Offshore geotechnical engineering

Principles and practice

Offshore geotechnical engineering
Principles and practice

E.T.R. Dean
Soil Models Limited

Published by Thomas Telford Limited, 40 Marsh Wall, London E14 9TP, UK.
www.thomastelford.com

Distributors for Thomas Telford books are
USA: ASCE Press, 1801 Alexander Bell Drive, Reston, VA 20191-4400
Australia: DA Books and Journals, 648 Whitehorse Road, Mitcham 3132, Victoria

First published 2010

Also available from Thomas Telford Limited
Disturbed soil properties and geotechnical design. A. Schofield. ISBN: 978-0-7277-2982-8
A short course in geotechnical site investigation. N. Simons, B. Menzies, M. Matthews.
ISBN: 978-0-7277-2948-4
ICE manual of geotechnical engineering. J. Burland, T. Chapman, H. Skinner and M. Brown.
ISBN: 978-0-7277-3652-9

www.icevirtuallibrary.com

A catalogue record for this book is available from the British Library

ISBN: 978-0-7277-3641-3

© Thomas Telford Limited 2010

Typeset by Academic + Technical, Bristol
Index created by Indexing Specialists (UK) Ltd, Hove, East Sussex
Printed and bound in Great Britain by Antony Rowe Limited, Chippenham

Dedication

Offshore geotechnical engineering owes much to the historical developments of soil mechanics by Karl Terzaghi, Donald Taylor, Arthur Casagrande, Ralph Peck, Harry Seed, Alec Skempton, Laurits Bjerrum, Andrew Schofield and others. A major part of our current knowledge of offshore geotechnical engineering has been developed by countless geotechnical engineers, managers, and others in the offshore industry itself. This book is dedicated to all those who have contributed to the subject, and who continue to contribute and share their knowledge.

Contents

Preface

Interest in the construction and development of offshore structures is increasing for several reasons. Demand for hydrocarbons makes offshore oil and gas commercially attractive. Increasing interest in renewable energy has made offshore wind farms attractive, and wave, current, and tidal energy systems will soon be financially viable. And artificial islands provide real estate not available onshore. All these structures are subject to significant geohazards, and require foundations to suit the structural weight and applied loads. Offshore geotechnical engineering is the practical science that addresses this.

This book presents the core design skills for this subject. It is self-contained, and can be used as a comprehensive primer for those new to offshore structures, or as a course text for students. It is advisable that readers have a prior understanding of soil mechanics and foundation engineering. Chapter 3 provides an overview of the main points, as they apply to offshore engineering, for readers without the advisable prerequisites.

The book is designed as an introduction to an extensive literature, but not as a replacement for that literature. Readers should also explore the offshore standards and codes of practice, listed at the start of this book. The most widely used practice has been API RP2A. Readers should also expect to read widely, particularly proceedings of the Offshore Technology Conference (OTC) held in Houston, Texas every May (www.otcnet.org). The following are also particularly recommended:

- Randolph, M.F., Cassidy, M.J., Gourvenec, S. and Erbrich, C.J. 2005. Challenges of offshore geotechnical engineering. State of the art paper. *16th International Conference on Soil Mechanics and Geotechnical Engineering*. Millpress Science Publishers, Vol. 1, 123–176.
- ISSMGE TC1 2005. *Geotechnical and Geophysical Investigations for Offshore and Nearshore Developments*. Technical Committee 1 of

the International Society of Soil Mechanics and Geotechnical Engineering. Downloadable from www.offshoregeohazards.org.

- Lunne, T., Robertson, P.K. and Powell, J.J.M. 1997. *Cone Penetration Testing in Geotechnical Engineering.* Blackie Academic and Professional.
- Schnaid, F. 2009. *In Situ Testing in Geotechnics: The Main Tests.* Taylor and Francis.
- Davis, R.O. and Selvadurai, A.P.S. 1996. *Elasticity and Geomechanics.* Cambridge University Press.
- Davis, R.O. and Selvadurai, A.P.S. 2002. *Plasticity and Geomechanics.* Cambridge University Press.

The offshore industry is very innovative. Research is well funded, and results are quickly and carefully used in practice. The book *Frontiers in Offshore Geotechnics* (edited by S. Gourvenec and M.J. Cassidy, and published by Taylor and Francis, 2005), describes some of the recent work.

Readers might like to consider becoming a member of the Society for Underwater Technology, the International Society of Offshore and Polar Engineers, and/or the Society of Petroleum Engineers. To work offshore, you will likely need to obtain, through an employer, a certificate of Basic Offshore Safety, Induction, and Emergency Training (BOSIET) including Helicopter Underwater Escape Training (HUET). It can also be helpful to obtain a seaman's card.

Good luck!

E.T. Richard Dean
2009

Acknowledgements

I would like to thank many friends and colleagues in the offshore industry who encouraged me to write this book and who made many constructive criticisms and suggestions for improvements to an early draft, including in alphabetical order:

- Dr Andrew J. Brennan, University of Dundee, UK
- Dr David Cathie, Christophe Jaeck, and others at Cathie Associates, Belgium
- Dr Dick Lyons and staff of Geotechnical Engineering and Marine Surveys (GEMS UK) Limited
- Dr Gopal Madabhushi, of Cambridge University, UK
- Dr Indrasenan Thusyanthan, of KW Limited, UK
- Dr Jack Templeton III, of Sage Engineering Inc, Houston, USA
- Dr Milutin Srbulov of Mott Macdonald Limited, UK
- Patrick Wong, ExxonMobil Development Company, Houston, USA
- Stefan Deokiesingh, Satesh Ramsaroop, and Kavita Fulchan and others of Capital Signal Company Limited, Trinidad.

I would also like to thank all my students at the University of the West Indies (UWI), who put up with the first drafts of the lecture notes, and Jennifer Pappin-Ramcharan, Unika Omowale, and others who assisted me greatly at UWI's Main Library in St. Augustine, Trinidad. I would like to thank the staff of Thomas Telford for their patient help and guidance, including Daniel Keirs, Jennifer Barratt, Terri Harding and others, as well as Debra Harding and other staff of the Institution of Civil Engineers' Library in London.

I would also like to thank friends and family for their patience while the book was being written, and my dear friend Jessie Moses for her sharp wit and warm encouragement during this time.

Permission to reproduced figures excerpted from copyrighted material is gratefully acknowledged, as indicated on relevant figures. Every effort has been made to ensure that appropriate acknowledgement has been made to previous copyrighted works quoted herein, and to contact all such copyright holders. If an omission in this matter have been made, the publishers and author apologise in advance, and shall rectify all errors brought to their attention in the next edition.

Any opinions that may be expressed in this book are mine alone, and do not necessarily represent the opinions of other persons or any organisations. All mistakes are mine: if you find one please contact the publisher.

Notation

Conventions

In this book, stress and strain are taken positive in compression. Work is taken as positive when it is done on a body, such as a body of soil. Angles are taken positive anticlockwise.

Full differentials are denoted using the pre-symbol d. For example, dx is the full differential for x. Differentials are always a result of starting by considering a small quantity, denoted using the symbol δ, then considering the case of smaller and smaller values of that quantity. For example, if a small change $\delta\sigma$ in stress occurs when a body is subjected to a small change δh in height, then the quantity $\delta\sigma/\delta h$ may tend to a limit as δh tends to zero. The limit is denoted as $d\sigma/dh$ if a full differential is relevant, or $\partial\sigma/\partial h$ if a partial differential is relevant.

Units

Most quantities in this book are in SI units, which are described in the paper entitled 'SI units for geotechnical engineering' (Committee on Definitions and Standards of the Geotechnical Division, 1983, *ASCE Journal of Geotechnical Engineering*, 109(12), 1534–1538). Exceptionally, Imperial units are used, e.g. some pile sizes given in inches, as this is common in the industry. The following conversion factors may be useful:

1 inch $= 25.4$ mm
1 foot $= 0.3048$ m
1 pound (mass) $= 0.453592$ kg
1 kip (force) $= 4.448222$ kN
1 kg/m^2 (force) $= 9.80665$ N/m^2
1 psi (pounds-per-square-inch, stress) $= 6.894757$ kPa
1 ksi (kips-per-square-inch, stress) $= 6.894757$ MPa
1 MN $= 1000$ kN

$$1\,\text{kN} = 1000\,\text{N}$$
$$1\,\text{Pa} = 1\,\text{N/m}^2$$

Some units involve an unmentioned application of the acceleration g of gravity, such as kg/m^2. It is best to avoid these units wherever possible, as great confusion can result. Mixed units can make sense, but are preferably avoided. For example, $1\,\text{kPa/ft}$ is the same as $1\,\text{kN/m}^2$ for each $0.3048\,\text{m}$, which equates to $1/0.3048 \approx 3.2808\,\text{kN/m}^2$ for every metre, so is about the same as $3.2808\,\text{kN/m}^3$.

Angles are assumed to be given in radians unless the symbol $^\circ$ for degrees is used. Conversion to consistent units is implicitly assumed in all arithmetic calculations. For example, $(1+\theta)\,e^{2\theta}$ evaluates to $(1+\pi)\,e^{2\pi}$ if $\theta = 180^\circ$. Another example: $\tan(45^\circ + \phi/2)$ evaluates to $\sqrt{3}$ if $\phi = \pi/6$ radians.

Fractions may be expressed as percentages or vice versa. Conversion to consistent units is implicitly assumed in all calculations. For example, $(1+w)$ evaluates to 2.5 if $w = 150\%$.

Notes

Where the same symbol is listed below with more than one meaning, the meaning will be clear from the context where the symbol is used.

Units are specified in square brackets, For instance, $[\text{ML}^{-1}\text{T}^{-2}]$ is a stress $(= \text{mass} \times \text{acceleration/area})$.

Symbols

a	adhesion $[\text{ML}^{-1}\text{T}^{-2}]$
a	constant [dimensionless]
a	radius [L]
a	lever arm [L]
A	constant [dimensionless]
A	area $[\text{L}^2]$
A	amplitude multiplication factor [dimensionless]
A	multiplier in $p - y$ calculation [dimensionless]
A_c	contact area $[\text{L}^2]$
A_0	initial area $[\text{L}^2]$
A_p	equivalent cross-sectional area of a pile $[\text{L}^2]$
A'	effective area $[\text{L}^2]$
A'	area of reduced foundation $[\text{L}^2]$
b	fraction [dimensionless]

b	constant [dimensionless]
B	constant [dimensionless]
B	footing breadth or diameter [L]
B'	equivalent footing breadth [L]
BHD	borehole depth [L]
$B(\gamma)$	function defining a backbone curve [$ML^{-1}T^{-2}$]
c	cohesion [$ML^{-1}T^{-2}$]
c	wave velocity [LT^{-1}]
c_h	coefficient of vertical consolidation, with horizontal drainage [L^2T^{-1}]
c_v	coefficient of vertical consolidation, with vertical drainage [L^2T^{-1}]
C	constant [dimensionless]
C	viscosity [MT^{-1}]
C	effective circumference [L]
C_c	coefficient of curvature [dimensionless]
C_c	compression index [dimensionless]
C_n	constant ($n = 0, 1, 2, 3\ldots$) [dimensionless]
$C_{(p)}$	factor in settlement calculation [dimensionless]
C_s	swelling index [dimensionless]
C_s	factor in settlement calculation [dimensionless]
C_u	coefficient of uniformity [dimensionless]
C_α	coefficient of secondary compression [dimensionless]
d	water depth [L]
d_0	adjusted depth [L]
D	water depth [L]
D	diameter [L]
D	constrained modulus [$ML^{-1}T^{-2}$]
D	damage [dimensionless]
D_N	damage ratio after N cycles [dimensionless]
D_n	largest nominal diameter of smallest n % of particles by dry weight [L]
e	void ratio [dimensionless]
e	eccentricity [L]
e_{EOP}	void ratio at the end of primary consolidation [dimensionless]
e_{max}	largest void ratio attainable by a standard procedure [dimensionless]
e_{min}	smallest void ratio attainable by a standard procedure [dimensionless]
E	Young's modulus [$ML^{-1}T^{-2}$]

E_g	pile group capacity factor [dimensionless]
E_p	equivalent Young's modulus for a pile material [$ML^{-1}T^{-2}$]
E_{py}	lateral soil reaction modulus [$ML^{-1}T^{-2}$]
E_{sec}	secant Young's modulus [$ML^{-1}T^{-2}$]
E_u	apparent Young's modulus for undrained conditions [$ML^{-1}T^{-2}$]
f	unit skin friction resistance stress [$ML^{-1}T^{-2}$]
f_{lim}	upper limit on the unit skin friction resistance stress [$ML^{-1}T^{-2}$]
f_r	reduction factor [dimensionless]
f_t	unit skin friction resistance stress for the pull-out of a pile [$ML^{-1}T^{-2}$]
F	environmental force [MLT^{-2}]
F	driving force [MLT^{-2}]
F_c	product of bearing capacity modifying factors for cohesion [dimensionless]
F_p	pile capacity factor [dimensionless]
F_q	product of bearing capacity modifying factors for surcharge [dimensionless]
F_{xc}	compressibility factor [dimensionless]
F_{xd}	depth factor [dimensionless]
F_{xi}	inclination factor [dimensionless]
F_{xs}	shape factor [dimensionless]
F_γ	product of bearing capacity modifying factors for self-weight [dimensionless]
FS	factor of safety [dimensionless]
g	acceleration due to earth's gravity, usually taken as $9.81\,\text{m/s}^2$
g	dimensionless parameter in shear modulus determination [dimensionless]
G	shear modulus [$ML^{-1}T^{-2}$]
G_{max}	shear modulus at infinitesimally small strain [$ML^{-1}T^{-2}$]
G_s	average specific gravity of particles [dimensionless]
$G(\omega)$	power spectral density [L^2T^2]
h	offset height [L]
h	peak-to-trough amplitude of sinusoidal undulation in as-laid pipe [L]
h_i	thickness of ith soil layer [L]
h_{xs}	excess head [L]
h_0	initial thickness of a soil layer [L]

H	height [L]
H	horizontal force [MLT^{-2}]
H_{iP}	horizontal force resultant evaluated at point P [MLT^{-2}]
H_{iQ}	horizontal force resultant evaluated at point Q [MLT^{-2}]
H_{i0}	reference horizontal load [MLT^{-2}]
H_{net}	net horizontal load [MLT^{-2}]
i	hydraulic gradient [dimensionless]
i_{crit}	critical hydraulic gradient [dimensionless]
I	moment of inertia [L^4]
I_r	rigidity index [dimensionless]
$I_{r,crit}$	critical rigidity index [dimensionless]
J	factor for a surface failure mechanism [dimensionless]
J_s	Smith damping [L^{-1}T]
k	hydraulic conductivity [LT^{-1}]
k	constant [dimensionless]
K	coefficient of lateral earth pressure [dimensionless]
K	bulk modulus [ML^{-1}T^{-2}]
K_a	active earth pressure coefficient [dimensionless]
K_h	effective horizontal stiffness at the hull level [MT^{-2}]
K_p	passive earth pressure coefficient [dimensionless]
K_s	punching shear coefficient [dimensionless]
K_T	torsional stiffness [ML^{2}T^{-2}]
K_0	coefficient of lateral earth pressure at rest [dimensionless]
$K_{0,nc}$	coefficient of lateral earth pressure at rest for a normally consolidated sample [dimensionless]
K_1	vertical stiffness [MT^{-2}]
K_2	horizontal stiffness [MT^{-2}]
K_3	rotational stiffness [ML^{2}T^{-2}]
K_1'	stiffness ratio [dimensionless]
L	lifetime in years [T]
L	lever arm [L]
L	water wavelength [L]
L	length of flow path [L]
L	leg length [L]
L	length of the longest side of a rectangular strip footing [L]
L_w	height from the spudcan bearing area to the centre of mass of a jackup
LI	liquidity index [dimensionless, fraction or %]

LL	liquid limit [dimensionless, fraction or %]
m	constant [dimensionless]
m	counter [dimensionless]
m_v	coefficient of volume change [$M^{-1}LT^2$]
M	mass [M]
M	overturning moment [ML^2T^{-2}]
M	series parameter [dimensionless]
M_h	mass of a hull [M]
M_{iP}	moment resultant evaluated at point P [ML^2T^{-2}]
M_{iQ}	moment resultant evaluated at point Q [ML^2T^{-2}]
M_{i0}	reference moment [ML^2T^{-2}]
n	porosity [dimensionless, fraction or %]
n	constant [dimensionless]
n	load spreading factor [dimensionless]
N	number of years [T]
N	stability number [dimensionless]
N	normal resistance per unit length [MT^{-2}]
N_c	cone factor [dimensionless]
N_c	bearing capacity factor for cohesion [dimensionless]
N_i	number of cycles of type i
$N_{i,f}$	number of cycles of type i required to reach a specified condition
N_k	cone factor [dimensionless]
N_{kt}	cone factor [dimensionless]
N_q	bearing capacity factor for surcharge [dimensionless]
N_q	pile end bearing capacity factor [dimensionless]
N_γ	bearing capacity factor for self-weight [dimensionless]
OCR	overconsolidation ratio
p	mean normal total stress [$ML^{-1}T^{-2}$]
p	pressure inside pipe [$ML^{-1}T^{-2}$]
p	lateral soil resistance force per unit length [MT^{-2}]
p'	mean normal effective stress [$ML^{-1}T^{-2}$]
p_1	probability of occurrence in a period of 1 year [dimensionless]
p_a	reference (standard atmospheric) pressure $= 100\,kN/m^2$
p_N	probability of occurrence in a period of N years [dimensionless]
p_u	ultimate lateral shaft resistance per unit length [MT^{-2}]
p_0	pressure amplitude [$ML^{-1}T^{-2}$]
P	length of pipe [L]
P	axial force [MLT^{-2}]

P	point load $[MLT^{-2}]$
P_f	force due to pressure in contained fluids $[MLT^{-2}]$
P_k	force contribution associated with the weight of the soil cover $[MLT^{-2}]$
P_t	negative of force in a pipe $[MLT^{-2}]$
PI	plasticity index [dimensionless, fraction or %]
PL	plastic limit [dimensionless, fraction or %]
q	deviator stress $[ML^{-1}T^{-2}]$
q	surcharge $[ML^{-1}T^{-2}]$
q	vertical effective stress at the level of the bearing area $[ML^{-1}T^{-2}]$
q	unit end bearing resistance stress $[ML^{-1}T^{-2}]$
q'	available bearing capacity $[ML^{-1}T^{-2}]$
q_c	cone resistance $[ML^{-1}T^{-2}]$
q_{lim}	upper limit on the unit end bearing resistance stress $[ML^{-1}T^{-2}]$
q_p	unit point resistance $[ML^{-1}T^{-2}]$
q_u	ultimate unit bearing capacity $[ML^{-1}T^{-2}]$
q_{ult}	ultimate unit bearing capacity $[ML^{-1}T^{-2}]$
$q_{u,net}$	net ultimate unit bearing capacity $[ML^{-1}T^{-2}]$
$q_{u,net,b}$	net ultimate unit bearing capacity of an underlying layer $[ML^{-1}T^{-2}]$
Q	volume flow rate $[L^3T^{-2}]$
Q	shear force $[MLT^{-2}]$
Q	vertical load capacity of a mudmat $[MLT^{-2}]$
Q_a	ultimate point resistance force on a steel annulus $[MLT^{-2}]$
Q_e	ultimate point resistance force beneath a soil plug $[MLT^{-2}]$
Q_p	ultimate point resistance force $[MLT^{-2}]$
Q_{si}	ultimate internal shaft friction resistance force for a coring pile $[MLT^{-2}]$
Q_{sx}	ultimate external shaft friction resistance force $[MLT^{-2}]$
Q_t	ultimate capacity in tension $[MLT^{-2}]$
Q_u	ultimate load $[MLT^{-2}]$
Q_{ws}	frictional resistance under the working load $[MLT^{-2}]$
r	radius $[L]$
r	radius of gyration $[L]$
r_f	failure ratio [dimensionless]
r_m	radius of zone of influence $[L]$
R	radial distance $[L]$
R	skirt resistance $[MLT^{-2}]$

R	lateral resistance [MLT^{-2}]
R	shear resistance per unit length [MT^{-2}]
R_i	load ratio [dimensionless]
R_p	skirt or dowel resistance due to end bearing [MLT^{-2}]
R_s	skirt or dowel resistance due to wall friction [MLT^{-2}]
R_s	shaft resistance per unit length [MT^{-2}]
RD	relative density [dimensionless, fraction or %]
s	settlement [L]
s_u	undrained shear strength [$ML^{-1}T^{-2}$]
$s_{u,nc}$	undrained shear strength for a normally consolidated sample [$ML^{-1}T^{-2}$]
$s_{u,remoulded}$	undrained shear strength for a remoulded sample [$ML^{-1}T^{-2}$]
S	degree of saturation [dimensionless, fraction or %]
S	leg spacing in elevation view [L]
S	shear resistance per unit length [MT^{-2}]
S_r	sensitivity to remoulding [dimensionless, fraction]
S_t	sensitivity [dimensionless, fraction]
SU	height of stick-up [L]
t	time [T]
t	wall thickness [L]
t	shaft resistance force per unit length [MT^{-2}]
t_{max}	maximum shaft resistance per unit length [MT^{-2}]
t_{EOP}	duration from the application of a load to the end of primary consolidation [T]
T	mass of tare [M]
T	wave period [T]
T	change in the temperature [°K]
T	anchor line tension [MLT^{-2}]
T_{end}	end torque [ML^2T^{-2}]
T_r	time factor [dimensionless]
T_{side}	side torque [ML^2T^{-2}]
T_v	time factor [dimensionless]
u	pore water pressure [$ML^{-1}T^{-2}$]
u_g	excess pore pressure generated at a point [$ML^{-1}T^{-2}$]
u_{xs}	excess water pressure [$ML^{-1}T^{-2}$]
u_0	water pressure on the seafloor [$ML^{-1}T^{-2}$]
u_0	initial velocity [LT^{-1}]
U	average degree of consolidation [dimensionless]
U_r	average degree of consolidation for radial drainage [dimensionless]

U_v	average degree of consolidation for vertical drainage [dimensionless]
v	vertical displacement [L]
v	discharge velocity [LT^{-1}]
v_r	discharge velocity in the radial direction [LT^{-1}]
v_z	discharge velocity in the z direction [LT^{-1}]
v_{sw}	velocity of a sound wave through water [LT^{-1}]
x	position coordinate [L]
x	depth below the seafloor [L]
x_R	depth of reduced resistance [L]
V	volume [L^3]
V	specific volume [dimensionless]
V	vertical load [MLT^{-2}]
V	vertical load capacity per unit length [MT^{-2}]
V_{iP}	vertical force resultant evaluated at point P [MLT^{-2}]
V_{iQ}	vertical force resultant evaluated at point Q [MLT^{-2}]
V_{it}	tension load capacity (positive for tension) [MLT^{-2}]
V_{i0}	reference vertical load [MLT^{-2}]
V_{ult}	ultimate vertical load [MLT^{-2}]
V_0	reference vertical load [MLT^{-2}]
w	vertical displacement [L]
w	width [L]
w	wall thickness [L]
w	water content [dimensionless, fraction or %]
w	force per unit length [MT^{-2}]
w	penetration distance [L]
w_i	initial force per unit length [MT^{-2}]
W'	buoyant weight [MLT^{-2}]
W_{max}	maximum buoyant weight of backfill [MLT^{-2}]
W_{net}	net vertical load [MLT^{-2}]
WD	water depth [L]
y	lateral displacement [L]
y_c	lateral offset due to construction tolerances [L]
y_c	reference displacement [L]
y_w	lever arm [L]
$y_{x,i}$	lateral displacement of point on the ith leg relative to the hull [L]
z	depth below the seafloor [L]
z_3	component of settlement due to settlement of material below the level of the pile tip [L]
z'	distance above a layer boundary [L]

z_{lim}	limiting depth of a stable vertical cut in clay [L]
Z	section modulus [L^3]
α	multiplier [dimensionless]
α	coefficient of thermal expansion [dimensionless, per K]
β	multiplier [dimensionless]
β	load inclination angle [dimensionless, radians or degrees]
β	wavenumber [L^{-1}]
δ	small change in (e.g. δx = small change in x)
δ	soil–pile friction angle [dimensionless, degrees or radians]
ε	phase lag [dimensionless, degrees or radians]
ε_{ax}	axial strain [dimensionless, fraction or %]
ε_c	axial strain at 50% of the maximum deviator stress in a UU test [dimensionless]
ε_{net}	net axial strain [dimensionless, fraction or %]
ε_r	radial strain [dimensionless, fraction or %]
ε_t	thermally induced strain [dimensionless, fraction or %]
ε_{vol}	volumetric strain [dimensionless, fraction or %]
ε_{xx}	axial strain in the x direction [dimensionless, fraction or %]
ε_{yy}	axial strain in the y direction [dimensionless, fraction or %]
ε_{zz}	axial strain in the z direction [dimensionless, fraction or %]
ϕ'	effective angle of internal friction [dimensionless, degrees or radians]
ϕ'_{cs}	effective angle of internal friction at a critical state [dimensionless, degrees or radians]
ϕ_{hi}	horizontal fixity at the ith spudcan [dimensionless]
ϕ'_{mob}	mobilised angle of effective (internal) friction [dimensionless, degrees or radians]
ϕ_{ri}	moment fixity at the ith spudcan [dimensionless]
γ	engineering shear strain [dimensionless, angle or fraction]
γ'	submerged unit weight [ML^{-2}T^{-2}]
γ_b	bulk unit weight [ML^{-2}T^{-2}]
γ_{bulk}	bulk unit weight [ML^{-2}T^{-2}]
γ_d	dry unit weight [ML^{-2}T^{-2}]
γ_{dry}	dry unit weight [ML^{-2}T^{-2}]
γ_{eng}	engineering shear strain [dimensionless, angle or fraction]
γ'_i	submerged unit weight of the ith soil layer [ML^{-2}T^{-2}]

γ_{rs}	engineering shear strain with respect to the r and s directions [dimensionless, angle or fraction]
γ_w	unit weight of water, usually taken as $9.8\,\text{kN/m}^3$ $[\text{ML}^{-2}\text{T}^{-2}]$
η	phase advance [dimensionless, degrees or radians]
η_w	pile group stiffness efficiency factor [dimensionless]
λ	wavenumber $[\text{L}^{-1}]$
λ	ratio of lengths [dimensionless]
λ	damage factor [dimensionless]
μ	Poisson's ratio [dimensionless]
μ_{sec}	secant Poisson's ratio [dimensionless]
θ	angle, or angular coordinate [dimensionless, degrees or radians]
θ_i	rotation of a hull [dimensionless, degrees or radians]
θ_i	rotation of the ith spudcan [dimensionless, degrees or radians]
ρ	mass density $[\text{ML}^{-3}]$
ρ	ratio of soil moduli [dimensionless]
ρ	rate of increase in the undrained shear strength with depth $[\text{ML}^{-2}\text{T}^{-2}]$
ρ'	buoyant density $[\text{ML}^{-3}]$
ρ_b	bulk density $[\text{ML}^{-3}]$
ρ_{bulk}	bulk density $[\text{ML}^{-3}]$
ρ_d	dry density $[\text{ML}^{-3}]$
ρ_{dry}	dry density $[\text{ML}^{-3}]$
ρ_p	density of pile material $[\text{ML}^{-3}]$
ρ_w	density of water, usually taken as $1000\,\text{kg/m}^3$ $[\text{ML}^{-3}]$
σ	normal total stress $[\text{ML}^{-1}\text{T}^{-2}]$
σ'	normal effective stress $[\text{ML}^{-1}\text{T}^{-2}]$
σ''	Skempton's normal effective stress $[\text{ML}^{-1}\text{T}^{-2}]$
σ'_a	axial effective stress $[\text{ML}^{-1}\text{T}^{-2}]$
σ'_a	active effective stress $[\text{ML}^{-1}\text{T}^{-2}]$
σ_{cell}	cell pressure $[\text{ML}^{-1}\text{T}^{-2}]$
σ_{centre}	total stress at the centre of a Mohr's circle $[\text{ML}^{-1}\text{T}^{-2}]$
σ'_{centre}	effective stress at the centre of a Mohr's circle $[\text{ML}^{-1}\text{T}^{-2}]$
σ_h	horizontal total stress $[\text{ML}^{-1}\text{T}^{-2}]$
σ'_h	horizontal effective stress $[\text{ML}^{-1}\text{T}^{-2}]$
$\sigma'_{h,\text{in situ}}$	in-situ horizontal effective stress $[\text{ML}^{-1}\text{T}^{-2}]$
$\sigma_{\substack{max \\ min}}$	maximum or minimum stress (maximum uses formula with $+$, minimum with $-$) $[\text{ML}^{-1}\text{T}^{-2}]$

σ'_p	passive effective stress $[ML^{-1}T^{-2}]$
σ_r	radial total stress $[ML^{-1}T^{-2}]$
σ'_r	radial effective stress $[ML^{-1}T^{-2}]$
σ_{radius}	radius of a Mohr's circle of total stress $[ML^{-1}T^{-2}]$
σ'_{radius}	radius of a Mohr's circle of effective stress $[ML^{-1}T^{-2}]$
σ_v	vertical total stress $[ML^{-1}T^{-2}]$
σ'_v	vertical effective stress $[ML^{-1}T^{-2}]$
σ'_{vc}	vertical effective pre-consolidation stress $[ML^{-1}T^{-2}]$
$\sigma'_{v,in\ situ}$	in-situ vertical effective stress $[ML^{-1}T^{-2}]$
σ'_θ	normal effective stress on a plane at an angle θ to a reference direction $[ML^{-1}T^{-2}]$
σ_a	axial total stress $[ML^{-1}T^{-2}]$
σ_θ	normal total stress on a plane at angle θ to a reference direction $[ML^{-1}T^{-2}]$
τ	shear stress $[ML^{-1}T^{-2}]$
τ_θ	shear stress on a plane at an angle θ to a reference direction $[ML^{-1}T^{-2}]$
ζ	depth beneath the seafloor $[L]$
χ_i	constant [dimensionless]
ω	circular frequency, usually expressed in radians/s $[T^{-1}]$
ω_n	natural circular frequency, usually expressed in radians/s $[T^{-1}]$
ψ	relative time $[T]$
ψ	parameter [dimensionless]
Δ	change in (e.g. Δx = change of x)
Δe	change in the void ratio
Δt	delay time $[T]$
Δu	increase in the water pressure $[ML^{-1}T^{-2}]$
$\Delta \sigma_0$	change in the total stress $[ML^{-1}T^{-2}]$
ξ	damping ratio [dimensionless]

Standards and codes of practice

ABS
Rules for Building and Classing Offshore Installation (1983)
Guide for Building and Classing Offshore LNG Terminals (2003)

ASTM
Vol. 04.08, *Soils and Rock* (1)
Vol. 04.09, *Soils and Rock* (2)

API RP2A
Planning, Designing and Constructing Fixed Offshore Platforms
WSD: *Working Stress Design*, 21st edition (2000) and supplements
1 to 3 (2005, 2007)
LRFD: *Load and Resistance Factor Design*, 1st edition (1993) and
supplement (1997)

API RP2N
*Planning, Designing and Constructing Structures and Pipelines for Arctic
Conditions*

API RP2SK
Design and Analysis of Stationkeeping Systems for Floating Structures

API RP2T
Planning, Designing and Constructing Tension Leg Platforms

API RP 1111
*Design, Construction, Operation and Maintenance of Offshore
Hydrocarbon Pipelines*

API Bull 2INT-DG
*Interim Guidance for Design of Offshore Structures for Hurricane
Conditions*

API Bull 2INT-EX
*Interim Guidance for Assessment of Existing Offshore Structures for
Hurricane Conditions*

API 95J
Gulf of Mexico Jackup Operations for Hurricane Season – Interim Recommendations

BS 1377
Methods of Test for Soils for Engineering Purposes
Part 1: General requirements and sample preparation
Part 2: Classification Tests
Part 3: Chemical and Electro-chemical Tests
Part 4: Compaction Tests
Part 5: Compressibility, Permeability and Durability Tests
Part 6: Consolidation and Permeability Tests
Part 7: Strength Tests – Total Stress
Part 8: Strength Tests – Effective Stress
Part 9: In-situ Tests

BS 4019
Specifications for Rotary Core Drilling Equipment

BS 5930
Code of Practice for Site Investigations

BS 6235
Code of Practice for Fixed Offshore Structures

CSA
Canadian Standards Association, Code for the Design, Construction and Installation of Fixed Offshore Structures

DNV
Offshore standards (OS) and recommended practices (RP), including:
Classification Note 30.4: *Foundations*
OS-J101: *Design of Offshore Wind Turbine Structures*
RP-C205: *Environmental Conditions and Environmental Loads*
RP-C207: *Statistical Representation of Soil Data*
RP-E301: *Design and Installation of Fluke Anchors in Clay*
RP-E302: *Design and Installation of Drag-in Plate Anchors in Clay*
RP-E303: *Geotechnical Design and Installation of Suction Anchors in Clay*
RP-F105: *Free Spanning Pipelines*
RP-F109: *On-Bottom Stability Design of Submarine Pipelines*
RP-F110: *Global Buckling of Submarine Pipelines*

GL
Germanischer Lloyd rules, including:
Standard for Geotechnical Site and Route Surveys
Guideline for the Certification of Offshore Wind Turbines
Offshore Installations – Structures

Eurocodes
2: *Design of Concrete Structures*
3: *Design of Steel Structures*
7: *Geotechnical Design*
8: *Design of Structures for Earthquake Resistance*

IEC 61400-3
Wind turbines – Part 3: Design requirements for offshore wind turbines

ISO 19900
General Requirements for Offshore Structures

ISO 19901
Specific Requirements for Offshore Structures
Part 1: *Metocean Design and Operating Considerations*
Part 2: *Seismic Design Procedures and Criteria*
Part 3: *Topsides Structure*
Part 4: *Geotechnical and Foundations Design Considerations*
Part 5: *Weight Control During Engineering Construction*
Part 6: *Marine Operations*
Part 7: *Stationkeeping Systems*

ISO 19902
Fixed Steel Offshore Structures

ISO 19903
Fixed Concrete Offshore Structures

ISO 19904
Floating Offshore Structures
Part 1: *Monohulls, Semi-submersibles, and Spars*
Part 2: *Tension Leg Platforms*

ISO 19905
Site Specific Assessment of Mobile Offshore Units
Part 1: *Jackups*
Part 2: *Jackups Commentary*

ISO 19906
Arctic Offshore Structures

ISO 22746-1
Geotechnical Investigation and Testing – Field Testing. Part 1: Electrical Cone and Piezocone Penetration Tests

SNAME TR-5A
Recommended Practice for Site-Specific Assessment of Mobile Jackup Units, Rev. 2 (2002)

UK HSE
Offshore Installations: Guidance of Design, Installation, and Certification, HMSO (1993; now withdrawn, parts reprinted as OTO reports available from the UK HSE)

Some useful websites

Conferences and societies

API	American Petroleum Institute, www.api.org
ASCE	American Society of Civil Engineers, www.asce.org
ASTM	American Society for Testing and Materials, www.astm.org
BSI	British Standards Institution, www.bsi-global.com
BWEA	British Wind Energy Association, www.bwea.com
DNV	Det Norske Veritas, www.dnv.com
EWEA	European Wind Energy Association, www.ewea.org
GL	Germanischer Lloyd, www.gl-group.com
ICE	Institution of Civil Engineers, www.ice.org.uk
ISO	International Standards Organization, www.iso.org
ISOPE	International Society of Offshore and Polar Engineers, www.isope.org
MMS	US Minerals Management Service, www.mms.gov
NGI	Norwegian Geotechnical Institute, www.ngi.no
OTC	Offshore Technology Conference, www.otcnet.org
SNAME	Society of Naval Architects and Marine Engineers, www.sname.org
SUT	Society for Underwater Technology, www.sut.org.uk
SPE	Society of Petroleum Engineers, www.spe.org

Large research groups

C-CORE	Centre for Cold Oceans Research, www.c-core.ca
COFS	Centre for Offshore Foundation Systems, www.cofs.uwa.edu.au
CUED	Cambridge University Engineering Department, www.eng.cam.ac.uk
DU	Delft University, Geoengineering, www.geo.citg.tudelft.nl

EERI	Earthquake Engineering Research Institute, www.eeri.org
HK	Hong Kong University of Science and Technology, www.ust.hk
ICL	Imperial College London, www3.imperial.ac.uk
NGI	Norwegian Geotechnical Institute, www.ngi.no
OUED	Oxford University Department of Engineering Science, www.eng.ox.ac.uk
OTRC	Offshore Technology Research Centre, otrc.tamu.edu

Journals

ASCE Journals, www.pubs.asce.org/journals

Canadian Geotechnical Journal, www.nrc-cnrc.gc.ca

Electronic Journal of Geotechnical Engineering, www.ejge.com

Geotechnical Engineering, www.thomastelford.com/journals

Géotechnique, www.thomastelford.com/journals

Royal Society London, www.royalsociety.org

Science Direct, www.sciencedirect.com

Soils and Foundations, www.jiban.or.jp

Geotechnical information and downloads

Geotechnical Engineering Directory, www.geotechnicaldirectory.com

Geotech Links, www.geotechlinks.com

Geotechnical and Geoenvironmental Software Directory, www.ggsd.com

Internet for Civil Engineers, www.icivilengineer.com

1

Introduction

This chapter describes the nature of the offshore civil engineering industry, the main types of offshore structure, the geohazards and environmental conditions to which they are subject, and the role of geotechnical engineering in their planning, design, construction, installation, monitoring and decommissioning.

1.1   Nature of offshore geotechnical engineering

1.1.1   General

Offshore structures are structures that are placed in specific locations in the sea or ocean for specific purposes. Examples include oil and gas platforms, offshore windfarm structures and artificial islands. Offshore geotechnical engineering is the branch of civil engineering concerned with the assessment of geohazards for these structures, and the design, construction, maintenance, and eventual decommissioning of their foundations. It differs from onshore geotechnical engineering in several ways:

- the clients and regulatory bodies are different
- many offshore structures are large (many stand over 100 m above the seabed, and some are considerably taller)
- the design life of an offshore structure is typically in the range 25–50 years
- most offshore structures are constructed in parts onshore, and are assembled offshore
- ground improvement is feasible offshore, but rather more expensive
- a larger range of geohazards can affect offshore structures
- offshore environmental loads include high lateral loads
- cyclic loading can be a major or even dominant design issue
- the environmental and financial cost of failure can be higher.

Like onshore geotechnical engineering, offshore geotechnical engineering involves strong interactions with other branches of engineering, particularly structural engineering, and with geology and geophysics. Constructability and installability are important aspects of design, as are reliability and robustness.

1.1.2 Historical development

The first offshore platform is considered to be a jacket structure named 'Superior'. This was an oil platform installed in 1947 about 30 km off the Louisiana coast, in a water depth of about 5 m (Yergin, 1993; Austin *et al.*, 2004). Figure 1.1 shows the main areas of offshore oil and gas developments today. There are over 10 000 offshore platforms (Chakrabati *et al.*, 2005). This translates to an average construction rate of about 200 platforms per year during the six decades since 1947.

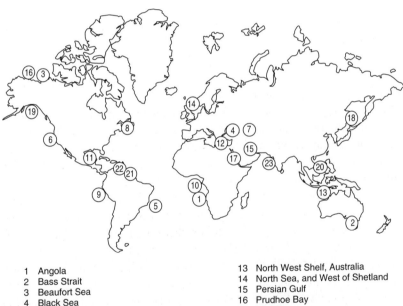

1 Angola	13 North West Shelf, Australia
2 Bass Strait	14 North Sea, and West of Shetland
3 Beaufort Sea	15 Persian Gulf
4 Black Sea	16 Prudhoe Bay
5 Brazil	17 Red Sea
6 California	18 Sakhalin
7 Caspian	19 South Alaska
8 Canada – Atlantic	20 South China Sea
9 Ecuador and Peru	21 Trinidad and Tobago
10 Gulf of Guinea (GOG), West Africa	22 Venezuela
11 Gulf of Mexico (GOM), and Bay of Campeche	23 West India
12 Mediterranean	

Fig. 1.1 Worldwide distribution of offshore oil and gas developments. (Data from McClelland (1974) and Poulos (1988), updated with data from www.rigzone.com, www.offshore-technology.com, www.otcnet.org, and elsewhere)

Platforms range from a few tens of tonnes of steel to a several hundred thousand tonnes of steel and concrete, in water depths from a metre to approaching 2 km.

Wind energy companies have also become interested in offshore construction, partly because the sea is relatively flat so that offshore wind has better power-generating characteristics than onshore, and partly to avoid adverse environmental impacts onshore (Leithead, 2007). Technologies for generating electricity from wave, tidal, and current power will also soon be sufficiently developed for significant offshore developments to begin (Kerr, 2007).

Real estate can sometimes be easier to construct offshore than buy onshore. Artificial offshore islands have been used to support airports, heavy industry parks and tourist destinations (Dean *et al.*, 2008). Mining the seafloor for manganese and other metals, and recovery of gas hydrates from the deep seabed, may be commercially feasible in the future (Takahara *et al.*, 1984; Collett, 2008). The deep seabed may also be a feasible solution for long-term storage of carbon dioxide (Schrag, 2008).

1.1.3   Types of offshore structure

The main types of bottom-founded offshore structure are jackups, jackets, pipelines, and gravity platforms. These are typically used in water depths up to about 120 m, although some have been installed in deeper waters. Tension-leg platforms, floaters, and semi-submersibles are used for water depths up to several kilometres.

Figure 1.2 shows a platform complex, offshore Nigeria. A jackup, shown on the left, is a mobile platform consisting of a hull and three or more retractable legs. The other three platforms are 'jackets'. A jacket is a fixed platform consisting of an open frame of steel tubulars, usually piled into the seabed, supporting a deck and topside modules. Small jackets are used as wellhead platforms, or as pumping stations along a pipeline. Larger jackets include drilling and production equipment.

Figure 1.3 shows the platform complex of Fig. 1.2 in end elevation. The jackup was floated into location with its hull in the water and its legs elevated. On arrival, the legs were lowered to the seabed and the hull was lifted out of the water by jacks installed on the hull. A cantilever structure was then extended out from the jackup, carrying the drilling derrick that is in the centre of the picture. The derrick is now drilling a well through a small wellhead platform. When the well

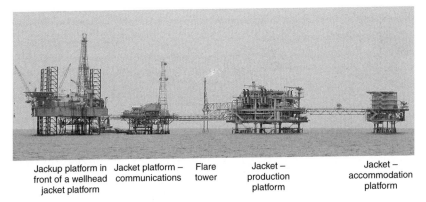

| Jackup platform in front of a wellhead jacket platform | Jacket platform – communications | Flare tower | Jacket – production platform | Jacket – accommodation platform |

Fig. 1.2 Platform complex, offshore Nigeria

is completed, it will be hooked up to a line to the production platform, which is behind the wellhead platform in this view. The flare
tower is connected to the production platform. It is used to burn off
unwanted gas that comes up the oil well with the oil. In this case, the
commercial value of the gas did not justify the cost of a pipeline to
shore.

Figure 1.4 shows two of the concrete gravity platforms that were
installed in the North Sea. This type of platform achieves stability
against lateral wave loading through its own weight. As shown by the
Condeep platform, a large gravity base structure (GBS) normally
includes a sub-sea caisson with a height of about one-third of the

| Flare tower | Supply boat | Jacket platforms | Jackup platform | Jackup hull |

Fig. 1.3 Flare tower, jackets, and jackup viewed from the left end of Fig. 1.2

4

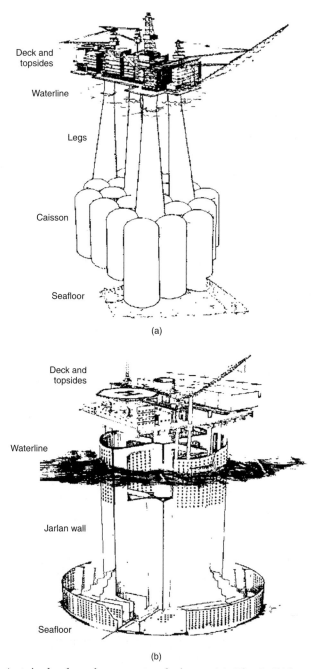

Deck and
topsides

Waterline

Legs

Caisson

Seafloor

(a)

Deck and
topsides

Waterline

Jarlan wall

Seafloor

(b)

Fig. 1.4 Artist's sketches of two gravity platforms. (a) The Gullfaks A Condeep platform in 134 m water depth. (b) The Frigg CDP-1 platform in 96 m water depth. (© 1994 Offshore Technology Conference: Moksnes et al., 1994)

water depth, one or more concrete legs, and a steel deck and topsides. The caisson is the foundation element, and provides weight and temporary oil storage. In the Frigg CDP-1, a special 'Jarlan wall' surrounds the central column which supports the deck and topsides. The Jarlan wall consists of a concrete wall with many holes. When waves flow against the wall, part of the wave energy is dissipated in the turbulence created by the flow of some of the water through the holes. This dissipation reduces the wave forces on the structure as a whole.

Pipelines are laid on or below the seabed to carry oil and gas to shore. Modern pipelines are often highly sophisticated systems that resist pressure, temperature, and corrosion from inside and outside, and with internal heating to prevent wax build-up. Tubes carrying different liquids may be bundled together, and the bundle may also contain electrical and fibre-optic cables for data transfer and control.

Artificial islands have been used as offshore platforms in relatively shallow waters, particularly in the US and Canadian parts of the Beaufort Sea, where ice sheets form for much or the year. Islands can also be mobile. A caisson-retained island is a caisson that is floated into location, sunk onto a prepared seabed berm, and filled with sand that is then compacted to give the required resistance when the ice later forms. When the time comes to depart, the sand in the core of the structure is fluidised and washed away, and the caisson is refloated and towed away.

Figure 1.5a shows a view of the Hutton tension leg platform (TLP), installed in the North Sea in 1984. At that time the water depth of 148 m was considered deep. The hull provides a buoyancy uplift force, and is kept in vertical position by legs that are in permanent tension. Thus, the hull does not move vertically as a large wave passes. The tension legs consist of tendons, each of which is a steel pipe that is attached to a foundation template that is piled into the seabed.

For waters up to a few hundred metres depth, a compliant tower can be a solution. Figure 1.5b shows the Benguela-Belize tower installed in about 390 m water depth. The 12 foundation piles were approximately 2.7 m in diameter and penetrated about 150 m into the seabed. For deeper waters still, while a TLP remains feasible, a permanently moored ship is also a solution. Figure 1.5c shows the field layout for the Girassol and Jasmin development, offshore Angola. The water depth is about ten times the depth at the Hutton TLP. The platform is an FPSO (floating production, storage, and offloading) vessel. Lines

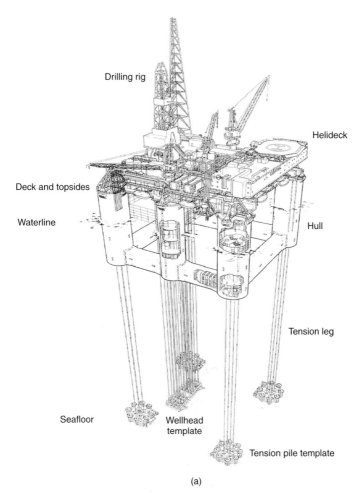

Drilling rig

Helideck

Deck and topsides

Waterline

Hull

Tension leg

Seafloor

Wellhead
template

Tension pile template

(a)

Fig. 1.5 Deepwater structures. (a) The Hutton TLP, installed in 1984 in 148 m water depth in the North Sea (Tetlow et al., 1983; Bradshaw et al., 1984, 1985). (b) The Bengula-Belize compliant piled tower, installed in approximately 390 m water depth, offshore West Africa (© 2006 Offshore Technology Conference: Will et al., 2006). (c) The Girrasol and Jasmin FPSO development – the illustration shows several kilometres of the seabed (© 2004 Offshore Technology Conference: Idelovichi and Zundel, 2004). The Girassol FPSO and sub-sea systems were installed in 1.35 km water depth, offshore Angola, and the first oil was produced in December 2001

from wellheads on the seafloor transport oil up to the vessel. The oil is processed there, and offloaded along hanging lines to a loading buoy. A tanker hooks up to the loading buoy, fills up with oil, and transports the oil to a shore refinery.

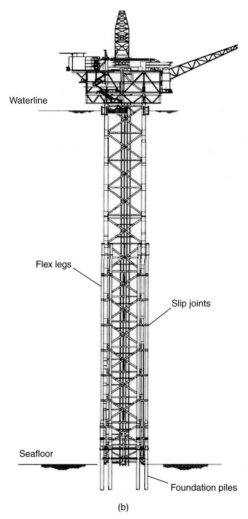

Waterline

Flex legs

Slip joints

Seafloor

Foundation piles

(b)

Fig. 1.5 Continued

Offshore structures are also now being built to harness the ocean's renewable energy. Figure 1.6 shows some of the wind towers at the North Hoyle windfarm, off the North Wales coast. Each tower supports a wind turbine and rotor assembly, typically 100 m above the waterline. The turbine generates electricity, which is fed along a sub-sea cable to land. North Hoyle has a maximum output of 60 MW, which provides energy to about 40 000 homes and represents a saving of about 160 000 tonnes of carbon dioxide per year (Carter, 2007). Offshore

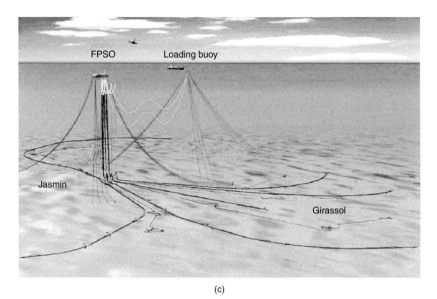

(c)

Fig. 1.5 Continued

Fig. 1.6 Offshore turbines and support structures at North Hoyle windfarm off the coast of North Wales (Ffrench et al., 2005). The nominal hub height is 70 m above the waterline. The rotor diameter is 80 m. The mean water depth is between 7 and 11 m over the site. The pile diameter is 4 m, installed to up to 33 m below the seafloor. Soil conditions consist of 10 m of sand and clay sediments, overlying mudstone and sandstone

windfarms are being developed mainly in Europe at present, but interest is developing elsewhere too.

1.1.4   Special features of environmental loading

The main environmental loads for offshore structures are wind, wave, and current loads. Ice loads may also be applicable. These loads are resisted by the structure and transmitted through the structure to the foundation. Therefore, values of the loads to be sustained by a foundation are usually determined as part of the structural analysis of the platform. For earthquakes, the opposite occurs. Ground shaking travels from an earthquake source, which may be many kilometres distant, through the ground, and through the foundations into the structure (Kramer, 1996).

Environmental loads are typically calculated as part of a structural analysis of the platform, from meteorological and oceanographic ('metocean') and other data that may be specified in terms of either spectra, time histories, or maximum values for particular return periods. The definition of a return period is the same as in onshore engineering: the return period of an event is an estimate of the average time interval between one occurrence and the next. For instance, a 100 year storm would occur, on average, $Y/100$ times in a period of Y years. In any one year, the probability p_1 of occurrence of an N-year event is approximately

$$p_1 = 1/N \tag{1.1}$$

Consider a design life of L years. The probability that the event will not happen in any one year is $1 - p_1$, so the probability that it will not happen in L years is $(1 - p_1)^L$. The probability that at least one event will happen in L years is

$$p_L = 1 - \left(1 - \frac{1}{N}\right)^L \tag{1.2}$$

Figure 1.7 shows this graphically. For example, there is a probability of about 18% that a structure with a design life of $L = 20$ years will experience the $N = 100$ year storm sometime in its design life. The probability of a set of conditions occurring is part of the calculation of the probability of failure, and is of interest to investors, insurers, and others, who may wish to balance the costs of an event with the extra costs of design and construction choices that reduce its likelihood of occurring (Kraft and Murff, 1975; Wu et al., 1989).

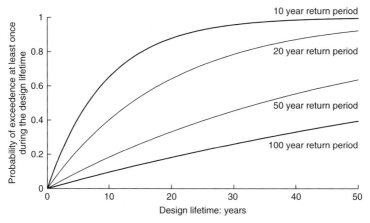

Fig. 1.7 Probability and return period

Except for wind, environmental loads act on the seafloor as well as on the structure. All of the environmental loads in the structure are primarily horizontal, but have noticeable vertical components. They also have significant cyclic components, and significant irregularity. For example, Fig. 1.8a shows a typical 4 minute time slice of the water level data at a North Sea location. The variations include some relatively short-period waves superimposed on longer wave periods. For linear waves, the relation between wave period T, wave length L, and water depth d is (e.g. Ippen, 1966)

$$L = \frac{gT^2}{2\pi} \tan h\left(\frac{2\pi d}{L}\right) \tag{1.3}$$

where $g = 9.81 \text{ m/s}^2$ is the acceleration due to gravity. For an extreme wave period of 16 seconds, in a water depth of 100 m, the wavelength is about 373 m, which is three times or four times the width of a large offshore structure. As a result, different parts of the structure experience cyclic wave forces that are partially out of phase.

The height of a breaking wave is about one-sixth of its wavelength in deep water, and about 0.8 times the water depth in shallow water. A typical 100 year wave in the North Sea has a wave height of about 30 m. Linear wave theory becomes rather approximate at large wave heights, and API RP2A (API, 2000) and other codes of practice require higher-order stream-function and non-linear Stokes theories to be used in wave force calculations.

Another complication is provided by vortex-shedding (Fig. 1.8b). As water passes a cylinder, such as a leg or bracing member on a

11

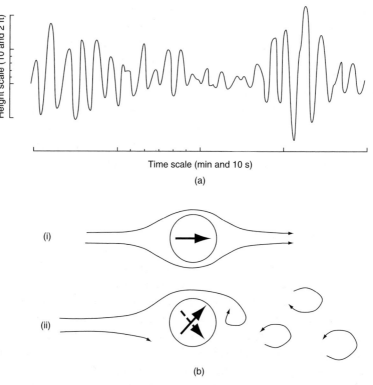

Fig. 1.8 Aspects of wave loading. (a) Example of a 4-minute portion of a wave record (© 1975 Offshore Technology Conference: Tricker, 1964; Lee and Focht, 1975). (b) Vortex shedding and vortex-induced vibrations as a wave or current passes a vertical pipe: (i) flow of a fluid past a cylinder in plan view, at low Reynold's number, showing smooth streamlines, and a steady force on the cylinder due to drag and inertia (Morison's equation); (ii) flow of a fluid past a cylinder in plan view, at high Reynold's number, showing development of vortices in the water, and oscillating forces on the cylinder

jacket platform, the flow is smooth if the speed of the water is low. At higher speeds, a succession of vortices form alternately on one side and the other of the cylinder as the water flows past, giving a component of alternating lateral force on the cylinder. Vortex-induced vibrations (VIVs) can develop if the rate of production of vortices matches a resonant frequency of the cylinder or structure.

Environmental loads thus contain many complex cyclic components. Soil behaviour is non-linear and inelastic under cyclic loading, even if only small strains occur (Atkinson, 2000). Cyclic loading can produce cumulative strains and cumulative development of excess pore pressures in the soil supporting an offshore structure. This can lead to progressive weakening during a storm. Excess pore pressure developed in the seabed as a result of one loading episode, such as a storm, can dissipate over subsequent time. Depending on the rate of dissipation, the soil response in a subsequent loading episode can be affected by residual effects from the earlier one. For these reasons, the structural analysis of a platform response generally involves significant interaction with geotechnical analysis. Design conditions may be specified in terms of a design storm, at the end of which a design extreme wave occurs.

1.1.5 Codes of practice

Several offshore standards and codes of practice are listed at the start of this book. Historically, the most widely used code is API RP2A. This was developed over many years, and has been validated by much engineering practice. It is updated periodically, both to incorporate the results of new research and experience and to address new challenges faced by the offshore industry. The last update was in 2007. Younger codes, including the ISO 19900 series, have copied much from API RP2A, but also tend to introduce some different features. For example, the DNV code for offshore windfarms, DNV-OS-J101, has slightly different expressions for some aspects of pile design. The series of new ISO 19900 standards will be completed by 2010, and API RP2A is to be re-structured (Wisch and Mangiavacchi, 2008).

As in other branches of civil engineering, offshore design standards are typically written in terms of ultimate limit states (ULSs) and serviceability limit states (SLSs). ULS events are extreme events that have a certain low probability of occurring during the design lifetime of a structure. An example is a 100-wave, which might occur only once in 100 years. A structure is required to survive ultimate events, though it may be allowed to sustain important damage. SLS events are less severe events, but more common, that a structure is required to remain serviceable in. For example, a structure should not settle excessively in moderately severe sea states, or sway so much that work becomes impossible.

Two other limit states are also considered. Accidental limit states (ALSs) are controllable events that are intended to not occur, but which have a significant probability of actually occurring. An example is a dropped object, or a ship impact against a structure. The character-istics of the accidents to be considered will be set by the platform designer. Fatigue limit states (FLSs) are limiting conditions or failures resulting from continued cyclic loading.

1.2   Development processes for offshore energy resources

1.2.1   Overview

Figure 1.9 shows an overview of the processes of identifying an offshore energy resource, arranging the legal framework, developing the resource, and decommissioning the development at the end of its productive life.

The time period between the first hydrocarbon discovery and the installation of a completed platform is typically 5 years or less (Digre *et al.*, 1989b). The productive life of a field is typically between 20

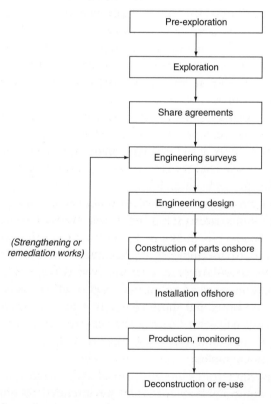

Fig. 1.9 Development process

and 50 years, although marginal fields may sometimes be economic over shorter periods. The design life for an offshore windfarm is of the same order (Carter, 2007). Design for periods longer than 50 years would entail increased costs to manage structural fatigue and corrosion.

1.2.2   Exploration

In pre-exploration, governments, energy companies, and academic institutions study an area to look for evidence of energy sources. For hydrocarbon resources, the geology of the area gives indications of the likelihood of the existence of hydrocarbon traps and other oil and gas sources. For renewable energy, metocean information gives information of where appropriate environmental conditions occur. If potentially commercial resources are found, the government will determine the boundaries of offshore exploration lots, and offers exploration licenses.

In exploration for hydrocarbon sources, geophysical surveys of licensed areas are run to determine whether and where the oil or gas is likely to be. These surveys typically penetrate several kilometres into the seabed, by acoustical and electrical means. If a possible oil reservoir is found, exploratory drilling may be carried out. For renewable energy, the focus is on wind, wave, current, or tidal characteristics. One or more anemometer masts may be installed offshore to measure wind speeds. Estimates are made of the amounts of energy available, and of its variability and reliability. A single hydrocarbon reservoir can often extend under the area covered by more than one exploration lot. The licensees make share agreements to determine which company will lead the development, and how costs and benefits are to be shared.

During this process, preliminary plans are made of the field development concepts. For hydrocarbon resources, the locations and types of platforms to be used are considered, and the routes of sub-sea pipelines or other methods to transport hydrocarbons ashore. For renewable energy, public consultation may be involved (CEEO, 2003) in determining the numbers and locations of wind or other energy generators to be placed offshore, and the cable route ashore. A supporting infrastructure plan may be needed. This may include construction or upgrading of ports and industrial support areas for oilfield supplies such as drilling equipment, pipes, muds, chemicals, and food, and for training people.

Once a resource has been found and government consents have been obtained, further survey work is carried out to determine engineering

Table 1.1 Surveys

Survey	Purpose
Bathymetry survey	To measure water depths, map the seafloor, identify seafloor hazards such as unevenness, slopes, fluid expulsion features, and collapses
Metocean study	To determine wind, wave, and current characteristics at the platform sites; these will form the basis of estimates of platform loading and of scour
Environmental baseline survey	To identify environmental issues and measure environmental flora and fauna populations, so that the site can be returned to its original condition after the production operations have finished
Geohazards assessment	To identify and plan the mitigation of geological and geotechnical hazards
Shallow geophysical survey	To identify soil layering and sub-bottom hazards such as geological faults, infilled ancient riverbeds, voids, shallow gas, and rock
Geotechnical survey	To verify soil layering and determine soil properties at the platform sites
Pipeline or cable route surveys	To identify bathymetry, soil conditions, and hazards along pipeline routes between different offshore platforms, and between platforms and onshore
Seismic risk assessment	To identify the seismicity of the area and determine spectra and/or acceleration time histories to be used in seismic design
Ice hazards and mitigation study	To determine ice loads and ways to manage them
Seafloor survey	Done just before installing a platform at a site, to check that the seafloor has not changed and hazards such as dropped objects, sand dunes, shipwrecks have not occurred there

and other design conditions and parameters. Table 1.1 lists some of the surveys that may be done.

1.2.3 Design, construction and installation

Preliminary geotechnical design is usually carried out as soon as relevant information is available. The properties and behaviours of the foundations partly determine the structural responses to environmental loads. A structural analysis will determine the loads to be supported by the foundations, but the result will depend partly on the foundation stiffness, which depends on those loads. For this reason, design is an iterative and interactive process.

Design calculations and plans are submitted, usually by the energy company, to a certifying body. Certifying bodies include the American Bureau of Shipping, Bureau Veritas, Det Norske Veritas, Germanischer Lloyd, Lloyd's Register of Shipping, and the Offshore Certification Bureau. Safety cases may also need to be made to a regulator, such as the UK Health and Safety Executive. Certification is a continuing process that includes the period of installation and pre-operational inspection.

Gerwick (2007) describes practical aspects of the construction, installation, remediation, and decommissioning of all types of marine and offshore structure. Platforms are partially constructed in dry dock facilities onshore. Towards the end of construction, a seafloor survey may be carried out at the planned offshore location, to check that no changes have occurred since the original bathymetric survey, and to ensure that there are no small-scale hazards on the seafloor, such as lost equipment, shipwrecks, jackup footprints, or undulations. The seabed may be prepared by clearing debris and/or levelling. Ground improvement works can also be done, such as installation of compaction piles, sand drains to accelerate consolidation of clay strata, or a seafloor berm needed to support some mobile islands.

The partially constructed platform is then moved offshore, by barge or by towing, and is installed at the target location with temporary support on the seabed. Positioning on location is controlled using data from the Differential Global Position System (DGPS), a system of satellites and onshore stations around the globe. The system measures position to a few centimetres accuracy. The installed position depends on controllability during installation, and can typically be within a metre of target for a jacket platform, or within a few metres for a gravity platform. Once the platform is resting on the seafloor, the foundation works are completed, and the platform deck and topsides modules are lifted on.

Sub-sea pipelines are laid by special vessels, and are buried in shallow waters as protection against snagging by fishing lines, ship's anchors, and from other hazards. After the relevant connections are made to a platform, everything is checked, and the platform is ready for its productive use.

1.2.4   Lifetime monitoring

Many offshore structures have comprehensive structural monitoring systems, often including foundation monitoring. Regular surveys are generally carried out including visual inspection of a platform, a review of equipment and maintenance records, and selective testing of safety systems (Mather, 2000). Additional survey requirements may be specified by the certifying authority. A structural engineer will inspect platforms regularly for corrosion and fatigue damage, and repairs can be carried out if necessary. Sub-sea inspections and maintenance can be done by a diver or by a remotely operated vehicle (ROV).

Sometimes a geotechnical issue arises, or new experience elsewhere indicates that previous design criteria may have been insufficient. An example is given by Berner *et al.* (1989), who describe the installation of belled piles following a reassessment of foundation reliability in carbonate soils.

Once an oil or gas reservoir is depleted, another use may be found for the structure. Some such platforms have been considered as support structures for offshore wind turbines. Most governments require that the offshore platform and associated facilities be eventually removed and the environment returned to its state before the platform was installed.

1.3   Geohazards

1.3.1   Introduction

Geohazards are hazards associated with geological or geotechnical features or processes in the vicinity of a planned offshore structure that may pose a threat to the integrity or serviceability of the structure and its foundations over its design lifetime. Geohazards are identified by a study of the geology, geomorphology, and geography of a region, and through geophysical and geotechnical surveys and investigations (Prior and Doyle, 1984; Dao *et al.*, 1985; Templeton *et al.*, 1985; Peuchen and Raap, 2007).

Figure 1.10a shows a well-used depiction of typical geohazards to be considered by the geotechnical engineer, including many geological features as well as landslides, carbonate sands, unconsolidated soils, gas hydrates, and disturbed sediments. Figure 1.10b shows another view considering deeper water. Some of these hazards are discussed further below. Figure 1.10c shows a simplified version of the approach by Power *et al.* (2005) to geohazards management. A geological model is developed of the region and of the platform site or pipeline route, and is used to predict how hazards may develop over the design lifetime of the structure. For each hazard, triggering likelihood is assessed. Threats are investigated, monitored, removed or avoided (Angeli *et al.*, 2005; Lane, 2005; Younes *et al.*, 2005; Galavazi *et al.*, 2006; Cauqil and Adamy, 2008; Hogan *et al.*, 2008).

1.3.2 Major events

Earthquakes are episodes of ground shaking that can last for a few seconds to a few minutes (Bolt, 2005). They are due to localised failures of parts of the earth's crust that are being pushed or sheared relative to one another by forces originating in the earth's mantle. They occur beneath land or beneath the ocean, where they are sometimes called seaquakes.

The 1929 Grand Banks earthquake had a magnitude of 7.2 with an epicentre about 400 km south of Newfoundland (Fine *et al.*, 2005). It was felt as far away as New York and Montreal. It occurred along two geological faults, and triggered a submarine landslide involving about 200 km^3 of soil. The slide turned into a turbidity current carrying mud and sand eastward about 1000 km at estimated speeds of about 60–100 km/h, breaking 12 submarine transatlantic telegraph cables. It caused a 15 m-high tsunami that struck the coast 3 hours after the earthquake. The tsunami was also recorded on the other side of the Atlantic Ocean.

The largest known landslide is the Storegga slide, offshore Norway. This occurred about 7000 years ago, and involved about several thousand cubic kilometres of material covering an area about 50 000 km^2 (Bryn *et al.*, 2005; Solheim *et al.*, 2005; Gafeira, 2009). The slide may have been caused by a gas hydrate event triggered by a global warming episode (Mienert *et al.*, 2005), or by an earthquake (Atakan and Ojeda, 2005). It was one of many that seem to have occurred in that area in the geological past. A 30 m tidal wave was created which reached the coasts of Norway and Scotland.

1.3.3 Submarine slope instabilities

Submarine slope instabilities, flowslides, debris flows, and mudflows can be triggered by earthquakes, and by slow events involving deposition of material on the upper surfaces of slopes, or erosion by current or other actions (including construction works) on slopes or at their bases. Submarine slides can be triggered by cyclic wave pressures (Henkel, 1970). Slopes can build up over time in and outside river estuaries,

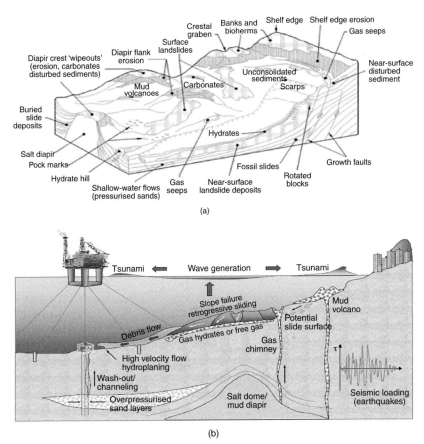

Fig. 1.10 Aspects of geohazards and their management. (a) A widely used summary of deepwater geohazards (© 2005 Offshore Technology Conference: Power et al., 2005). (b) More geohazards (© 2007 Offshore Technology Conference: Strout and Tjelta, 2007). (c) Management process (simplified from Power et al., 2005)

due to deposition of sediment as the velocity of the water slows as it enters the ocean. The effects can stretch many kilometres out to sea for large rivers (Roberts *et al.*, 1976; Coleman *et al.*, 1978; Templeton *et al.*, 1985). Larger particles settle faster, while clays can travel many hundreds of kilometres. Slopes steepen over time, eventually reaching a height and steepness that causes the slope to fail (Mulder and Cochonat, 1996; Huhnerbach and Masson, 2004; Masson *et al.*, 2006).

Sliding soil can break into blocks and smaller lumps as it moves, creating a debris flow or turbidity current that is lubricated by the water entrained within it. The flow can continue for many hundreds

20

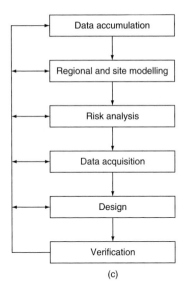

(c)

Fig. 1.10 Continued

of kilometres from the original source of the slide (Felix and Peakall, 2006). Platforms are designed to avoid generating a slope failure, and to resist the forces from turbidity currents and debris flows generated elsewhere.

1.3.4   Seabed geology and variability

The seabed is rarely uniform, flat, or featureless. Soil layering beneath the seafloor is not necessarily uniform in the lateral directions, and geological faults are common, with layer boundaries on one side of a fault displaced vertically compared with the other side. Active faults can move suddenly from time to time, creating a small or large earthquake as they do. They can also move by creeping. It is unwise to locate an offshore structure close to a fault, or across it. However, it happens. For long pipelines, there may be little choice but to cross fault lines. Special fault-crossing structures can be designed to allow for likely fault movements with pipeline damage.

Mud volcanoes are cones of mud on the seafloor that have been formed in the same way as lava volcanoes, except that fine-grained soil is ejected from deep beneath the seabed, instead of magma (Camerlenghi *et al.*, 1995).

Karst ground occurs in some offshore areas. This consists of soluble rock that has been partially dissolved by groundwater, at a period of geological history when the water surface was different from now. The dissolution can leave sinkholes, cavities, and cave systems at shallow depth (Waltham, 2000). Karst conditions can be readily detected by geophysical surveys. They develop primarily in strong limestones and dolomites. Similar features occur in weaker limestones, chalk, sabkhas, and cemented carbonate sands, though on smaller scales. Sabkhas are flat, very saline areas of sand or silt that are deposited on land and often contain soft nodules and veins of gypsum or anhydrite (Boggs, 2006). They are then covered over by other sediments, and become part of a seabed as a result of crustal movement.

1.3.5   Seabed materials

Unconsolidated sediments are silts and clays that were deposited relatively recently, and which have not finished the process of primary consolidation. This means the soils have not had time to gain strength from the compressive strains associated with dissipation of excess pore pressures. The sediments are unusually weak materials.

Calcareous and carbonate soils can be identified by their reaction with dilute hydrochloric acid, which produces carbon dioxide that bubbles off. The grains are made partially or wholly or calcium carbonate, and may be formed of the skeletal remains of microscopic marine plant and animal life. Calcium carbonate is a relatively soft mineral, compared with silica-based soils (Mitchell and Soga, 2005). It dissolves very slowly in seawater, but can precipitate out and form a calcite cement that binds soil grains together. The binding is very variable. This and the crushability of the grains make carbonate sands unreliable foundation materials (Murff, 1987; Jewell and Khorshid, 2000; Kolk, 2000).

Shallow gas may occur in the form of small bubbles in the pore fluid of a soil, or as layers of solid gas hydrate. If disturbed by drilling, the hydrate can volatilise from the solid into a gas. Gas can bubble up explosively through a drill pipe. The gas can be hydrogen sulfide, which smells like rotten eggs and is highly poisonous. It also numbs people's sense of smell. By the time you can no longer smell it, you have inhaled enough to present a major danger of death. Areas where shallow gas occurs are called 'sour gas' fields. Work in these areas is feasible and safe provided people are prepared, the appropriate detectors are used, and emergency equipment is available.

Gas hydrates are crystalline solids consisting of gas molecules, with each molecule surrounded by a cage of water molecules. Methane hydrate looks like water ice, is stable in ocean floor sediments at water depths greater than 300 m, and can exist in solid form at elevated temperatures if the water pressure is sufficiently high (Shipley *et al.*, 1979; Neurauter and Bryant, 1989). Hydrates are a potential source of energy, and may amount to more than double the world's other hydrocarbon reserves. They can be readily detected by geophysical surveys. In deep water, they can cement loose sediments in a surface layer several hundred meters thick. The drilling of a well through a gas hydrate body, and heating by warm drilling fluids and hot recovered hydrocarbons, can cause the hydrate to sublimate, turning the soil layer into a mixture of soil grains, water and gas. This can severely damage a foundation. Siriwardane and Smith (2006) found that hydrate-related slope instability could occur for slopes as low as 2–5°.

Sand dunes can move along the seafloor by a process of erosion from one side and deposition on the other. Their movement can bury submerged structures, creating serviceability and maintenance problems. Their weight can cause settlements and local foundation failures. Some seabeds are composed of thick deposits of ancient sand dunes that have piled up on top of each other. This can produce complex variations of strength and density in the seabed.

A hard seabed is hazardous. A hardpan surface is inconvenient if an excavation is to be made in the seabed (Randell *et al.*, 2008). Intact rock layers are harder to drive piles through compared with most soils, and will grip an installed pile less strongly, giving less shaft resistance to vertical loading. Grouted piles provide an alternative, but are generally more expensive. A hardpan layer may overly weaker materials, and there can be places immediately below an intact rock later where relatively large voids can be stable. Generally, a hard stratum overlying a weaker one presents a danger that a foundation intended to rest on the hard stratum may fail by punching through into the weaker one.

1.3.6 Other hazards

Previous uses of a seabed can create hazards. For example, if a jackup is set down on a location, its foundations disturb the seabed. This creates a 'footprint' problem when that jackup leaves and another jackup is used later at the site, with a different geometry of foundations (Jardine *et al.*, 2001; Dean and Serra, 2004). The seabed is also used for anchoring ships and for trawler fishing, and there are shipwrecks. All these represent hazards to offshore structures, and can be detected in a geophysical survey or side-scan sonar survey.

Drilling fluids are often under high pressure, both during site investigations for a platform, and during drilling an oil well. Hydraulic fracture and/or local liquefaction of the seabed can result if the pressures are too high or are not adequately contained. These problems can be avoided by proper geotechnical design. Marine ecosystems can also be hazards for offshore structures. Marine plant and animal growth on offshore structures increases the environmental loads on the structures by making their surfaces rougher and their dimensions larger. Burrowing sea creatures have the potential to remove foundation material from beneath or beside a structure.

Some seafloor areas have been used as munitions dumping grounds, or as military practice areas. Munitions or unexploded ordinance (UXO) risks can be particularly important in areas where there has been recent war. These risks are best managed by specialists (Halpin and Morrison, 2009).

1.4   Geotechnical design

1.4.1   Objectives

Geotechnical design is the process of planning, choosing, specifying, and inspecting solutions for foundations and earthworks. It is part of the development processes of an offshore energy resource. It involves investigation, concepts, judgement, modelling, calculations, checking, and reports. It essentially results in a set of technical instructions to a contractor.

Part of the aim is to ensure that, although a chosen technical solution may sustain some expected damage over a design lifetime, it can survive extreme events in the damaged condition, such as an extreme storm, can remain serviceable for an acceptable proportion of the structure's design life, and will not cause failure to other parts of the structure or other structures.

For offshore design, expected damage can include corrosion, effects of marine growth, effects of seafloor erosion or scour, and cumulative effects of cyclic loading on the soil.

Scour is a process by which the movement of water over a granular soil surface causes grains to be picked up and transported elsewhere (Niedoroda *et al.*, 1981; Whitehouse, 1998; Sumer *et al.*, 2005). Figure 1.11a illustrates the type of result that can occur beneath the base of a jacket platform. 'Global scour' is scour over the entire area of a platform footprint. It occurs because the structural elements force moving water to accelerate around the elements, producing an increase in water particle velocity compared with areas outside the footprint, and so a small increase in the rate of general scour. Global scour affects the stresses in the seabed over a wide area. 'Local scour' is scour in the immediate vicinity of a structural element such as a pile. It occurs because of the local high increases in water velocity here. Local scour affects stresses in the seabed only to a shallow depth.

Figure 1.11b shows aspects of the mechanics of scour around a pile. The development of small vortices as the water passes the pile tends to increase the water velocity at the soil surface, and this causes material to be picked up by the water. This in turn causes a depression that can accentuate the scouring effect. Scour is similar to erosion, but has more complex aspects in the offshore environment, due to wave effects and changes of direction of the fluid. Figure 1.11b shows a simple erosion model that is strictly valid for a very specific water depth. Erosion is most marked for a middle range of particle sizes, corresponding to sands. Erosion requires higher water velocities in fine-grained soils, partly because of electric forces between clay grains. Erosion requires higher velocities for gravels, because of the higher weight of the gravel particles relative to the erosive forces.

1.4.2 Design tools

An understanding of soil mechanics is a key design tool, and in particular how soil can interact with structural behaviours. This book aims to provide a starting point. Many references are also given to sources in the literature which provide more information.

The standards and codes of practice listed at the start of this book contain valuable guidance, and the appropriate standard must of course be followed when agreed in a contract.

Commercial software exists to carry out most of the repetitive design tasks, and should generally be used, for the following reasons. First, it has been validated, and so is less likely to be in error compared with a hand calculation, unless the input data are wrong. Second, it is faster, and so frees the engineer to think and judge, and for other important parts of the design process.

Centrifuge model testing is a routine part of creative geotechnical design and research for offshore structures (Schofield, 1980; Rowe, 1983; Taylor, 1995; Murff, 1996; Springman, 2002). A simple centrifuge model is a $1/N$ scale model of a foundation, tested under a centrifugal acceleration equivalent to N times the acceleration of

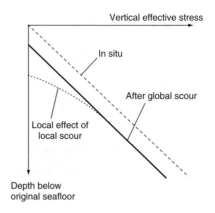

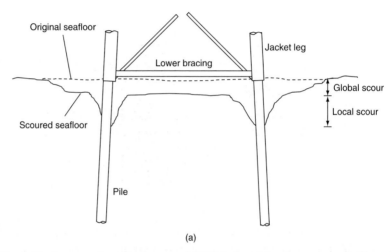

(a)

Fig. 1.11 Aspects of seafloor scour. (a) Global and local scour, and effects on vertical effective stresses in the soil. (b) Vortex development and associated scour as water flow around a circular cylinder intersecting the seafloor (© 1981 Offshore Technology Conference: Niederoda et al., 1981). (c) Hjulström diagram showing critical current velocity to move grains on a plane bed at 1 m water depth, adapted from Sundborg (1956) and Boggs (2006), with approximate transport/sedimentation boundary added

earth's gravity. The soil is not scaled: the same soil is used in the model as at full scale. The fluid used in the model may be N times more viscous than water. Scales of $N = 100$ are common. The arrangements ensure that the soil in the centrifuge experiences the same stresses as at full scale, and so behaves in the same way as at full scale.

Finite element calculations are also becoming a major design (Potts and Zdravkovic, 1999; Templeton, 2008). However, the validity of

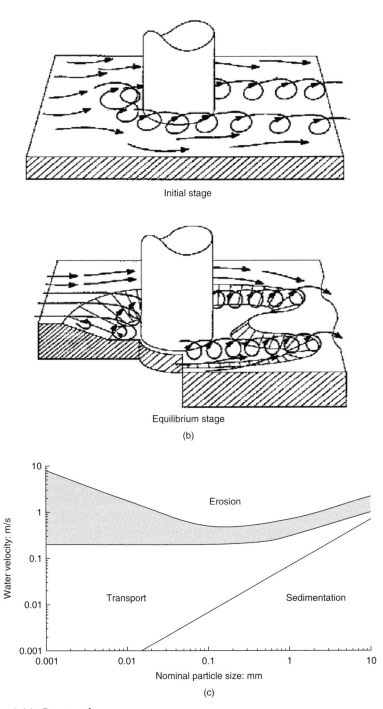

Initial stage

Equilibrium stage

(b)

Erosion

Transport

Sedimentation

Fig. 1.11 Continued

the results depends on the validity of the theories that the software applies. The theory of cyclic loading is presently somewhat qualitative and approximate, and sound engineering judgement is required. The software gives answers based on the theory, but the theory needs further development.

Probably the most important design tool is the designer's sense and good judgement, updated by continuously evolving personal experience and the documented experiences of others. New discoveries and methods in offshore geotechnical engineering are published in the proceedings of the Offshore Technology Conference and the Offshore and Polar Engineering Conference, held annually, and in refereed technical journals.

1.4.3   Records

As in other engineering disciplines, comprehensive and accurate record keeping is essential for all relevant observations, design calculations, software versions, decisions, recommendations, and supporting arguments. Record keeping is an important part of a company's quality system.

2

Offshore surveys and site investigations

Chapter 2 looks at the various types of offshore survey, covering how to interpret results from geophysical surveys for geotechnical purposes, understand the technologies and some of the soil mechanics theory underlying offshore surveys and investigations, and how to plan, participate in, and report these activities.

2.1   Introduction

2.1.1   Purpose and types of investigation

An offshore survey for engineering purposes is a study to determine the conditions, hazards, and parameters for an engineering design (Atkins, 2004). Surveys relating to geotechnical work include:

- *preliminary study*: a desk study of a few weeks' duration to extract engineering data from geological survey reports and to determine what is already known in published documents and company archives, and from technical data providers
- *shallow geophysical survey*: a field study using non-intrusive devices such as echosounders for bathymetry and sound sources for sub-seafloor surveying, done as part of a geohazards survey and to help plan and support a subsequent geotechnical survey or investigation
- *shallow-penetration geotechnical survey*: a field study with in-situ testing and soil sampling to a few metres below the seafloor, and with subsequent laboratory testing, for pipeline routes and small structures
- *deep-penetration geotechnical investigation*: a field study with in-situ testing and soil sampling to up to 120 m or more below the seafloor, with extensive laboratory testing, done for the sites of fixed and mobile offshore platforms.

One of the outputs from the surveys will normally be a geohazards assessment, and there is normally a separate seismic hazard survey if there is an earthquake risk. A meteorological and oceanographic (met-ocean) survey will be done to determine wind, wave and current conditions for the area of interest. An environmental baseline survey may be done to determine flora and fauna in the area of interest; most regulatory authorities require the environment be returned to its previous state at the end of a field development.

An excellent detailed description of surveys of offshore and nearshore projects is provided by ISSMGE TC1 (2005). Specific survey requirements are also detailed in API RP2A (API, 2000), ISO 19902 (ISO, 2007), ISO 19903 (ISO, 2006), and other offshore codes of practice.

2.1.2 *Project management issues*

All offshore survey work requires careful and intense planning and project management. Most works are international in character, with personnel and equipment being mobilised from different countries and even continents to work intensely for short periods at locations offshore. A typical management team includes:

- a project manager
- an operations manager
- a geophysics manager
- a geotechnical engineering manager or engineer
- a laboratory manager
- a country manager
- a local shipping and general agent.

The project manager will also be able to call on the services of a contracts manager, an HSE (health, safety, and environmental) manager, and a quality system manager. The work on a particular survey project passes through the typical stages of:

- planning
- mobilisation
- work
- demobilisation of offshore equipment and people
- onshore testing and analysis
- final reporting.

Daily reports are typically submitted for operational matters and technical progress. Engineering field reports are issued either in the field or (more commonly) from a head office within a few days after the field-work is completed. The final report is normally required within 6 weeks of the field demobilisation. Final engineering reports are inputs to the contractual process for construction.

2.1.3 Health and safety and environmental issues

Offshore working is nowadays very safe and environmentally friendly, primarily because of the seriousness with which energy company clients treat HSE issues. Every project is normally required to have a safety plan, which will detail health and safety policies, procedures, training, and arrangements for the work, including medical evacuation if it becomes necessary. Medevac and anti-piracy arrangements are made before the cruise starts.

Typically, there will be a kick-off briefing at the start of the offshore work, and a lifeboat drill and possibly a shallow gas drill and a reminder of the man-overboard procedure. There will be clean and dirty areas on a ship, and workers coming in from dirty areas must clean up before entering office, eating, or accommodation spaces. People will typically work 12 hour shifts, and will be required to maintain good hygiene. There will be daily briefings on the work that is planned for that day, and 'toolbox talks' covering anything from general safety issues and the task in hand.

Geophysical and geotechnical surveys involve a considerable amount of working with cranes and on a deck that may be windy, wet, moving, and, sometimes, slippery. Personal protective equipment is usually mandatory, and geotechnical personnel can be expect to be provided with (and be required to use) steel-tipped boots, fire-resistant overalls, gloves, safety glasses, a lifejacket, and a hard hat. Working areas will have eyewash facilities and a first aid kit available for minor cuts and bruises. There will normally be an onboard medical room and an offshore medic.

Clients insist that environmentally responsible procedures be adopted, and that compounds that are to be discharged to the environment are safe. For example, seismic survey ships typically employ a large-mammal lookout who will stop the survey work if the sound energy sources are likely to cause harm. On drilling ships, guar gum is often used as a drilling mud, and is edible. Ships are normally equipped with oil spill remediation kits, and machines are fitted with containment trays to catch any small spills. Garbage is typically stored on the vessel and disposed of at local facilities during port calls.

2.1.4   Offshore positioning and water depths

The measurement of positions and the interpretation of water depths offshore is usually the responsibility of a specialist surveyor.

Geographic positions are typically determined using the Differential Global Positioning System (DGPS), based around 24 satellites and a number of ground stations (ISSMGE TC1, 2005; Lekkerkerk *et al.*, 2006). Receivers on a boat decode the signals and calculate geographical positions usually to within about ±0.1 m. The position is normally described in terms of easting and northing in metres, referred to the WGS84 spheroid. This is a set of local spherical models of the earth's surface. Latitude and longitudes are obtained by conversion from the WGS84 values. The measurement systems are calibrated by bar checks that are usually carried out at the start and end of each phase of job for survey work.

The water depth at a location varies due to daily or twice-daily tides, and over longer durations, and is affected by atmospheric weather, and by the earth's rotation and the Coriolis forces it generates. Lekkerkerk *et al.* (2006) describe how a daily tidal wave is generated in the Antarctic Ocean and travels northwards, being deflected by land masses, arriving at the English Channel a little more than a day later. This type of astronomically generated tide is predictable in advance, including the effects of landmasses and varying water depths. Predictions are published as tide tables (e.g. UKHO, 2004).

Depths on marine charts may be referenced to 'chart datum', which is defined differently in different regions. Depths measured by echosounders will normally be corrected for tides, and expressed either in terms of a depth at the lowest astronomical tide (LAT), or depth relative to a chart datum.

2.2   Shallow geophysical surveys

2.2.1   Introduction

A geophysical survey is an exploration by non-intrusive methods (Games, 1985; OSIF, 2000; Keary *et al.*, 2002; Atkins, 2004; Fugro, 2005; ISSMGE TC1, 2005; Lekkerkerk *et al.*, 2006). This type of survey can include bathymetry to measure water depths, sonar surveys to image the seafloor and objects on it, and sub-bottom profiling surveys to measure soil stratigraphies, estimate soil types, and identify irregularities and lateral variability. Geophysical surveys are a necessary precursor to geotechnical surveys and investigations. (Sieck, 1975;

Williams and Aurora, 1982; Pelletier *et al.*, 1997; Ehlers *et al.*, 2008). They are also used to find sand and gravel deposits for island construction or other commercial exploitation (Nebrija *et al.*, 1978).

Figure 2.1a illustrates the measurement of water depth using an echosounder. A sound pulse is emitted from a source, travels outwards and downwards to the seabed, is reflected back up, and arrives at a receiver at a time Δt after it was emitted. By measuring Δt and knowing the velocity of sound through water and the distances L and d_0, the water depth can be deduced. The sound frequency used is typically in the range 10–500 kHz. The speed of sound is around 1400–1500 m/s in water, depending on a variety of factors, including temperature, salinity, and contaminants load. The accuracy can be as good as ±0.1 m in 100 m water depth, but depends on a variety of factors, including the hardness of the seafloor soils. A dense sand or rock seabed can give a clear reflection. Weak reflections giving less accurate results can occur if the seabed is very soft silt or clay (Winterwerp, 2005).

Figure 2.1b illustrates a multi-channel system, with up to 50 or more echosounders deployed on structural members protruding either side of a survey boat. The spacing between transducers may be between about 1 and 3 m. Figure 2.1c depicts the more recent swathe bathymetry technique, where a transducer array is used to measure depths along a swathe at right angles from the ship (Denbigh, 1989). Swathe widths are limited to about four times the water depth for measurements accurate to a few centimetres, provided the seafloor soils are sufficiently strong to give a clear reflection. These systems can also be angled to inspect slopes (Fig. 2.1d).

Sound navigation and ranging (sonar) systems are commonly used for imaging the seafloor and obstacles on it. Active sonar systems send out sound pulses, while passive sonar systems monitor the sounds emitted by the objects they are tracking. Active scanning sonar systems can be used to monitor a rapidly changing sub-sea environment. Ship-borne sonar systems can be very powerful, imaging objects and seafloors that can be several kilometres from the sound source. The frequency used determines the depth capabilities of the system. High frequencies (100–450 kHz) are used for water depths up to 300 m or so. Medium frequencies (30–100 kHz) are used for medium-depth waters, to 3000 m or so. Low frequencies (12–18 kHz) are useful for very deep waters (>6000 m).

Figure 2.2a shows a typical arrangement for seismic reflection surveys. A survey ship works an area in a grid pattern. It travels along survey

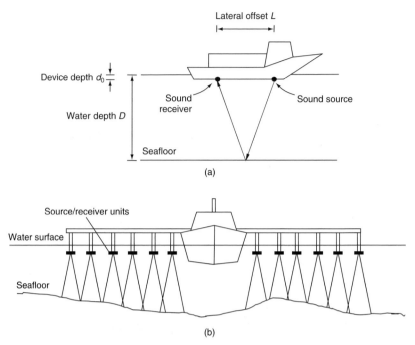

Fig. 2.1 Echosounding systems for measurement of water depth. (a) Travel of a sound wave from a source to a seafloor, reflection, and travel to a receiver. (b) Multi-system array; each echosounder measures the average depth to the seafloor over a small angle; software on board the boat combines the data to give a contour map of what is observed. (c) Swathe bathymetry using a multi-beam system. (d) Multi-beam system turned at an angle for slope inspection

lines, pulling with it an energy source and a number of receivers. Energy sources include sparkers, boomers, and pingers, which operate at different frequencies, and chirp profiles, which scan through a range of frequencies. The source is activated in an explosive burst every few seconds, and the sound waves travel to and into the seabed, being reflected and refracted at the seafloor and at internal boundaries between soil layers of different wave transmission characteristics. The reflected signals are picked up by the receivers. The signal times and strengths are transmitted to computer systems onboard the vessel that decode the information and present it in terms of contour maps or other visualisations.

Figure 2.2b shows a typical arrangement for a seismic refraction survey, which requires energy sources and receivers close to or in contact with the seafloor (Fortin *et al.*, 1987; Pedotti *et al.*, 1990).

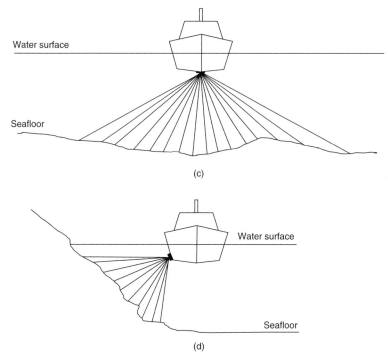

(c)

(d)

Fig. 2.1 Continued

These surveys are particularly useful for cable and pipeline routes, where fine detail is required of the upper 3 m of the seabed. A similar system is also used for a seabed resistivity survey. A sledge is pulled along the seafloor, and emits a signal into the seabed. The sledge pulls a trail of receivers that pick up the signals and pass them up the umbilical to onboard computers which analyse the data and present them in engineering visualisations (Atkins, 2004; Kolk and Wegerif, 2005). The sledge can weigh up to a tonne, and is required to be stationary on the seafloor during each pulse and measurement cycle. A device on the deck of the vessel alternately pays out and pulls in cable, so that the sled moves along the seabed in jerks while the vessel steams ahead at 3–4 knots. The systems work in water depths up to 350 m or so.

Seismic reflection and sonar systems can also be fitted to 'towfish' that are towed behind a ship under the control of an operator on board (Fig. 2.2c). This is convenient for pipeline routes which may be several kilometres to several hundred kilometres long. Small systems can also be fitted to remotely operated vehicles (ROVs) for use in and around a particular location (Fig. 2.2d). The sonar systems are

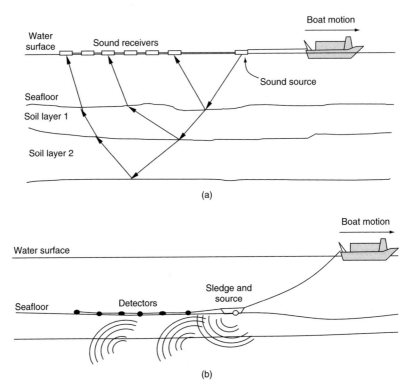

Fig. 2.2 Deployment of towed, directed and autonomous systems. (a) Typical arrangement for ship-borne seismic surveying. (b) A system pulled along the seafloor. (c) Towfish system. (d) Operations of remotely operated vehicles (ROVs) and autonomous underwater vehicles (AUVs)

often dual frequency, with frequencies up to 1 MHz for accurate imaging, and from 50 kHz upwards for operations requiring less accuracy. Vertically mounted sonar is used for ROV inspections of seabed objects, trenches, cables and pipelines. Sidescan sonar is used to image obstacles in front of the ROV. Side-scan sonar mounted on towfish are used to monitor seabed morphology. Side-scan and vertical systems can be used together, and with underwater cameras and remotely operated tools for underwater construction operations.

Small systems can also be fitted to autonomous underwater vehicles (AUVs). These operate under onboard power, and are preprogrammed, so do not require umbilical connections. They are useful for deepwater sites, where umbilical lengths can create difficulties for ROVs (Campbell *et al.*, 2005).

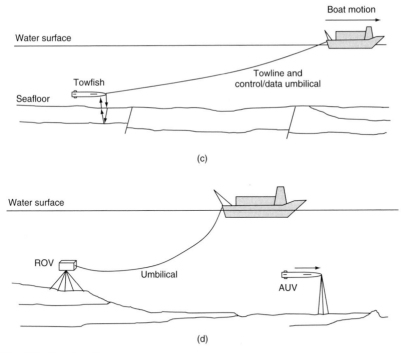

Fig. 2.2 Continued

2.2.2 Examples of geotechnical uses of sonar and sub-bottom survey data

Experience from the use of geophysical data in geotechnical studies has shown that the seabed is rarely flat and rarely uniform. It contains significant irregularities that can affect foundation design. Consequently, integrated geological, geophysical, and geotechnical interpretations of site survey data can provide considerably more useful information than straightforward geotechnical interpretations alone (Williams and Aurora, 1982; McKenzie *et al.*, 1984; Campbell *et al.*, 1988; Nauroy *et al.*, 1994).

Figure 2.3a shows an example of soil layering and geological faults identified by an AUV survey. The information was important in the assessment of lateral levels and variability of soil layering, and the identification of the faults allowed those areas to be avoided in the deployment of a seabed structure. AUV sub-bottom profiles (Fig. 2.3b) showed that one of the geotechnical cores and the associated cone penetration test (CPT, described later) had been carried out in a sinkhole. This provided an understanding of why the geotechnical data from these

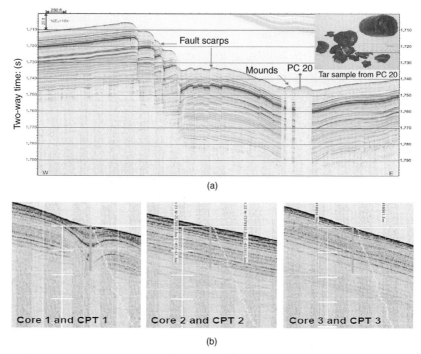

Fig. 2.3 Examples of geotechnical applications of geophysical survey data. (a) An AUV sub-bottom profile showing soil layering and geological faults. The horizontal scale is 10 × the vertical scale. The depth of the profile is about 250 feet, and the width is about 5000 feet (about 1 mile) (© 2008 Offshore Technology Conference: Williamson et al., 2008). (b) An AUV sub-bottom profile was undertaken to verify the soil stratigraphy at three locations where core sampling of the seabed had been undertaken and in-situ cone penetration tests (CPTs) had been done. The profiles explained how the data from Core 1 and CPT 1 related to the data for the other two positions (© 2008 Offshore Technology Conference: Ehlers et al., 2008). (c) A seafloor landslide with mass transport deposit (MTD) and recent hemipelagic slide infill (© 2007 Offshore Technology Conference: Solheim et al., 2007). (d) Example of the use of geophysical data to find suitable locations for three anchor piles. This is a plan view showing depth contours and the surface expressions of geological faults that had been identified in a sub-bottom geophysical survey (© 2005 Offshore Technology Conference Campbell et al., 2005)

tests differed from the other two locations, and allowed the engineer to avoid an incorrect inference concerning lateral dip of the soil layer boundaries.

Figure 2.3c is a larger-scale plot with a width of several kilometres. It shows a landslide mass, and allows the engineer to correctly understand and interpret geotechnical data in the area. This dipping of strata seen

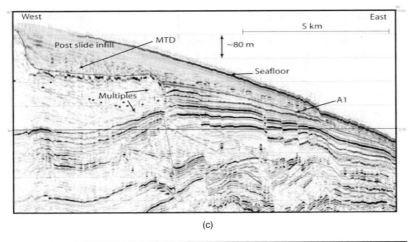

(c)

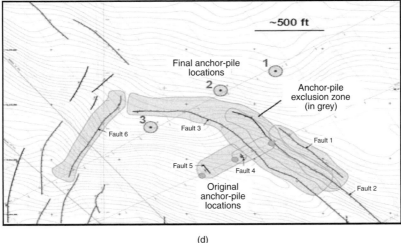

(d)

Fig. 2.3 Continued

here is common in many offshore regions. Soil layers can have appreciable dips. In one case, a jackup was deployed about 100 m from the originally planned location: soil strata at the actual location had a dip of about 6°, and predictions for the engineering response of the foundations gave results that were about $100 \times \tan 6° = 10.5$ m different than calculated on the basis of the measured soil layers and properties. The reason became apparent when the geophysical data were provided.

Figure 2.3d shows an example where the planned locations of three large anchor piles was changed as a result of geophysical data which indicated that the originally planned locations were too close to geological faults.

2.2.3   Other surveying methods

Existing sledge-based seismic (sound) systems apply pressure waves to the seabed (P-waves). A newer system using surface waves is described by Puech *et al.* (2004). A sledge-mounted shear wave generator and detection system is described by Vaneste *et al.* (2007). Resistivity surveys also use a sledge and streamer system towed along the seafloor (Scott *et al.*, 1983; Puech and Tuenter, 2002). Pulses of electrical current are passed from a device on the sledge, through the soil, into transducers on the streamer system, with the circuit being completed back to the sledge. The data are processed in much the same way as a seismic refraction survey.

In a ground-penetrating radar survey, a radar system is pointed into the ground, and the reflected electromagnetic waves are used to build up a picture of sub-bottom reflectors (Eyles and Meulendyk, 2008). In gravity and magnetometer surveys, devices that measure variations in the magnitude and direction of the earth's gravity or in its magnetic field is carried along with the vessel or an aircraft. Special compensation systems are needed to account for vessel motions and the vessel's magnetic properties. Data are sensed automatically, stored on hard disk, and plotted as a map. Contours are interpreted in terms of geological bodies beneath the seafloor.

In radiometric surveying, natural radioactivity is monitored. This can be done from aircraft or ships. Detector types that can be used over water include Geiger counters, scintillation counters, and gamma-ray spectrometers (Kearey *et al.*, 2002).

2.3   Shallow-penetration geotechnical surveys

2.3.1   Introduction

A geotechnical survey is an investigation of the seabed to determine the nature and engineering properties of the soils and other materials there, and to determine one or more simplified soil profiles and properties assignments for purposes of design.

A shallow penetration explores only the first few metres below the seafloor. The survey will be carried out for a light seabed structure, or at kilometre intervals along the proposed route of a cable or pipeline.

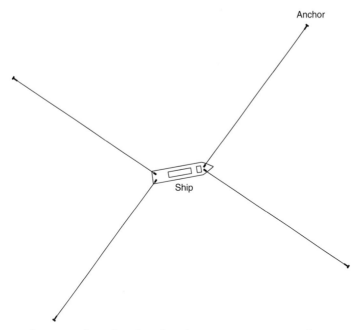

Fig. 2.4 Plan view of vessel anchored on four-point mooring spread

Special drilling equipment is not required, and the survey is often done from the same vessel as does the shallow geophysical survey. The opportunity is often taken to collect some of the soil and seawater samples needed for an environmental baseline survey.

For geotechnical surveys along proposed cable or pipeline routes, a programme of geotechnical sampling and testing will be carried out, typically at intervals of 1 km or so along the proposed route, with extra stops either side of locations where the geophysics has identified a change in the seabed conditions, such as a geological fault, the end of a soil layer, or an ancient riverbed. Samples are normally subject to visual–manual inspection, and may be subjected to preliminary laboratory testing on board the survey vessel, They are then packed and transported ashore for further laboratory testing.

Shallow penetration sampling may take a few hours at a location, and the vessel will need to be held stationary. Anchoring on a four-point mooring plan may be employed (Fig. 2.4), but this can take a considerable amount of valuable time to set up. In a 'dynamically positioned' (DP) ship, thrusters below the waterline apply thrusts to counter the motions induced by wind, wave, and current, so that the ship can stay on station without anchors.

41

2.3.2 Grab and box sampling systems

A grab sampler consists of two spring-loaded, clamshell jaws (Fig. 2.5b). The sampler is primed open on the deck of the survey vessel, then lifted over the side and lowered to the seabed. On contact with the seabed, the jaws snap shut, cutting a few inches of soil from the seabed. The sampler is then lifted to the vessel, and the sample is examined.

A box corer (Fig. 2.5c) is a similar system that operates using a frame. An open-bottomed box is lowered to the seafloor and penetrates a short distance into the seabed. A mechanical system then releases a base plate

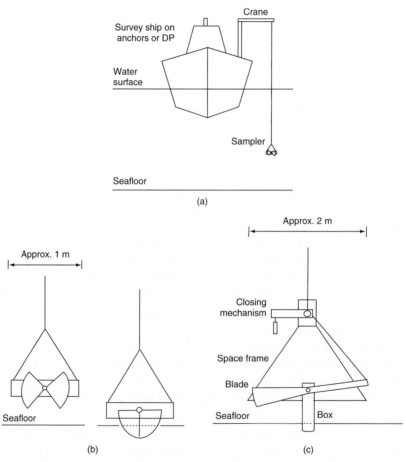

Fig. 2.5 Grab and box samplers. (a) Sampler lowered to the seafloor. (b) Grab sampler above the seafloor (left), and with jaws closed on the seafloor (right). (c) Box corer penetrating the seafloor

which cuts under the base of the box and so collects the soil, and the sampler is lifted back to the ship and the soil is examined.

Box and grab samples allow the soil type in the upper few inches of the seabed to be identified, but provide no information about what is below. Box samples can be of high quality, and reliable density, moisture content, and strength tests can be done on sub-samples cored from the box sample on deck. Grab samples are highly disturbed, and essentially provide only soil classification data.

2.3.3 *Tube sampling systems*

Push samples can be obtained by lowering a heavy frame to the seabed and using a motor on the frame to push a stainless steel or aluminium tube into the seabed (Fig. 2.6a). Typically, the tube will be 1–3 m long, and 8–10 cm in diameter. A non-return valve at the top allows water to flow out as soil enters the tube. The lower end of the tube will have a cutting edge. The soil experiences some straining as the sample tube is pushed into it, but generally the quality that can be achieved with tube samples is considered good. A core catcher can be fitted to prevent loose soil from falling out, but this causes disturbance as the soil enters the tube.

In a vibrocorer (Fig. 2.6b), the sample tube is fitted onto the bottom of a vibration system that is supported by a light frame. The frame is lowered to the seabed on a wire and with an umbilical. The motor is started, and the motion of the eccentric masses induces up and down forces on the corer, which sinks into the seabed. The system is then lifted up and onto deck. Vibrocores are partially disturbed due to the vibratory motion. Density and water content measurements on recovered clays may be reliable, but the cyclic loading vibratory motion will often have reduced sample strengths significantly.

In a gravity corer or drop sampler (Fig. 2.6c), a weighted tube is lowered to about 10 m above the seafloor and then released. The tube drops onto the seafloor and cuts into the seabed. The mass of the deployed system can be up to a tonne. The corer is deployed from a deck crane with a free-fall winch capability. A typical coring tube will have a diameter of 10 cm, and may be equipped with an internal piston to improve sample quality or with a segmented internal plastic liner. Penetrations up to at least 8 m can be possible in clays, depending on the clay strengths.

In an advanced device such as the Kullenberg piston corer (Fig. 2.6d), a pilot mass is fitted onto a trigger arm and contacts the seabed before

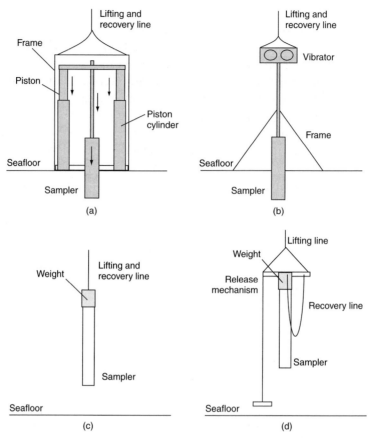

Fig. 2.6 Examples of tube samplers. (a) Push sampling. (b) Vibrocore. (c) Simple drop sampler with seafloor-triggered release. (d) Gravity sampler with seafloor-triggered release

the main corer. The contact releases a trigger, and the main tube free-falls to the seabed. A short lifting wire is used to retrieve the sample, eliminating the need for a free-fall winch on deck. While a Kullenberg core is widely accepted to be less disturbed than a vibrocore or simple drop sampler, Borel *et al.* (2002, 2005) reported that it can disturb soil to such an extent that strength data from the core are unacceptable for geotechnical engineering purposes.

Quality is improved in the STACOR® piston corer (Wong *et al.*, 2008), which includes a base plate which is linked to the corer in a way that provide improved control of the piston. Samples up to 30 m long can in principle be recovered.

2.3.4 In-situ testing

The purpose of in-situ testing is to determine the strength properties of the soils as they exist in the seabed. In-situ tests have the advantage of avoiding effects of disturbances to the soil during sampling. Schnaid (2009) describes the main techniques involved, including cone penetration, vane, pressuremeter, dilatometer, and other tests.

In a CPT (Fig. 2.7a), a cone-tipped tube is pushed into the seabed, and the end resistance and side friction is measured by load cells within the body of the device. Advanced devices also have pore pressure transducers fitted at the cone and/or behind it. The pore pressure measurements assist in identifying the soil type, and dissipation tests

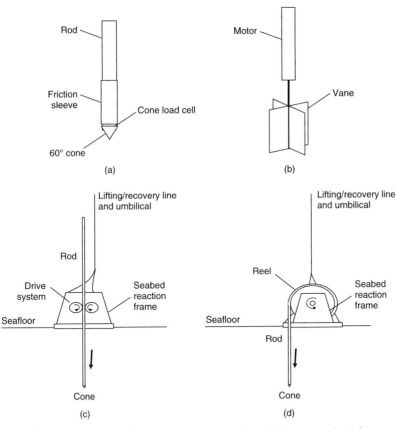

Fig. 2.7 Commonly used in-situ testing systems for shallow geotechnical investigations. (a) Cone penetrometer and rod. (b) Vane device. (c) Wheel-drive system: straight rod with a standard cone. (d) Mini-CPT system: coiled rod with a small cone

can be carried out to measure the consolidation and permeability characteristics of the in-situ soils. In a vane test (Fig 2.7b), a cruciform vane is pushed into the seabed and rotated, and the torque and rotation are measured.

Figure 2.7c illustrates one system used to push the cone into the seabed for shallow surveys (a similar system is used for vane tests). A wheel-drive unit mounted on a frame is lowered to the seabed. The CPT rod is then driven downwards into the seabed by the wheel-drive, and data are transmitted up the umbilical to the controller on board the vessel. Figure 2.7d illustrates another system, in which the CPT rod consists of a tube that is wound on a reel on the frame. To push the cone into the seabed, the reel is unwound, and the CPT rod passes through a straightener before it passes down into the soil.

2.4   Deep-penetration geotechnical site investigations

2.4.1   Overview

The aim of a geotechnical site investigation is to determine the soil layering at the locations of the structures planned for the location, and to measure engineering properties of the soils there (Andresen et al., 1979). For a jackup, an investigation of the first 30–50 m of the seabed may be required (SNAME, 2002). For a piled jacket platform, the first 100–130 m of seafloor may be investigated (Bainbridge, 1975; Semple and Rigden, 1983). For a large gravity platform, borings may extend to 200 m or more below the seafloor (George and Shaw, 1976; Amundsen et al., 1985; Thompson and Long, 1989).

The scope of a particular investigation should normally be specifically tailored to produce the information that will be required for a particular design of structure and for the loading conditions to be considered. The investigation is an important part of the design work, and is not done simply to fulfil permitting requirements. If more than one platform type is being considered, the investigation should provide sufficient data for each. Otherwise, if the design is changed after an investigation is done, another investigation may be needed (George and Shaw, 1976).

The investigation normally includes in-situ testing, sampling, laboratory testing offshore, and further laboratory testing onshore. The results will be used to identify the soil layers at the location and to determine their density, strength, and other characteristics. Preliminary design calculations may be required during the investigation. Factual and design results from the fieldwork are written up in a field report within a few days of the end of a borehole or investigation. A final factual report is usually completed within six weeks. An engineering design report is often required at the same time.

2.4.2   Geotechnical vessels

The most common vessel is a dedicated geotechnical drillship. Other possibilities include a jackup, semi-submersible, hovercraft, structural frame, trailer, or amphibious vehicle, depending on the water depth and metocean conditions. A deep borehole may take several days to complete, and several boreholes may be required for a given location. The ship may be held in place by a four-point mooring system. Alternatively, the ship may be dynamically positioned – a 'DP' ship.

Figure 2.8 shows a common layout for a drillship. The layout is centred on the drilling derrick, typically consisting of an open framework tower 20 m high or so. The best-quality geotechnical data are obtained if the derrick is in the centre of the vessel, where movements of the vessel – due to pitch, yaw, and roll – are least. To achieve this, the vessel is fitted with a moonpool, which is a hole in the centre of the ship through which drilling operations are conducted. The drillstring will pass down through the moonpool, through a seabed reaction frame and then into the seabed. The seabed reaction frame is typically stored in a recess beneath the moonpool during vessel transits between locations. For added stability during drilling, a heave compensation system is fitted in such a way that the drillstring is caused to move, relative to the ship, opposite to the motion of the ship relative to the seabed. This minimises the motion of the drillpipe relative to the bottom of the borehole, and so allows the driller to keep a uniform pressure on the drill bit at the bottom during drilling.

On deck, there will be a pipe rack where the drillpipe and collars are stored. Winches will be arranged around the derrick to lift objects and lower them into the borehole. There will be a mud-mixing system, for preparing drilling mud, and a generator for producing electrical power. There will be a workshop for the drilling system, a soils laboratory, and an office. The workshop, laboratory, and office may be integral with the ship, or may be standard cargo containers fitted out for workshop, laboratory, and office operations. There will be ship management facilities, including positioning and communications systems. There will be ships stores, a drilling store, accommodation for about 35 persons, a galley, a medical centre, washing and laundry facilities, and a garbage collection and storage system.

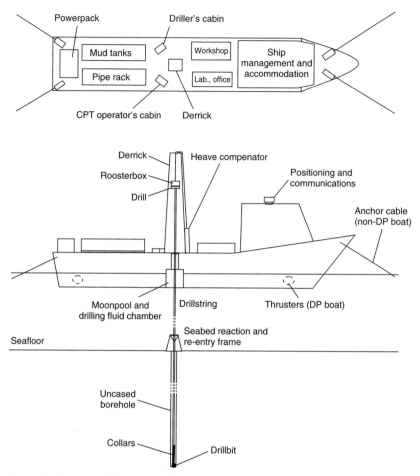

Fig. 2.8 Example of features and drilling arrangements for a geotechnical drilling ship

Personnel on board a drill ship include ship's personnel, client representatives, a medical officer, security personnel, and drilling and geotechnical personnel. The ship is normally supported by a local agent onshore, and operations and advisory personnel from the investigation company. Modern ships have satellite phone, fax, email and Internet access.

The drilling and geotechnical crews are typically headed by a party chief or team leader, whose job usually includes instructing the ship's captain, handling contractual matters with client representatives, liaising with head office and with local services provides onshore, and generally managing the offshore operations. The drilling crews are usually guided by a drilling supervisor, and a mud engineer from an oilfield supply company may also be present if there are difficult soil conditions. There are normally two drilling crews, one for the day shift and one for the night shift, including a driller, assistant driller, CPT operator, and one or two roughnecks. There will be two geotechnical crews on a long job, each consisting of a geotechnical engineer and a laboratory assistant. Fewer geotechnical personnel may be employed for short jobs. One of the two geotechnical engineers may be designated as the lead engineer for a particular location, and will take final responsibility for the geotechnical interpretation and reporting for that location.

2.4.3   Drilling operations

Drilling, sampling, and in-situ testing for onshore works are described by Clayton *et al.* (1982), Lowe and Zaccheo (1991), Mayne *et al.* (2001), Terzaghi *et al.* (1996), Hunt (2005), Schnaid (2009) and others. Technical standards include ASTM D 6032 (ASTM, 2009) and BS 5930 (BSI, 1999). All the onshore technologies, techniques, and standards apply offshore (Lunne, 2001).

Figure 2.9 illustrates how a borehole is progressed. The drillstring consists of segments of pipe that screw into each other. Typically, the pipe is 5 inches in diameter, and may be in 3 m, 5 m, 9 m, or other segment lengths. When a section of pipe gets to deck level, drilling is stopped, and the pipe is lifted a short distance and clamped at the drilling deck. The drill can then be lifted away, and a new section of pipe lifted into place and screwed onto the top of the clamped pipe. The drill is then screwed onto the top of the next pipe section, the drillstring is released, and drilling of the borehole continues.

Figure 2.9 also illustrates one of the methods used to measure the depth to the bottom of a borehole. The driller knows the length P of drillpipe that has been installed, and the stickup length SU above the deck when the pipe is resting in the bottom of the hole. The driller will have measured the height H of the drilldeck above the waterline at the start of the borehole, and will check this occasionally. The water depth WD is measured by an echosounder at the time of interest. The depth BHD of the bottom of the borehole below the seafloor at the time of interest is thus

$$BHD = P - (SU + H + WD) \qquad (2.1)$$

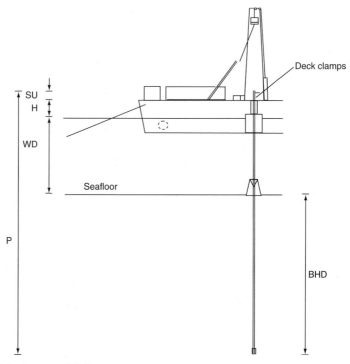

Fig. 2.9 Aspects of drilling operations

This calculation ensures that tidal and other variations of water depth are properly accounted for and that BHD is truly the depth below the seafloor. The calculation is done with echosounder measurements made before every soil sample is taken and before any in-situ test is done. The echosounder will have been checked at the start of the borehole by reference to physical measurements made with the aid of in-situ testing equipment and the drillstring.

Figure 2.10 illustrates schematically some of the processes that occur during drilling at the bottom of a borehole. The drillpipe is rotated as the drillbit is pressed onto the bottom of the borehole. A dragbit is often used, consisting of teeth projecting a few centimetres downwards, roughened by tungsten welds. The teeth drag across the soil, breaking it, to form cuttings. Viscous drilling mud is pumped down the centre of the drillstring, and passes through vents in the drillbit. It picks up the cuttings, and transports them upwards in the annulus between the drillpipe and the soil at the borehole wall. Some of the drilling mud passes into the pore spaces of sand and gravel strata. A gelling agent in the mud causes it to slowly solidify and forms a cake in the

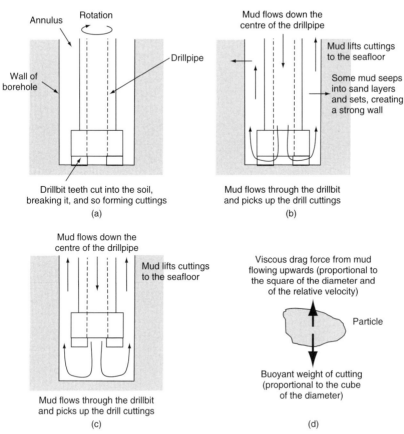

Fig. 2.10 *Some geotechnical processes in the borehole. (a) Elements of the bottom of the drillstring (annulus width exaggerated for clarity). (b) Mud flows in the borehole. (c) Flushing the borehole prior to sampling. (d) Forces on a particle of cuttings*

soil around the borehole. This helps to prevent the sides of the borehole from collapsing. Mud may also be mixed with barites to increase its weight and so prevent borehole collapse in difficult drilling conditions. Cuttings are usually vented to the seafloor at the level of the seabed frame, but can be collected if necessary.

On modern vessels the control systems allow the driller to check the mud pressure and flow rate, the bit weight (vertical load applied to the soil), the torque on the drill during drilling, and other parameters. All these parameters can also be recorded, and the records stored digitally for later analysis. The driller also keeps a written log. Driller's logs are usually presented as an appendix in the field report, together with

51

drilling parameter records and the mud engineer's records, if available. These logs provide useful support to the separate logs kept by the geotechnical engineers and laboratory staff.

2.4.4   Soil-sampling operations

Figure 2.11 illustrates three common types of soil-sampling devices. Most offshore soil samples are obtained using a push-in Shelby tube sampler, consisting of a duraluminium or stainless steel tube, typically 1 me long and with a diameter of 51 mm or (preferably) 76 mm. The sampler is described in detail in ASTM D 1587. Piston corers incorporate a piston that moves upwards as the corer is pushed into the soil, holding the soil and reducing disturbance. Split spoons are deployed for hammer sampling, as described in ASTM D 1586 and in BS 5930.

Figure 2.12 illustrates one sampling procedure. Rotation of the drill-string is stopped, and the string is lifted away from the bottom of the hole. The hole is then cleaned by flushing mud through the string, lifting all cuttings away from the bottom of the hole and transporting them to the seafloor. The mud flow is then stopped, and the drillpipe is clamped, to the seabed frame or to the drilling deck if there is no frame. The mud valve at the top of the drillstring is opened, and a sampling tube and associated equipment is lowered down the centre of the drillstring on a wireline. The equipment latches into the bottom of the string. Depending on the type of drilling system being used, the string may then be pushed downwards under the control of systems on the ship or in the seabed frame, or the downhole equipment may push the tube out of the bottom on the static drillstring into the soil.

The sample tube has a non-return valve at the top which allows water to exit when soil enters the tube, but stops water being sucked in. The tube or drillstring is pulled up so that the tube comes out of the soil, the valve closes, and the sample stays in the tube. The latch releases the tube, which is winched up the string, then lowered to the deck. The mud valve is then closed, and drilling operations restart.

2.4.5   Rock-coring operations

In hard rock, a dragbit will drill slowly, and a core stub will form if the rock in the centre of the drillbit does not break. As the drillbit cuts downwards, the cylindrical stub stays where it is, and so moves upwards relative to the drillbit, and into the drillpipe. When the stub reaches

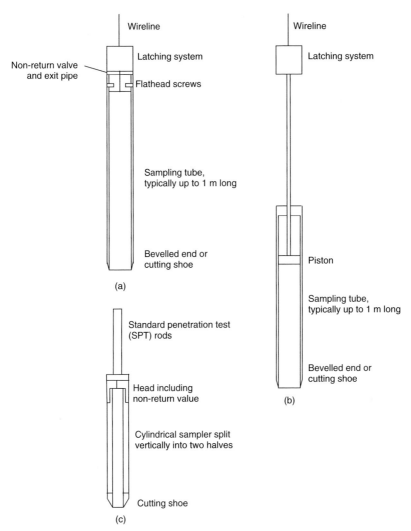

Fig. 2.11 Soil sampling devices. (a) Shelby tube sampler. (b) Piston sampler. (c) Split spoon sampler

a certain height, it will start to block the mud flow, and the driller will see this on the drilling monitors. A danger is that the core stub will fracture at its base and block the drillbit, necessitating lengthy remedial measures.

For drilling and sampling in rock, a core barrel is fitted inside the pipe. This is a tubular steel casing, typically with an internal plastic liner. To install the core barrel, drilling is stopped, and mud flow is stopped. The

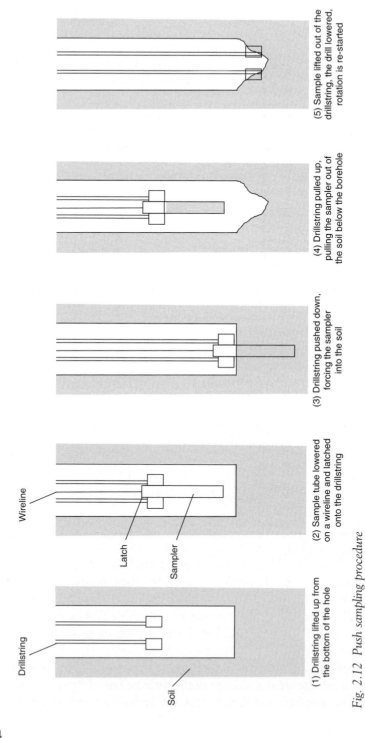

Fig. 2.12 Push sampling procedure

drillstring is lifted away from the bottom of the hole, the mud valve at the top of the drillstring is opened, the core barrel is dropped down the string, and the driller listens to hear the click as it latches into place at the bottom. The mud valve is then closed, the drillstring is lowered, and drilling restarts. As the drilling continues, the rock core rises up inside the coring tube.

A typical coring tube is 1.5 to 3 m long. When full, or when the driller detects that the rock layer has been passed and the drillbit is again in soil, the tube is removed. To do this, the drilling is stopped, the mud flow is stopped, and an overshot grab is lowered down the centre of the drillstring. The overshot attaches to the top of the top of the core barrel, which is then pulled up and out of the drillstring.

2.4.6   In-situ testing – CPT, T-bar, and ball penetrometer tests

In-situ penetration testing involves pressing an object into the ground at the bottom of the borehole, and measuring the soil resistance and other parameters.

Figure 2.13a illustrates the standard cone penetrometer, consisting of a cone and friction sleeve. The standard cone has an apex angle of $60°$ and a cross-sectional area of $10\,cm^2$, corresponding to a diameter of $3.56\,cm$. It is pushed into the soil at $20\,mm/s$ (ISSMFE, 1989; Lunne *et al.*, 1997).

Electrical transducers measure the soil resistance on the cone tip as it penetrates into the soil, and the frictional resistance on the sleeve. The maximum capacity for the cone loadcell is typically $100\,MPa$, implying that the unit can apply a force of $10\,cm^2 \times 100\,MPa = 100\,kN$ to the soil. The reaction to this force is supplied by the weights of the drillpipe and seabed reaction frame.

Other devices have also been used. In the piezocone (PCPT or CPTU), one or more transducers to measure pore water pressure are installed on the device. The standard nomenclature u_1, u_2, and u_3 for these pressures is shown in Fig. 2.13b (Bayne and Tjelta, 1987; Lunne *et al.*, 1997). Other devices include a T-bar, sphere, and flat plate, sketched in Fig. 2.13c (Lunne *et al.*, 2005; Yafrate and DeJong, 2005; Audibert *et al.*, 2008). For the T-bar, soil resistance can usefully be measured during pull-out as well as during penetration, and a comparison of pull-out and penetration measurements gives a measure of the sensitivity of the soil to prior straining. The plate test provides a larger bearing area, and is useful for soft soils.

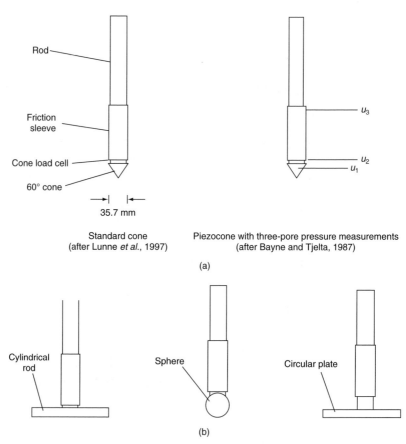

Fig. 2.13 Cone penetrometer devices. (a) Standard cone (after Lunne et al., 1997) (left) and piezocone with three-pore pressure measurements (after Bayne and Tjelta, 1987) (right). (b) T-bar, ball, and plate penetrometers (after Lunne et al., 2005; Yafrate and DeJong, 2005)

Several systems and procedures are available for pushing the devices into the soil. Figure 2.14a illustrates the basics of the test procedure for one system. Rotation of the drill is stopped, and the drilling mud is flushed through to clean the hole and remove cuttings from the base and annulus. The drillstring is then clamped to the seabed frame, the mudvalve at the top of the string is opened, and a CPT unit is lowered through it. The unit is up to 7 m or so in length, and includes a drive system and a 3 m-long CPT rod with a sleeve and cone. Power, control signals, and data signals are provided through an umbilical. When the unit arrives at the drill collars, it is latched in at the bottom of the drillstring. The drive unit then pushes the rods out of the CPT housing and into the soil. The

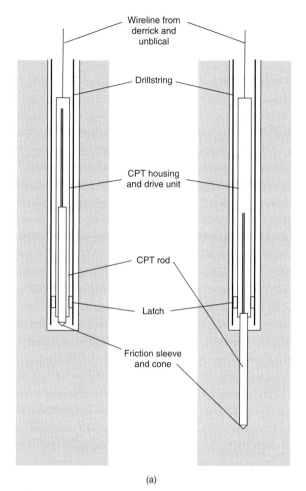

(a)

Fig. 2.14 Deployment and types of results for the downhole cone penetrometer.
(a) One method of carrying out a downhole CPT test. (b) Example of individual
CPT records not yet processed to remove start-up effects (Focht et al., 1986).
(c) Example of a continuous record assembled from several CPT pushes and
correlated with soil layering (Bayne and Tjelta, 1987)

drive unit may then be used to retract the rod, and the system is then lifted
out of the drillstring so that drilling can restart.

In an alternative system, the drillstring is first lifted 3 m above the
bottom of the borehole, then clamped at the seabed frame. A CPT
unit is then lowered through the string and latched with the CPT rod
protruding 3 m below the drag bit. Hydraulic actuators on the seabed
frame are then used to drive drillstring downwards, pushing the CPT
into the soil.

57

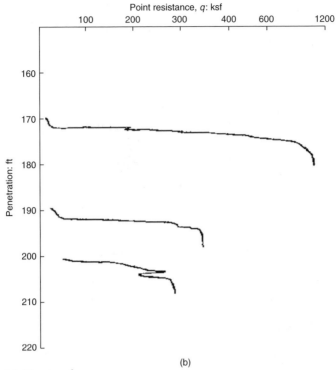

Fig. 2.14 *Continued*

The standard rate of penetration is 2 cm/s. Typically, a CPT stroke will be 1.5 or 3 m, depending on the type of unit used, so the test will take between 75 seconds and 1.5 minutes. The cone, sleeve, and pore pressure data are displayed on the CPT operator's computer during penetration, and penetration will be stopped if the soil resistance exceeds the limit of the loadcells, typically 100 MPa. When the test is done, the CPT unit is unlatched from the drillstring and lifted out, the mud flow is restarted, and drilling is recommenced.

Figure 2.14b shows results of three cone tests, starting at around 170, 190, and 200 feet below the seafloor. In each record, the first 1 foot of the record shows a build-up of cone resistance. This is because the failure mechanism in the soil around the cone is affected by the presence of the ground surface at the bottom of the borehole. A certain distance is needed in order for this effect to disappear. Only the latter part of the record is representative of in-situ conditions.

Figure 2.14c shows an example of a continuous CPT record that has been assembled by joining records from several CPTs together, after

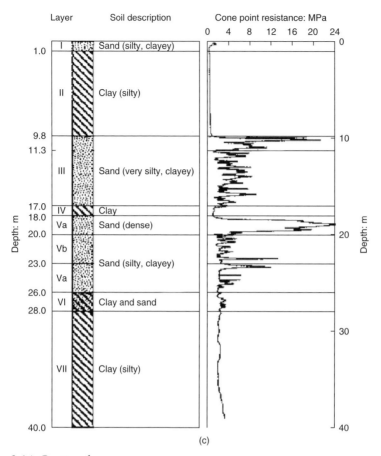

Fig. 2.14 Continued

judiciously removing the initial parts of the records. The data show the typical, very different types of response obtained in clay, sand, and clayey sand. By careful examination of the data, the change of cone resistance just below 18 m penetration is found to be delayed compared with the layer boundary. This is like the effect near the bottom of the borehole, and occurs because the failure mechanism around the cone tip remains affected by the upper layer as the cone penetrates a little way into the lower layer. The data also show considerable variability below 20 m, which may indicate that the soil consists of alternating seams of sand and clay.

Further aspects of the interpretation of CPT data are discussed in Section 2.7.

2.4.7   Other in-situ testing devices

Downhole vane tests are useful for clay soils (Chandler, 1988). A vane assembly with an electrical umbilical, a latch, a motor, and a cruciform vane is lowered to the bottom of the borehole, and the vane is pressed into the soil there. The vane is then rotated, and the torque required to do this and the amount of rotation is measured.

A standard penetration test (SPT) can be carried out offshore. The test is carried out in the same way as an onshore SPT (see ASTM D 1586), but requires a jackup or other stable platform that provides an offshore working level that does not move in relation to the seabed. Drilling is stopped, the drillstring is lifted a short way off the seabed, mud flow is stopped, and the mud valve at the top of the drillstring is opened. A thick-walled split spoon sampler (see Fig. 2.11c) is attached to rigid SPT rods and passed down into the borehole until it rests on the seabed. A drop hammer is attached to the upper rod. Marks are made on the rod at 3 inch intervals, and the hammering is started. A count is made of the number of blows to penetrate the sampler for each 3 inches of penetration. The number N of blows for the last 12 inches of penetration is the SPT N-value. The results can be used to estimate soil strength (Schnaid, 2009), and the split spoon sampler provides a disturbed soil sample that can be classified.

In a downhole self-boring pressuremeter test, a system consisting of a driving module and pressuremeter module is lowered down the centre of the drillstring. The cylindrical pressuremeter is driven into the soil below the bottom of the borehole, and a diaphragm is then inflated to press the soil radially outwards. The pressures required and the inflation achieved are measured. Data interpretation is similar to onshore pressuremeter tests (Faÿ et al., 1985; Houlsby, 1990; Clarke, 1995; Schnaid, 2009). In the dilatometer, a blade is pushed into the soil, and a device in the blade is inflated. The pressure and the amount of inflation are measured. Data interpretation is similar to onshore tests (Schnaid, 2009).

Burgess et al. (1983) describe a number of other in-situ technologies that have been developed primarily onshore but can also be useful offshore. Such devices include:

- natural gamma logger, to detect soil layering (Ayres and Theilen, 2001)
- electrical conductivity, for water content and related parameters (Campanella and Kokan, 1993)

- seismic cone, for shear wave velocity for earthquake analysis (Campanella and Davies, 1994)
- BAT/DGP (deep water gas probe), to sample pore water and pore gas (Mokkelbost and Strandvik, 1999)
- piezoprobe, to measure the pore pressure and coefficient of consolidation (Dutt *et al.*, 1997)
- nuclear density probe, to measure the in-situ density of sands (Tjelta *et al.*, 1985)
- heat flow probe, to measure the thermal properties of soils (Zelinski *et al.*, 1986)
- hydraulic fracture test, to assess the conductor setting depth (Aldridge and Haland, 1991).

Further information is provided by Lunne (2001).

2.5 Visual–manual sample inspection, logging, and packing

2.5.1 Overview

Sample procedures offshore are the same for shallow geotechnical surveys or deep-site investigations, and follow the procedures, methods, and terminologies given in standards including ASTM D 6032, BS 1377 (BSI, 1990), and BS 5930. ASTM and BS standards are slightly different. Useful texts also include Hunt (2005) and Head (2006). Different companies have different ways of managing and recording the activities, in accordance with the standards.

An example of an offshore sample log sheet is shown in Fig. 2.15. The record is for sample P23 taken with the bottom of the borehole 22 m below the seafloor. This is BHD from equation (2.1). The upper 42 cm of soil consisted of firm dark greenish grey silty clay. A density test D1 and two strength tests TV1 and PP1 were done on this part of the sample, with results at the bottom right showing strengths of 86 and 90 kPa, respectively. The lower 20 cm of the sample consisted of sand with occasional shell fragments. A density test was done. The 62 cm-long sample was stored in bag B1 (upper 10 cm), quart sample Q2, bag B3, and bag B4. The bag samples are disturbed samples, but will give information about soil types. The quart sample is an undisturbed sample, and will be tested later to obtain the strength and deformation characteristics of the clay.

Occasionally, samples are sealed in their Shelby tubes by waxing the ends, but this provides virtually no field information. Some of the

Soil Sample Data Sheet							

XYZ Offshore Geotechnics Ltd

Project Name	*West Saco*	Project No.	0907	Site	*Site 12*
Borehole No.	*BH2*	Sample No.	*P23*	Depth	*22.0m*
Time *22.40* Sampling Method	*P*	Sampler Type	*S*	Hammer Blows	

Abbreviations:

					PP	Pocket Penetrometer	H	Hammer	S	3" Shelby
									2"S	2" Shelby
B	Bag sample	W	Water content	TV	Torvane	P	Push	1½ S/S	1½" Split spoon
Q	Quart sample	D	Density	MV	Miniature vane	R	Piston	2 S/S	2" Split spoon

SPL LENGTH (m)	SPL TYPE & No.	VISUAL DESCRIPTION Consistency or density / structure / colour / sec. soil type / PRIMARY SOIL TYPE / inclusions	LOG	TEST RESULTS	REMARKS
	B1				D1 @ 0.1m
	Q2	*Firm dark greenish grey silty CLAY*			
	B3				*TV1 @ 0.4m* *PP1 @ 0.4m*
0.42m					
	B4	*Fine to coarse brown SAND with occasional shell fragments*			D2 @ 0.5m
0.62m					

WATER CONTENT AND DENSITY							TORVANE				PENETROMETER			
Test no.	*D1*	*D 2*	3	4	5		Test	Adaptor	Reading	Su (kPa)	Test	Adaptor	Reading	Su (kPa)
Tin no.	*47*	*48*												
Wet wt. + tare (g)	*53.5*	*58.1*					1	*A*	*4.3*	*86*	1	*N*	*4.5*	*90*
Dry wt. + tare (g)	*39.1*	*49.8*					2				2			
Wt. of water (g)	*14.4*	*8.3*					3				3			
Wt. of tare (g)	*2*	*2*					4				4			
Dry wt. (g)	*37.1*	*47.8*					5				5			
Water Content (%)	*39*	*17*					6				6			
Wet den. (Mg/m³)	*1.78*	*1.93*					7				7			
Dry den. (Mg/m³)	*1.28*	*1.65*					8				8			
Depth (m)	*22.1*	*22.5*												

By: *LTE*	Date: *20/5/09*	Checked: *RDE*	Date: *21/5/09*	Processed: *GEN*	Date: *21/5/09*

Fig. 2.15 Example of a sample log sheet

inspected samples may be subjected to onboard laboratory testing. All samples, whether tested or not, are stored and shipped onshore for further tests.

2.5.2 Push samples: initial procedures

At the start of the borehole, clays may be encountered that are soft enough for miniature vane testing. On receipt of a sample, the first action by the geotechnical crew is to inspect the lower end of the sample. If it is soft clay without sand or gravel intrusions, a miniature vane test is done. The tube is upended and clamped, a miniature vane is pushed into the soil in the tube, and a motor is started to rotate the vane in the sample. The maximum torque is converted by a calibration factor to an undrained shear strength. A residual strength may be measured by continuing the rotation until the torque is constant.

After the vane test, if appropriate, the sample is extruded by fitting the sample tube horizontally into a holder, and using a piston to push the soil sample out onto a sample tray. The tray may be lubricated lightly to prevent soil disturbance. Care is taken to prevent the sample from bending or cracking during this process. Horizontal extrusion offshore is often more practical than vertical extrusion, because a vertically extruded sample has no lateral support and may collapse, particularly if the vessel is moving at the time. Extrusion may be in the opposite direction to the direction of entry, so that the sample is pushed out of the end that it entered. This can be practical partly because full-length samples are not always obtained.

The top of the sample is inspected to ensure that original soil has been obtained, rather than remoulded or reworked cuttings. Cuttings may appear as a few centimetres of very uniform gravel, or as soft, mashed-up soil, possibly containing bits of gelled drilling mud. The gravel is there because the driller made a mistake, and the upwards velocity of the drilling fluid in the borehole was insufficient to lift cuttings larger than gravel size; in other words, the gravity force in Fig. 2.10d was larger than the viscous force for a particular size of cutting that corresponded to the gravel. Larger particles will also have not been lifted: they will have fallen back onto the drillbit and been broken up by it. Mashed soil occurs if the upwards flow of drilling mud was stopped too early, so that some of the smaller particles fell back down during the period between stopping the mud flow and starting the push sample. If cuttings are found, they are normally removed (unless the client requires them to be kept).

After separating out any cuttings, the sample is then cleaned. If an aluminium sampling tube has been used, there may be back streaks from aluminium hydroxide that has scraped off the tube and stained the sample. A palette knife is used to scrape away the black streaks. The sample is then photographed. The sample is normally arranged with a metre rule to show scale, a greyscale chart, a standard Munsell colour chart, and a label giving the job number, the borehole identification, the sample identifier, and the depth of the top of the sample below the seafloor.

The sample is transferred to a laboratory bench, and is gently probed to determine whether it is mainly gravel, sand, silt, or clay, or whether there are seams of more than one soil type. Any surface features are also noted, such as gas blisters, which indicate the presence of gas in the soil. A smell of rotten eggs indicates the presence of hydrogen sulfide gas, which is poisonous. A record is made in the sample log of the length of the sample, the main soil types, and positions of boundaries between different soil types.

2.5.3   Immediate tests on sand samples

A plan for sectioning the sample is made. For a uniform sand, this will just involve deciding the number of bags the sample will be put into, and dividing the sample into segments for this. If there are two different layers of sand, the different parts are put into different bags. One or two moisture content and/or density measurements are done. A small steel cylinder or 'density ring' of known volume is pushed into the sample, scraping away material from around the ring, scraping flat the ends, then pushing the material in the ring out onto a numbered tray for weighing, drying, and reweighing later.

An offshore carbonate content test is usually carried out to determine whether the soil grains are composed of calcium carbonate. A small amount of soil is dropped into a shallow pan containing dilute hydrochloric acid, and the resulting bubbling observed. Calcium carbonate reacts with the acid, to produce calcium chloride, water, and carbon dioxide:

$$CaCO_3 + 2HCl \rightarrow CaCl_2 + H_2O + CO_2 \qquad (2.2)$$

Calcium chloride is soluble in water, so the solids that remain after the reaction is complete are the non-carbonate parts of the soil. Carbon dioxide creates bubbles, and in a simple offshore test, strong effervescence is taken to indicate that the soil contains a lot of calcium carbonate, and this is confined by observing how much of the sample remains afterwards. This is just a preliminary test, and if it finds carbonate, then more exact measurements are done onshore.

The main sand sample, that has not been carbonate tested, is then broken up and inspected to determine its detailed nature, including colour, particle size (considered in terms of fine, medium, or coarse sand sizes: see Chapter 3), estimated degree of clayey or silty components, occurrence of silt or clay pockets, gravel inclusions, rootlets, other organic matter, shells, corals, and any other notable characteristics. This is all logged.

The broken material is stored in a strong plastic bag or other container. The bag is usually put in a second bag as a precaution against leaks. The bag is labelled and stored. The number of bags used for the sand or gravel components of the sample, their positions in the sample, and all findings are noted on the sample log sheet. The density and moisture content samples are weighed and placed in an oven at 105°C. They will be taken out of the oven 24 hours later and weighed dry. The results will be written on the sample sheet and used to infer the density and the moisture content.

2.5.4 Immediate tests on cohesive samples

If the sample is mainly silt or clay, a plan for sectioning the sample is made, as far as possible so as to be able to get at least one 'UU' sample of length about 17 cm, and one 'quart' sample of about 20 cm. The sections avoid areas near the top of the sample where the soil may be softer than elsewhere, due to disturbance, and areas near the bottom if a miniature vane test was done there. Figure 2.16a shows an example for a long clay sample, using a common naming system for subsamples. Two undisturbed parts will be cut out, in this case labelled UU2 for later triaxial testing on the ship, and Q4 for later testing onshore. The remaining parts of the sample are subject to immediate tests, and then bagged.

Before sectioning, density tests are done in regions outside the UU and quart samples, and small-scale strength tests are also performed if there is enough material. In a torvane test (Fig. 2.16b), a flat cruciform vane attached to a circular plate is pushed onto a flat part of the sample, and then rotated until a shear failure occurs in the soil over a disk at the level of the tips of the blades. The maximum torque is multiplied by a calibration factor to get an estimate of the undrained shear strength. In a pocket penetrometer test (Fig. 2.16c), a rod is pushed into the soil. This causes a bearing capacity failure on a 6 mm diameter area. The force is measured by a spring device in the body of the penetrometer, and is multiplied by a calibration factor to get an estimate of the undrained shear strength. The torvane and pocket penetrometer tests are highly sensitive to small non-uniformities and intrusions in the soil, such as sand pockets or silt partings. Many engineers use these devices only if there is no other data available, preferring to follow API RP2A and ISO 19902 in relying primarily on triaxial, minivane, and CPT data.

The sectioning is then done. The UU sample may be wrapped in thin plastic or cling film to prevent any change in the moisture content while

65

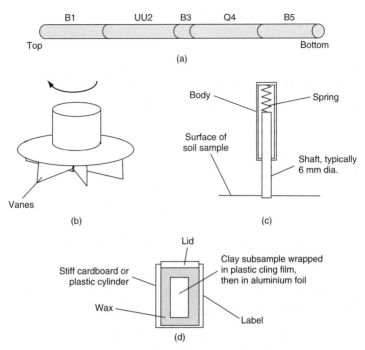

Fig. 2.16 Aspects of offshore procedures for clay samples. (a) Example of a sectioning plan for a clay sample. (b) Handheld torvane device. (c) Pocket penetrometer. (d) Section through a cylindrical clay sample packed in a quart container ready for transportation ashore

the sample is temporarily stored before the offshore triaxial test. The quart sample is typically wrapped in cling film, then in aluminium foil, then placed in a cardboard or plastic cylinder and surrounded with liquid wax, which cools and solidifies (Fig. 2.16d). This protects the sample during subsequent transportation ashore. The remaining parts of the original tube sample are inspected to determine the detailed nature of the soil, in terms of colour, secondary particle size (sandy or gravelly silts and clays), structure (defined in BS 5930: examples include laminations, blocks, fissures, and fracture planes), and inclusions (such as seams, lenses, or pockets of other soil types, or shell or coral fragments).

The material is then placed in labelled bags for storage. Like the granular samples, the density and moisture content samples are weighed and placed in an oven at 105°C. They will be taken out of the oven 24 hours later and weighed dry, and the results will be used to infer density and moisture content.

2.5.5 Disturbed soil samples

Disturbed samples are inspected in the same way as for undisturbed samples, but measurements of density, water content, and strength are not usually reliable. Disturbed samples are thus simply inspected, tested for carbonate content (sands), and bagged. All observations and measurements are recorded on a sample log sheet.

2.5.6 Rock cores

A core barrel sample may or may not contain a rock core. If it contains soil, the soil is inspected and logged in the same way as a disturbed sample, noting layer boundaries that may be more common in the longer core barrel samples.

If a core barrel contains rock, it may be fragmented, possibly with soil seams between fragments. One procedure is as follows. The sample is extruded and photographed, and the major rock segments are drawn to scale on a rock core log. The following quantities are determined (ASTM D 6032; BS 5930; Norbury *et al.*, 1986):

- Total core recovery (TCR): the total length of the core recovered, as a fraction of the distance drilled through the rock with the core barrel in place.
- Solid core recovery (SCR): total length of the rock layer in the core (i.e. excluding seams of soil) as a fraction of the distance drilled through the rock with the core barrel in place.
- Rock quality designation (RQD): total length of rock pieces longer than 100 mm, as a fraction of the distance drilled through the rock with the core barrel in place.

The soil samples are inspected as disturbed samples, logged, and bagged. The rock fragments and bagged soil samples are stored in a core box in the order in which they occurred in the sample.

2.5.7 Sample storage and manifests

Methods of storing and transporting samples are described in ASTM D 3213 (soils) and ASTM D 5079 (rocks). Principal requirements are to ensure that the receiving laboratory receives the subsamples in a state as close as possible to their original state, and that the recipients know where the samples come from. Samples and subsamples in their individual bags or waxed boxes are typically stored in strong boxes on the vessel. Each strong box might contain 20 or so samples, packed so that they do not move. Each sample and subsample will be labelled with a job number, the site name, the borehole number, the sample number, the depth, and the subsample number.

Boxes are kept in a place that is not subject to ship vibrations, with a constant, cool temperature and constant humidity. Each box is labelled, and the samples it contains are listed on a manifest for customs purposes, and for the receiving laboratory. (Special arrangements may be needed in advance, as many countries restrict the import of soils due to agriculture protection reasons.) Arrangements for lifting the sample boxes off the vehicle and transporting them, sometimes by air, to the onshore laboratory will need to be planned. Lifting from ship to shore is critical, or from drill ship to supply ship. Dropping a sample box at that stage can result in an entire borehole having to be redrilled.

2.6 Offshore laboratory testing

2.6.1 Overview

The purpose of laboratory testing is to measure the properties of the soils recovered from the seabed that are used as inputs to geotechnical calculations. A few tests are carried out offshore, during the fieldwork. However, test results can be affected by vibrations and by the rocking motions of a ship in bad weather. Consequently, most of the laboratory tests are done onshore.

Table 2.1 lists some of the main volumetric and gravimetric quantities used to describe soils. The parameters can be defined in terms of

Table 2.1 Gravimetric and volumetric descriptions of offshore soils

Void ratio:	Porosity:	Specific volume:
$e = \dfrac{V_a + V_w}{V_s} = \dfrac{n}{1-n}$	$n = \dfrac{V_a + V_w}{V_a + V_w + V_s} = \dfrac{e}{1+e}$	$V = \dfrac{V_a + V_w + V_s}{V_s} = 1+e$
Carbonate content:	(Gravimetric) moisture content:	Degree of saturation:
$CC = \dfrac{M_{CaCO_3}}{M_s}$	$w = \dfrac{V_w}{G_s V_s} = \dfrac{Se}{G_s} = \dfrac{\rho_b - \rho_d}{\rho_d}$	$S = \dfrac{V_w}{V_a + V_w}$
Bulk density:	Dry density:	Buoyant density:
$\rho_b = \dfrac{(G_s + Se)\rho_w}{1+e}$	$\rho_d = \dfrac{G_s \rho_w}{1+e} = \dfrac{\rho_b}{1+w}$	$\rho' = \rho_b - \rho_w$
Bulk unit weight:	Dry unit weight:	Submerged unit weight:
$\gamma_b = \rho_b g$	$\gamma_d = \rho_d g$	$\gamma' = \rho' g$

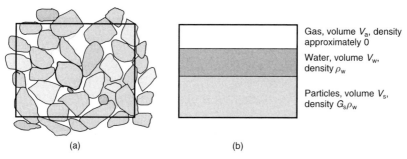

Fig. 2.17 Phase diagram and measures of volume, density, and unit weight. (a) Actual soil, containing soil particles, water, and gas. (b) Conceptual model, showing volumes and densities

a 'phase diagram' (Fig. 2.17), in which a volume of soil is considered to contain a volume V_s of solids, V_w of liquid (usually water), and V_a of gas. The parameters listed in Table 2.1 are described in more detail below.

Density samples and moisture content samples will have been placed in an oven for drying. The dried samples are weighed offshore, and results are used to deduce water contents, densities, and unit weights. Offshore triaxial tests are carried out on cohesive samples if a preliminary design calculation is required immediately the fieldwork is completed.

2.6.2 Densities, carbonate content, and moisture content

In a moisture content or density test, a sample of wet soil is placed on a tray whose weight T is known. The mass M_1 of the soil plus tray is measured, typically to the nearest 0.1 g. The sample and tray is then placed in an oven and dried for 24 hours at 105°C. The mass M_2 of the tray plus soil is measured. The gravimetric water content w of the soil is defined as the mass of the water divided by the dry mass of the soil:

$$w = \frac{M_1 - M_2}{M_2 - T} \tag{2.3}$$

The result is usually expressed as a percentage. For example, $M_1 = 38$ g, $M_2 = 22$ g, and $T = 2$ g gives a water content of 30%. Typical gravimetric water contents for a sand are around 20–30%. Values for a clay can be much larger, and can be greater than 100%. Gravimetric water contents are different to volumetric water contents, which are used in environmental studies.

69

The carbonate content of a soil is the ratio of the mass of calcium carbonate in its grains to the mass of the soil grains. It is usually estimated offshore using the hydrochloric acid test described earlier. For more exact measurements, the ASTM D 4373 procedure, or an equivalent, may be used.

The bulk density ρ_b of the soil is defined as the mass of the original soil divided by its volume V^{ring}, is the volume of the density ring:

$$\rho_b = \frac{M_1 - T}{V^{\text{ring}}} \tag{2.4}$$

The dry density is the mass of soil after drying divided by the original volume:

$$\rho_d = \frac{M_2 - T}{V^{\text{ring}}} = \frac{\rho_b}{1 + w} \tag{2.5}$$

Typical values are between about 1500 and 2200 kg/m³. The bulk and dry unit weights of the soil, γ_{bulk} and γ_{dry}, are defined as the densities multiplied by the acceleration $g = 9.81$ m/s² of gravity. For example, a soil with a bulk density of 1800 kg/m³ will have a unit weight of $1800 \times 9.81/1000 \approx 17.6$ kN/m³. It is also useful to define a submerged unit weight γ', as the bulk unit weight less the unit weight $\gamma_w \approx 9.8$ kN/m³ of water:

$$\gamma' = \gamma_{\text{bulk}} - \gamma_w \tag{2.6}$$

Submerged unit weight takes account of buoyancy effects, and is directly useful in calculating the in-situ stress state of the soil (see Section 2.6.4).

2.6.3 Soil mechanics interpretations

Soil particles such as siliceous sands and gravels are hard and impermeable. Particles of fine-grained silts and clays also have these characteristics. Except for carbonate and some volcanic soils, particles do not bend, deform, or break easily, and water does not dissolve in them. Consequently, other explanations are needed for the measurable water content of soils, and for stresses and observable deformations that can occur to soils.

Figure 2.18 illustrates the soil mechanics explanations for these and other features. Soil particles come in many shapes and sizes, and do not fit snugly together. When a collection or aggregate of particles are pressed together, they come into contact on relatively small areas that can almost

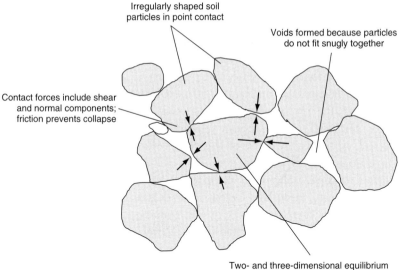

Irregularly shaped soil
particles in point contact

Voids formed because particles
do not fit snugly together

Contact forces include shear
and normal components;
friction prevents collapse

Two- and three-dimensional equilibrium
of a particle requires forces to spread out

Fig. 2.18 Particle mechanical origins and explanations for fundamental engineering parameters

be regarded as point contacts. Elsewhere, voids are formed where the shapes of particles in point contact do not match. In most soils, the voids are all connected, and water and gas can exist in them and flow through them. This is why soils have water contents. Exceptionally, particles of volcanic soils such as pumice can contain intra-particle voids, which started out as gas bubbles within molten lava that eventually solidified and broke up to form the soil. Some offshore carbonate soils are formed from the skeletons of many tiny marine animals, and the particles that the skeletons form have many complex shapes, and may include intra-particle voids.

The process of drying soil in an oven for 24 hours at 105°C is a standard procedure that is designed to remove the majority of water from the inter-particle voids. Different drying processes are feasible, such as by hot plate, air-drying, or microwave (Mendoza and Orozco, 1999; ASTM D 4643). For clays, water molecules close to the surface of particles are partially bound to the particles, forming a double layer in which electrical forces are important (Mitchell and Soga, 2005). However, the standard or equivalent process represents the definition of water content for engineering purposes. The pore water of offshore soils typically contains sodium chloride and other dissolved salts and

71

substances. Some of these precipitate out during the drying process, implying that the dry mass measured after drying may be larger than the actual mass of particles. However, the effect is small, except perhaps for very soft soils (Noorany, 1984). The standard or equivalent process is the reference for most engineering purposes.

The inter-particle void ratio, e, of a soil is defined as the ratio of the volume of the inter-particle voids divided by the volume of solids. The void ratio is directly related to the porosity $n = e/(1 + e)$ of the soil, which is the ratio of the void volume to the volume of the whole soil, and to specific volume $V = 1 + e$, which is the ratio of the macroscopic volume to the particle volume. It is also related to relative density, described below. The degree of saturation S of the voids is defined as the ratio of the volume of water in the voids divided by the volume of the voids. Many offshore soils exist in a state of 100% saturation, but soils with voids that are partially filled with gas also occur, and have S less than 100%. Dry soils correspond to $S = 0$.

The ratio of the volume of water to the volume of solids is S times e. The average specific gravity G_s of the solids is defined as the ratio of the average density of the solids in the soil divided by the average density of water. Then, the moisture content is $w = Se/G_s$. The specific gravity can be measured using a water pycnometer, based on Archimedes' principle, or a gas pycnometer (ASTM D 854 and ASTM D 5550). Typical values are in the range 2.5–2.7, depending on mineralogy, with $G_s = 2.65$ being typical for quartz or silica sands, and $G_s = 2.64$ for kaolinite clays (e.g. Lambe and Whitman, 1979).

Typical values of the void ratio for a sand are in the range 0.5–1.2. Values for a clay can be higher. For a sand, estimates of the minimum and maximum possible void ratios e_{min} and e_{max} can be obtained using laboratory tests described in ASTM (D 4253 and ASTM D 4254), and in BS 1377:4. The relative density of a particular body of sand, denoted as RD, is calculated from the void ratio of that body as

$$RD = \frac{e_{max} - e}{e_{max} - e_{min}} \tag{2.7}$$

Relative density is usually expressed as a percentage. It is also termed the density index, denoted as I_D. Lambe and Whitman (1979) describe the relative density categories listed in Table 2.2. For example, a sand layer with a void ratio of 0.9, a minimum void ratio of 0.6, and a

Table 2.2 Some terminology for relative density

Adjective	Very loose	Loose	Medium dense	Dense	Very dense
RD range	<15%	15–35%	35–65%	65–85%	>85%

maximum void ratio of 1 would be described as loose, while the same sand in a different layer with a different void ratio of 0.7 would be described as dense sand. In-situ relative densities less than 0% are very uncommon. Values a little greater than 100% sometimes occur, and are thought to be caused by the compaction due to pressure variations on the seabed induced by water waves (Bjerrum, 1973).

Now, a unit volume of soil contains a volume $Se/(1+e)$ of water with a density of $\rho_w \approx 1000 \, kg/m^3$, and a volume $1/(1+e)$ of solids with a density $\rho_w G_s$. Hence, the bulk and dry densities of the soil are, respectively,

$$\rho_b = \frac{G_s + Se}{1+e} \rho_w = (1+w)\rho_d \tag{2.8}$$

$$\rho_d = \frac{G_s}{1+e} \rho_w \tag{2.9}$$

Consequently, if the specific gravity and dry density are known, the void ratio may be inferred from equation (2.9), and the degree of saturation can then be inferred from equation (2.8). Alternatively, if it is known that the degree of saturation is 100%, the void ratio and specific gravity can be deduced from the measured bulk and dry densities.

2.6.4 Calculation of in-situ stresses in the soils in the seabed

At a given depth below the seafloor, some components of stress are due to the weight of material above that depth. If the soil is fully saturated, there will be a unique value of equilibrium pore water pressure, dependent on depth below the water surface. Some stress will also be transmitted through the particles, and across inter-particle contacts from one particle to another. The contact forces can have tangential and normal components, and are limited by the frictional characteristics of the contacts, and by the possibilities and restrictions on particle movements resulting from other particles. Soil deformations occur, not from deformations of particles but from large-scale slippage and rolling motions of particles relative to one another (Schofield and Wroth, 1968; Cundall *et al.*, 1982).

At the macroscopic scale, stress is defined as a force per unit area. If the force is at right angles to the area, the stress is a normal stress, conventionally denoted using the symbol σ. Terzaghi's principle of effective stress states that the component σ' of normal stress that is effective in determining soil stiffness and in relation to limiting conditions is equal to the total normal stress σ less the pore water pressure u:

$$\sigma' = \sigma - u \tag{2.10}$$

This applies for dry and fully saturated soils only. Stress for partially saturated soil is still a matter of research (Fredlund and Rahardjo, 1993; Fredlund, 2006). Vertical and horizontal stresses must be calculated for the purposes of planning laboratory tests, and this will now be described.

Figure 2.19 shows an example of part of the calculation of stress in a seabed. The example is for a position that is 22 m below the seafloor, in a water depth of 75 m. The soil layering consists of:

- layer 1 with a thickness of 4 m and bulk unit weight 16.6 kN/m^3
- layer 2 with a thickness of 9 m and bulk unit weight of 18.3 kN/m^3
- layer 3 with a bulk unit weight of 17.9 kN/m^3.

The total vertical stress above a given depth z below the seafloor is the total weight of material bearing on a horizontal unit area at that depth. By convention in soil mechanics generally, the effect of atmospheric pressure is ignored. If the seafloor is flat and the seabed is laterally uniform, the in-situ total vertical stress σ_v is determined in general as

$$\sigma_v = \gamma_w D \int_{z=0}^{z} \gamma_{bulk} \, dz \tag{2.11}$$

where D is the water depth. For the example in Fig. 2.19, the total stress at any given depth z below the seabed is calculated using the bulk unit weights as shown. The pore water pressure u at a given depth z is determined in general as:

$$u = \gamma_w(D + z) \tag{2.12}$$

where γ_w is the unit weight of water, usually taken to be the same for the water in the soil as for the water in the sea. This calculation assumes full saturation. For the example in Fig. 2.19, the unit weight of water has been taken as 9.8 kN/m^3. Applying Terzaghi's principle of effective stress, equation (2.10), with the general equations (2.11) and (2.12),

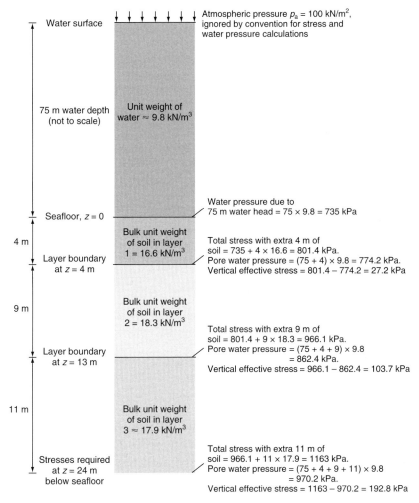

Fig. 2.19 Example of calculations for vertical total stress, pore pressure, and vertical effective stresses in a fully saturated, laterally uniform seabed

the vertical effective stress σ'_v at a given depth is

$$\sigma'_v = \sigma_v - u = \int_{z=0}^{z} (\gamma_{\text{bulk}} - \gamma_{\text{w}}) \, dz \qquad (2.13)$$

The water depth cancels in the calculation, and the submerged unit weight affects the calculation directly.

Two more steps are required to fully determine the state of stress in the soil. Because of the way the effective stress is transmitted from one particle to another through inter-particle contacts, the vertical effective

75

stress tends to spread out with depth, thereby creating a horizontal component σ'_h of effective stress. This is typically calculated as

$$\sigma'_h = K\sigma'_v \tag{2.14}$$

where K is the coefficient of lateral earth pressure. For many locations, the geological history of the site has not involved lateral compression or expansion, and the soils will have experienced compression and unloading only in the vertical direction during their history after deposition. The one-dimensional condition is termed the 'at-rest' condition, and the value of K for this condition is denoted as K_0, pronounced 'kay nought', and termed the coefficient of lateral earth pressure at rest.

K_0 depends on many factors. Typical values range from about 0.35 to 2 or more for sands, and 0.6 to 2 or more for clays. Having used it to calculate the horizontal (lateral) effective stress, the total lateral stress σ_h is calculated using Terzaghi's equation in reverse:

$$\sigma_h = \sigma'_h + u \tag{2.15}$$

Finally, it can be useful to calculate the mean normal total stress p and the mean normal effective stress p':

$$p = (\sigma_v + 2\sigma_h)/3 \tag{2.16}$$

$$p' = (\sigma'_v + 2\sigma'_h)/3 = p - u \tag{2.17}$$

The horizontal stresses are counted twice because there are two orthogonal horizontal directions but only one vertical direction.

If voids are partially filled with gas, the above equations are not so useful. If water collects around the particle contacts, the surface tension at the gas–water interface can pull the particles together, adding to the inter-particle contact forces. Relative particle motion is affected because it requires changes to the areas and shapes of the air–water interfaces. Also, if there is enough water to form a continuous path from the open sea into a given point in the seabed, then the average density of the fluid above that point is less that it would be for a fully saturated soil.

2.6.5 Triaxial test

The triaxial device is regarded as the most reliable way of measuring the undrained shear strength and the deformation characteristics of clays (API RP2A, ISO 19902). It is also reliable for silts and sands, and is one of the most reliable laboratory strength tests onshore, where its use became widespread after the publication of Bishop and Henkel's

(1957) book. The triaxial device can be used in many different ways, described in ASTM D 2850, ASTM D 4767, and ASTM D 5311, and in parts 7 and 8 of BS 1377. The most common test offshore is the unconsolidated undrained UU test, described below. Other types of triaxial test are described in Chapter 3. The triaxial cell is impractical for very soft clays, and the miniature vane test is used for these soils.

Figure 2.20a shows key features of the triaxial cell, and some aspects of sample preparation are sketched in Fig. 2.20b. The apparatus is designed to test a cylindrical soil sample. The sample diameter for testing offshore soils is determined by the internal diameter of the sampling tubes, and is typically 70 mm in diameter and about 140 mm high. In terms of onshore soil mechanics, these are large-diameter tests, can give better-quality results.

The triaxial cell itself is the central portion of the apparatus, consisting of a strong Perspex cylinder with a top and a base. The soil sample is placed on a metal pedestal in the middle of the cell. It is enclosed by a rubber membrane, which is surrounded by water under pressure. The sample will be loaded vertically through a plate placed on top. The rubber membrane prevents this water from entering the soil. The cell is fitted with a cell pressure line, to allow water under pressure to enter the volume outside the membrane-enclosed sample. It is also fitted with a sample drainage line connected to an independent water system. Tests in which this line is blocked off are called undrained tests. The line may be fitted with a pore pressure transducer to measure the water pressure in the sample. Tests in which the line is open, and the rate of straining is sufficiently slow to allow water to move freely through the sample without significantly affecting pore pressure, are called drained tests. A burette system allows the volume of water that flows into or out of the sample during the test to be measured.

The triaxial cell is placed in a loading frame which incorporates a motor and a system for measuring the axial load applied to the sample. The most common system consists of a stiff proving ring and dial gauge. When axial load is applied to the ring, it squashes slightly, and the change in height is measured by the dial gauge and converted to a force via a calibration factor. Axial load is transferred into the sample by a ram which extends downwards from the base of the proving ring, through a greased bushing, and onto the loading plate on top of the sample. During testing, the motor will push the base of the triaxial cell upwards. The ram will stay where it is relative to the loading frame, implying that the ram moves downwards relative to the soil sample. The compression of the sample is measured by a displacement gauge.

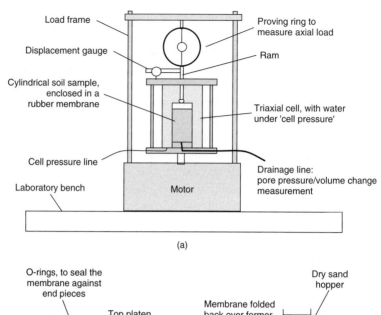

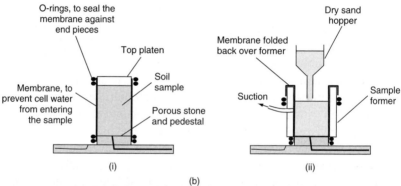

Fig. 2.20 Technology and examples of results for unconsolidated undrained (UU) triaxial tests. (a) Soil sample set up in a triaxial cell ready for testing. (b) Preparation of clay and sand samples: (i) clay sample installed with a rubber membrane and O-rings; (ii) preparation of a sand sample using a hopper and a cylindrical former – tamping may be needed for each sand layer to achieve the intended density. (c) Examples of results for UU tests. Tests 1 and 2 are good results. Test 3 has a seating error, and either there was friction in the apparatus or a less-stiff proving ring should have been used. (d) Some types of failure

One end is attached to the ram, the other to the top of the moving triaxial cell.

During a compression test, the axial load on the sample is increased and the sample compresses vertically, and may expand laterally. The linear axial strain ε_{ax} is defined as the reduction in height, s, divided

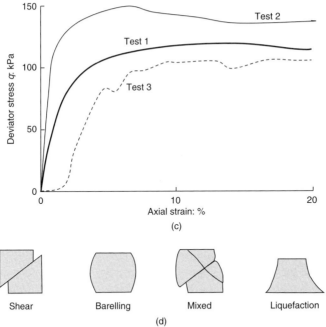

Fig. 2.20 *Continued*

by the initial height h_0 of the sample:

$$\text{generally:} \quad \varepsilon_{ax} = \frac{s}{h_0} \tag{2.18}$$

The settlement is measured by the settlement gauge, and is positive in compression. In general, tests are continued to 20% axial strain, or until the sample collapses. For a drained test, the linear radial strain ε_r is computed using the measured linear volumetric strain ε_{vol}, taken positive in compression:

$$\text{generally:} \quad \varepsilon_r = \sqrt{\frac{1 - \varepsilon_{vol}}{1 - \varepsilon_{ax}}} - 1 \tag{2.19}$$

where ε_{vol} is the reduction of volume divided by the initial volume. In an undrained test on a fully saturated soil, the volume strain is almost zero, because soil particles and water are almost incompressible. As a result, the axial compression causes an increase of the cross-sectional area of sample, and the radial strain is negative. If the area at the start of the test was A_0, the area A at some stage during the test is

$$\text{constant volume test:} \quad A = \frac{A_0}{1 - \varepsilon_{ax}} \tag{2.20}$$

79

A is sometimes called the corrected area of the sample. For example, for a 70 mm diameter sample, the initial area is $(\pi/4) \times 70^2 \approx 3848.5 \text{ mm}^2$. By the time the sample has been compressed axially by 20%, the area has become $3848.5 \approx 4810.6 \text{ mm}^2$.

The stresses on the sample consist of the cell pressure σ_{cell}, the deviator stress $q = F/A$ due to the ram force F divided by the corrected area A, and the pore fluid pressure u in the sample. The axial force is measured using the proving ring. From these quantities, several other measures of stress can be calculated. The axial total stress is $\sigma_a = \sigma_{\text{cell}} + q$, and the radial total stress is $\sigma_r = \sigma_{\text{cell}}$. The stresses are under the control of the operator, and it is usual to carry out a UU test with the cell pressure equal to the estimated in-situ mean total normal stress, equation (2.16). In the triaxial cell, the effective stresses are

$$\sigma'_a = \sigma_a - u = \sigma'_r + q \tag{2.21}$$

$$\sigma'_r = \sigma_r - u \tag{2.22}$$

The mean normal total stress p can be calculated using equation (2.16), taking the axial stress to be the vertical stress and the radial stresses to be the horizontal stresses. Similarly, the mean normal effective stress p' is computed using equation (2.17).

Figure 2.20c shows some typical results. The deviator stress q is plotted versus axial strain. Tests 1 and 2 are both good tests. The undrained shear strength of a soil is taken to be one-half of the maximum deviator stress in the test, or as one-half of the deviator stress at 20% strain if the deviator stress continues to rise throughout the test. For example, for test 1, the maximum deviator stress is 120 kPa, so the undrained shear strength of this soil is 60 kPa. For certain engineering calculations, the strain ε_c at one-half of the maximum deviator stress is required. For test 1, this is the strain at a deviator stress of 60 kPa, which is about 1.1%.

Test 3 in Fig. 2.20c has quality issues. The sample appears to have been seated badly, giving an initial soft response for about 2% axial strain. The waviness in the response is not a soil behaviour. It may have been caused by slip–stick behaviour in the system, which can produce waviness in a smoothed graph plot. The slip–stick might indicate friction in the triaxial system, which would need to be investigated, or it might be because the proving ring used for the test was too stiff, in which case a softer ring should be used. Useful data can be extracted from the graph, although the measurement of ε_c will require a judgmental shift of origin and may be somewhat subjective.

Figure 2.20d shows some common modes of collapse or 'failure' of soil samples. Shear failure involves development of a slip surface in the sample. The angle of the surface to the vertical may be of interest, but its meaning is not yet fully understood. Barrelling occurs for softer soils. More complex modes are possible too. Although tests offshore are usually only done on clay samples, silts and sands can be tested onshore. A sand sample may fail by shearing, barrelling, or by liquefaction, where the soil appears to collapse and become a liquid. Silts can also fail in this mode, but may become solid again when bent.

The first UU test on a clay sub-sample is an 'undisturbed' test, meaning that care is taken not to subject the soil to mechanical disturbance before testing. After an undisturbed test, the clay sample will be remoulded, reformed, and then retested. Remoulding involves breaking the sample into lumps, pressing and shearing the lumps, reforming a sample, then repeating the process several times. This destroys the original 'fabric' of the soil, replacing it with a fabric with every part of the sample has had a recent history of severe shearing, with the directions of shearing now randomly oriented. The remoulded sample is then retested, and the sensitivity of the sample to remoulding is determined:

$$S_r = \frac{\text{undisturbed shear strength}}{\text{remoulded shear strength}} \qquad (2.23)$$

For soils with sensitivities much larger than about 2, careful consideration is needed of the potential for remoulding during design events in the field, and the consequences of that.

2.7   Interpreting CPT data

As noted earlier and in relation to Fig. 2.14, CPT data can provide clear indications of the positions of boundaries between two layers that have different cone response characteristics. CPT data can also be used to identify soil types and estimate strength and other soil characteristics.

When a standard cone is pushed into soil, the soil is forced to flow outwards as the cone moves in. An idea of the strains experienced by the soil can be obtained by considering a small soil element just off the centreline below a 60° cone. As the cone pushes the element, the shape of the element will change to conform somewhat to the shape of the cone. Hence, the element is likely to experience an engineering shear strain of about 30° as it passes the tip, and the reverse as it passes the top of the cone. This severe deformation is likely to cause most soils to reach limiting stresses. Also, the element is being pushed against the surrounding soil. The lateral effective stresses and lateral stiffness of the in-situ soil can affect the resistance to penetration. The lateral stress may increase in the element, and soil will press harder against the friction sleeve. This is likely to increase the friction there.

These considerations indicate that CPT results will be affected by soil strength, stiffness, and in-situ stress. More precise analyses have been presented by Baligh and Levadoux (1986), Teh and Houlsby (1988, 1991), and others, and correlations between cone measurements and a variety of engineering parameters are summarised in Lunne *et al.* (1997), Schnaid (2009), and others.

Several proposals have been made for correlating cone parameters to soil type. Figure 2.21a shows part of a proposal by Robertson *et al.* (1986). The soil types range from clean sands, with low friction ratios and high cone resistances, to clays and peats, with high friction ratios and low cone resistances. Other charts have been proposed in the literature, and are discussed by Lunne *et al.* (1997), Schneider *et al.* (2008), and Schnaid (2009). It is important to recognise that the charts are based on experience, which is limited, and only give an approximate idea of soil type.

Lunne *et al.* (1997) summarise 14 proposals for relations of the following form between cone resistance and undrained shear strength s_u:

$$s_u = \frac{q_c - \sigma}{N_c} \tag{2.24}$$

where σ is a measure of the in-situ total stress and N_c is a cone factor, sometimes denoted N_k or N_{kt} depending on the context. Depending on the proposal, the stress may be the in-situ horizontal, vertical, or mean normal stress. Values for the cone factor are typically in the range 10–20, depending on soil plasticity, horizontal stress, stiffness, and other factors (Teh and Houlsby, 1988; Schnaid, 1990).

A practical problem in site investigation is to know what factor to use. A practical approach is to adjust the cone factor that is used for a clay layer until agreement is obtained between cone results and UU or miniature vane test results.

The strengths of sands are normally characterised in terms of a friction angle, which is typically correlated with relative density. Several authors have carried out calibration chamber tests in which a sand of known relative density is subjected to a known vertical stress in a calibration chamber, and a cone test is then performed. Results can often be expressed in the form

$$q_c = C_0(\sigma')^{c_1} \exp(C_2 \, RD) \tag{2.25}$$

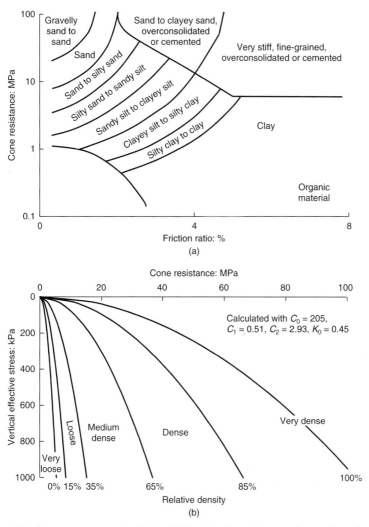

Fig. 2.21 Interpretation methods for CPTs. (a) Part of a correlation for soil type by Robertson et al. (1986). (b) Correlations of cone resistance, in-situ vertical effective stress, and relative density of clean sands (after Baldi et al., 1986; ISO 19902)

where q_c is the cone resistance in kN/m^2, C_0, C_1, and C_2 are constants, σ' is a measure of effective stress in kPa, and RD is the relative density.

Figure 2.21b illustrates the curves suggested by ISO 19902, based on Baldi et al. (1986). For these curves, σ' is the mean normal effective stress, and is obtained from the vertical effective stress using a value for the coefficient of lateral earth pressure K_0. Each curve represents a relation between cone resistance and vertical effective stress for a particular relative density. The five relative density categories described by Lambe and Whitman (1979) are marked. The curves show that, for a given relative density, the cone resistance increases with increasing vertical effective stress. For a given vertical effective stress, the resistance increases with relative density.

The curves are slightly incompatible with the chart of Fig. 2.21a, in the following way. The chart indicates that the cone resistance for sand does not reduce below about 7 MPa. The curves of Fig. 2.21b allow that sand can have smaller cone resistances if the stresses and relative densities are sufficiently low. Some engineers prefer to use Lunne and Christophersen's (1983) curves, which can give relative densities that are smaller for a given cone resistance and vertical effective stress. Another issue is that the coefficient of lateral earth pressure is not usually known. This simply illustrates that engineering judgement is required when using charts and curves.

For calcareous and carbonate sand layers, cone penetration results depend strongly on the degree of cementation, and are highly unreliable indicators of strength. Jewell and Khorshid (2000) describe an experience at the Rankine A platform site, offshore Australia, where CPT data had indicated relatively strong sands. During subsequent pile installation, however, the first pile that was placed on the seabed dropped 60 m into the seabed at the start of pile driving. The reason was essentially that the seabed was composed of calcareous and carbonate sands. The cost of remedial actions was around A\$340 million. In practice, some engineers nowadays use the correlations for siliceous sands to estimate the relative density of carbonate sands, but use different pile design methods, such as the methods of Kolk (2000).

By combining empirical relationships between cone resistance and strength with empirical relationships between strength and other parameters, it is possible to develop empirical relationships between cone resistance and other factors, including soil stiffness, friction angle, coefficient of lateral earth pressure, and elastic properties. These and other aspects are discussed by Lunne *et al.* (1997) and Schnaid (2009).

2.8   Developing a geotechnical site model

2.8.1   *Introduction*

A geotechnical site model is a description of the geotechnical conditions at the site of a planned or actual offshore structure, forming a sufficient basis for geotechnical design. API RP2A and ISO 19902 indicate that the model should be based on an integrated assessment of geophysical and geotechnical data. Ideally, the model will include a description of the present site conditions, an understanding of how the present site conditions came to be formed in the geological and recent past, and an assessment of how these conditions may change over the design life-time of the structure.

Model development starts at the stage of the desk study, and the model evolves as new data are obtained. Important aspects of the model include simplified models of the soil layering or stratigraphy at a location, sometimes called the 'design soil profile', together with the engineering properties of each layer in the profile. Some of the fundamental properties are:

- layer thickness
- submerged unit weight
- undrained shear strength for clay layers
- relative density and/or friction angle for granular layers
- carbonate content for granular layers.

Part of this information will become available during the site investi-gation, and this will be added to during the subsequent laboratory testing. Details of the laboratory tests that are usually done are given in Chapter 3, but a summary is also given in Section 2.8.2. There will often be some scatter in the data, and this is discussed in Section 2.8.3.

Site investigation results are normally presented on a detailed borehole log, supported by graphs and charts. Logging software is highly recommended. Figure 2.14c shows part of a simplified borehole log. The log presents both factual data and a simplified interpretation of soil layering.

2.8.2   Onshore laboratory testing

The cost of a laboratory test is small compared with the cost of an offshore project or the cost of an engineering problem that happens offshore. Consequently, cost is not usually an issue when deciding on a programme of laboratory tests. All possible efforts are made to get as much information from the recovered samples as possible. Time and laboratory availability are more often the constraining factors.

It is usual to carry out classification tests on every recovered sample if there is enough material. This includes grain size analysis,

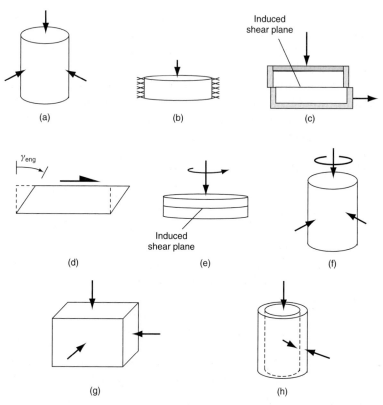

Fig. 2.22 Schematics of test conditions for some common onshore laboratory strength and deformations tests. (a) Triaxial. (b) Oedometer. (c) Direct shear. (d) Simple shear. (e) Ring shear. (f) Resonant column. (g) True triaxial. (h) Hollow cylinder

plasticity tests for cohesive samples, and carbonate tests for sands. Mineralogy tests and X-ray photomicrographs of soil particles are sometimes done, particularly if there are indications of problematic mineralogies. Depending on the type of structure to be built, permeability tests may be done to estimate rates of flow of water through coarse-grained soils.

Figure 2.22 illustrates some of the available tests for strength and deformation characteristics of recovered soils. Three common types of test are:

(a) Triaxial tests: onshore laboratories can typically explore a wider range of test conditions than offshore.

(b) Oedometer tests, which involve compressing a disk of soil vertically. These tests are done to estimate settlements under vertical loads, and to investigate the consolidation and time-dependent characteristics of the soil.

(c) Direct shear tests, done to estimate the friction angle of sands or the undrained shear strength of clays. In these tests, a horizontal shear plane is induced in the soil sample, and the associated stress conditions are measured.

Other tests are more specialised, including:

(d) Simple shear tests, in which a disk of soil is sheared through an angle. This avoids problems of stress concentration and non-uniform distribution of strains and effective stress in direct shear.

(e) Ring shear tests, in which a disk of soil is twisted to induce a circular shear plane. The upper part of the ring of soil is then rotated over the lower part, and the stress conditions on the induced failure plane are measured.

(f) Resonant column tests, in which a cylinder of soil is subjected to torsional vibrations. These tests are done to determine parameters for earthquake analysis.

(g) True triaxial tests, in which a cube of soil is subjected to variations of normal stress in three perpendicular directions. This can be particularly useful for anisotropic and stress path tests.

(h) Hollow cylinder tests, in which a tube of soil contained in a rubber membrane is subjected to inner and outer pressures as well as axial load and torsion.

Further details are given in Chapter 3, and in Hunt (2005), Head (2006), and other sources in the technical literature.

After testing at an onshore laboratory, it is normal for the client to require samples to be kept for a minimum period, typically 2 years, to assist in clarifying any subsequent queries.

2.8.3 Managing scatter

It is usual to plot laboratory data on a graph versus depth below the seafloor. The graphs almost always show some scatter, and some simplifications are usually necessary for the purposes of design. Figure 2.23 shows an example. The soil profile consists entirely of clay. Data points representing many measurements of undrained shear strength have been plotted versus depth, and show some scatter.

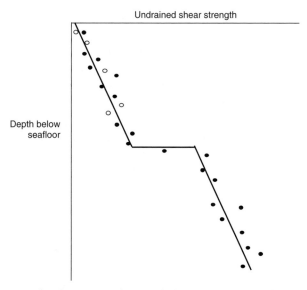

Fig. 2.23 Example of scatter in data, and the stepped profile of undrained shear strength versus depth below seafloor

The method used to manage scatter always involves application of engineering judgement, and always depends on the uses to which the final results will be put. Engineering judgement is required to assess the quality of the data. For example, if one of the triaxial test results was like test 3 in Fig. 2.20c, then that result might be given less credibility than other, better-quality, tests. Judgement also involves the application of engineering knowledge and experience, and it happens that this leads to an expectation that clay strengths will usually increase with depth, sometimes with step increases, as in Fig. 2.23. The geological origins of this kind of step profile are described in Chapter 3.

The application is important too. If the engineering task is to ensure that a pile can support a given load, then a 'conservative' approach is to err on the low side in terms of estimating shear strength. That would produce predictions for ultimate capacity that would be expected to be less than the actual capacity. By contrast, if the task is to ensure that a pile can be driven into the seabed, it can be conservative to err on the high side, since that would be expected to lead to overestimates of resistance. That will in turn lead to the provision of more powerful pile-driving equipment, so that there may be greater confidence that the actual resistance can be overcome by that equipment.

2.8.4 Developing design soil profiles and engineering parameters

Different companies have different ways of developing design profiles and parameters. For many locations, the soils data are complex, not always as complete as would be ideally desired, and occasionally contra-dictory in places. Sometimes there are conflicts of opinion between laboratory staff, who often believe that everything possible should be put on a log whether or not it affects engineering calculations, and engineers, who recognise that design calculations only use simplified models. Sound engineering judgement and a disciplined method can help. One method is illustrated in Fig. 2.24:

(1) Data Preparation. The data available from a geotechnical survey or site investigation typically includes driller's logs, sample description

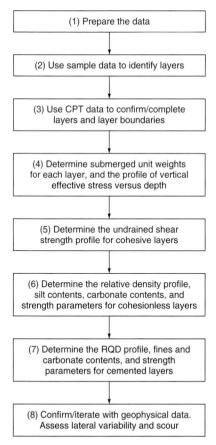

Fig. 2.24 *Example of steps for developing a geotechnical site model*

sheets, laboratory test results, and in-situ test results. In some investigations, the drilling parameters such as mud pressure and bit weight will be recorded. Step 1 is to collect all of the available information and put it into a manageable order.

(2) *Identifying soil layers.* The sample data sheets will contain descriptions of the soils as written up by the laboratory technician or attending engineer at the time of visual–manual investigation. These descriptions can vary from short to lengthy. For the purposes of most engineering calculations, a first decision is to determine which of the following four categories a soil falls into:
   – siliceous sand or gravel, for which drained design methods will usually be used
   – carbonate sand or gravel, for which special caution is needed
   – silt or clay, for which undrained design methods will usually be used
   – cemented soil or rock.

Most engineering calculations are not very sensitive to thin layers, although there are some important exceptions discussed later in this book. Some companies consider a 'layer' to be not thinner than a metre or so, but also ensure that soft seams that may be problematic are always noted on the borehole log.

Consecutive samples with the same category are normally considered to potentially be parts of the same soil layer. Thus, having gone through all the sample sheets a relatively small number of distinct soil layers is found. However, it is now feasible that two soil layers with different soil properties have been mistakenly considered to be one soil layer. A check is therefore made on the graphs of water content, density, strength, and so on to verify that the properties of what is considered to be a single layer are reasonably consistent throughout the layer thickness. If not, the layer is split into two or more layers having distinct engineering properties.

(3) *Identify the depths of layer boundaries below the seafloor.* A full sample of soil may not have been recovered in all samples, so there will be gaps. Thus, it will often not be possible to determine where one soil layer ends and the next starts. CPT data often provide a very clear indication of layer boundary depths, remembering, however, that the CPT data are also affected by layer boundaries (see Fig. 2.14b). Another useful source of information can be the drillers' logs, as the drillers may have made a note of where drilling conditions changed.

Steps 1 to 3 have essentially finished the work of developing a design stratigraphy. It will typically have produced between a few soil layers for a shallow borehole and up to about 30 distinct soil layers for a deep borehole. The subsequent steps are primarily focused on the development of engineering parameters for each soil layer, taking due account of any scatter in data:

(4) *Determine submerged unit weights and vertical effective stresses.* Measured submerged unit weights are plotted versus depth below the seafloor. There will be some scatter in the plot, but it is usually possible to select a single representative value for any given soil layer. Occasionally, there is a clear and significant linear increase of submerged unit weight with depth. Based on the values or linear trends assigned to each soil layer, a graph of vertical effective stress versus depth below the seafloor can be drawn.

(5) *Cohesive layers.* The main strength parameter for clay and cohesive silt layers is the undrained shear strength of the material. It is measured reliably by the laboratory miniature vane tests and by triaxial testing. Estimates are also usually available on the basis of torvane and pocket penetrometer tests. CPT data are also useful, providing the correct cone factor is known. As was indicated by the data in Figs 2.23 undrained shear strength usually increases with depth below the seafloor. However the strength of an underlying soil layer can sometimes be less than for an overlying one, producing a sawtooth profile, and occasionally the data will indicate strength that is constant with depth, or reducing with depth.

(6) *Cohesionless layers.* For sands and gravels, the primary measure of shear strength is a friction angle, which correlates with relative density. It is usual to assume that a single sand layer has a constant relative density and a constant friction angle. This is not necessarily accurate for thick sand layers, and can be very inaccurate in seabeds that have been formed from sand dunes. Sound engineering judgement is needed.

(7) *Cemented layers.* Data may be available in terms of RQD, unconfined compressive strength, index strength, or wave velocity. Cemented soil layers are sometimes treated as granular soils for the purposes of driven pile design. Friction cannot exceed the frictional strength of the rock. Local experience is an essential guide.

(8) *Lateral variability.* Where there are several sets of boreholes in close proximity, it is possible to estimate lateral variability by comparing the levels, thicknesses, and engineering properties of similar strata

in the different boreholes. Geophysical data can be highly useful for this purpose.

It is useful to again note that the borehole log and design stratigraphy are just parts of a geotechnical site model, and that other parts can be important too. Recent examples include Lane (2005), Liedtke *et al.* (2006), Bryn *et al.* (2007), Ehlers *et al.* (2008), amongst others.

3

Soil mechanics

Chapter 3 covers the main processes of the formation of offshore soils, the classifications of offshore soils and rocks, and the different ways that basic soil mechanics theories are applied in many offshore contexts.

3.1   Formation of offshore soils

Many offshore soils are formed in the same way as onshore soils, as part of the rock cycle. Terrestrial rock surfaces that are exposed to the atmosphere are subject to weathering, and are slowly but continuously broken down by the cyclic actions of wetting and drying by rain, cyclic stress changes associated with daily and seasonal changes of temperature, physical breakage by ice action, chemical action through chemicals in rain and surface run-off, and the physical actions of living things from microbes to people (Price, 2008). The rock fragments formed in this way travel downslope by gravity, and are subjected to further weathering, together with impact and abrasive actions. Some fragments are transported by gravity or surface run-off water into streams, where they experience further breakage as they are pushed downstream. The soils are transported to the sea, and are deposited on the seafloor, buried under further sediment, compacted over millions of years, and moved by geological processes, eventually to rise and form new land and rock surfaces, when the process continues.

The process produces particles of various sizes. Sands formed in this way typically have a silica-based mineralogy, giving very hard, almost incompressible, rounded or angular particles, often with few or no internal weakness. Clays are typically formed from silica–aluminate minerals. Their shapes may be rounded, stick-like, tubular, plate-like, flake-like, or other. Montmorillonite mineralogy produces clay particles that have a high affinity for water molecules. This can result in very open structures at the microscopic scale, with a clay soil containing more water than solids. Quick clays are of this type, and have been responsible for many onshore landslides of slopes of only a few degrees (Cornforth, 2005; Mitchell and Soga, 2005).

Very fine silt and clay particles travel more or less in suspension, while coarser fragments are pushed along the stream or river bed as bedload. Sands and coarse silts may travel as bedload in periods of slow river motion, but in suspension in periods of faster motion. When the river reaches the ocean, the water slows down. Coarse particles are deposited first, and so gravel and sand banks are typically found in and close to estuaries. Longshore currents may then pick up and transport these particles along the coast, where further erosion on cliffs adds to the sediment load. Coarse silts tend to settle to the seabed further out. The deposition creates slopes on the seabed which slowly steepen until they become so unstable as to fail in a submarine landslide (Coleman *et al.*, 1978; Masson *et al.*, 2006). Finer particles take longer to settle out, and can be transported hundreds of kilometres into the ocean.

Sands and silts can also be transported by wind. Sahara sand can be blown from Africa to America. Particle sizes from boulders to clays can be picked up by glaciers and be transported many kilometres out to sea, and the boulders in boulder clays are thought to be the result of boulders being dropped from melting ice. Bjerrum (1973) describes the geological history of the soils on the seabed of the North Sea (Fig. 3.1). About 20 000 years ago, at the peak of the last ice age, the sea level was about 100 m lower than it is today. Glaciers originating in Britain and Scandinavia covered much of the North Sea. When the earth warmed, the ice cover melted, but there were colder periods that allowed the ice to move back over the area. The result was the formation of terminal moraines, and much of the coarser material presently covering the area is believed to be the result of the subsequent transportation of this material by sea water. Clay deposits are thought to have been brought into the area by the meltwater from glaciers, and left in deep depressions in the sands where the ocean currents could not move them.

One type of soil that is special to oceans is carbonate soil, formed in the sea from the skeletons of micro-organisms (Murff, 1987; Le Tirant *et al.*, 1994). When these creatures die, the skeletons fall slowly to the sea floor, and build into thick layers over millennia. The skeletons consist primarily of calcium carbonate, which dissolves very slowly in seawater. The 'carbonate compensation depth' (CCD) is the water depth below which the rate at which calcium carbonate can dissolve exceeds the rate of supply of carbonate materials from above. It depends on temperature and other factors, but is typically around 3.5–5 km at

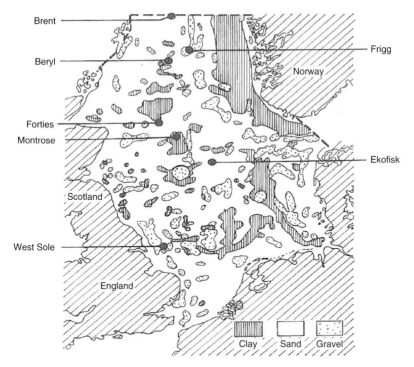

Fig. 3.1 Map of the North Sea, showing the distribution of bottom sediments (reproduced with permission from Bjerrum (1973))

the present time. Carbonate soil deposits cannot form below the CCD, but they can be transported there by flowslides or other events. Calcareous sands are typically found between 30°N latitude and 30°S latitude, and exceptionally outside these latitudes, including the Bass Strait, Australia.

Calcareous sands can be problematic foundation materials. Carbonate sand particles are soft compared with siliceous sands, and can have very complicated shapes. After a carbonate soil is formed, carbonate can dissolve in the water in the soil, and precipitate out as a weak calcite cement at interparticle contacts. This creates a weakly cemented soil that can appear to be strong, but be very brittle. Jewell and Khorshid (2000) describe the Rankine experience, where a first pile was found to free-fall 60 m into a seabed that had been previously identified as a strong one. Subsequent piles at the site of the North Rankine A platform were also found to give very low penetration resistances. The total cost of the problem and the research needed to solve it exceeded A$340 million.

Dead corals are another type of carbonate soil. They are formed from living corals which died in past centuries and millennia, and were buried under subsequent sediments, and sometimes eroded to reappear at the seabed. Corals can be very variable foundation materials.

Keller (1967) proposes that ocean sediments can be divided into six classes. Classes 1 and 2 are fluvial marine sand–silts and fluvial marine silt–clays, both derived from the rock cycle weathering onshore and transported to the ocean primarily by rivers. Class 3, inorganic pelagic clay, is a deep-ocean inorganic deposit. Classes 4 and 5 are siliceous oozes and calcareous oozes, consisting of deep-ocean deposits with significant to dominant proportions of minute skeletal material. Class 6 is calcareous sand and silt, predominantly shell fragments and coral debris.

Materials at and beneath the seabed can include rocks. All of the onshore rock types are also found offshore, and are formed by the same processes. Cemented sands, sandstones, siltstones, and claystones may be formed by the slow deposition of cement in the corresponding soils, and/or by pressure bonding at interparticle contacts as a result of high overburden stress coupled with heat from the earth's core. Gypsum crystals consist of calcium sulfate dihydrate, and can lead to long-term settlement problems due to time-dependent deformations, even under constant loads. Submarine volcanoes also contribute to the range of soils found offshore (Menard, 1964). Volcanic soils can also be part of the fluvial marine soils of terrestrial origin.

3.2 Classification and basic properties of offshore soils

3.2.1 Particle sizes

Offshore soils are classified according to the Unified Soil Classification System (USCS), which is described in ASTM D 2487 and ASTM D 2488 (ASTM, 2009), and in BS 5930 (BSI, 1999). Slightly different versions of the USCS apply in different countries. The principal classification tests are the particle size distribution test and the Atterberg (liquid and plastic) limit tests. Carbonate content is another key classification test that is absolutely necessary for coarse-grained offshore soils.

Figure 3.2 shows an example of particle size distribution (PSD) curve for a soil. The percentage by dry weight finer than a given nominal diameter is plotted vertically, versus nominal particle diameter plotted horizontally. The coarse-grained part of the curve, for nominal diameters greater than 75 µm, is measured by drying a sample of soil, and passing it through a stack of sieves of various sized-openings. The

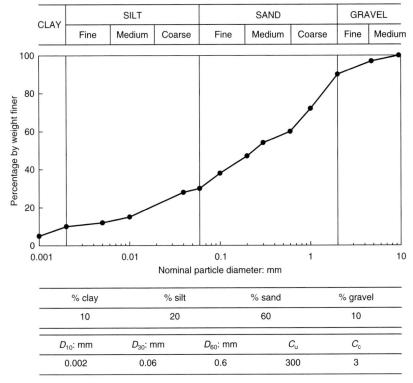

% clay	% silt	% sand	% gravel
10	20	60	10

D_{10}: mm	D_{30}: mm	D_{60}: mm	C_u	C_c
0.002	0.06	0.6	300	3

Fig. 3.2 Example of a particle size distribution, annotated using BS size ranges

nominal diameter is the size of a sieve opening through which the particle can just pass. The fine-grained part of the curve, smaller than 60 μm, is measured using a hydrometer. The nominal diameter is the diameter of a spherical particle that would fall through water at a terminal velocity equal to the terminal velocity of the actual particle.

Some of the size ranges are slightly different in the ASTM and BS systems. For example, ASTM D 653 defines a sand as 'particles of rock that will pass the No. 4 (4.75 mm) sieve and be retained on the No. 200 (75 μm) U.S. standard sieve', while Table 13 of BS 5930 defines sand-sized particles as between 0.06 and 2 mm. Both agree that clay sizes are less than 2 μm.

The effective size of a soil, D_{10}, is the largest nominal diameter in the smallest 10% of particles. Similarly, the D_{30} and D_{60} sizes refer to the smallest 30 and 60% of particle sizes. The coefficient of uniformity, C_u, is defined as the ratio D_{60}/D_{10}. If the coefficient of uniformity is greater than about 3, the soil is 'well-graded' or 'poorly sorted'. A soil with a lower value is 'poorly graded' or 'well sorted'. The coefficient of curvature or grading is $C_c = D_{30}^2/(D_{60}D_{10})$.

Some soils contain gaps where there are almost no particles. This shows up in the PSD as a flat portion between two steeper portions of the curve. If the flat portion extends over a width corresponding to one soil group, the soil is called 'gap-graded'. If there is significant flow of fluid through a gap-graded soil, the flow can carry away the smaller particles through gaps formed between larger particles, leaving a loose and weak skeleton of just the larger particles.

3.2.2 Particle aggregates

A soil body consists of an aggregate of particles held together by the compressive forces induced by an outside agency, such as by gravity or by the application of load to a foundation. The particles are not identical, even for a uniform soil. They have different shapes, and do not fit snugly together. Spaces or 'voids' are formed when the particles are in contact. Water and gas may exist in the voids. Many different particle arrangements are possible, particularly for fine-grained soils, in which particles tend to be far from spherical. Platy clay particles may be stacked in bookend-type structures. Crisp-like clay particles may be joined at their edges, to form structures resembling irregular rooms.

The soil fabric refers to the spatial arrangement of particles and voids, including orientations of particles relative to one another, and numbers and orientations of interparticle contacts (Brewer, 1964; Oda, 1978). The fabric occurs at the microscopic scale of a few tens or hundreds of particles, and at the mesoscopic scale of thousands and millions of particles. It affects strength and stiffness, and is associated with soil anisotropy, but knowledge of how this occurs is far from complete (Mitchell and Soga, 2005; Yang *et al.*, 2008). Fabric and anisotropy can sometimes help to explain scatter in strength data (Pelletier *et al.*, 1997).

Offshore soils can show structural features such as fissures and shear planes. A blocky clay is one that separates easily into small cube-shaped blocks. Partings are thin seams of silt or fine sand in a clay soil, and can be identified when an otherwise stiff or hard clay breaks easily on a plane that is usually horizontal. Laminations, seams, and lenses are small bedding features, and different engineers may use different definitions for these terms. Some soils consist of alternating beds of sand and clay, with each bed being a few centimetres thick. A pragmatic approach is often adopted: the interbedded region is modelled as either a uniform sand or a uniform clay, and the worst case scenario is used for design.

3.2.3   Plasticity and index properties of fine-grained soils

Fine-grained soils such as clays and silts have the characteristic of mouldability at moderate water contents. This is the ability to be deformed plastically without cracking and without flowing like a liquid. The ranges of water contents at which this can occur are different for different fine-grained soils.

The liquid limit (LL) of a fine-grained soil is defined as the highest water content at which the material is considered to be a plastic, remouldable solid. It is measured using the Casagrande device or the fallcone (ASTM D 4318; Koumoto and Houlsby, 2001). Soil deposits at water contents higher than this are considered to be liquids for most engineering purposes. The plastic limit (PL) is the lowest water content at which the soil can be deformed without cracking. It is usually measured by rolling a thread of material between the fingers.

Typically, a fine-grained soil will have a water content w between the liquid and plastic limits, and is said to be a plastic solid. The plasticity index $PI = LL - PL$ of a soil is a measure of the ability of a soil to retain water. A low plasticity index means that the addition of only a small amount of water can turn a strong soil, at or near the PL, into a weak one, at or near the liquid limit. A high plasticity index means that the soil is highly compressible. The liquidity index of a sample of the soil is

$$LI = 100\% \times \frac{w - PL}{PI} \tag{3.1}$$

where w is the in-situ water content. The liquidity index is a measure of the weakness of that sample. Both plasticity and liquidity index are usually expressed as a percentage. A soil at the plastic limit ($w = PL$) has a liquidity index of zero, and is relatively strong, whereas a different sample of the same soil but at its liquid limit ($w = LL$) has an LI of 100%, and is on the borderline between a plastic solid and a liquid.

For classification purposes, the liquid limit and plasticity index of a soil are plotted on a plasticity chart. The ASTM chart is shown in Fig. 3.3a, the British chart in Fig. 3.3b. The A-line separates clays (plotting above the line and represented by the symbol C), from silts (below the line and represented by M). It was suggested by Casagrande (1948), based on his experience. Its sloping part has $PI = 0.73(LL - 20)$, which implies $PL \approx 15 + LL/4$. In the ASTM chart, the difference between low and high plasticity is set at a liquid limit of 50%, and there is a region of low-plasticity silty clay (CL-ML). In the British chart, there are five plasticity classes: low, intermediate, high, very high, and extremely high. There is no silty clay region.

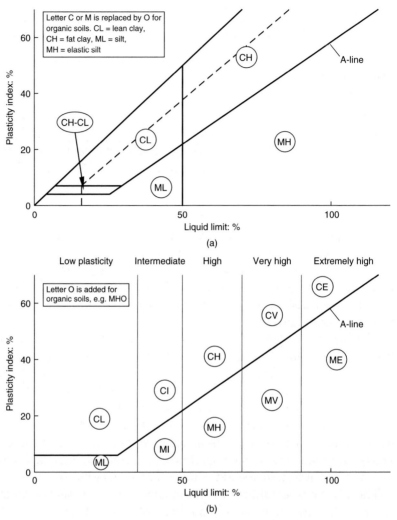

Fig. 3.3 Plasticity charts. (a) ASTM D 2487 chart. (b) BS 5930 chart

3.2.4 Classification of soils and rocks

Figure 3.4 illustrates the basic steps used in the ASTM version of the USCS. First, is the soil fine-grained or coarse-grained? For fine-grained soils, the main soil type is determined from the plasticity chart, and additional descriptive terms are determined from particle size data. For coarse-grained soils, the main soil type is determined from the particle size, and additional descriptive terms are determined from

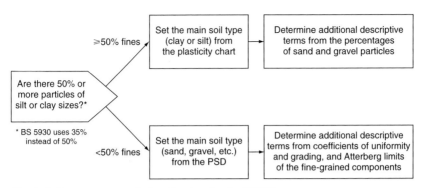

Fig. 3.4 Basic steps in soil classification by the USCS

size and plasticity. The final result of the classification process is a precisely defined name, and a letter designation. For instance, ASTM D 2487 uses the term 'gravelly lean clay with sand' to mean, precisely, an inorganic CL material with 30% or more particles larger than the No. 200 sieve size (75 μm), with 15% or more sand, and more sand than gravel.

Classification of cemented materials is often done using a modification of Clarke and Walker's (1977) classification scheme, which is shown in Fig. 3.5. The scheme was originally proposed for Middle Eastern sedimentary rocks, and is based on three parameters: induration, carbonate content, and grain size. Induration is the degree to which the rock has undergone hardening by precipitation of cement out of water. Materials are considered in four groups: non-indurated, slightly indurated, moderately indurated, or highly indurated. Carbonate content and grain size determine subgroup classifications.

The scheme is useful but has some minor issues. The shear strength categories do not fit well with BS 5930, and the break-levels of 10 and 90% on the carbonate content axes do not fit well with breaks of 20 and 80% in Kolk's (2000) widely accepted recommendations for engineering design in calcareous and carbonate soils. Other rocks are also encountered offshore, including chloride rocks such as rock salt, or sulfate rocks such as gypsum, anhydrite, or potash. These materials can exist in thick beds that can exhibit significant time-dependent creep and settlement under sustained load (Shiri and Pashnehtala, 2006). General classification schemes for carbonate soils and rocks are discussed by Bieniawski (1979), King et al. (1980), and Le Tirant et al. (1994), and the BS 5930 descriptions are discussed by Dearman (1995).

101

Degree of induration	Approximate unconfined compressive strength	ADDITIONAL DESCRIPTIVE TERMS BASED ON ORIGIN OF CONSTITUENT PARTICLES				TOTAL CARBONATE CONTENT (constituent particles plus matrix)
		NOT DISCERNIBLE		BIOCLASTIC (organic) OOLITE (inorganic)	SHELL (organic) CORAL (organic) ALGAL (organic) PISOLITES (inorganic)	
		INCREASING GRAIN SIZE OF PARTICULATE DEPOSITS → 0.002 mm	0.060 mm	2 mm	60 mm	
Non-indurated	Very soft to hard (<36 to >300 kN/m^2)	CARBONATE MUD	CARBONATE SILT	CARBONATE SAND	CARBONATE GRAVEL	90%
		Clayey CARBONATE MUD	Siliceous CARBONATE SILT ①	Siliceous CARBONATE SAND ①	Mixed carbonate and non-carbonate GRAVEL ②	50%
		Calcareous CLAY	Calcareous SILT ①	Calcareous silica SAND ①		10%
		CLAY	SILT	Silica SAND	GRAVEL	
Slightly indurated	Hard to moderately weak (0.3 to 12.5 MN/m^2)	CALCILUTITE (carb. claystone)	CALCISILITITE (carb. siltstone)	CALCARENITE (carb. sandstone)	CALCIRUDITE (carb. conglomerate or breccia)	90%
		Clayey CALCILUTITE	Siliceous CALCISILITITE	Siliceous CALCARENITE	Conglomerate CALCIRUDITE ②	50%
		Calcareous CLAYSTONE	Calcareous SILTSTONE	Calcareous SANDSTONE	Calcareous CONGLOMERATE	10%
		CLAYSTONE	SILTSTONE	SANDSTONE	CONGLOMERATE or BRECCIA	
Moderately indurated	Moderately strong to strong (12.5 to 100 MN/m^2)	Fine-grained LIMESTONE		Detrial LIMESTONE	CONGLOMERATE LIMESTONE	90%
		Fine-grained Argillaceous LIMESTONE	Fine-grained Siliceous LIMESTONE	Siliceous detrital LIMESTONE	Conglomerate LIMESTONE ②	50%
		Calcareous CLAYSTONE	Calcareous SILTSTONE	Calcareous SANDSTONE	Calcareous CONGLOMERATE	10%
		CLAYSTONE	SILTSTONE	SANDSTONE	CONGLOMERATE or BRECCIA	
Highly indurated	Strong to extremely strong (70 to >200 MN/m^2)	CRYSTALLINE LIMESTONE OR MARBLE (tends towards uniformity of grain size and loss of original texture)				50%
		Conventional metamorphic nomenclature applies in this section				

Fig. 3.5 Clarke and Walker's (1977) scheme for classifying Middle Eastern sedimentary, siliceous or carbonate cemented soils and rocks

3.3   Stress and strain in soils

3.3.1   *Terzaghi's principle of effective stress*

Consider a small macroscopic cross-sectional area A in an element of soil, where A is much larger than the cross-sectional area of a particle. Let N and S be the normal and shear forces which, if acting on one side of the area, would equilibrate all of the forces and pressures from the particles and water acting against the other side. Then, $\sigma = N/A$ is the total normal stress acting on the soil in the direction normal to the area, and $\tau = S/A$ is the total shear stress.

Skempton (1960) proposed a particle mechanical interpretation of stress, sketched in Fig. 3.6a. Suppose a wavy surface is drawn through the soil, as nearly flat as possible but only passing through voids and the boundaries between particles at interparticle contacts. Consider a cross-sectional area A, and let A_c be the net contact area between the particles. The total normal force on the area is made up of a force $u(A - A_c)$ due to the pore fluid pressure u, and an intergranular force equal to the total force less this. Dividing by A, an intergranular stress σ'' is obtained:

$$\sigma'' = \sigma - u(A - A_c)/A = (\sigma - u) + uA_c/A \qquad (3.2)$$

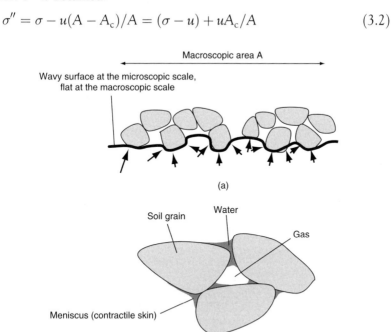

Macroscopic area A

Wavy surface at the microscopic scale,
flat at the macroscopic scale

(a)

Soil grain   Water

Gas

Meniscus (contractile skin)

(b)

Fig. 3.6 Interparticle forces and stress. (a) Skempton's (1960) model. (b) The extra complication of air–water interfaces in partially saturated soil

For hard particles, the contact area ratio A_c/A would be very small, much less than 0.001, for example. Terzaghi (1936) had earlier proposed that the quantity

$$\sigma' = \sigma - u \qquad (3.3)$$

would be effective in the stress–strain and strength properties of the particle aggregate. This equation is Terzaghi's principle of effective stress, and σ' is termed the normal effective stress.

Terzaghi's principle is usually used, rather than Skempton's stress. It applies for fully saturated soils, and for dry soils ($u=0$), and leads directly to the equations for in-situ effective stresses developed in Chapter 2. It does not apply for partially saturated or gassy soils (Fig. 3.6b), for which the microstructure also includes surface tension effects due to water–gas boundaries (Fredlund and Rahardjo, 1993; Fredlund, 2006).

3.3.2 Mohr's circles of effective and total stress

Mohr's circles of stress and strain in soils are described by Lambe and Whitman (1979), Bowles (1996), Parry (2004), and others.

Figure 3.7a shows the total stresses and pore pressure u acting on the sides of a square element of soil seen in end view. Consider another plane through the soil, at an angle θ, as shown in Fig. 3.7b. Let σ_θ and τ_θ be the total normal and shear stresses on this plan, respectively, and let the hypotenuse of the right-angled triangle have a length equal to 1 unit. Then, $\sigma_\theta 1$ and $\tau_\theta 1$ are the forces on the plane per unit length in the direction at right angles to the view shown. The other sides have lengths $\cos\theta$ and $\sin\theta$, and the forces per unit length on these sides are obtained by multiplying the lengths by the relevant stresses. Considering the equilibrium of the triangular element in the directions normal and tangential to the inclined edges, and applying standard trigonometric formulae, gives

$$\sigma_\theta = \frac{\sigma_v + \sigma_h}{2} + \frac{\sigma_v - \sigma_h}{2}\cos 2\theta - \tau\sin 2\theta \qquad (3.4)$$

$$\tau_\theta = \frac{\sigma_v - \sigma_h}{2}\sin 2\theta + \tau\cos 2\theta \qquad (3.5)$$

If the results are plotted on a graph as a function of θ, they form a circle. In Fig. 3.7c, the circle on the right is Mohr's circle of total stress. The stresses on the horizontal and vertical planes in Fig. 3.7a are plotted at points (σ_v, τ) and (σ_h, τ) respectively. The stresses $(\sigma_\theta, \tau_\theta)$ for the

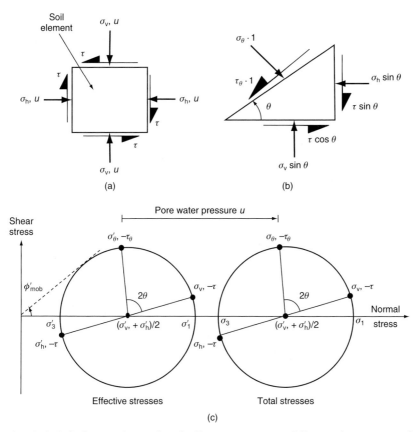

Fig. 3.7 *Calculations for total and effective stresses on different planes in a soil body. (a) Total stresses and pore pressure in two dimensions. (b) Equilibrium calculation. (c) Mohr's circles of effective and total stresses*

inclined plane are obtained by rotating around the circle by an angle 2θ, as shown. The principal total stresses are the normal stresses $\sigma_1 = \sigma_{\text{centre}} + \sigma_{\text{radius}}$ (major) and $\sigma_3 = \sigma_{\text{centre}} - \sigma_{\text{radius}}$ (minor), where the circle crosses the axis. The physical planes at angles $-\sin^{-1}(\tau/\sigma_{\text{radius}})$ and this $+90°$ are planes on which no shear stress occurs. The normals to these planes are the principal directions of total stress for the two-dimensional view being considered.

By subtracting the pore water pressure u from the normal stresses, corresponding results for effective stress are obtained. Because of Terzaghi's principle, Mohr's circle of effective stress is obtained by translation from the total stress circle by an amount representing the pore water pressure. The effective circle is left of the total if the pore

105

pressure is positive, and right of it, if negative. The effective radius is the same as the total radius. The principal effective stresses occur on the same planes and directions as the principal total stresses, and are equal to those less the pore pressure. Terzaghi's principle applies so that, for example, the effective stress on the plane at angle θ is given by $\sigma'_\theta = \sigma_\theta - u$. The friction angle on a plane at angle θ in the soil is $\phi'_\theta = \tan^{-1}(|\tau_\theta / \sigma'_\theta|)$. The largest angle for all possible planes is the mobilised friction angle. For the Mohr diagram in two dimensions:

$$\phi'_{mob} = \frac{\sigma'_{radius}}{\sigma'_{centre}} = \frac{\sigma_{radius}}{(\sigma'_v + \sigma'_h)/2} \tag{3.6}$$

The physical planes on which this maximum occurs are the planes of maximum stress obliquity. The maximum possible value of this maximum is a measure of the frictional strength of the soil, and depends on the state of the soil.

3.3.3   Mohr's circles and laboratory tests

Mohr's circles can be used to compare different types of laboratory test. Figure 3.8 illustrates this for triaxial and simple shear tests.

Figure 3.8a illustrates features of a triaxial test carried out on a cylindrical specimen. If the cell pressure is σ_{cell}, the deviator stress is q, and the pore water pressure is u, then the radial effective stress is $\sigma'_r = \sigma_{cell} - u$, and the axial effective stress is $\sigma'_r + q$. The stress state referred to axes of the apparatus plots as two points on the normal stress axis of the Mohr diagram. As the triaxial test progresses, the points move along the axis but never leave it. The circle may expand or contract, and its centre may move. A graph of radius versus the stress at its centre would represent a type of 'stress path' for the test. Different stress paths could be applied to different samples, and the results compared.

Figure 3.8b illustrates a type of simple shear test. The sample is subjected to a shear stress τ under conditions of no lateral strain. It is possible to do the test at constant vertical effective stress σ'_v. The lateral effective stress σ'_h changes in some way that depends on the constitutive laws of the soil. The Mohr's circle may expand or contract during the test, and its radius and centre may change, but the point representing effective stresses on the horizontal plane will stay at the same constant vertical effective stress in the diagram. Consequently, the directions of the principal axes of stress rotate in physical space during the test.

In the Cambridge simple shear device, the sample is rectangular, whereas it is cylindrical and confined by a wire-reinforced rubber

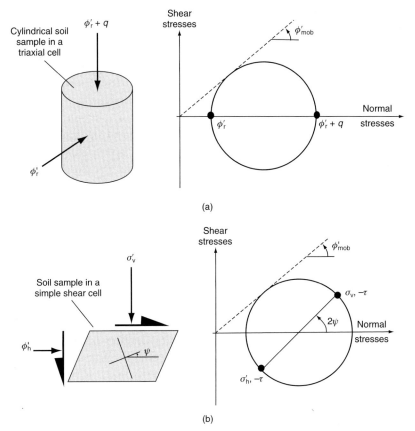

Fig. 3.8 Using Mohr's circles to compare triaxial and simple shear tests. (a) Triaxial test: principal effective stresses in the fixed axial and radial directions. (b) Simple shear test: physical directions of principal effective stresses rotate as the test progresses

membrane in the Geonor apparatus (Airey, 1984; Airey and Wood, 1987). The mobilised angle of friction will be the same at corresponding stages in a triaxial test and a simple shear test if the following equality holds:

$$\phi'_{mob} = \frac{q}{2\sigma'_r + q} \sqrt{\frac{(\sigma'_v - \sigma'_h)^2 + 4\tau^2}{(\sigma'_v + \sigma'_h)^2}} \tag{3.7}$$

It is possible to control the radial and deviator stresses in the triaxial cell. Consequently, the same stress paths can be applied to two samples in terms of the radius and centre of the Mohr's circle. This allows the effect of principal axis rotation to be identified.

107

3.3.4 Macroscopic strain in soils

One might ask how strains can occur in a soil if the soil particles are sufficiently hard that Terzaghi's principle of effective stress applies. This is explored at particulate scale in numerical simulations by Cundall *et al.* (1982) and others, and some implications are discussed by Cundall (2001). The answer may be that soil particles do deform a little, not enough to affect the principle significantly, but enough for small changes to occur in the position and orientation of particles relative to one another. For sufficiently large changes of stress, slip can occur at interparticle contacts. As this occurs, asperities on the surfaces of particles can be broken, and particles may occasionally crack or crush. These processes result in major changes to the shapes and sizes of some of the voids in the body.

One consequence is that macroscopic volumes of soil have a property of 'dilatancy', meaning a tendency to change in volume when a shear stress is applied. The generic term includes increases in volume (dilatant behaviour) and decreases (contractive behaviour, or negative dilatancy). For a fully saturated soil, dilatancy requires that water be sucked into soil or expelled from it during stress–strain processes. Two extreme conditions are recognised. In fully drained conditions, strains occur sufficiently slowly that any changes in pore pressure due to this effect are negligible. In fully undrained conditions, the flow of water into or out of a soil element is prevented. As a result, particle movements are constrained, and shearing produces changes in pore water pressure.

3.4   Fluid flow through soils

3.4.1   General

Water can flow through the connected void spaces of soils in ways that are similar to flow through pipes. Figure 3.9a shows how this flow disperses the fluid molecules. Water molecules that start at points 1, 2, and 3 travel along different tortuous paths through the soil matrix, with different path lengths and speeds, so that the molecules emerge from the soil in dispersed locations and at dispersed times.

Fluid flow is primarily driven by differences of excess pore pressure between different parts of a soil body, defined as pore pressures that are different from the values that would occur under static conditions. For offshore soils, the sea surface acts as the uppermost water table, In Fig. 3.9b, the pore water pressure for equilibrium conditions is the product of the unit weight of water γ_w and the depth $(z + D)$ of a point below the sea surface, where D is the water depth and z is the

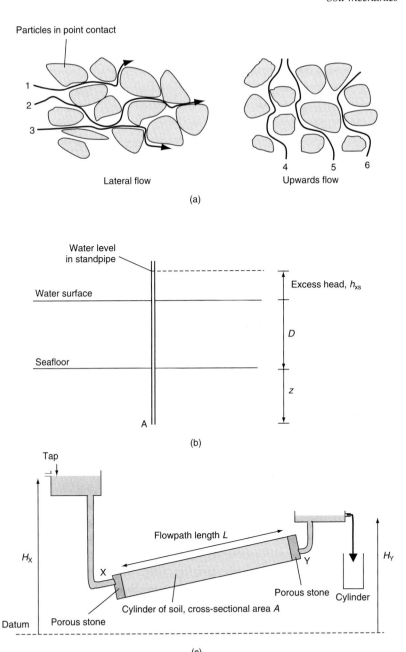

Particles in point contact

Lateral flow

Upwards flow

(a)

Water level in standpipe

Water surface

Excess head, h_{xs}

D

Seafloor

z

A

(b)

Tap

Flowpath length L

H_X

X

Y

H_Y

Porous stone Cylinder

Cylinder of soil, cross-sectional area A

Datum Porous stone

(c)

Fig. 3.9 Excess pore pressures and fluid flow. (a) Tortuous paths of water molecules flowing through a soil matrix. (b) Concept of excess head at a point A in the seabed. (c) Principle of the laboratory apparatus used for measuring hydraulic conductivity

109

depth of the point below the seafloor. So, if the pore water pressure at point A is u, an excess pore pressure u_{xs} is calculated as

$$u_{xs} = u - \gamma_w(z + D) \qquad (3.8)$$

The excess pore pressure at a point can be measured using an electrical probe (Dunlap *et al.*, 1978; Kolk and Wegerif, 2005), or in principle by inserting a standpipe in the soil to the point in question, and waiting for the water level in the standpipe to come into equilibrium. In that case, as sketched in Fig. 3.9b:

$$u_{xs} = \gamma_w h_{xs} \qquad (3.9)$$

It is possible for the excess head h_{xs} to be positive or negative. It is positive in a marine clay that is being deposited rapidly on the seafloor, as the rapid deposition increases the stresses on the soil, and it takes time for the water to be squeezed out of the deposited soil (Dunlap *et al.*, 1978; Sangrey *et al.*, 1979). It can also be positive if there is artesian water in one or more of the soil layers. Storms and earthquakes induce cycling loading of the seabed that can cause increases of pore pressure (Williams *et al.*, 1981; Demars and Vanover, 1985; Pappin, 1991).

3.4.2 Darcy's Law

Darcy carried out laboratory experiments on the flow of water through soils, and discovered that the rate of flow between two points was proportional to the difference in excess pore pressures between the points, and inversely proportional to the distance between them. Figure 3.9c shows a generalisation of his apparatus. Water flows through a cylinder containing soil, from a point X to a point Y. If the effects of the porous stones are neglected, then the hydraulic gradient i in the soil is defined to be the head difference $H_X - H_Y$ divided by the length L of the flowpath through the soil:

$$i = \frac{H_X - H_Y}{L} = \frac{\Delta u_{xs}}{\gamma_w L} \qquad (3.10)$$

where Δu_{xs} is the difference in excess pore pressure between X and Y. The apparatus allows the volume flow rate Q to be measured, equal to the volume of fluid flowing through the soil per unit time. The discharge velocity v is defined to be the volume flow rate Q divided by the macroscopic cross-sectional area A of the soil. Darcy's law is

$$v = \frac{Q}{A} = ki \qquad (3.11)$$

where k is the hydraulic conductivity of the soil to the fluid, with units of velocity. It was historically called the coefficient of permeability, but that term is now used for a different quantity.

The laboratory constant head and falling head permeameter apparatuses are similar in concept to Fig. 3.9c, but are usually arranged vertically (see ASTM D 2434). Hydraulic conductivity can also be deduced from consolidation tests (see ASTM D 2435, and Section 3.11). It can be measured in the field by downhole packer tests, and can be assessed from cone penetration dissipation tests (Lunne and Christoffersen, 1983). Well tests can be used to measure in-situ permeability onshore. A push-in cone permeameter was developed by Lowry *et al.* (1999).

Field measurements typically show that hydraulic conductivity is larger for flow in the horizontal direction compared with the vertical. Typical values of k range from about 10^{-10} cm/s for the least permeable clays, through 10^{-5} cm/s for a medium silt, to about 10^{-1} cm/s for a coarse beach sand (Lambe and Whitman, 1979). Hazen (1892) gives $k \approx cD_{10}^2$ as a rough approximation, where D_{10} is the effective particle size of a sand (in millimetres). Hazen's value for c was 100 cm/s, so that a sand with an effective size of 0.1 mm would have a permeability of 1 cm/s. Lambe and Whitman (1979) analysed published data giving values between 1 and 42 cm/s. They also discuss the Kozeny–Carman equation, which makes k proportional to $e^3/(1+e)$, where e is void ratio, and to other parameters.

3.4.3 Limitations of Darcy's law

Darcy's law only applies if the flow of water through the pore spaces of the soil is laminar. If the velocity is sufficiently high, the flow becomes turbulent. This starts at a Reynolds number $\mathrm{Re} = \rho v D / \mu$ of about 10, where ρ is the mass density of the flowing fluid and v is the interstitial velocity through a pore channel of diameter D. The density of water is about 1000 kg/m^3, and its dynamic viscosity μ is about 10^{-3} Pa.s. Hence, the transition to turbulent flow starts when $vD = 10^{-5}$ m^2/s. Combining this with Hazen's equation and assuming $i = 1$ shows that turbulent flow is unlikely for silts or clays.

Darcy's law breaks down if the effective stresses in the soil become so low that the frictional strength of the soil becomes negligible in comparison with natural variations of stress in the soil body. If a positive excess pore pressure u_{xs} has been induced at some depth z in a uniform soil layer, for example as a result of cyclic loading, the vertical effective stress at that depth will be

$$\sigma'_v = \gamma'z - u_{xs} = (\gamma' - i\gamma_w)z = (1 - i/i_{crit})\gamma'z \qquad (3.12)$$

Now $i = u_{xs}/\gamma'$ is the upwards hydraulic gradient. When i gets close to the critical hydraulic gradient $i_{crit} = \gamma'/\gamma_w$, the vertical effective stress reduces to such an extent that the soil loses much of its strength and stiffness, and gravitational–hydraulic instabilities start to occur. These result in the development of a network of pipes or flow channels along which relatively rapid water flows develop, entraining some sand, separated by regions of soft but still solid soil. There is continual erosion along the flow channels, and continual evolution of the pipework geometries.

If the upwards flow rate is increased further, more pipes develop, until the entire sand body appears to be boiling, with sand everywhere in a state of motion (Terzaghi *et al.*, 1996). If the level of the external water surface is then reduced, the sand solidifies by settling out. A condensation front develops from the bottom of the cylinder of sand, and moves upwards as more sand grains settle onto the solid surface at the front. The upwards velocity of the front is related to the limiting rate of settlement of sand grains through the fluid, and to the difference in the void ratio between the sand in the fluidised bed, and the relative density of the sand that has condensed out at the bottom of the cylinder (Heidari and James, 1982).

Darcy's law does not explain the flow of water through soils during the process of secondary compression (see Section 3.11.3).

3.4.4 Further aspects of fluid flow

Equations for the flow of fluids through multiple soil layers with different hydraulic conductivities are derived by Terzaghi *et al.* (1996) and in other textbooks. Advanced aspects of fluid flow are described by Cedergren (1997) and others, including the construction of flownets for flow in two dimensions. Software to calculate flow for two- or three-dimensional situations is readily available commercially.

A sand boil involves the upwards transport of sand from some depth, through a pipe that forms rather like pipes during fluidisation, to the soil surface. Sand boils commonly occur onshore after a strong earthquake. They occur offshore for a similar reason, and also in association with high sub-seafloor pore pressures induced by other processes such as seafloor spreading. The event causes high pore water pressure to develop at some depth below the surface, and a pipe develops through the overlying material. The process can be readily reproduced in the laboratory (Yang and Elgamal, 2001).

Mud volcanoes are also associated with high sub-surface pore pressures, but can be larger, rising several hundred metres above the seafloor (Yusifov and Rabinowitz, 2004; Judd and Hovland, 2007). They may be linked to geological faults. Periods of mud volcano activity may coincide with times of rapidly increasing vertical stress associated with high sedimentation rates, or with regional contraction due to compressive tectonic forces.

Fredlund and Rahardjo (1993) review the permeability of partially saturated soils. The soils contain gas–water menisci and discontinuous water that can act to prevent the flow of water through the voids.

3.5   Compressibility and yielding of soils

3.5.1   *One-dimensional compression and swelling*

In the oedometer test (Fig. 3.10a), a cylindrical sample is subjected to changes of vertical stress, without allowing lateral strains to occur. Compression with no lateral straining is called 'one-dimensional compression'. The sample height reduces from h_0 to h, say, and its void ratio reduces from e_0, to e. By considering the phase diagram, it can be shown that the settlement $s = h_0 - h$ is given by

$$s = h_0 \frac{e_0 - e}{1 + e_0} = h_0 m_v \, \Delta\sigma'_v \tag{3.13}$$

where m_v is the coefficient of volume change, and $\Delta\sigma'_v$ is the overall change of vertical effective stress. If the void ratio is known at one stage during the test, then the void ratio can be known at any other stage by measuring the settlement. At the field scale, if the change in void ratio for any given change in stress is known, then the settlement for a soil layer of thickness h_0 can be inferred.

The usual test procedure is to apply an increase in vertical stress σ_v. This causes an immediate increase in pore water pressure in the soil, which causes water to start to flow out of the sample. The process of squeezing water out of a clay sample is called primary consolidation, and is discussed in Section 3.11.2. The pore water pressure gradually reduces as water moves out of the soil, and so the vertical effective stress gradually increases. The term 'end of primary' or EOP denotes the time at which the pore water pressure returns to its original, equilibrium, value. For some soils, a process of creep or 'secondary compression' continues after EOP. Secondary compression is discussed in Section 3.11.3.

Figure 3.10b shows typical EOP results for a clay (e.g. Roscoe and Burland, 1968). The vertical effective stress is plotted horizontally,

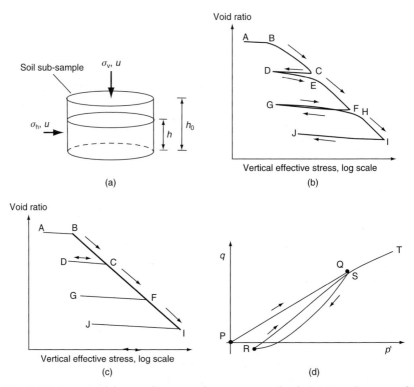

Fig. 3.10 Aspects of the one-dimensional compression of soil. (a) One-dimensional compression. (b) Typical result for a clay or silt (e.g. Roscoe and Burland, 1968; Lambe and Whitman, 1979). (c) Simplification. (d) Typical load–unload–reload stress path

usually on a log scale, versus the void ratio vertically. Starting from point A, the initial response is stiff, with little reduction in the void ratio until the soil state reaches B. Yielding starts at B, and the subsequent response is less stiff. On unloading from C, the initial response is stiff along a swelling curve CD. This shows that response BC was elastoplastic, since the compressive strain from B to C was not fully recovered on unloading. There was irreversible frictional sliding of particles relative to one another, and/or some particle breakage. On reloading from D, the response does not follow the unloading line but reaches yield at E, then responds elastoplastically. The yield stress at E is larger than the previous yield stress at B, and the material is said to have 'hardened'. The subsequent unloading from F is large, and a hysteresis loop is formed on unloading to G and then reloading to H.

The elastoplastic curve is called the normal consolidation line (NCL), the normal compression line, the virgin compression line (VCL), the one-dimensional compression or consolidation line or curve, or the asymptotic one-dimensional compression line or curve. Figure 3.10c shows a commonly used simplification. The NCL is represented by a straight line on a semi-log or double-log plot. Swelling and reloading curves are represented by straight elastic lines. In the traditional, single-log formulation, the lines are given by

$$\text{NCL:} \quad e + C_c \log_{10}(\sigma'_v) = \text{constant} \tag{3.14a}$$

$$\text{elastic line:} \quad e + C_s \log_{10}(\sigma'_v) = \text{constant} \tag{3.14b}$$

where C_c is the compression index and C_s is the swelling index. The constant in the first equation is a material parameter, while the constant in the second is different for different elastic lines. Double-log and Napierian-log forms of the equations are described by Schofield and Wroth (1968), Butterfield (1979), Hashiguchi (1995), and others. The coefficient of volume change is

$$m_v = \frac{\text{vertical strain}}{\text{change of vertical stress}} \tag{3.15}$$

(Lambe and Whitman, 1979). For infinitesimally small changes of void ratio, the tangent value of m_v is obtained by differentiation:

$$m_v = \frac{1}{D} = \frac{-1}{1+e} \frac{de}{d\sigma'_v} = \frac{C}{\ln(10)(1+e)\sigma'_v} \tag{3.16}$$

where D is the constrained modulus of the soil. The last expression gives the differential expression for a traditional, single-log line with constant C. The value of m_v on the NCL is obtained by putting $C = C_c$. The value on an elastic line is obtained with $C = C_s$.

Siliceous sands appear to follow similar behaviours, but with an NCL at larger values of vertical effective stress. However, yield points are less clearly defined, and the swelling lines are very flat, indicating very stiff responses (Lee and Seed, 1987). Carbonate sands appear to show similar responses to clay (Coop, 2000; Carter *et al.*, 2000; Islam *et al.*, 2004).

3.5.2 Overconsolidation ratio and K_0

For any given soil state, there is a unique intersection of the elastic line through that state and the NCL. The stress at this intersection is the pre-consolidation stress σ'_{vc}. Consideration of Fig. 3.10b indicates that the pre-consolidation stress is also the maximum vertical effective stress that the soil has experienced in its history. The overconsolidation ratio (OCR) of a soil is the ratio of the pre-consolidation stress divided by the in-situ vertical stress σ'_v. A material with an OCR of 1 is called 'normally consolidated'. A material with an OCR of between 1 and about 3 is lightly overconsolidated. An OCR > 8 is heavily overconsolidated. Jamiolkowski *et al.* (1985) summarise processes by which a soil can become overconsolidated. One is mechanical, by a stress history in which the vertical effective stress in the soil reaches a maximum and then reduces, for example as a result of erosion of overlying layers. Another is desiccation, which is possible for an offshore soil if the soil was once a dry land surface (Abu-Hejleh and Znidarčić, 1995). Other processes include drained creep (ageing) and physicochemical processes such as cementation, ion exchange, and thixotropy.

In some oedometer devices it is possible to measure the lateral total stress imposed by the walls of the device to maintain the one-dimensional strain condition. The coefficient of lateral earth pressure at rest, K_0, can then be calculated as the ratio of the lateral effective stress to the vertical effective stress. Many soils are found to exhibit the following trend:

$$K_0 = K_{0,nc}\, OCR^n \tag{3.17a}$$

$$K_{0,nc} = 1 - \sin \phi'_{cs} \tag{3.17b}$$

where $K_{0,nc}$ is the value of K_0 on the virgin compression line (at OCR $= 1$), ϕ'_{cs} is the critical state friction angle of the soil (discussed in Section 3.6), and the exponent n is typically between 0.32 for low-plasticity clays and 0.42 for high-plasticity ones. For clays, $n \approx \sin \phi'_{cs}$ (Mayne and Kulhawy, 1982). Equation (3.17b) is Jaky's (1944) approximate empirical formula. Some other empirical equations are discussed by Wroth and Houlsby (1985).

3.5.3 *Proportional straining*

Because there are no lateral strains in one-dimensional tests, the ratio of the strains in the radial (x, y) and axial (z) directions is $0:0:1$. More generally, a 'strain increment' can be defined as a strain whose magnitude is negligibly small, but whose sign is determined. If an apparatus applies principal strains ε_x, ε_y, and ε_z in the fixed orthogonal directions x, y, and z, then a 'proportional straining test' has a ratio $d\varepsilon_x : d\varepsilon_y : d\varepsilon_z$ that is constant. For example, isotropic compression and swelling has a ratio of $1:1:1$. Undrained compression in the z-direction has a ratio of $-1:-1:2$. A 'critical state' can be reached by undrained proportional straining, and is defined as a soil state at which the soil can be sheared continuously at constant volume and constant effective stress (Schofield and Wroth, 1968). It is an asymptotic state, attained by a strain increment ratio $a{:}b{:}c$ with $a + b + c = 0$. The critical state stress ratio for triaxial compression is denoted by $q/p' = M$, and is related to the critical state friction angle ϕ'_{cs} in the Mohr diagram by $\sin \phi'_{cs} = 3M/(6 + M)$.

The proportional straining of sands and clays has been investigated by Topolnicki *et al.* (1990), Chu and Lo (1994), and others, using triaxial and true triaxial apparatuses. Except for constant-volume straining, typical responses are similar to those for one-dimensional compression. During compressive loading, the state of the soil approaches and then follows an asymptotic curve relating the void ratio and the mean normal effective stress. The asymptotic curves for different types of proportional straining are parallel to one another when plotted in the relevant semi-log or log axes. For different asymptotic states at a given void ratio, the effective stresses for different strain-increment ratios are different. If the effective stresses are plotted on a stress diagram, they form a locus of asymptotic proportional straining states for that void ratio. Topolnicki *et al.* (1990) called the relation between strain-increment ratios and asymptotic stress ratios on such a locus a 'kind of flow rule'.

3.5.4   *Monotonic loading behaviours*

In a standard drained triaxial test, the radial effective stress is kept constant while the deviator stress is increased (compression test), decreased (extension test), or cycled (cyclic test). Volume strains are determined from measurements of the initial or final sample volume, and the changes of volume due to water flowing into or out of the sample. In an undrained triaxial test, water is not allowed to flow into or out of the sample during the test.

Figure 3.11 shows the results of some standard drained triaxial tests on samples of a siliceous Ham River sand. The responses are highly non-linear. Although not evidenced from this plot, the responses are inelastic because stress–strain curves in unloading would not retrace the loading curve. The loose samples experienced volumetric compression during shearing, with the least compression for the sample under the smallest radial stress. For the dense tests, the lightly confined sample experienced negative volume strain. Peak values of deviator stress depend on the confining stress. Thus, the sand does not have a unique shear strength, but one that varies with confining stress. At large strain, the deviator stresses for the loose samples appear to tend

117

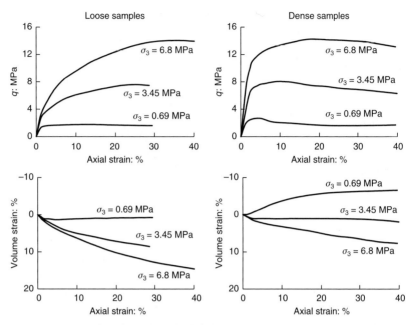

Fig. 3.11 Drained monotonic triaxial behaviours of Ham River sand. Skinner's (1964–1966) tests as reported by Bishop (1966) are shown here converted to SI units, and illustrate the nature of an unloading response AB

to become constant, and the volume strains may be tending towards constant values. Thus, the samples may be tending asymptotically towards critical states.

Figure 3.12a shows the results of undrained triaxial tests in two samples of London Clay. The tests have been replotted from original data using the relation $p' = p - u$. For the test starting at an effective confining stress of 103 kPa, a peak deviator stress occurs at about 480 kPa, at a vertical compressive strain of about 4%. The stress path corresponds to the development of positive pore pressure initially, but negative pore pressure by the end of the test. The sample is approaching a critical state by the time 10% strain is reached. For the test at an initial effective confining stress of 59 300 kPa, the stress–strain curve shows much greater ductility, with plastic yielding starting at around 3000 kPa deviator stress, and without a significant peak strength. Positive pore pressure developed during the test.

Figure 3.12b shows typical undrained triaxial results for some siliceous sands. For a dense sample, the deviator stress continues to increase to a relatively large value. This is interpreted as a 'dilatant' response. The intermediate sample experiences 'limited liquefaction'. The

118

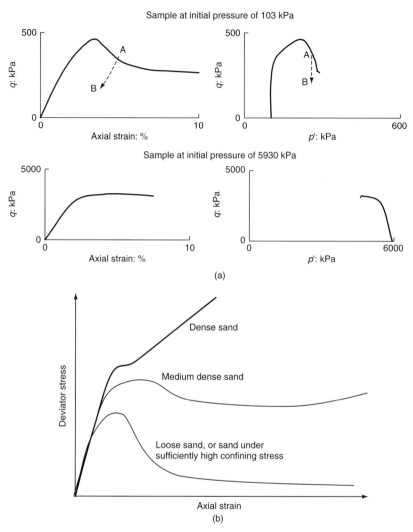

Fig. 3.12 *Undrained monotonic triaxal behaviours. (a) Stress–strain curves and effective stress paths for samples of London Clay (Bishop et al., 1965), and type of unloading response AB. (b) Undrained triaxial responses of some sands in monotonic triaxial loading. The 'initial liquefaction' response of the loose sample is associated with a large increase in the pore water pressure during the test, and a consequent reduction in the mean normal effective stress and frictional strength (e.g. Castro, 1969)*

deviator stress reaches an approximately 'steady state' value after a small strain, but then begins to increase again at large strain. For the loosest sample, the peak deviator stress occurred at less than 1% axial strain, followed by a large reduction in the deviator stress, followed by the development of large strain at a very low deviator stress. The reduction is called 'initial liquefaction' (Vaid and Chern, 1985), and is discussed in a wider context in Section 3.10.4.

3.5.5 Cyclic loading behaviours

A cycle is termed 'one-way' if the average value of the stress that varies during the cycle is greater than the magnitude of the cyclic component, so that the sign of the stress that varies does not change during the test. A cycle is termed 'two-way' if the sign changes. In general, one-way cycles are less damaging than two-way ones.

Figure 3.13 shows an example of drained triaxial loading and one-way cycling of kaolin clay. The initial response AB is very stiff at small strain, with a yield point perhaps identifiable at B at a deviator stress of about 40 kPa. For the small unload–reload cycle CDE, the soil response was essentially elastic, with reloading DE tracing almost the same path as the unloading CD. For the larger cycle FGH, a hysteresis loop appears. These cycles are rather similar to the one-dimensional cycles of Fig. 3.10. The yield stress at H in Fig. 3.13 is larger than at E, so the material has hardened between E and H. For the largest cycle IJK, the hysteresis is very pronounced. A Bauschinger effect appears to be developing, and the curve might be interpreted as showing a yield point in unloading at about 50 kPa.

Figure 3.14 shows results of two-way cyclic loading tests on a sand and on a clay. In both tests, the mean normal effective stress reduces by a

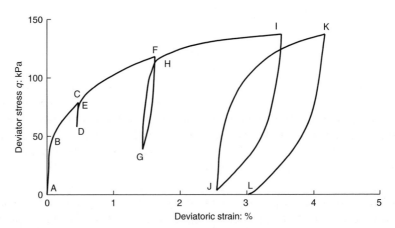

Fig. 3.13 Drained responses: triaxal test on kaolin clay (reproduced with permission, from Roscoe and Burland, 1968. © Cambridge University Press)

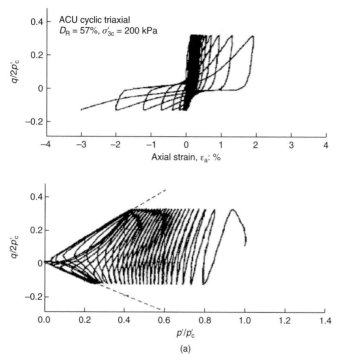

Fig. 3.14 Examples of soil responses in two-way cyclic undrained triaxial tests. (a) Sacramento River sand (originally from Boulanger and Truman, 1996). (b) Cloverdale clay (adapted from Zergoun and Vaid, 1994). (Reproduced with permission of the ASCE from Boulanger and Idriss, 2007). In both cases, the stress–strain response is initially stiff, but degrades as cycling continues. The effective pressure starts high, and reduces

relatively large amount in the first cycle, then by smaller amounts per cycle as the cycling continues. This kind of response is termed 'cyclic mobility' (Vaid and Chern, 1985). The stress–strain loops are initially steep, but gradually collapse. Low stiffness can develop in the middle of each loop. After many cycles, the stress paths become limited by specific stress ratio lines, and start to resemble deformed figures-of-eight or 'butterfly' shapes.

France and Sangrey (1977) reported different behaviours for one-way cyclic triaxial tests on a clay, with one-way cycles stabilising without a catastrophic increase in the pore water pressure. For undrained cycling below a 'critical level of cyclic loading' (CLCL), continued cycling resulted in a stable equilibrium being reached, with no further change in the effective stress path and no further accumulation of strain, but with hysteresis within a cycle.

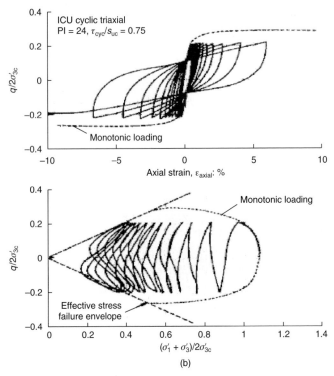

Fig. 3.14 *Continued*

3.5.6 *Constitutive models*

A constitutive model is a mathematical description of stress–strain behaviours. The development of such descriptions is a highly specialised task. Many models have been proposed, reviewed by Hashiguchi (1985), Scott (1985), Loret (1990a,b) and others. A model can be useful if it can be calibrated from field or test data and then used to extrapolate to slightly different field conditions elsewhere. A model need not necessarily represent all possible constitutive behaviours.

Soils are not isotropic, linear, or elastic (Atkinson, 2000). However, the model of isotropic, linear-elastic behaviour can be adapted and be useful for small-strain processes (see Section 3.8). For larger strains, the idea of a 'linear-elastic, plastic' model can also be adapted to advantage. In this model, a yield point occurs at some value of stress, after which the stiffness reduces. Graham *et al.* (1988) describe procedures by which yield points can be identified from curved stress–strain results. Because more than one stress is involved, yield points for different tests

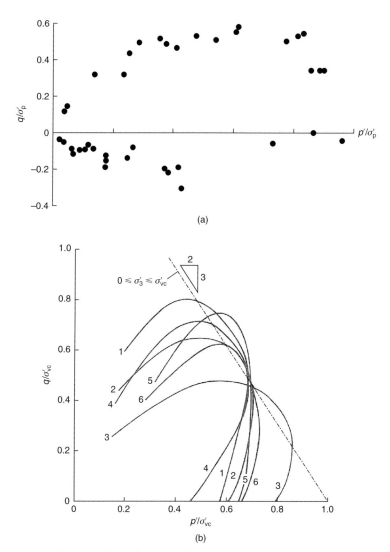

Fig. 3.15 Behaviours of one-dimensionally compressed and unloaded clay. (a) Yield points for Drammen clay, plotted in terms of Cambridge parameters normalised by preconsolidation pressure σ_p (data from Larsson and Sallfors, 1981). (b) Normalised yield loci for various clays (reproduced with permission from Graham et al., 1988)

can be plotted in stress space. Yield points for different tests all starting from the same soil state form a 'yield locus' or 'yield envelope'.

Figure 3.15a shows data from yield points measured in monotonic loading tests on undisturbed samples of Drammen clay. The yield locus is not symmetric about the horizontal (p') axis but is aligned

123

more with the stress ratio associated with K_0 compression. Graham *et al.* (1988) found a similar type of alignment for published data on several onshore clays. Figure 3.15b shows some of their results, normalised by an estimated pre-consolidation stress. Al-Tabbaa (1984) found that isotropic samples of kaolin clay would develop an anisotropic yield locus when subjected to anisotropic stress history. Since an isotropic stress history produces a yield locus centred on the p' axis, Al-Tabbaa's data suggest that the shape or orientation of the yield locus is perhaps not a fixed property of the soil but instead may depend on the stress history.

Yamamuro and Kaliakin (2005) present some of the prominent modelling ideas. Most include the concept of critical states, (for clays) or 'steady states' (for sands) (Poulos, 1981; Jefferies and Been, 2006). Schofield and Wroth (1968) and Schofield (2005) describe the influential original Cam clay model, which adapted and extended ideas from Hill's (1950) theory of metal plasticity, and from concepts of hardening of Drucker *et al.* (1957). A pointed yield envelope shape was assumed, and was also the state boundary surface of the model and its asymptotic proportional straining surface. Roscoe and Burland (1968) proposed a modified Cam clay with an elliptical envelope. This theory is now widely used (Atkinson and Bransby, 1978; Muir Wood, 1991a). Sekiguchi and Ohta (1987) proposed a yield envelope that matched the data on anisotropic soils better.

The search continues for a practical model that is not limited to a small subset of constitutive behaviours. Anisotropy and cyclic loading effects are of particular interest for offshore applications. Subsequent models have included those of Hashiguchi and Ueno (1978), Dafalias and Hermann (1980), Pande and Sharma (1983), Davies and Newson (1992), Cottechia and Chandler (1997), Gajo and Muir Wood (1999), Li and Dafalias (2004), Dean (2007a,b), Schweiger *et al.* (2009), and others.

3.6 Practical approaches for soil strength

3.6.1 *Measures of strength*

Strength is a measure of stress at some condition that is considered to be limiting. It is different from plastic yielding. For instance, yielding in one-dimensional compression occurs when the pre-consolidation stress is reached, but this is not an unstable process and is not a limiting condition in constitutive behaviour (although at the field scale it may be limiting in respect of the associated settlement). In constitutive terms, strength is a concept for stress ratios equal or greater than the critical state stress ratio, or at stress ratios associated with liquefaction. In

124

some situations, slip surfaces or ruptures surfaces develop in the soil under sufficiently high shear stress, or cracks may form.

Strength can be expressed in terms of the shear stress in a test, or the radius of the Mohr's circle, or half of the deviator stress in an undrained triaxial test, or as a friction angle, or in another convenient way. The undrained strength is the shear strength measured in a test without drainage. It is now usually represented by the symbol s_u, instead of the historical c_u. The drained strength is measured in a test with drainage. It is usually expressed as the mobilised friction angle at the limiting condition. Many design calculations for sands involve drained conditions, and so sand strength is often expressed in terms of a drained friction angle. Because of the correlation between strength and relative density, relative density values are sometimes used instead.

The peak strength occurs at the maximum value of the stress quantity. The critical state strength is the value when the sample has reached a critical state. The steady state strength is when a sand reaches a steady state (Poulos, 1981). The residual strength is the value after huge strains have been applied, usually including large displacements on a slickensided rupture surface. The residual strength is typically measured in a ring shear apparatus (Stark and Contreras, 1996; Kelly *et al.*, 2003).

The in-situ strength is the strength of the soil in situ. Commonly, the in-situ strength within a clay layer increases linearly with the depth below the seafloor. Undisturbed strengths are measured on samples that have been taken from the ground in a way that ideally produces no sample disturbance. In practice, some disturbance always occurs (see Section 3.12). Remoulded clay strengths are measured by first thoroughly working the clay, shearing and distorting it to destroy any in-situ fabric, so that every part reaches the limiting shear stress, with the physical directions of the history randomly distributed in the sample. The strength of a reconstituted clay is a strength measured on a sample that that been totally broken up, such as by mixing with water at two or more times the water content, and has then been recompressed. Reconstitution destroys all the in-situ structure and fabric. Non-cohesive soil samples are usually highly disturbed, since the sand will have broken up during the visual inspection and will have been stored in a bag. In effect, sand strengths measured using bag samples are reconstituted strengths.

Strength can depend on the cyclic loading history (described in Section 3.7), and on the rate at which monotonic (or cyclic) strains are applied to the soil. This can be important in design calculations for boat impact, and for seismic analysis. The theory of viscoplasticity may assist in modelling rate effects. In practice, rate effects are more often addressed by conducting triaxial tests on similar samples at different strain rates. A typical rate effect is an increase of undrained shear strength by 10% or so for an increase in the strain rate by a factor of 10. It is also feasible for strength to be less at higher strain rates.

3.6.2 Strengths and Mohr's circles

Figure 3.16a illustrates the Mohr–Coulomb strength criterion. If the normal stress on a plane in the soil body is σ, then the shear stress on

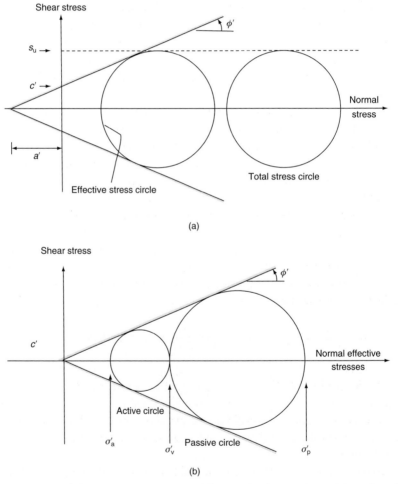

(a)

(b)

Fig. 3.16 *Mohr circle criterion. (a) Mohr–Coulomb criterion and total and effective stress circles. (b) Effective stress circles and active and passive pressures for a purely frictional material*

that plane is limited by a relation of the form

$$|\tau| \leq c + \sigma \tan \phi = (a + \sigma) \tan \phi \tag{3.18}$$

where c represents cohesion, ϕ is a friction angle, and a is adhesion (Janbu, 1985). Since there are many planes through a point in a soil body, an entire Mohr's circle of stress must lie within the lines defined by this equation.

For undrained analyses, ϕ is usually taken to be zero. c is the undrained shear strength s_u, and is the radius of the Mohr's circle of effective stress that just touches the failure envelope. It is therefore half of the deviator stress in the triaxial cell when the relevant strength condition is reached. Because of Terzaghi's principle of effective stress, a variety of different total stress circles correspond to the same effective stress circle. They all have the same radius. One of them has a minor total stress equal to zero. This circle corresponds to the total stresses at failure in unconfined compression.

For drained conditions, the strength parameters are denoted as effective parameters c' and ϕ'. Drained cohesion is usually considered to be unreliable, and is taken as zero for design purposes. If $c' = 0$, then ϕ' can be shown to be the angle to the horizontal of the steepest slope that can be constructed from the material, subject to the relevant strength condition. Peak ϕ' is sometimes called the angle of repose.

In several offshore design scenarios, like onshore, principal effective stress directions are known to be vertical and horizontal, and a calculation is required for the minimum and maximum possible horizontal effective stresses. From the geometry of Fig. 3.16b, the smallest and largest normal effective stresses σ'_a and σ'_p are related to the vertical effective stress σ'_v by

$$\text{active:} \quad \sigma'_a = K_a \sigma'_v, \quad K_a = \frac{1 - \sin\phi}{1 + \sin\phi} = \tan^2\left(45° - \frac{\phi}{2}\right) \tag{3.19a}$$

$$\text{passive:} \quad \sigma'_p = K_p \sigma'_v, \quad K_p = \frac{1 + \sin\phi}{1 - \sin\phi} = \tan^2\left(45° + \frac{\phi}{2}\right) \tag{3.19b}$$

K_a and K_p are the active and passive earth pressure coefficients respectively. Their values are limits on the coefficient of earth pressure K, and its value K_0 at rest.

In the phenomena of fluidisation and liquefaction, the pore water pressure increases due to constitutive reasons, and the vertical effective stress reduces to a small value. Hence, the active and passive effective pressures reduce. The limiting shear stress given by the Mohr–Coulomb failure

127

criterion becomes small, and the material can behave like a liquid with virtually no shear strength. When shear strains are applied, the particles are forced back into contact, and the shear stress can then recover.

3.6.3 Clay strengths

The undisturbed undrained shear strength of a clay layer is not a constant, but generally increases with decreasing void ratio. Since the vertical, over-burden, stress increases with depth below the seafloor, the void ratio decreases with depth, and the undrained shear strength is generally larger at greater depths. The effect can be observable in offshore data even for clay layers of only a few metres thickness, as well as over the depth of a deep borehole.

The undrained shear strength is often considered to be related to the in-situ vertical effective stress and the OCR by

$$s_u = s_{u,nc}\, \text{OCR}^m \qquad\qquad (3.20a)$$

with

$$s_{u,nc} = k\sigma'_v \qquad\qquad (3.20b)$$

where k and m are material constants (Wroth and Houlsby, 1985). Skempton (1960) proposed that $k = 0.11 + 0.0037\text{PI}$, with PI as a percentage. For example, a clay with a PI of 20% would have $k \approx 0.184$, using this relation. Semple and Gemeinhardt (1981) found that $k = 0.2$ and $m = 0.85$ fitted the data from Gulf of Mexico clays well.

Equations (3.20a,b) provide part of an explanation for certain step increases that occur for many offshore locations in a plot of clay strength versus depth. Figure 3.17 shows a geological history with historical deposition to a level higher than the present seafloor, followed by erosion to below the present seafloor, followed by deposition to the present seafloor. The history produces a profile of the OCR versus depth of the form shown. Using this with equations (3.20a,b) produces the step increase of undrained shear strength at the base of the final clay layer to have been deposited.

An 'underconsolidated clay' is one whose apparent overconsolidation ratio is less than 1, and whose strength is less than the value $s_{u,nc}$. A likely explanation is that excess pore pressures exist in the soil, resulting in an overestimate of σ'_v, and so an overestimate of $s_{u,nc}$. By using equations (3.20a,b) to infer the vertical effective stress, then using equation (3.12), the excess pore pressure can be estimated. One scenario where this is feasible is where clay is being deposited relatively rapidly

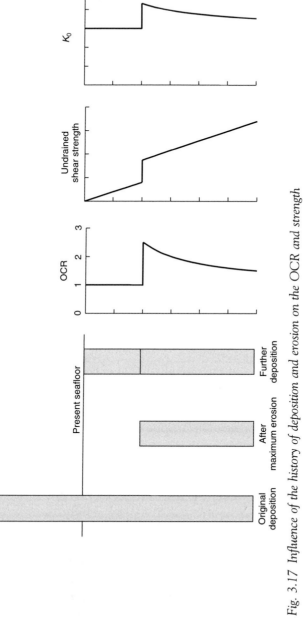

Fig. 3.17 Influence of the history of deposition and erosion on the OCR and strength

on the seafloor. As the clay column increases in height, a soil element in the column experiences an increasing total vertical stress. Positive excess pore pressures develop, causing water to flow upwards, out of the clay, so that the clay can compact and take up some of the extra overburden. If the rate of clay deposition is large, excess pore pressures may persist for some time in the soil. Another possible cause of a reduction in the vertical effective stress is an underlying stratum containing artesian water pressure.

For several clays, remoulded shear strength is related to the liquidity index LI of the soil by the empirical relation $s_{u,remoulded} \approx (170/100^{LI})$ kPa, where the liquidity index is expressed as a fraction (Wroth and Wood, 1978; Wroth, 1979). On this basis, for instance, a clay at a liquidity index of 50% has a strength of about 17 kPa. Sensitivity to remoulding is defined as the ratio of the strength of an undisturbed sample divided by the remoulded strength. A typical, insensitive, clay may have a sensitivity of around 2. Highly sensitive clays can be problematic, partly because it is likely that the disturbance that occurred during sampling has significantly reduced the strength compared with its value in the ground, and partly because possible progressive failure can occur in sensitive soils.

3.6.4 Stress–dilatancy theory

In Rowe's (1962) stress–dilatancy theory, strength parameters are related to dilation, and this is used to help explain differences in parameters measured in triaxial and other tests. Figure 3.18 shows data for the relation between the friction angle at failure in tests on Ham River sand, and the rate of dilation of the sand at failure, defined as the negative of the rate of volumetric compression strain divided by the rate of axial strain in the triaxial apparatus. The data show an approximately linear relation with:

$$\sin \phi' = \sin \phi'_{cs} + k(-d\varepsilon_{vol}/d\varepsilon_1) \qquad (3.21)$$

where ϕ'_{cs} is the friction angle at a critical state, when no volume change occurs so that the rate of dilation is zero, and k is related to the slope of the line through the data. It can be seen from this that cohesion is essentially related to dilation. For offshore foundations, cyclic loading can reduce the amount of dilation that is available for subsequent monotonic loading. Consequently, only the critical state friction angle is reliable in the long term.

Bolton (1986) has developed stress–dilatancy theory further, by identifying relations between dilation and relative density. This further

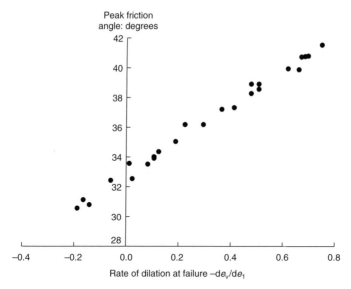

Fig. 3.18 The stress–dilatancy approach: data from 25 tests on Ham River sand at radial effective pressures between 0.7 and 28 MPa, for initially loose and initially dense samples (Bishop, 1966)

clarifies differences between strength parameters measured in triaxial and plane strain tests, and helps explain why it is reasonable to consider that the design strength of a sand is related to its relative density.

3.6.5 Other strength criteria

Many other proposals for limiting stresses have been reviewed by Chen and Liu (1990). Amongst these are the Drucker–Prager criterion (Drucker and Prager, 1952), and the Tresca and Von Mises criteria, which are particularly useful in undrained plasticity analyses (Schofield and Wroth, 1968; Houlsby and Wroth, 1982). Strength parameters may be the same or different for triaxial compression and extension (Parry, 1958; Hight *et al.*, 1994). A criterion by Lade and Duncan (1975) allows for this.

3.7   Practical approaches for cyclic loading

3.7.1   General

As noted earlier, cyclic loading can be an important design issue for offshore foundations, and is sometimes the dominant issue. If the soil is undrained or partially drained during cyclic loading, excess pore pressures can be generated by the constitutive response of the soils. If the soil is drained or partially drained, volume changes occur. These changes, and associated changes in the effective stress and the fabric, result in changes in the soil stiffness and the soil strength. They can induce ground movements, including small or large settlements, or failure. Excess pore pressures start to dissipate as soon as they are generated, and this can be modelled using consolidation theory (see Section 3.11). Nevertheless, changes that occur during one episode of severe cyclic loading, such as a winter storm, can persist in the ground and affect the soil response and platform integrity in subsequent episodes.

Foss *et al.* (1978) pointed out that failure due to cyclic loading can happen in different ways. In Fig. 3.19a, a sample is loaded with a deviator stress that increases monotonically from point a to b, where the sample fails. Alternatively, the sample may be subjected to some cycling, followed by a monotonic loading to failure at c at a lower deviator stress. The ratio of the shear or deviator stress at c to the value at b is the cyclic strength ratio. Another possibility is that the sample can be cycled continuously until its stress state either stabilises, or until it 'fails by cyclic loading' at point d.

Several authors report data showing that cyclic loading can affect the strength of clay (e.g. Hyde and Ward, 1986; Hyde and Conn, 1987; Ding *et al.*, 2007). Figure 3.19b shows data from undisturbed and remoulded samples for which the strength of the soil measured after the cycling has reduced compared with the strength without cycles. Figure 3.19c shows an effect of cyclic loading on soil stiffness. The vertical axis represents the ratio of the shear modulus of the soil after cycling to the modulus for the first cycle. In this case, the ratio is 1 for small cycles, indicating that these have little effect. For the largest cycles, the ratio reduces to about 0.9 after only 20 cycles.

Figure 3.19d shows a typical increase in the mean pore pressure during undrained cycling of a sand. When this occurs at constant total stress, it reduces the effective stresses, and so reduces the shear strength of the soil. If the soil loses all its strength, it is said to have 'liquefied by cyclic loading' (Vaid and Chern, 1985). Liquefaction is discussed further in Section 3.10.4.

A simple design approach is to apply an adjustment factor to a method for monotonic or 'static' loading. This is done, for example, in the API RP2A procedure for p–y analysis for lateral pile deflections (see Chapter 5). A more sophisticated approach is to use the 'stress

132

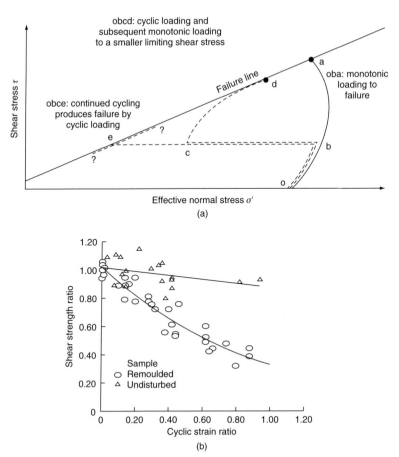

Fig. 3.19 Some effects of cyclic loading. (a) Different concepts of the effects of cyclic loading on strength (after Foss et al., 1978). (b) Post-cyclic strength ratios for a marine clay from the South China Sea (reproduced with permission, from Wang and Lu, 2008. © ISOPE). (c) Evolution of the shear modulus in Toyoura sand (reproduced with permission, from Kim and Choo, 2005. © ISOPE). (d) Typical development of excess pore pressures in undrained cycling

path' method. The loading process for a structure is analysed using one set of soil stiffness properties, and the results are used to determine the stress paths experienced by the soil. The stress paths are then applied to soil samples in the laboratory, and the relevant stiffnesses are measured. The structural analysis is then repeated using the new soil properties, and the analysis is repeated until convergence is reached between analysis and the tests.

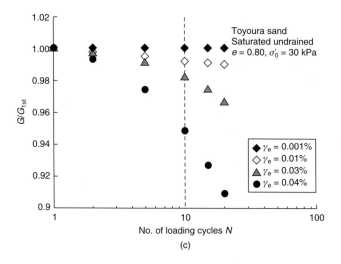

(c)

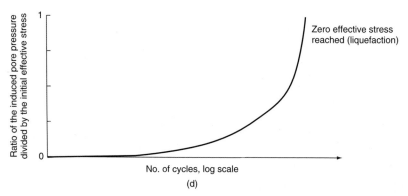

(d)

Fig. 3.19 Continued

3.7.2 Phase transformation

Ishihara *et al.* (1975) proposed a concept of 'phase transformation', which can be very useful in mapping the effects of cyclic loading. A similar concept of 'characteristic states' is described by Luong and Sidaner (1981). Figure 3.20 shows this. In this concept, soil is considered to behave in a contractive manner if the triaxial stress ratio q/p' lies between the values of the phase transformation or characteristic state lines. It behaves in a dilative manner at higher stress ratios.

For a one-way cycle that starts at a stress ratio less than the characteristic value, cycling will either cause compaction, if drained, or the development of positive excess pore pressures if undrained. In the

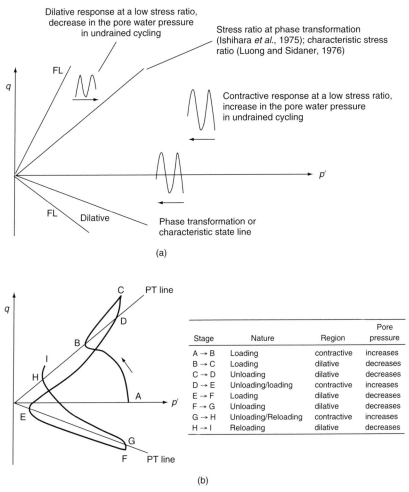

Fig. 3.20 Concept of phase transformation or the characteristic stress ratio. (a) Behaviours related to the stress ratio. (b) Formation of butterfly cycles

latter case, the stress path will move leftwards, and may eventually stabilise on the characteristic or phase transformation line.

For a two-way undrained cycle starting at A in Fig. 3.20b, the initial response involves increases of pore water pressure, so that the stress path moves leftwards as the mean normal effective stress reduces. However, once the phase transformation line is crossed at B, the material dilates, and the pore pressure decreases, making the mean normal effective stress increase. On unloading from C, the initial response may be dilative, but becomes contractive after the stress

135

path crosses into the contractive region at D. The pore pressure increases, and the mean normal effective stress decreases until E, when the samples cross into the dilative region. The behaviour produces a figure-of-eight loop, sometimes called a 'butterfly cycle'. These cycles occur once the stress has reduced sufficiently that the phase transformation lines are crossed twice in each cycle.

Hyde *et al.* (2006) reported data on the liquefaction and cyclic mobility of a low-plasticity silt, and proposed an initial phase transformation (IPT) line at a stress ratio lower than at phase transformation. They found that contractive responses did not start in monotonic loading until the IPT line was crossed.

3.7.3 Stress–strain relations: Masing's rule

Masing's (1926) rule is familiar in metal plasticity, and can be usefully applied to soils if the stress path has stabilised and the severe non-linearities associated with phase transformation do not occur. Its application to soils is discussed by Pyke (1979), Kramer (1996), and others.

In Fig. 3.21, the first loading curve ABCDEF is considered to be a 'backbone' curve for cyclic loading. If the material is unloaded from point E, the unloading curve is constructed by rotating the backbone curve through 180°, expanding it by a factor of 2 in all directions, and fixing its start point to E. Thus, the unloading curve $A'B'C'D'E'$ is a scaled, rotated copy of ABCDE. If the unloading continues past E', the original backbone curve applies along $E'F$. If the material is reloaded from E', it follows $A''B''C'' \ldots$, which is a scaled, unrotated copy of ABC with its start point attached at E'. When this curve intersects the original backbone curve, the original curve will then be followed until the next reversal.

Kramer (1996) notes that two additional rules are required in order to uniquely determine the stress–strain curve in irregular cycles. One is that, if an unloading or reloading curve exceeds the maximum past strain and intersects the backbone curve, it follows the backbone curve until the next stress reversal. Another is that, if an unloading or reloading curve crosses an unloading or reloading curve from the previous cycle, the stress–strain curve follows the previous cycle. Taken together with the original rules, the rules form an 'extended Masing model'.

Masing's rules make the assumption that the backbone curve is stable, and that the cyclic response is also stable. However, this may often not

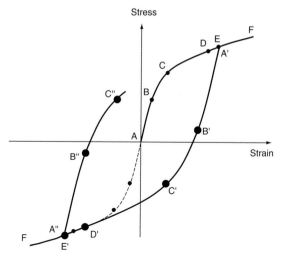

Fig. 3.21 Masing's (1926) rule

be the case. In practice, it may be feasible to incorporate gradual changes to the backbone curve as cyclic loading effects accumulate.

3.7.4 Miner's law and S/N plots

Figure 3.22a illustrates the concept of an *S/N* plot, adapted from the analysis of fatigue in materials (e.g. Jackson and Dhir, 1996). A driving parameter *S*, such as the cyclic stress amplitude, is plotted versus the number *N* of cycles required to achieve a certain condition. For example, the condition may be a certain cumulative strain, or a certain excess pore pressure. The driving parameter is typically normalised by dividing by a reference quantity.

The laboratory data on which an *S/N* plot are based may be of uniform stress cycles. However, the structural analysis of the platform for a particular storm or earthquake may reveal that non-uniform cycles occur in the soil, or a sequence of uniform cycles of different magnitudes. Estimates of effects of non-uniform cycles can often be made using Miner's law of cumulative damage (Young *et al.*, 1975):

$$D = \sum \frac{N_i}{N_{if}} \tag{3.22}$$

where *D* represents a measure of damage, with 0 corresponding to no damage and $D=1$ to a failure or other limit, N_i represents the number of cycles of a given type, and N_{if} is the number of cycles of

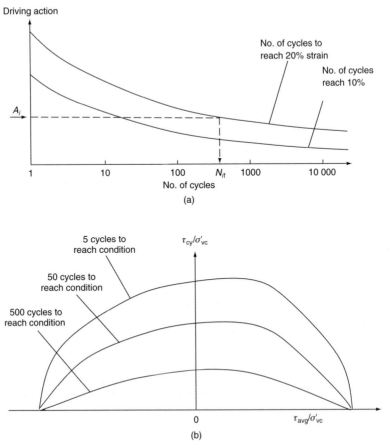

Fig. 3.22 Some practical concepts for cyclic loading. (a) S/N plots. (b) Contour plots

that type and characteristic that would be required to reach the failure or other limit in a test starting at $D = 0$.

Miner's law can give useful first estimates of damage. It can also be helpful in determining the number of uniform cycles that are 'equivalent' to a given number of irregular cycles, by requiring that the damage for the irregular and equivalent uniform cycles be the same. However, damage does not necessarily add up in a simple linear manner, so the accuracy of Miner's law may be limited.

3.7.5 Contour mapping

Figure 3.22b illustrates the concept of contour mapping, developed particularly for application to gravity platforms (Eide and Andersen, 1984; Andersen, 1991).

In this case, the horizontal axis represents an average shear stress divided by a reference stress. The vertical axis represents the normalised cyclic component. Based on laboratory data, points are plotted on the diagram, representing the number of cycles required to achieve a certain condition during cyclic loading. Contours are then inferred that join stress states for which the condition is achieved in a certain number of cycles. The contours then allow interpolation to stress states which were not quite the same as the states during the laboratory tests.

Different reference parameters can be used, for example the vertical effective stress or the pre-consolidation stress. Many different types of contour plot can be developed. For example, instead of plotting numbers of cycles to achieve a given strain, contours of strains achieved after a given number of cycles can be plotted. Multidimensional contour plotting is feasible by software.

3.8   Theory of applied elasticity

3.8.1   *Isotropic linear elasticity*

The theory of isotropic, linear elasticity is familiar from applications in structural mechanics. Few materials conform to its assumptions, but the theory is, nevertheless, useful for design. Applications to soils are described in textbooks such as Lambe and Whitman (1979), Bowles (1996), and Das (2004). Davis and Selvadurai (1996) provide a very clear and comprehensive summary. All of the approaches used onshore can also be used offshore. In particular, adaptations of the theory are useful to estimate settlements, cyclic loading effects, foundation stiffness, and seismic responses, amongst other purposes.

The theory is an application of Hooke's law to isotropic materials. It assumes that changes in stress applied to a body are related by linear equations to associated strains. For an isotropic material, stress–strain relations are also independent of the orientation of the body. For a soil that obeys Terzaghi's principal of effective stress, the equations relative to fixed orthogonal axes $\{x, y, z\}$ may be written as

$$
\begin{bmatrix} \varepsilon_{xx} \\ \varepsilon_{yy} \\ \varepsilon_{zz} \end{bmatrix} = \frac{1}{E} \begin{bmatrix} 1 & -\mu & -\mu \\ -\mu & 1 & -\mu \\ -\mu & -\mu & 1 \end{bmatrix} \begin{bmatrix} \Delta\sigma'_{xx} \\ \Delta\sigma'_{yy} \\ \Delta\sigma'_{zz} \end{bmatrix}
\tag{3.23a}
$$

$$
\gamma_{rs} = \frac{\Delta\tau_{rs}}{G}
\tag{3.23b}
$$

$$G = \frac{E}{2(1 + \mu)} \tag{3.23c}$$

where ε_x represents normal strains in the direction of the s-axis ($s = x$, y, or z), γ are engineering shear strains, $\Delta\sigma'$ are changes in the normal effective stress, $\Delta\tau$ are changes in the shear stress, and 'rs' is 'xy', 'yz', or 'zx'. The material parameters E and G are the drained Young's modulus and the shear modulus, respectively, and μ is Poisson's ratio. The relation between E, G, and μ may be derived using the Mohr's circle constructions for stress and strain. Adding the three equations contained in the matrix equation gives

$$\varepsilon_{vol} = \frac{\Delta p'}{K} \tag{3.23d}$$

$$K = \frac{E}{3(1 - 2\mu)} \tag{3.23e}$$

where $\varepsilon_{vol} = \varepsilon_{xx} + \varepsilon_{yy} + \varepsilon_{zz}$ is the volume strain, $\Delta p'$ is the change in the mean normal effective stress, and K is the bulk modulus of the soil. The inverse of the matrix equation is

$$\begin{bmatrix} \Delta\sigma'_{xx} \\ \Delta\sigma'_{yy} \\ \Delta\sigma'_{zz} \end{bmatrix} = \frac{E}{(1 + \mu)(1 - 2\mu)} \begin{bmatrix} 1 - \mu & \mu & \mu \\ \mu & 1 - \mu & \mu \\ \mu & \mu & 1 - \mu \end{bmatrix} \begin{bmatrix} \varepsilon_{xx} \\ \varepsilon_{yy} \\ \varepsilon_{zz} \end{bmatrix} \tag{3.23f}$$

All the moduli E, G, and K are positive for a stable material, and μ is between -1 and $1/2$.

The theory of elasticity assumes that the elastic parameters are constants. In practice, as described later, they are not so for soils. In particular, they depend on strain. Das (2004) gives typical small-strain values of Young's modulus in the range 10–100 MPa for loose to dense sand, and 4–100 MPa for soft to stiff clay. Lambe and Whitman (1979) gives values of 100–700 MPa for loose to dense sands under repeated loading. Kramer (1996) summarises empirical relations for shear modulus. Hardin and Black (1968) gave a formula for G for angular crushed quartz sand equivalent to

$$G = \frac{(2.973 - e)^2}{1 + e} \sqrt{p_a p'} \tag{3.24a}$$

where e is the void ratio, $p_a = 100$ kPa is atmospheric pressure, and p' is the mean normal effective stress. For an Ottawa sand with rounded grains, a similar formula was given with different constants and a different exponent for p'. Other expressions of the same general form have been proposed by Hardin (1978), Jamiolkowski *et al.* (1991), and others. For clays, a first approximation is

$$G = ks_u \qquad (3.24b)$$

where s_u is the undrained shear strength, and k is in the region of several hundred to several thousand. Like all empirical relations, these equations have been developed from data on a limited number of soils, and do not necessarily apply to all soils. Das (2004) gives Poisson's ratios in the range 0.15–0.5.

Consider the special case of the undrained behaviour of a fully saturated soil. Because water and soil particles are both virtually incompressible compared with the volume strains that can occur under drained conditions, it is usually assumed that undrained deformations occur at constant volume. Hence, $\varepsilon_{vol} = 0$, and the mean normal effective stress will not change. From Terzaghi's principle of effective stress, this implies that $\Delta u = -\Delta p$, where Δp is the change in the mean total stress. Changes in the effective stress $\Delta\sigma'$ equal the corresponding changes in the total stress $\Delta\sigma$ less Δu. Using these results to substitute for the changes in the effective stress in equation (3.23a) gives

$$\begin{bmatrix} \varepsilon_x \\ \varepsilon_y \\ \varepsilon_z \end{bmatrix} = \frac{1}{E_u} \begin{bmatrix} 1 & -1/2 & -1/2 \\ -1/2 & 1 & -1/2 \\ -1/2 & -1/2 & 1 \end{bmatrix} \begin{bmatrix} \Delta\sigma_x \\ \Delta\sigma_y \\ \Delta\sigma_z \end{bmatrix} \qquad (3.25a)$$

$$E_u = 3G \qquad (3.25b)$$

for undrained conditions, and equations (3.23b) and (3.23c) apply without change. Because equations (3.23a) and (3.25a) are similar in form, E_u is sometimes called the undrained Young's modulus of the soil, and it is sometimes said that Poisson's ratio is 1/2 for undrained conditions. Thus formulae for drained conditions using E and μ can be converted to formulae for undrained conditions be changing E to E_u and μ to 1/2.

3.8.2 Measurement of elastic properties

In principle, elastic properties are measured by comparing results of a laboratory or field test with predictions based in the theory of elasticity. In practice, soil is not linear, not elastic, and not isotropic. Adjustments are made to fit the theory to the reality.

Figure 3.23a(i) shows the results of a drained triaxial test on Ham River sand. The radial effective stress was constant during the test. Application of the elastic equations for triaxial conditions in this case leads to a prediction that the slope of the curve of the deviator stress versus the axial strain should be the Young's modulus E. For any point A on the curve, a secant modulus E_{sec} can be defined as

$$E_{sec} = \frac{q \text{ at } A}{\varepsilon_{ax} \text{ at } A} \tag{3.26a}$$

This has the effect that, if the elastic theory is applied for an event in which the change of deviator stress is the same as the change from zero to A, the theory will predict the correct strain at A, even though it will not predict correct strains between zero and A. This can be valuable in design, as long as the change in the stress can be calculated independently.

Application of the elastic equations gives a relation between Poisson's ratio and the ratio of volumetric to axial strains. The secant Poisson's ratio μ_{sec} at A is

$$\mu_{sec} = \frac{1}{2}\left(1 - \frac{\varepsilon_{vol} \text{ at } A}{\varepsilon_{ax} \text{ at } A}\right) \tag{3.26b}$$

Figure 3.23a(ii) shows the variations in the secant Young's modulus and the secant Poisson's ratio with strain for this test. The secant Young's modulus reduces towards zero as the deviator reaches a constant value and the strain continues to increase. The secant Poisson's ratio increases towards 1/2 as the volume strain over the test tends to become constant as the strain increases.

Figure 3.23b shows that several different secant quantities can be defined for cyclic loading, depending on what use is to be made of the results. For example, for analysing one-way cycles, a secant modulus could be inferred from the difference between the stresses at B and C, divided by the difference in the strains between B and C. For two-way cycles, differences over ranges such as D and E could be useful. Obviously, the values of the secant elastic parameters in cyclic loading depend on how they are defined, and also on strain amplitudes.

Figure 3.23c shows typical variations in the ratio G_{sec}/G_{max} with the cyclic shear strain amplitude, where G_{sec} is the secant modulus for stable cycles at a particle strain amplitude, and G_{max} is the secant modulus for infinitesimally small strain amplitudes. For many soils, the shear

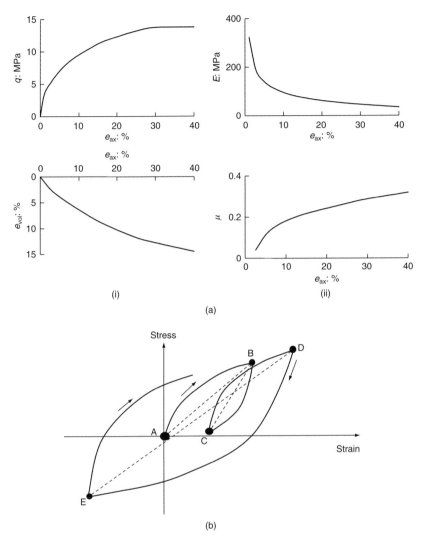

Fig. 3.23 Measuring elastic parameters from data. (a) Example using drained triaxial test data to infer secant Young's modulus and Poisson's ratio: (i) original data; (ii) inferred secant elastic parameters. Data are for test 29 on Ham River sand from Fig. 18 of Bishop (1966). (b) Examples of different secant stiffness values for cyclic loading. AB for initial loading, BC for small cycles, DE for larger cycles, etc. (c) Typical variations of G/G_{max} with cyclic strain amplitude

modulus is typically close to its maximum value only if the shear strains are less than 0.001–0.01%, depending on the plasticity index, the confining stress, the OCR, and other factors. Further information is given by Kramer (1996).

143

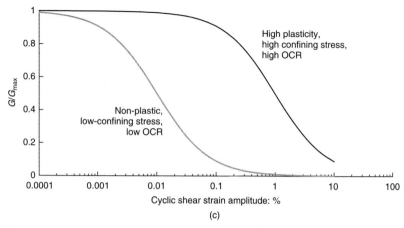

Fig. 3.23 Continued

3.8.3 Application to shallow foundations

Several offshore foundations approximate to a rigid, circular foundation of diameter B resting on the surface of an infinite, uniform, linear isotropic elastic half-space. Suppose the foundation is subjected to vertical load V, horizontal load H, moment M about a line through the bearing area of the foundation, and torque T. Table 3.1 gives the elastic relations between the loads and corresponding displacements v and h, and the rotations θ and ψ.

Theoretically, Bell (1991) and Cassidy (1999) note that the equation for the shear stiffness K_2 is inconsistent with the equations for K_1 and K_3, since the latter were calculated assuming a frictionless base. Similar remarks may apply for the torsional stiffness K_T. For very small strains, the shear modulus in the equations might be taken as G_{max}. For larger strains, a reduced value is needed. Dean (2008) explores how this might be calculated using the concept of a yield envelope for the footing.

Table 3.1 Stiffness equations for a rigid circular footing

Vertical	Horizontal	Overturning	Torsional
$\dfrac{V}{v} = K_1 = \dfrac{2GB}{1-\mu}$	$\dfrac{H}{h} = K_2 = \dfrac{16GB(1-\mu)}{7-8\mu}$	$\dfrac{M}{\theta} = K_3 = \dfrac{GB^3}{3(1-\mu)}$	$\dfrac{T}{\psi} = K_T = \dfrac{2GB^3}{3}$

See Figure 4.6a. Stiffnesses assume the soil is a uniform, isotropic, linear elastic half-space with shear modulus G and Poisson's ratio μ. Based on API RP2A and SNAME TR-5A. $\mu = 0.5$ for undrained conditions. DNV-RP-E302 and DNV-OS-J101) give the horizontal stiffness K_2 as $4GB/(2-\mu)$. See DNV (1992) for damping coefficient and effective mass parameters

3.8.4 *Application to seismic analysis*

Analysis of the earthquake response of an offshore structure and the soils supporting it is required if the structure is in region of seismic risk. This is the case for many offshore regions. In principle, the analysis can be done by a finite element program. In practice, it is only recently that details of such work have been published (Templeton, 2008).

Kramer (1996) presents a comprehensive treatment of geotechnical earthquake engineering. Srvbulov (2008) describes simplified case histories and calculation examples for onshore structures. An earthquake is caused by sudden movements of soil or rock, usually in association with the build-up and then sudden release of primarily lateral stress in deep ground as a result of tectonic movements. The resulting shaking is transmitted through the materials as pressure and shear waves.

In a simplified analysis, a specified time history of shaking is assumed to occur at some 'bedrock' stratum, at some depth below the seafloor. A one-dimensional geotechnical analysis is carried out to determine how the horizontal ground shaking is transmitted up the soil column, and how a shear wave is partially reflected and partially transmitted at boundaries between one soil layer and the next, and reflected at the seafloor. Freeware such as the SHAKE and EERA programs may be used (available on the Internet), and quality-assured commercial software is available (Bardet, 2002).

The results of the analysis are used as input motions for the offshore structure. For a wide foundation, the interface between the soil and the structure may be modelled using springs and dashpots. The input motions are input at one end of the spring–dashpot system, and the consequent structural motions are the result of interaction between the soil model and the structural model. For a piled foundation, the soil motions are input into axial and lateral soil springs attached to a pile, and the pile is modelled as part of the structure. The springs are determined from $p–y$, $t–z$, and $Q–z$ curves, as described in Chapter 5.

The analysis is usually iterative, because the elastic spring stiffness and damping properties representing the soil responses depend on cyclic strain amplitude. Thus, the strain amplitudes obtained from one structural analysis are checked against the values used to determine the soil parameters for that analysis, If necessary, a subsequent analysis is done using adjusted parameters. Once convergence has been reached for the structural and geotechnical calculations, further analyses are carried out to check (a) the degradation in strength of the clay layers, and its effects on structural stability, and (b) the possibility of liquefaction of sandy soils. Strength degradation is assessed by direct laboratory testing, or

145

by S/N or other techniques described in Section 3.7. Liquefaction assessment is discussed in Section 3.10.4.

3.9   Theory of bearing capacity

3.9.1   *Introduction*

Bearing capacity calculations offshore are the same as onshore, except that submerged unit weights are usually used instead of bulk unit weights. Special considerations are needed if gassy soils are encountered.

Consider a pad foundation of area A that is subjected to a load that has a vertical component V. If the load is increased, there will come a point at which the foundation can be said to 'fail'. The failure may be sudden, or may simply be a foundation movement that is judged to be intolerable. In traditional terminology, the average stress V/A at the point of failure is called the ultimate bearing capacity q_u, and the value of the vertical load at this point is called the ultimate vertical load Q_u. Some engineers use the phrase 'unit bearing capacity' for q_u, and 'bearing capacity' for Q_u. To avoid confusion, this book uses 'unit bearing capacity' for q_u, and 'load' for Q_u.

Das (2004) reviews the history of bearing capacity theory. Terzaghi (1943) was the first to present a comprehensive theory. His equation is based on plasticity theory. Adjustments were later made to cater for situations outside the range of the plasticity equations, and for soil compressibility. Meyerhof (1963) developed a formalism that is now known as the general bearing capacity equation. It is described in textbooks such as those by Lambe and Whitman (1979), Bowles (1996), and Das (2004). Vesic (1963, 1973) proposed the general shear, local shear, and punching shear failure mechanisms. Calculations are carried out using limit analysis and/or plasticity theory, and are described in detail by Calladine (2000), Chen and Liu (1990), Davis and Selvadurai (2002), and others. The general strength parameters c and ϕ are often used, based on the Mohr's circle construction. In offshore practice, an undrained calculation is usually done by taking c to be the undrained shear strength and $\phi = 0$. A drained, log-term calculation is done taking $c = 0$ and ϕ equal to the drained friction angle ϕ' of the soil.

Conventional bearing capacity theory does not implicitly account for excess pore pressures that may have been generated in the soil as a result of previous events, such as previous storms or the early part of the present storm. Consequently, some adjustment may be needed to the strength parameters.

146

3.9.2 Bearing capacity under vertical and horizontal loads

Consider a foundation of breadth B, with a bearing area at depth D below the seafloor, bearing on a fully saturated, submerged soil of uniform density and strength. The foundation is subjected to a vertical load V and a lateral load H, giving a load inclination angle $\beta = \tan^{-1}(H/V)$. The unit ultimate bearing capacity of q_u is the value of V/A at failure, and can be conveniently written as

$$q_u = cN_cF_c + qN_qF_q + \tfrac{1}{2}\gamma'BN_\gamma F_\gamma \tag{3.27a}$$

where q is the vertical effective stress in the in-situ soil at the level of the bearing area A, and γ' is the submerged unit weight of the soil.

Table 3.2 shows bearing capacity factors as functions of the friction angle ϕ. The equations for N_c and N_q were derived by Prandtl (1923) and Reissner (1924). The equation for N_c in terms of N_q can be derived by comparing the bearing capacity of a soil with strength parameters (c, ϕ) and the capacity of a similar soil with $c=0$ but with a surcharge $q=c/\tan\phi$. The equation for N_c gives $N_c = \pi + 2$ when ϕ is zero. The equation for N_q is different to the equation used in Terzaghi's original formulation, which is considered to be incorrect (Das, 2004). However, in many cases it is not too inaccurate, and is still used by some designers onshore.

For the self-weight factor, two expressions are commonly quoted in the literature. The first was given by Caquot and Kerisel (1953) and

Table 3.2 Bearing capacity

	Cohesion term	Surcharge term	Self-weight term
Bearing capacity factors	$N_c = \dfrac{N_q - 1}{\tan\phi}$	$N_q = e^{\pi\tan\phi}\tan^2\left(45° + \dfrac{\phi}{2}\right)$	$N_\gamma = 2(N_q + 1)\tan\phi$ or $N_\gamma = 1.5(N_q - 1)\tan\phi$
Shape factors	$F_{cs} = 1 + \dfrac{B}{L}\dfrac{N_q}{N_c}$	$F_{qs} = 1 + \dfrac{B}{L}\tan\phi$	$F_{\gamma s} = 1 - 0.4\dfrac{B}{L}$
Depth factors	$F_{cd} = 1 + 0.4F^*(D/B)$	$F_{qd} = 1 + 2(1 - \sin\phi)^2 \times \tan\phi F^*(D/B)$	$F_{\gamma d} = 1$
Inclination factors		$F_{\gamma i} = F_{qi}\left(1 - \dfrac{\beta}{90°}\right)^2$	$F_{\gamma i} = \left(1 - \dfrac{\beta}{\phi}\right)^2$
Compressibility factors	If $I_r > I_{r,crit}$, then $F_{cc} = 1$ If $I_r < I_{r,crit}$, then $F_{cc} = F_{\gamma c} - \dfrac{1 - F_{\gamma c}}{N_c \tan\phi}$	If $I_r \geq I_{r,crit}$, then $F_{qc} = F_{\gamma c} = 1$ If $I_r < I_{r,crit}$, then $F_{qc} = F_{\gamma c} = \left(\dfrac{I_r}{I_{r,crit}}\right)^{4\sin\phi/[3(1+\sin\phi)]}$	

Note: $F^*(x) = x$ if $x < 1$, and $F^*(x) = \tan^{-1}(x)$ if $x > 1$

Vesic (1973). The second is smaller, and credited to Hansen (1970). It is not clear why these eminent authors disagreed, but some light on the matter is shed by Michalowski (1997) and Davis and Selvadurai (2002). It seems that it is difficult to include self-weight in an algebraic plasticity analysis. In practice, the first formula is sometimes used for upper-bound estimates of q_u, and Hansen's expression is used for lower-bound estimates.

The modifying factors F_c, F_q, and F_γ are all 1 for the case of a strip footing loaded vertically and on the surface of a flat soil body. For other conditions, based on Das (2004), each factor F_x is composed of multiples of modifying factors. For instance:

$$F_x = F_{xs}F_{xd}F_{xi} \cdots \tag{3.27b}$$

where F_{xs} is a modifying factor depending on the shape of the bearing area in plan view, F_{xd} depends on the depth of embedment D, F_{xi} accounts for load inclination, and F_{xc} accounts for soil compressibility. All of these differences affect the failure mechanisms involved, and, in particular, the mechanism for a circular footing under pure vertical load can be axisymmetric. There are also factors for ground inclination, base area inclination, and other effects.

Bowles (1996) summarises various different formulae that have been proposed by various authors for various modifying factors. Table 3.2 lists some of the expressions. For shape factors, L is the longest side of a rectangular foundation area, and B is the shortest side. For a circular foundation, $L = B$ is the diameter. For depth factors, several authors have pointed out that the change at $D/B = 1$ produces an unrealistic step change in the bearing capacity at this depth ratio. Dean (2008) observed that this produces an incorrect prediction of a punch-through failure at $D/B = 1$ in jackup analyses. He recommended that the $\tan^{-1}$ formula be used at all depth ratios.

For compressibility, the original approach used with Terzaghi's equation involved multiplying the friction angle by 2/3. A more scientific basis was established by Vesic (1973), who developed compressibility factors using a cavity expansion approach. The results depend on a rigidity index I_r and a critical rigidity index $I_{r,crit}$, defined as:

$$I_r = \frac{G}{c + q' \tan \phi} \tag{3.28a}$$

$$I_{r,crit} = \frac{1}{2} \exp\left[\left(3.3 - 0.45\frac{B}{L} \right) \tan\left(45° + \frac{\phi}{2} \right) \right] \tag{3.28b}$$

where G is a measure of the small-strain elastic shear modulus of the soil at a depth of $B/2$ below the bearing area, and q' is the in-situ vertical effective stress at that depth. Measurement of G is discussed in Section 3.8.2. The equation for F_{qc} and $F_{\gamma c}$ in Table 3.2 is algebraically equivalent to Vesic's (1973) equation 16, and to Das's (2004) equation 3.39. For N_{cc}, the present author suggests the expression listed in Table 3.2, which uses N_c instead of N_q, which was used in Vesic's (1973) equation 11. For the special case of $\phi = 0$, this expression reduces to

$$F_{cc} = \frac{4}{3N_c} \ln\left(\frac{I_r}{I_{r,crit}}\right)$$
(3.28c)

This gives operationally the same values as Vesic's (1973) equation 17 and Das's (2004) equation 3.40. The factor cannot be used for rigidity indices less than about 1/50 of the critical value.

For triangular footings, several opinions have developed in the literature regarding shape factors. One is to assume that the bearing capacity is the same as a circular footing of equal area, which makes $B/L = 1$ in the shape factor equations. Another is to assume that B/L equals the ratio of the shortest altitude of the triangle to its longest side. For a $45°$ right-angled triangle, this is equivalent to taking $B/L = 0.5$.

3.9.3 Bearing capacity with overturning moment

Consider an overturning moment M applied to a rigid footing, in addition to vertical and horizontal loads. The conventional approach involves two steps. First, the actual loads by equivalent loads V and H only, with the line of action of the vertical load offset horizontally by the eccentricity $e = M/V$. A reduced foundation is developed which will provide a vertical reaction force at the same eccentricity. Second, a linear distribution of vertical stress is assumed across the entire bearing area, and a check is made that the distribution does not imply tensile bearing stress anywhere.

The first step in the procedure is illustrated for a circular foundation on clay in Fig. 3.24a. Using the effective area and length-to-breadth ratios given in API RP2A, the ultimate vertical load V_{ult} on the foundation of diameter B is given by

$$V_{ult} = A'q_{ult} = A'N_c F_{cs} F_{cd} F_{ci} F_{cc} s_u$$
(3.29a)

149

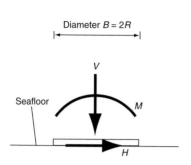

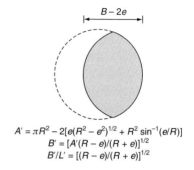

$$A' = \pi R^2 - 2[e(R^2 - e^2)^{1/2} + R^2 \sin^{-1}(e/R)]$$
$$B' = [A'(R - e)/(R + e)]^{1/2}$$
$$B'/L' = [(R - e)/(R + e)]^{1/2}$$

Elevation showing combined loads {V, H, M}

Plan view of equivalent foundation, and equivalent area A' and length to breadth ratio L'/B'

(a)

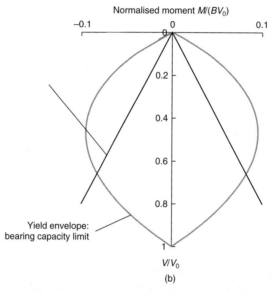

(b)

Fig. 3.24 *Some concepts for bearing capacity calculations for a foundation under combined vertical, horizontal, and moment loading. (a) Reduced foundation for a moment M applied to a circular foundation of diameter B = 2R, in accordance with API RP2A. (b) Example interpretation of the bearing capacity formula in terms of a yield envelope*

where A' is the area of the reduced foundation. Using Table 3.2 to determine the shape, depth, and inclination factors gives

$$V_{ult} = V_0 \frac{A'}{A} \left(\frac{N_c\sqrt{B + 2e} + \sqrt{B - 2e}}{(N_c + 1)\sqrt{B + 2e}} \right) \left[1 - \frac{2}{\pi}\tan^{-1}\left(\frac{H}{V}\right) \right] \quad (3.29b)$$

150

with

$$V_0 = \frac{\pi B^2}{4}(N_c + 1)F_{cd}F_{cc}s_u \tag{3.29c}$$

The ultimate load has to be obtained by solving equation (3.29b) when $V = V_{ult}$ on the right-hand side. The second step in the procedure would then be to calculate the minimum and maximum normal bearing stresses as

$$\sigma_{min}^{max} = \frac{V}{A} \pm \frac{M}{Z} \tag{3.30}$$

where A is the area of the actual bearing area and Z is its elastic section modulus. The limitation means the eccentricity cannot be greater than Z/A. For a rectangular footing, $Z/A = B/6$, so the line of action of the vertical load must be within the middle third of the actual foundation. For a circle, $Z/A = B/8$, so the line of action must stay within the middle quarter if tension is to be avoided.

3.9.4 Bearing capacity and yield envelopes

The idea of using a yield envelope to describe bearing capacity under combined loading was suggested by Roscoe and Schofield (1956), and was further developed by Ticof (1977), Butterfield and Ticof (1979), Tanaka (1984), Osborne *et al.* (1991), and others, who show how a yield envelope can be developed from a conventional bearing capacity analysis. Figure 3.24b illustrates equation (3.29b) plotted in this way. The axes are the vertical load and the normalised moment e/B. The different curves are for different values of the load ratio H/V. The plot represents a yield envelope in the three-dimensional loadspace $\{V, H, M/B\}$. The size of the envelope is measured by V_0. The limit $|e/B| < 1/4$ plots as two planes.

3.10   Other stability analyses

3.10.1 Slope stability

Slope stability is important offshore because the seabed is not flat. Some offshore platforms are located on or near slopes, and some are on or near a continental rise that represents the transition between a continental margin and the deep ocean. Even platforms that are close to shore can be at risk, owing to the possibility of coastline collapse (Locart and Mienert, 2002; Stowe, 2003; Yalçıner *et al.*, 2003; Sultan *et al.*, 2007).

All of the methods developed for onshore slopes can be used offshore. Earthquake effects on slope stability are also considered in the same way. These methods are described in textbooks such as those by Bowles (1996) and Das (2004), and in specialist books such as those by Abramson *et al.* (1996), Cornforth (2005), and Cheng and Lau (2008). Poulos (1988) provides an extensive summary of submarine slope stability. Two factors are different compared with above-water slopes. First, provided the slope is fully submerged and the soil is fully saturated, submerged unit weights are used instead of bulk unit weights, in undrained as well as drained calculations. Second, account must be taken of water pressures acting on the seafloor, and cyclic wave loading effects on seabed pore pressures and strength.

Figure 3.25a illustrates aspects of the effects of wave pressures on a seabed. The wave pressure follows an approximately sinusoidal variation, with a magnitude decreasing exponentially with water depth (eg. Ippen, 1966). One of the effects is to reduce the factor of safety against slope failure, and this can cause the slope to fail if it is already close to failure. The wave is, of course, travelling, so there may not be time for a failure to occur. Nevertheless, it is normally prudent to include wave loading effects in all slope stability calculations, as well as in bearing capacity calculation and other calculations for structures such as a gravity platform, where the caisson base is a significant fraction of the wavelength.

Fung (1965) showed that, if the seabed is a uniform, linear, isotropic elastic half-space, wave pressures induce changes in stress in the seabed that reduce exponentially with depth (Fig. 3.25b). Ishihara and Yamazaki (1984) showed that, under simplifying assumptions, the radius of the Mohr's circle of change of stress is constant at any particular depth z, and that the directions of the principal change in stress rotate during a wave cycle. This gives a rather complex cyclic loading action. Excess pore pressures may develop in the soil, for instance as a result of storm loading, and these pressures will dissipate over time after the storm. The dissipation can be accompanied by changes in the void ratio and associated changes in the soil strength. Data and models of this process have been proposed by Putnam (1949), Liu (1973), Demars (1983), Finn *et al.* (1983), Demars and Vanover (1985), Poulos (1988), and others. It is entirely feasible that, in severe storms, some relatively loose sandy seabeds can liquefy.

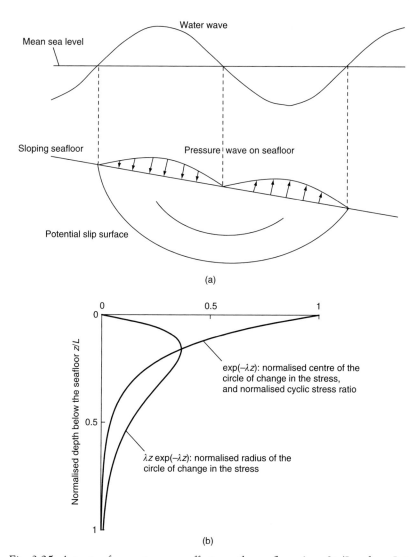

Fig. 3.25 Aspects of wave pressure effects on the seafloor. $\lambda = 2p/L$, where L is the wavelength. (a) Water pressures act on a sloping seafloor and increase the moment, tending to cause sliding on a potential slip surface. (b) Variation in the magnitude of effects with normalised depths below the seafloor

3.10.2 Trench stability

Figure 3.26 shows a vertically sided trench cut into a seabed of uniform clay with an undrained shear strength s_u. Let u_0 be the water pressure on the seafloor, and let γ_{bulk} be the bulk unit weight of the soil. The vertical

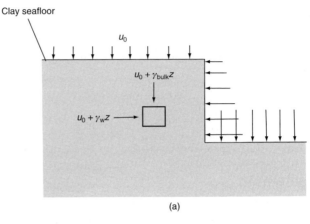

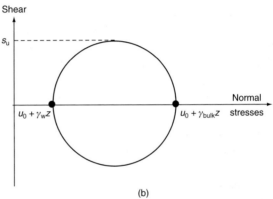

Fig. 3.26 *Stability calculation for a submerged vertically sided trench in clay.* (a) *Stresses on the seafloor and in the clay.* (b) *Limiting Mohr's circle of total stress, undrained case*

total stress at some depth z beneath the original seafloor is $u_0 + \gamma_{bulk} z$. The lateral total stress acting on the side of the trench at the same depth is $u_0 + \gamma_w z$, where γ_w is the unit weight of the seawater. Hence, the diameter of Mohr's circle of total stress is $\gamma' z$, where γ' is the submerged unit weight of the soil. If the limiting diameter is $2s_u$, the limiting stable trench depth z_{lim} is

$$z_{lim} = \frac{2s_u}{\gamma'} \tag{3.31}$$

Davis and Selvadurai (2002) note that, based on plasticity theory, this is strictly a lower-bound estimate of the limiting trench depth that will remain standing in the short term. A simple upper-bound calculation gives twice this limit. In the long term, the stability will be governed by a drained calculation. The side of the trench will collapse, and take up a slope angle ϕ' equal to the drained friction angle of the soil.

3.10.3 Hydraulic fracture

Hydraulic fracture is a process by which a crack is caused to occur in a soil body by the application of high fluid pressure at some point (Overy and Dean, 1986). The process is used to improve oil recovery from deep reservoirs (Hubbert and Willis, 1957; Yew, 1997). It also represents a hazard during the drilling of an oil well, or of a geotechnical borehole, and is one of the criteria that is involved in calculating the 'conductor setting depth' for wells (Schotman and Hospers, 1992).

Consider a well being drilled into the seabed from a jackup or a fixed platform. Drilling mud is pumped down the drillstring and rises up along the outside of the string. The mud lifts soil and rock cuttings from the drillbit and transports them upwards. The lower part of the borehole may initially be uncased, with the sides of the borehole supported by the soil strength and/or the effect of mud cake. Mud and cuttings pass up through this part of the hole, then into a steel tube called a conductor. This transports the cuttings through the water column and up to receiving systems on the platform deck. The conductor only penetrates a certain depth below the seafloor. Its top is higher than the level of seawater, and the drilling mud and cuttings have a different density, so the water pressure at the top of the uncased part of the borehole will be higher than the equilibrium value there. If the excess pressure is too large, it can cause a crack to develop in the soil. In general, the crack is either horizontal or vertical.

A simple, traditional analysis for hydraulic fracture is as follows, based on Bjerrum *et al.* (1972), but ignoring soil strength. Let the fluid pressure be $u_0 + \Delta u$ at the conductor setting depth, where u_0 is the in-situ pore water pressure in the soil at P. Let the in-situ total vertical and horizontal stresses be given by

$$\sigma_v = u_0 + \sigma_v' \tag{3.32a}$$

$$\sigma_h = u_0 + K_0 \sigma_v' \tag{3.32b}$$

where σ'_v is the vertical effective stress and K_0 is the coefficient of lateral earth pressure. If the increasing fluid pressure reaches the total vertical stress, it may be possible for a horizontal crack to open, and be held open by the fluid pressure. If the pressure reaches the horizontal total stress, a vertical crack may theoretically open, and be held open by the water pressure. Hence, the limiting conditions are

$$\text{if } K_0 \leq 1, \Delta u \leq K_0\sigma'_v \text{ to avoid a vertical crack} \qquad (3.33a)$$

$$\text{if } K_0 \geq 1, \Delta u \leq \sigma'_v \text{ to avoid a horizontal crack} \qquad (3.33b)$$

Hence, a simple procedure to estimate conductor setting depth is to plot the horizontal and vertical effective stress versus depth, and to determine the minimum depth below which a given value Δu of pressure is lower than these effective stresses, with an adequate factor of safety.

In practice, conductor setting depths have been found to be satisfactory that are considerably less than values calculated by the simplified theory. Part of the problem is likely to be the estimation of K_0. However, another factor is that soil strength has been ignored in the analysis. Aldridge and Haaland (1991) showed that additional fluid pressures can be tolerated without fracture in a cohesive soil if its undrained shear strength s_u is taken into account. Further analyses have been proposed by Schotman and Hospers (1992) for conductor setting in sand, and by Andersen and Lunne (1994), Andersen *et al.* (1994), Kennedy *et al.* (2004a,b), Xia and Moore (2006), and others.

3.10.4 Liquefaction assessment

Liquefaction offshore is assessed in the same ways as onshore, except that cyclic loading due to water waves is an additional driver that is not present onshore. Jefferies and Been (2006) and de Groot *et al.* (2006) present comprehensive reviews. Vaid and Chern (1985) summarised some of the terminology:

(a) Liquefaction and limited liquefaction in monotonic loading, with the deviator stress either reducing to a low value or reducing and then recovering, and with large concurrent strains (see Fig. 3.12b).
(b) Liquefaction due to cyclic loading: a point is reached at which the deviator stress that could be sustained in previous cycles can no longer be sustained, and the soil collapses with a rapid increase in the pore water pressure and strain, reaching a state where the mean normal effective stress is zero or near zero, and the deviator

or shear stress is similarly very small in comparison with the values previously attained during cycling.

(c) Cyclic mobility: the stress–strain diagram during cyclic loading develops into a shape where there is virtually no secant stiffness over a range of strain, but with a recovery once a certain amount of strain has occurred (see Fig. 3.14a).

(d) Limited liquefaction due to cyclic loading: the deviator stress reduces with a concurrent increase in the pore water pressure and a large strain, but recovers once a certain amount of strain has occurred.

Bardet (2002) summarises several constitutive models of liquefaction. More recent developments include Elgamel *et al.* (2003), Mroz *et al.* (2003), Park and Byrne (2004), and Jefferies and Been (2006).

In practice, liquefaction potential as a result of cyclic loading is assessed by comparing soil shear stresses calculated for the process of interest, such as a storm, with data from laboratory tests. Examples of liquefaction assessments for offshore structures are provided by Rahman *et al.* (1977), Clukey *et al.* (1980a), Sully *et al.* (1995), and others. Typically, laboratory data that mimic the imposed conditions in the seabed are used to construct a curve of the number of cycles required to cause liquefaction, versus a cyclic stress or strain amplitude. Representative values of the normalised amplitude and the number of cycles are calculated for the episode of cyclic loading in question, and plotted on the diagram. If the number of cycles exceeds the number required to cause liquefaction, then liquefaction is judged to be likely.

Liquefaction as a result of an earthquake is assessed by a similar procedure originally developed by Seed and his co-workers (Seed and Idriss, 1970, 1971; Seed and Peacock, 1971; Seed *et al.*, 1991). It is described by Kramer (1996), Chen and Scawthorne (2003), Day (2007), and others, and a recent update is described by Youd *et al.* (2001). For a given sand layer in the soil profile, a representative value of the cyclic shear stress ratio (CSR) is determined for the particular event being studied. This is a measure of the ratio of the shear stress induced by the earthquake divided by the in-situ vertical effective stress. The result is plotted on a graph of CSR versus cone penetration test (CPT) resistance. The plotted point is compared with a threshold curve which depends on earthquake magnitude and other factors, and which separates a conditions where liquefaction occurs (high CRS, low CPT resistance), from conditions where it does not.

3.11   Consolidation and other time-related processes

3.11.1 Introduction

Primary consolidation is a process of squeezing water out of a soil under drained conditions, or of sucking water in, in association with elastic rebound due to stress removal. It involves interaction between compressibility and fluid flow, and is rapid in sands and slow in clays. Secondary consolidation is a creep phenomenon whose physical drivers are not well understood. Theories of primary and secondary consolidation are well established and described in textbooks such as those by Lambe and Whitman (1979), Terzaghi *et al.* (1996), Bowles (1996), and Das (2004). Related theories of vertical and horizontal drainage have been developed by Rendulic (1935), Barron (1948), Olson (1977), Olson and Li (2002), and others.

One of the ways that consolidation theory can be used for offshore design is illustrated in Fig. 3.27. Excess pore pressures are induced in the seabed by various loads and the consequent changes of total stress. Various methods are available to determine the excess pore pressures generated by these processes. Consolidation is the process by which they dissipate over time, in association with changes in the effective stress, void ratio, stiffness, and soil strength. The changes in stiffness affect the subsequent responses to loads, and the changes in strength affect the subsequent factors of safety against various forms of failure.

3.11.2 Primary consolidation

Figures 3.28a and 3.28b show two scenarios where a theory of vertical consolidation can be relevant offshore. In Fig. 3.28a, a wide structure is placed on a seabed consisting of a thin clay layer overlying sand or gravel. The load will induce positive excess pore pressures in the clay, and these can drain mainly vertically into the sand. In Fig. 2.28b, the underling layer is relatively impermeable, intact rock. The excess pore pressures will dissipate primarily by radial flow of water out from under the base. In both cases, vertical settlements will occur over time as the clay layer slowly compresses.

At the same time, the structure may be subject to shear loading from water waves, and so may transfer cyclic shear stresses into the soil. These stresses can generate further excess pore pressures. A storm may occur, resulting in a rapid increase in the generation rate. Between storms, dissipation by consolidation can continue. Over a

158

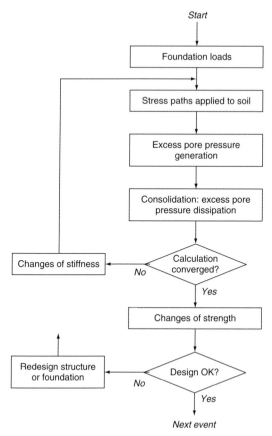

Fig. 3.27 Example of the use of consolidation calculations within an iterative geo-technical and structural design process

longer period of time, the soil will compact and harden, and this will cause the rate of generation of excess pore pressures to reduce. A state might eventually develop in which no further significant generation occurs.

Figure 3.28c shows a simplification of the problem, in which a cylinder of soil of radius R is compressed vertically. Vertical, radial, and angular coordinates z, r, q, respectively, can be defined as indicated. The soil is assumed to move only vertically, so that no radial or circumferential strains occur, This is reasonable, since the surfaces of the structure and of the underlying soil layer are likely to be rough.

159

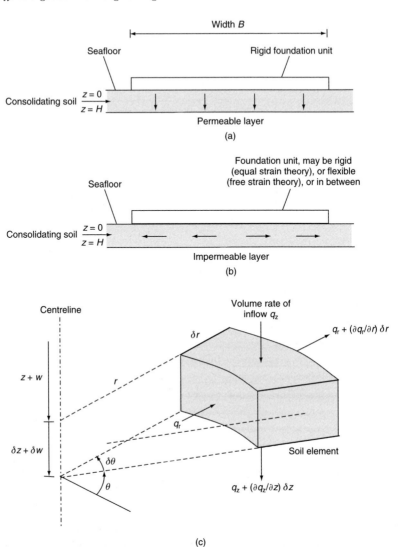

Fig. 3.28 Consolidation analysis for a soil layer of thickness H much less than the width B of the foundation. (a) Mainly vertical flow to the underlying permeable layer. (b) Mainly radial flow outwards and then up to the seafloor. (c) Considerations of flow and volume strain for a soil element

Because of the axisymmetry of the problem about the central axis, none of the variables involved in the calculation are expected to depend on the angular coordinate θ. Let p be the excess pore pressure at a general point (z, r) at some time t. By using Darcy's law to calculate the discharge velocities on the surfaces of the element, the rate of compressive volume strain of the element is found to be

$$\frac{\partial e_{vol}}{\partial t} = -\frac{\partial^2 w}{\partial t\,\partial z} = \left[-k_v\frac{\partial^2 u_{xs}}{\partial z^2} + \frac{k_h}{r}\frac{\partial}{\partial r}\left(r\frac{\partial u_{xs}}{\partial r}\right)\right] \qquad (3.34)$$

where k_v and k_r are the vertical and horizontal hydraulic conductivities of the soil, respectively, and w is the vertical settlement of the soil at position r, z, θ and time t. Following Terzaghi *et al.* (1996), but taking account of Seed and Rahman's (1977) proposals for pore pressure generation in offshore foundation soils, it is assumed that the change in the vertical effective stress at a general point in the soil, since the start of the analysis, is the sum of a component associated with volume change less a component u_g due to the generation of excess pore pressures at that point:

$$\Delta\sigma_v' = \frac{e_{vol}}{m_v} - u_g \qquad (3.35)$$

where m_v is the familiar coefficient of volume change. Finally, from Terzaghi's principle of effective stress, the change in the vertical effective stress equals the change in the vertical total stress less the change in the excess pore pressure. Using this to substitute for the change in the vertical effective stress in equation (3.35), then using the result to substitute for the volume strain in equation (3.34), and rearranging, gives

$$\frac{\partial u_{xs}}{\partial t} = \left[c_v\frac{\partial^2 u_{xs}}{\partial z^2} + \frac{c_h}{r}\frac{\partial}{\partial r}\left(r\frac{\partial u_{xs}}{\partial r}\right)\right] + \left(\frac{\partial\Delta\sigma_v}{\partial t} + \frac{\partial u_g}{\partial t}\right) \qquad (3.36)$$

where $c_v = k_v/\gamma_w m_v$ and $c_h = k_h/\gamma_w m_v$ are coefficients of consolidation. The coefficients thus represent an interaction between the permeabilities of the soil, represented by k_v and k_h, and the compressibility of the soil, represented by m_v. Equation (3.34) also represents a soil–structure interaction, since the stiffness of the structure will provide a relation between w and the change in the total vertical stress.

Table 3.3 lists three solutions, and Fig. 3.29 illustrates them in the form of familiar diagrams of pore pressure isochrones and degree of consolidation. The first is the solution of Terzaghi's equation without radial flow. The second is the 'equal strains' solution for radial flow alone, assuming that the vertical displacement of the soil is a function of z and t but not of the radial coordinate r. This corresponds to a rigid structure, and results in a vertical total stress that is a function

Table 3.3 Theories for vertical consolidation (see Figs 3.28 and 3.29)

(a) Vertical drainage (Terzaghi's theory of one-dimensional consolidation)

Time factor	$T_v = \dfrac{c_v t}{H^2}$

Excess pore pressure $\quad\quad \dfrac{u_{xs}}{\Delta\sigma_0} = \displaystyle\sum_{m=0}^{\infty} \dfrac{2}{M} \sin\left(\dfrac{Mz'}{H}\right) \exp(-M^2 T_v)$

Average degree of consolidation $\quad\quad U = 1 - \displaystyle\sum_{m=0}^{\infty} \dfrac{2}{M^2} \exp(-M^2 T_v)$

Parameters $\quad\quad z' = H - z, M = \dfrac{\pi}{2}(2m+1)$

(b) Radial drainage, free strain condition

Time factor $\quad\quad T_r = \dfrac{c_h t}{R^2}$

Excess pore pressure $\quad\quad \dfrac{u_{xs}}{\Delta\sigma_0} = \displaystyle\sum_{n=1}^{\infty} \dfrac{2}{M} \dfrac{J_0(Mr/R)}{J_1(M)} \exp(-M^2 T_r)$

Average degree of consolidation $\quad\quad U = 1 - \displaystyle\sum_{m=0}^{\infty} \dfrac{4}{M^2} \exp(-M^2 T_r)$

Parameters $\quad\quad$ M is the nth root of $J_0(M) = 0$,
J_0 and J_1 are the Bessel functions of the first kind, of zero and first order, respectively

(c) Radial drainage, equal strains condition

Time factor $\quad\quad T_r = \dfrac{c_h t}{R^2}$

Excess pore pressure $\quad\quad \dfrac{u_{xs}}{\Delta\sigma_0} = 2\left(1 - \dfrac{r^2}{R^2}\right)\exp(-8T_r)$

Average degree of consolidation $\quad\quad U = 1 - \exp(-8T_r)$

Sources: (a) from Craig (2004), (b) and (c) from Olson and Lai (1989, 2002) with changed notation

of the radius. The third is the 'free strain' solution for radial flow alone, assuming that the vertical displacement can be a function of the radius and that the vertical total stress is independent of the radius. This applies for a flexible structure. Carillo (1942) demonstrated that the combined degree of consolidation U satisfies

$$1 - U = (1 - U_v)(1 - U_r) \tag{3.37}$$

where U_v is the degree of consolidation for purely vertical flow, representing the fraction of the long-term settlement that would be achieved for purely vertical flow at a given time, and U_r is the degree of consolidation for purely radial flow, representing the fraction achieved for radial flow.

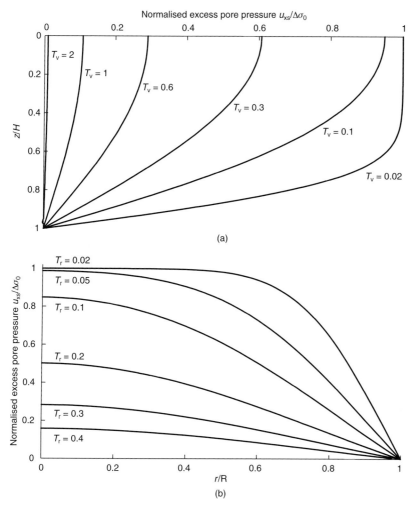

Fig. 3.29 Consolidation analysis for a soil layer of thickness H much less than the width B of the foundation. (a) Excess pore pressure isochrones: vertical drainage only. (b) Excess pore pressure isochrones: radial drainage, free strains case. (c) Excess pore pressure isochrones: radial drainage, equal strains case. (d) Average degree of consolidation versus the time factor

3.11.3 Secondary compression

Secondary compression occurs during and after primary consolidation, but is not driven by the excess pore pressure gradient (Mesri and Vardhanabhuti, 2005). It can be particularly significant for silts and silty clays, and is believed to be responsible for major unexpected settlements

163

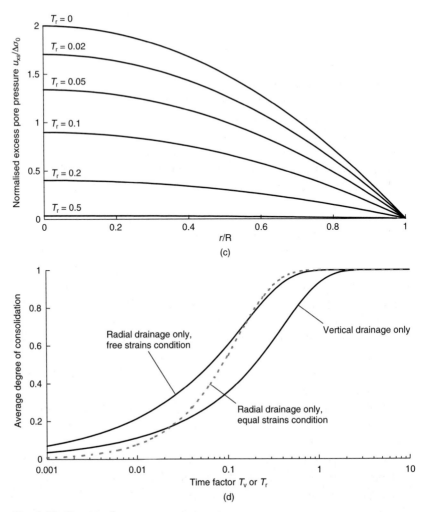

Fig. 3.29 Continued

of over 11 m for the offshore island supporting KIA international airport. The driving mechanisms for secondary compression are still the subject of research, and there is some uncertainty on the best way to model it. A commonly used approach is to calculate secondary compression as if it starts at the end of primary consolidation, with

$$e = e_{EOP} - C_{\alpha} \log(t/t_{EOP}) \tag{3.38}$$

where e is the void ratio of the soil at time t after the start of primary consolidation, e_{EOP} is the void ratio at the end of primary consolidation,

164

when the pore water pressures are sensibly zero, and C_α is the secondary compression index.

Mesri and Castro (1987) propose that C_α is related to the primary compression index C_c. A typical value of C_α/C_c is 5% (Ladd *et al.*, 1977) but may reduce with time (Mesri and Godlewski, 1977). This leads to a prediction that the void ratio continues to decrease indefinitely, which is not physically possible, but the effect is not usually relevant considering the typical design lifetime of a structure. Secondary compression is related to drained creep, and is one of the phenomena that the visco-plasticity modelling approach aims to model (Sekiguchi and Ohta, 1977; Kim and Leroueil, 2001; Zhu and Yin, 2001).

3.11.4 Other time-related processes

Ageing is the process by which the properties of a soil change over time. Ageing effects differ from cyclic loading effects, changes in the pore pressure, and from development of cementation in carbonate soils. Ageing can cause soil strengths to increase or to decrease. Bjerrum (1967) reviewed some of its effects for North Sea soils, and proposed a concept of 'delayed compression' as an alternative to secondary compression. Ageing of sands is reviewed by Baxter (1999), Leon *et al.* (2006), and others. Its significant effects on pile capacity are discussed by Jardine *et al.* (2006).

Thixotropy can also have important effects (Mitchell, 1960; Mitchell and Idriss, 2001). Thixotropic effects are more pronounced in montmorillonite clays and least in kaolin (Poulos, 1988).

The process of cementation of a soil can also cause changes in the soil properties, and depends on the amount of cementitious material available in the pore fluid. Cementation develops in carbonate sands through the slow dissolution of particles and precipitation of calcite cement at interparticle contacts. The process is spatially variable, so that some carbonate sand deposits are cemented in some places and uncemented in others.

3.12 Sample integrity

3.12.1 Sampling disturbance

Several authors investigated the effects of the inevitable small or large degree of sample disturbance that occurs when a soil sample is extracted from the ground and set up in a laboratory ready for a test, including Hight (1993), Hight *et al.* (1994), Lunne *et al.* (1998, 2006), Santagata

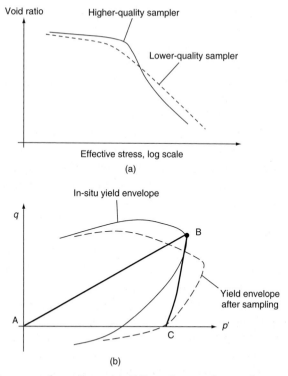

Fig. 3.30 Some sampling effects. (a) Effect of a sampler on the one-dimensional behaviour of clays (redrawn from Hight, 1993). (b) Simple interpretation of undrained unloading during sampling: normally consolidated sample

and Germaine (2002), Clayton and Siddique (2001), and Long (2003, 2006). X-ray radiographs can be used to assess sample uniformity prior to testing, or indeed during and after testing (Allen *et al.*, 1978; ASTM D 4452).

Figure 3.30a shows the effects of sampling on Bothkennar clay (Hight, 1993). The dashed curve shows the characteristic shape of an oedometer test result for a clay sample obtained using a piston sampler, which is regarded as a good-quality sampler and better than a simple Shelby push sampler. The solid curve shows data for the same soil sampled using the Sherbrooke sampler described by Lefebvre and Poulin (1979), which is considered to be of better-quality than a piston sampler. The higher-quality sampler has a stiffer initial response, and a higher preconsolidation stress, and its post-yield response is different.

Baligh *et al.* (1987) and Hight (1993) report finite element calculations that indicate that some parts of a sample can experience shear strains of 5% or more as a sampler is pushed downwards into the soil. These strains are very significant, as some soils will undergo shear failure in a triaxial cell at less than this; in effect, the sampling process can pre-fail a sample, which can have a significant effect on the response measured subsequently in a triaxial cell.

Figure 3.30b shows a simplified concept of what happens to a normally consolidated clay during sampling. The clay has been subjected to one-dimensional loading along AB during its geological history. If the sampling process is rapid and gentle enough, the clay will be unloaded under undrained conditions, reaching $q = 0$ when it is extracted from the sampling tube. But a stress path for undrained unloading will push out the yield envelope, and may cause its orientation in stress space to change, as shown by the dashed curve. Although the effect may not seem great, it may potentially affect the strength and stiffness of the soil in subsequent laboratory testing.

These and other investigations show that sampling effects can be complex and significant, even if all care is taken to minimise soil disturbance. The SHANSEP (stress history and normalised soil engineering parameters) approach is sometimes used in an attempt to reverse some of the effects of sampling, but has limitations for sensitive clays (Ladd and Foott, 1974; Ladd and Assouz, 1983; Bradshaw *et al.*, 2000; Hiroyuki *et al.*, 2003; Le *et al.*, 2008). Recent developments of deepwater samplers have included sophisticated computer analyses of sampling disturbance effects (Lunne *et al.*, 2008).

3.12.2 Reconstitution of sands

Sand samples are usually obtained from the seabed as bag samples, with all in-situ fabric lost. For testing purposes, the sand is reconstituted in a former of the relevant shape and size, and may be tamped to achieve the same relative density as the estimated in-situ value.

Several authors have found that the sample preparation method can have a major effect on the stiffness and volumetric response in drained tests, and a noticeable effect on the strength at large strains (e.g. Oda, 1972; Ladd *et al.*, 1977). For undrained testing, Fig. 3.31 shows typical effects of the sample preparation method on the liquefaction resistance measured in a laboratory. The number of cycles to initial liquefaction at a given cyclic stress ratio can be very different for different preparation techniques.

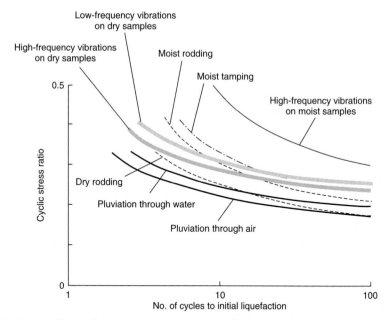

Fig. 3.31 Effects of the sample preparation method on the liquefaction resistance of Monterey sand. (Simplifed from a much-quoted diagram by Townsend, 1978)

The problem of sample preparation effects has been investigated by many researchers, including Ladd (1974, 1977), Silver *et al.* (1976), Castro and Poulos (1977), Mulilis *et al.* (1977, 1978), Marcuson and Townsend (1978), Vaid *et al.* (1999), and Porcino and Marciano (2008). For onshore sites, it is possible to freeze the ground and so take samples that have been disturbed only by the freezing process (Harris, 1995; Ghionna and Porcino, 2006).

4

Jackup platforms

Chapter 4 looks at the geotechnical procedures and special hazards for mobile jackup platforms, covering how to perform preload checks and bearing capacity and sliding checks, and appreciate the geotechnical aspects of dynamic structural analysis, and geotechnical aspects of site departure.

4.1 Introduction

4.1.1 Types of jackup

A jackup is a mobile, self-elevating offshore platform consisting of a hull that supports drilling and other topside equipment, and three or more retractable legs passing through the hull (McClelland et al., 1982; Young et al., 1984; Vazquez et al., 2005). A unit moves onto location, sets its legs onto the seabed, and raises its hull out of the water.

Figure 4.1a shows an independent-legged jackup. A large unit will operate in up to about 150 m water depth. It has a triangular hull 80 m or so long. Its legs consist of a frame structure 10 m or so square in plan view, supported on independent foundations called 'spudcans' that may be up to 20 m or so in diameter. A smaller independent-legged jackup may have tubular legs. Figure 4.1b shows a mat-supported jackup. The foundation consists of a single mat to which the legs are permanently attached. The unit is suitable for soft soil sites where large foundation area may be required, but can also be used on sandy seabeds. (Turner et al., 1987; Murff and Young, 2008; Templeton, 2008).

A liftboat is a self-propelled unit fitted with jacking systems and legs, used mainly for coastal and river works (Fig. 4.2b) (Oser and Huston, 1992).

4.1.2 Uses of offshore jackups

A large jackup may be used as a standalone platform, drilling exploration wells in the open sea. The wells are capped off on completion, and the

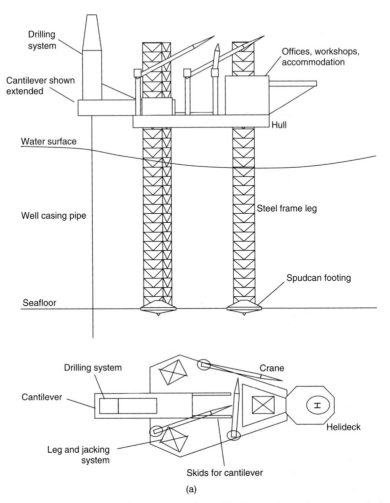

Fig. 4.1 Large offshore jackups. (a) Independent-leg jackup: elevation and plan views of the hull and topsides. (b) Mat-supported jackup: elevation view and plan view of mat

jackup moves elsewhere. The well may later be connected to a sub-sea flowline to a nearby fixed platform. A jackup can also be used to drill wells through a previously installed fixed-jacket platform. The unit is installed close to the jacket. The cantilever that supports a drilling derrick is then extended over the smaller jacket platform, and one or more oilwells or gas wells are drilled through a pre-installed template on the jacket. Typically, a jackup may drill several production wells on a first visit. More wells may be drilled on a second visit, which may be by a different jackup. Water or gas injection wells may be drilled to recover the last of the hydrocarbons.

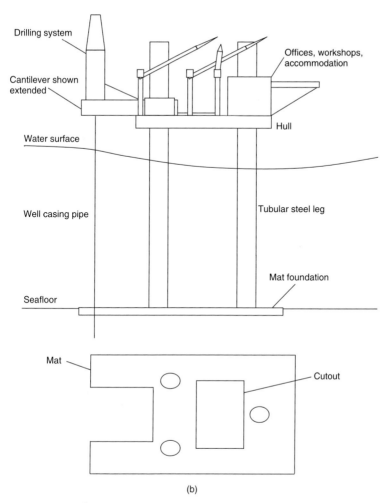

Fig. 4.1 *Continued*

Cholley *et al.* (2008) describe a multi-footing mega-jackup proposed to support an offshore LNG plant. Jackups are also used for offshore site investigations, offshore construction, and as temporary accommodation platforms or as fixed accommodation or drilling platforms. Small jackups have been used as construction platforms for installing offshore wind-farm structures (Zaaijer and Henderson, 2004).

4.1.3 *Safety and codes of practice*
Unlike most other platforms, jackups are intended for use at many different locations during their design life. Design calculations must

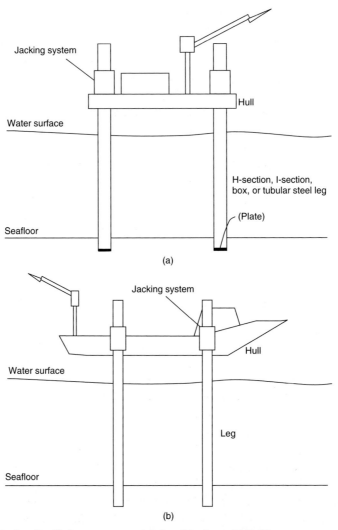

Fig. 4.2 *Small self-elevating units. (a) Small jackup. (b) Liftboat*

consider the range of environmental and foundation conditions that a given unit may experience during its design lifetime. This depends primarily on the maximum water depth the jackup is designed for. The designer will want a spudcan that will be suitable for seabeds consisting of anything from very soft clays to very dense sands. Once the jackup is built and commissioned, a site-specific assessment will be made for each location where the unit is to be used.

Guidelines for site-specific assessment for jackups were published by SNAME as TR-5A (SNAME, 1991), and later updated (SNAME, 2002).

A considerable amount of investigation into the reliability of the SNAME code and of jackups in general has been carried out (MSL, 1998, 2002a,b; Nelson *et al.*, 2000; Cassidy *et al.*, 2002a,b; Morandi, 2003). A new standard for independent-legged jackups, ISO 19905 (parts 1 and 2) is expected by 2010. It may include modifications to the SNAME (2002) recommendations, based on experience since 2002. It may subsequently be extended to include mat-supported units. Useful guidance is also provided by Dier and Carroll (2004) and Vazquez *et al.* (2005).

Jackups and other offshore installations are routinely shut down and evacuated in advance of hurricanes (API, 2006). The evacuated platforms are occasionally lost in the storm. API publishes guidelines for hurricanes (see the list of codes and standards at the start of this book). The US Minerals Management Service reviews damages after hurricanes in the Gulf of Mexico (Sharples, 2002, 2004; Sharples and Stiff, 2009; Templeton *et al.*, 2009).

4.2 Independent-legged jackups

4.2.1 Types of foundation

Figure 4.3 shows some of the foundations that have been used on independent-legged jackups. Light jackups for port and coastal use may have simple tubular or H-section steel legs that penetrate the seafloor until the required bearing capacity is achieved. In some cases, a flat bearing plate may be used.

Modern large jackups generally use a double-cone arrangement, including a smaller central cone to assist in installing the unit on or in the seabed. The arrangement is typically hexagonal or octagonal in plan view, and can often be considered to be circular for purposes of geotechnical analysis. The use of skirted spudcans is a relatively new development (Svanø and Tjelta, 1993; Eide *et al.*, 1996; Jostad and Andersen, 2006; Andersen *et al.*, 2008).

4.2.2 Installation procedures

To install a large independent-legged jackup, the unit is moved onto site and a preloading operation is carried out. The purpose is to proof-test the foundation soils and to strengthen them by increasing their bearing capacity. Figure 4.4 shows the procedure:

(a) The jackup is towed too close to the final location, and the legs are lowered onto the seabed. The hull is raised slightly to provide a

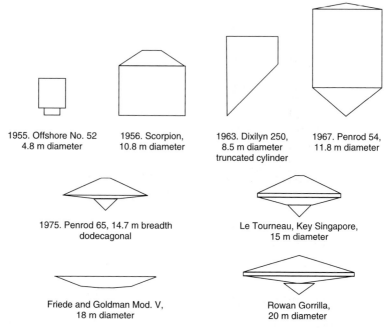

1955. Offshore No. 52   1956. Scorpion,   1963. Dixilyn 250,   1967. Penrod 54,
   4.8 m diameter   10.8 m diameter   8.5 m diameter   11.8 m diameter
                                               truncated cylinder

1975. Penrod 65, 14.7 m breadth   Le Tourneau, Key Singapore,
          dodecagonal   15 m diameter

Friede and Goldman Mod. V,   Rowan Gorrilla,
       18 m diameter   20 m diameter

Fig. 4.3 Types of foundation used for various jackups (not to scale). (Data from Young et al., 1984; McNeilan and Bugno, 1985; Hambly et al., 1990; Hayward et al., 2003)

small foundation load, and the jackup is dragged into the final position.

(b) The hull is raised a short distance out of the water. Water ballast is pumped on board, such that the vertical load on individual spud-cans increases to typically twice the working vertical load.

(c) The preload is held for some time, typically several hours, so that any excess pore pressures induced in the foundation soils can dissipate.

(d) The preload is dumped to sea, and the hull is raised to its final working height.

Preloading induces bearing capacity failure in the soil beneath and around each spudcan, causing the spudcan to penetrate into the seabed until the soil resistance equals the applied load.

A punch-through failure can occur during preloading if the spudcan breaks through a hard soil layer, such as dense sand, and pushes rapidly into a softer layer, such as soft clay (McClelland et al., 1982; Young et al., 1984; Hambly, 1985; Fujii et al., 1989; Aust, 1997; Brennan et al., 2006). This can result in the jackup toppling over and one or more

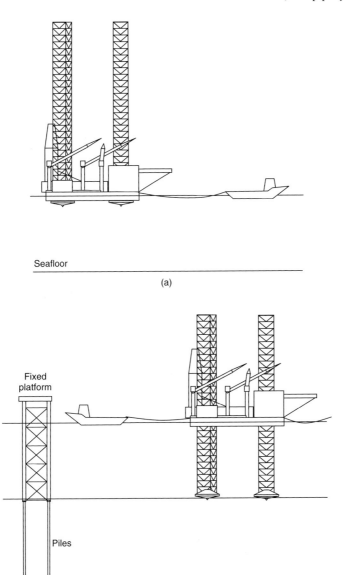

Seafloor

(a)

Fixed
platform

Piles

(a)

Fig. 4.4 *Installation procedure for work over a preinstalled fixed platform. (a) Jackup towed to location. (b) Legs in the seabed, jackup dragged to final position. (c) Hull raised slightly out of the water, leg being preloaded. (d) Hull raised to final elevation, cantilever extended, drilling through template on fixed platform*

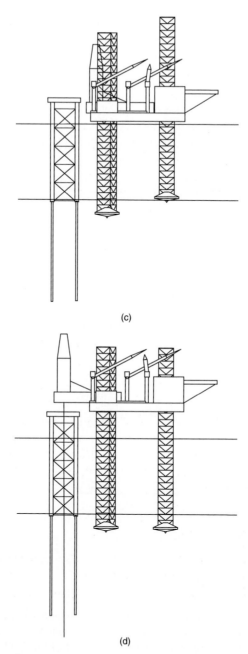

(c)

(d)

Fig. 4.4 Continued

legs being severely bent or broken. To reduce the risks involved, modern jackups are able to preload spudcans individually. A single operative will be able to monitor all three legs during the operation, and will be able to dump the preload rapidly if a problem arises.

4.2.3 Types of geotechnical calculation

Jackups are unusual in that they are mobile structures, and a designer will not necessarily know the foundation conditions that apply at all of the locations at which a jackup is used during its design life. For each new site, SNAME (2002) recommends that a site-specific assessment be done. This may include:

- an assessment of geohazards
- a foundation assessment for installation, commonly including a 'preload check'
- a foundation assessment for operations, including a sliding check and an overturning check
- an assessment of effects of the jackup on nearby structures
- a leg extraction assessment, for when the jackup is moved off site to another location.

SNAME's criteria are arranged so that, if it is safe to preload a jackup at a site to double the working vertical load, it is likely to be safe to operate the jackup at that site. For this reason, a site-specific assessment for a standalone jackup is often limited to simply the preload, sliding, and overturning checks. If a jackup cannot be preloaded safely in this way, or it does not have the ballast tank capability to do so, more detailed calculations may be required, either:

- a bearing capacity and sliding check or
- a displacements check.

If a jackup satisfies the first check, there may be no need to do the second. Both calculations involve dynamic analysis accounting for soil stiffness as well as strength. The checks are summarised later.

4.2.4 Site investigations

It is always wise, and is mandatory in some regulatory areas, to carry out a geophysical investigation of a platform site before a geotechnical investigation is done (UKOAA, 1997; Noble Denton, 2003). The geophysical investigation will include a bathymetry survey, a seafloor survey for debris and unevenness, and shallow seismic sub-bottom profiling. The survey will be able to identify hazards such as rock outcrops, shallow gas, or highly variable stratification. For standalone drilling, it is usually possible to move the jackup location a few hundred metres to avoid a rock outcrop, for example.

Specific requirements for the geotechnical investigation include at least one main borehole to a depth below the seafloor of at least 30 m, or to 1.5 spudcan diameters below the expected depth of spudcan penetration into the seabed, whichever is the greater. A typical geotechnical investigation for a large jackup may include a single main borehole at the location of the planned centre of the jackup, and at least one cone penetration test (CPT) hole a few metres away, typically to at least 20 m below the seafloor. Additional borings will be done if needed to verify missing information or potential problems identified in the main borehole. Data are evaluated as they are obtained. Occasionally, a CPT hole is carried out under the planned location of each spudcan, to check for lateral variability of soil strata and properties.

The investigation is normally done from a geotechnical drillship or semi-submersible. Occasionally, the work is carried out from the jackup itself, using the oilwell drilling equipment on the jackup. However, there are several disadvantages. The jackup does not usually have the heave compensation equipment that would be available on a drillship, so it needs to be stabilised on the seafloor during the 24 hours or so of the geotechnical investigation. As a result, the seafloor is disturbed, and the data in the upper few metres may not be reliable. Another problem is that the foundation risks are unknown until the investigation is done, so the jackup is being used in a less safe manner than would otherwise be the case. Also, if it is found that the jackup cannot be safely deployed, the resulting disruption to the client's drilling programme can be more severe than if the geotechnical work was done well in advance.

A preload check will normally be done during the investigation, and will be reported to the client together with the field data and analyses. It is advisable to alert the client to potential geohazards in the report, and to any limitations, particularly if there is a potential for lateral variability of the soils.

4.3   Foundation assessment for installation

4.3.1   *Seafloor hazards*
Figure 4.5 illustrates some special hazards during installation (Kee and Imms, 1984). Construction debris and rock outcrops can damage

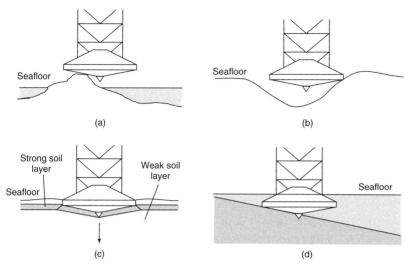

Fig. 4.5 Some seafloor hazards during installation. (a) Rock outcrop or hard sea-floor debris. (b) Footprints, or softened remoulded volumes, from previous jackup deployments. (c) Punch-through failure: a hard soil layer overlying a soft layer. (d) Sloping hard stratum or seabed

spudcans by focusing the soil reaction forces on small areas (Fig. 4.5a). This can cause local overstress in the steel, and excessive bending moments in the legs. A naturally uneven seafloor may also lead to leg bending, but may sometimes be corrected by light dredging. A uniform hard rocky seabed is also hazardous because most spudcans will not be able to support the weight of the jackup on their tip cones.

A common hazard for jackups being deployed at a fixed platform site is the footprints problem (Fig. 4.5b), where the previous deployment of a different jackup has left depressions in the seabed, caused by the previous jackup's spudcans. The depressions do not match the positions of the spudcans for the new jackup. This can cause a spudcan to slide into an old footprint, inducing leg bending, and preventing proper alignment with the fixed platform. Jardine *et al.* (2001) developed a technique called 'stomping' to counteract this at soft clay sites. One of the spudcans is used to push down in many different places around the old footprints, creating uniformity by collapsing them and remoulding the clay everywhere. Some other approaches are discussed by Dean and Serra (2004) and others.

Punch-through is a major hazard at some locations (Fig. 4.5c). The most common cause is a hard soil or rock layer overlying a softer soil. The spudcan breaks through the hard layer, and penetrates rapidly until either a sufficient soil resistance is encountered or the jackup hull enters the water, and buoyancy reduces the leg load sufficiently to stop the motion. Punch-through can also occur if there are gas voids in the seabed, or gas hydrates close to sublimation, or other seabed anomalies.

Sloping soil strata can be hazardous (Fig. 4.5d). The legs of a large jackup may be 50 m or more apart. If the soil strata at the location have significant dips, the penetrations of different spudcans into the seabed can be significantly different. For example, a 6° dip can result in penetrations that are $50 \times \tan 6° \approx 5$ m different at different spud-cans. Or it may be that a dense sand layer is 5 m thinner at one spudcan than another, giving a punch-through danger that might not be apparent if only average strata depths were measured in the site investigation. Sometimes, a standalone jackup will be deployed within a relatively large positional tolerance from the location of the site investigation, resulting in a significantly different foundation risk if the strata are steeply sloping.

If the jackup is installed close to an existing piled platform, soil can be pushed past the piles during preloading. This may potentially bend the piles, and the remoulding of the soil can weaken it and so reduce the ultimate pile capacity (Mirza *et al.*, 1988). Subsurface interactions may also occur if a jackup is deployed near any structure, such as a gravity platform, an anchor, a pipeline, a quay wall in a port, or, indeed, another jackup. Siciliano *et al.* (1990) report data from centri-fuge model tests that indicated that soil displacements at one spudcan radius from the edge of a spudcan would typically be less that 0.02 times the spudcan radius, and that effects on a pile at this distance were small. However, Tan *et al.* (2006) carried out finite element analyses and concluded that a stress change of 110 MPa could occur in a pile that was about three spudcan radii from the spudcan centreline. Tests by Leung *et al.* (2006) tend to confirm that effects are small at a distance of one spudcan diameter between the pile and the spudcan edge.

4.3.2 Preloading calculations – an overview

Preloading calculations are carried out to predict the relation between leg load and spudcan penetration, and to determine the safety of the planned operation, particularly in respect of the possibility of punch-through.

The information needed consists of the spudcan geometry, jackup parameters, and the soil layering, unit weights, and strength parameters.

Spudcan geometry is normally modelled in a simple way, as sketched in Fig. 4.6a for a symmetrical spudcan. An up-to-date drawing is required, including any modifications made to the spudcans after construction. The preload value is also needed, defined as the maximum load applied to a foundation during preloading. This is the sum of the effects of the static jackup weight plus added water ballast. It equals the difference between the load on the spudcan before the spudcan touches the seafloor and the maximum load on the spudcan. It is also useful to know how much uncontrolled penetration of a spudcan can be tolerated without overstressing a leg or connection.

In an ideal world, a leg penetration calculation might start with the spudcan just above the seafloor, and consider what happens to the soil as the spudcan is pushed down into the seabed. However, such calculations require significant computing resources (Carrington *et al.*, 2003; Kellezi and Stromann, 2003, Kellezi *et al.*, 2005a,b). In practice, a 'wished-in-place method' is used. Conventional bearing capacity calculations are carried out for many assumed spudcan tip penetrations. At each, the spudcan is assumed to have arrived without disturbing the soil. Several failure modes at that penetration may be considered, and the most critical one is assumed as the limiting mechanism.

The calculations usually assume the spudcan bearing area is circular. For shallow penetrations (Fig. 4.6a), before the widest part of the spudcan penetrates the seafloor, the bearing area is assumed to be at the level of the seafloor. Its diameter B is assumed to be the value that has the same area as the area of intersection with the original seafloor. Soil heave is not accounted for in the calculations, but should be considered when the results are assessed. For deeper penetrations (Figs 4.6b–4.6d), the bearing area is assumed to be at the widest part of the spudcan, and calculations are done as if the spudcan were a simple circular cylinder with its base at this level. For very deep penetrations (Fig. 4.6d), soil flows around the spudcan as a result of the penetration. The weight of this 'backflow' reduces the net bearing capacity of the foundation.

4.3.3 *Backflow and infill*

In onshore bearing capacity calculations, the ultimate bearing capacity q_u is the largest vertical stress that can be applied to the soil, averaged over the bearing area, assuming the space above the bearing area has been excavated (e.g. Das, 2004). The net ultimate bearing capacity $q_{u,net}$ is defined as the difference $q_u - q$ between the ultimate bearing

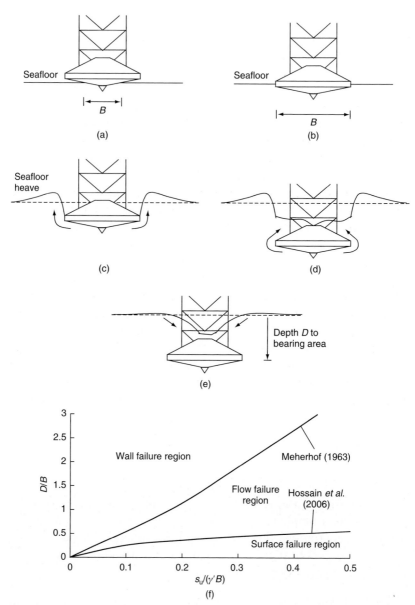

Fig. 4.6 Spudcan penetration, failure modes, backflow, and infill. (a) Spudcan before the maximum bearing area is reached. (b) Spudcan after the maximum bearing area is reached. (c) Surface failure during initial penetration into soft clay (after Hossain et al., 2006). (d) Flow failure creating backflow during further penetration into soft clay (after Hossain et al., 2006). (e) Wall failure creating infill during subsequent operations (interpreted after Hossain et al., 2006). (f) Comparison of failure modes for a clay with a uniform shear strength

capacity and the in-situ vertical overburden stress q at the level of the bearing area. If the density of the footing is the same as the soil, q_{net} is a measure of the bearing capacity that would apply if the hole above the bearing area was backfilled with the soil.

For offshore jackup foundations, the situation is different. The spudcan is pushed into the seabed, displacing some of the soil there. Figures 4.6c and 4.6d summarise experimental data and finite element calculations by Hossain *et al.* (2003, 2005a, 2006) that show how this happens for a clay seabed. As the spudcan penetrates the soil, a small pile of soil is initially formed outside the rim of the spudcan. On further penetration, an open hole develops, with material flowing around from underneath the spudcan. On further penetration, more material flows around, but this now flows onto the top of the spudcan. This 'backflow' stabilises the wall of the hole, so that a wall collapse need not occur during a preloading operation. Figure 4.6e shows how a wall failure might develop in an open hole during subsequent operations. For instance, this might occur if there is softening of the seabed after spudcan installation. The material involved in this collapse is called 'infill'.

Backflow and infill apply loads to the foundation bearing area, and so reduce the additional load that the bearing area can support. This can be accounted for in a bearing capacity calculation as follows. The maximum buoyant weight W_{max} of material on top of a spudcan is approximately

$$W_{max} \approx qA - \gamma'V \tag{4.1}$$

where q is the in-situ vertical effective stress at the level of the bearing area, A is that area, γ' is the submerged unit weight of the soil, and V is the volume of soil displaced by the spudcan. Some of the backflow may be held up by the leg bracing. Note that $q=0$ for the situation of Fig. 4.6a, when the bearing area is still at the seafloor. If it is assumed that a fraction b of the maximum does occur, then an available bearing capacity q' can be defined for this situation as

$$q' = q_u - bW_{max}/A = q_{u,net} + [b\gamma'V/A - (1-b)q] \tag{4.2}$$

where $q_{u,net} = q_u - q$. SNAME (2002) applies equation (4.1) to all its preload formulae. The formulae used in the present book will be for the net bearing capacity. The value plotted on a leg load–displacement curve is the product $q'A$ of the effective capacity and the bearing area.

To determine whether backflow will occur in clay soil, SNAME (2002) adopted Meyerhof's (1972) calculation for the stability of an unsupported slurry-field trench in clay. However, Meyerhof's calculation assumed that the trench wall would fail by collapsing into the slurry. This corresponds to the wall failure mechanism of Fig. 4.6e, and would occur if the hole depth D satisfies

$$\text{wall failure if} \quad \frac{D}{B} > N\frac{s_u}{\gamma'B} \tag{4.3}$$

where s_u is the average undrained shear strength over the depth D, γ' is the average submerged unit weight of the soil, and N is a stability number plotted in SNAME's (2002) Fig. 6.3 as a function of D/B. For the different situations of backflow during preloading, the recommendations of Hossain et al. (2006) may be followed. Their experimental and analytical results indicated that flow failure occurs if

$$\text{flow failure if} \quad \frac{D}{B} > \left(\frac{s_{uD}}{\gamma'B}\right)^{0.55} - 0.25\left(\frac{s_{uD}}{\gamma'B}\right) \tag{4.4}$$

where s_{uD} is the undrained shear strength of the clay at the depth of the spudcan bearing area, and the notation D here denotes the penetration depth, and B the diameter of the spudcan bearing area (this notation is used in SNAME (2002), while Hossain et al. use H and D for these quantities, respectively). Figure 4.6f compares the two mechanisms. Flow failure is always more critical during the preloading phase.

For a spudcan bearing on a uniform sand layer, it is rare for the penetration to be such that backflow or infill is possible. However, backflow may be feasible in loose sands, or infill may be feasible in special cases where a spudcan is placed in a hollow between moving sandbanks, for example. During preloading, the sand is likely to flow until its angle of repose ϕ' is achieved. For layered soils, backflow and inflow can occur if the sand layers collapse, pulling clay layers with them.

4.3.4   Interpreting leg penetration curves
Leg penetration calculations are described in Section 4.3.5. Results are plotted on a graph of leg load versus spudcan tip penetration versus leg load (Fig. 4.7a). Leg load is the soil resistance less the weight of the backflow. Figures 4.7b–4.7g show some common types of results:

- *Figure 4.7b.* The vertical load on the spudcan increases with penetration, and no instability is likely during loading to the

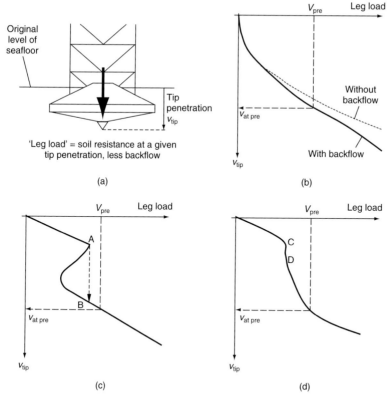

'Leg load' = soil resistance at a given
tip penetration, less backflow

(a)

(b)

(c)

(d)

Fig. 4.7 *Interpreting preloading curves. (a) Definition of terms. (b) Curves indicating no problems, unless there is significant lateral variability. (c) Curve indicating punch-through during preloading. (d) Curve indicating small punch-through during preloading, which may be controllable. (e) Curve with a low factor of safety against punch-through during preloading and subsequent operations. (f) Curve with a low factor of safety against punch-through during preloading and subsequent operations. (g) Curve indicating rapid penetration and potential P–Δ failure during preloading*

required preload. Additionally, the ultimate capacity of the spudcan would continue to increase if an extra load were applied. No problems are indicated here. The penetration v_{tip} at the preload V_{pre} is read from the graph using the curve with or without backflow, depending on whether backflow is predicted. The actual penetration will be checked, and any significant difference between the prediction and the actual value will be investigated.

• *Figure 4.7c.* A punch-through is indicated at point A, before the preload is reached. If the applied load increases marginally above

185

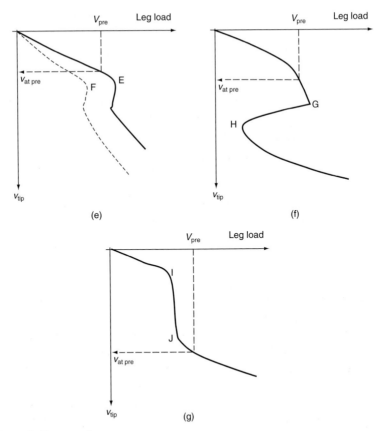

Fig. 4.7 *Continued*

A, the foundation will no longer be able to support the load, and a rapid penetration will occur until point B, where the bearing capacity next matches the applied bearing stress. The client must be alerted to this danger, and the values of the leg load and the leg penetration at point A provided in the written assessment, together with the punch-through distance from A to B. If this distance is small, the rig movers may be able to control the ballast systems to allow the penetration to take place without danger or damage.

• *Figure 4.7d.* A punch-through is indicated at point C, but the punch-through distance CD is relatively small. The client needs to be warned that there may be a short, rapid penetration at this load level. However, the prediction is sensitive to small variations in soil properties and layer thicknesses.

- *Figure 4.7e.* A punch-through is not indicated during loading to the planned preload, but would occur at E if the spudcan was only marginally overloaded. There is also the possibility that some of the engineering parameters may be slightly inaccurate, or that the thicknesses of the spoil layers are not quite as indicated, due to lateral variability of the soils. If the actual graph was that shown dashed, a punch-through would occur at F. One way to define a factor of safety for this situation is as

$$FS = \frac{\text{leg load at punch-through } (E)}{\text{maximum planned leg load}} \qquad (4.5)$$

The client needs to be warned that the factor of safety against punch-through at the maximum preload is low.

- *Figure 4.7f.* A punch-through is not indicated up to the planned preload, but would occur at point G. Moreover, the leg load at point H is below the planned preload, and may even be below the working load of the jackup. The strong response at G is probably due to a strong soil layer (this can be checked from the detailed calculations), so the results are very sensitive to the accuracy of the thickness of this layer and its strength parameters.
- *Figure 4.7g.* A punch-through is not indicated but the rate of increase in the ultimate leg load with penetration is very small from I to J. This creates three potential problems. First, if the actual soil properties or layering is only slightly different from the values used in the calculations, the actual penetration during preloading may be quite different from the predicted values. Second, a rapid penetration may nevertheless occur if the rig movers are unable to control the rate of ballasting accurately. Third, a $P - \Delta$ failure may occur, described in Section 4.4.

In summary, the engineer is primarily looking for possibilities of punch-through or rapid penetration, and is taking account of the fact that the data on which the assessment is made may contain some inaccuracies.

The value of penetration is also important. In normally consolidated or underconsolidated clays, a jackup leg may penetrate 30 m or more into the seabed. The penetration must be predicted accurately so as to ensure that the jackup has enough leg length. Also, during subsequent operations, the clay will consolidate and may gain in strength, potentially resulting in difficulties extracting the spudcan at the end of the deployment. Leg extraction is discussed further in Section 4.8.

4.3.5   *Bearing capacity calculations*

The main text of SNAME (2002) considers several possible failure mechanisms for a spudcan penetrating into soil profiles consisting of layers of clay, siliceous sand, and/or siliceous gravel soils. Calcareous and carbonate soils are considered by Poulos and Chua (1985), Dutt and Ingram (1988), Yeung and Carter (1989), Randolph *et al.* (1993), Le Tirant *et al.* (1994), Pan (1999), Randolph and Erbrich (1999), Erbrich (2005), Yamamoto *et al.* (2005, 2008a), and others.

The calculation methods for sands and gravels assume drained behaviour. The soil strength is characterised by the effective angle ϕ' of internal friction, measured in a triaxial or direct shear test or estimated from in-situ test data. The methods for clays assume undrained behaviour. Soil strength is characterised by the undrained shear strength s_u, which may be estimated using triaxial or vane tests, for example. For silts, some drainage may occur during the time needed to complete the preloading operation. SNAME (2002) recommends that both drained and undrained calculations be done, and the worst case result used.

All of the formulae assume that the spudcan bears on only one or two soil layers. For more than two layers, a procedure is recommended in which calculations are carried out for deeper penetrations first. When a three-layer situation arises (Fig. 4.8), the lower two layers are replaced by an equivalent single layer with the same bearing capacity as if the spudcan were at the top of those two layers. This procedure is repeated as necessary.

Figure 4.9a shows the application of a conventional plane strain failure mechanism to the axisymmetric problem of a spudcan penetrating clay. Provided the cone has a rough enough surface and the cone height is not too large, the entire cone will remain in the active wedge, and so may have little effect on the results. Hossain *et al.* (2006) found experimentally that the actual mechanism changes from surface failure to flow failure. For a spudcan bearing on uniform clay, SNAME (2002) uses the familiar general bearing capacity equation described in Chapter 3, with factors listed in Table 3.2. The accuracy of depth factors in clay was investigated using finite elements by Salgado *et al.* (2004), Edwards *et al.* (2005), Gourvenec (2008), and others. Several authors observe that Hansen's (1970) equations produce a step change at $D/B = 1$ (Bowles, 1996; Martin, 1994). Dean (2008) suggested that, to avoid a spurious punch-through prediction at $D/B = 1$, the expression for F_{cd} at $D/B \geq 1$ be used at all D/B ratios.

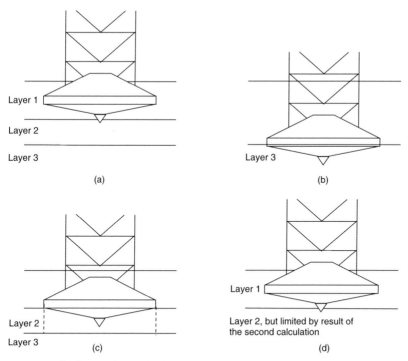

Fig. 4.8 Calculations for multiple layers. (a) Actual situation. (b) First calculation. (c) Second calculation. (d) Third calculation

If the strength of the clay increases with depth, the undrained shear strength for the calculation may be taken as the strength at a depth $B/2$ below the level of the spudcan bearing area. Alternatively, SNAME (2002) allows for the use of Davis and Booker's (1973) calculation, or the more recent calculation by Houlsby and Martin (2003) that accounts for the inclination of the base of a spudcan to the horizontal. Menzies and Roper (2008) compared several methods, and concluded that Houlsby and Martin's (2003) method generally provided lower bounds on the spudcan load to achieve a given penetration, SNAME's (2002) methods sometimes underpredict and sometimes overpredict, and the proposals of Hossain *et al.* (2006) generally provide upper bounds on the spudcan load to achieve a given penetration.

For a spudcan on clay overlying a softer soil layer, a punching motion can develop. Figure 4.9b shows the mechanism observed in centrifuge model tests by Hossain *et al.* (2005b). SNAME (2002) adapts the

189

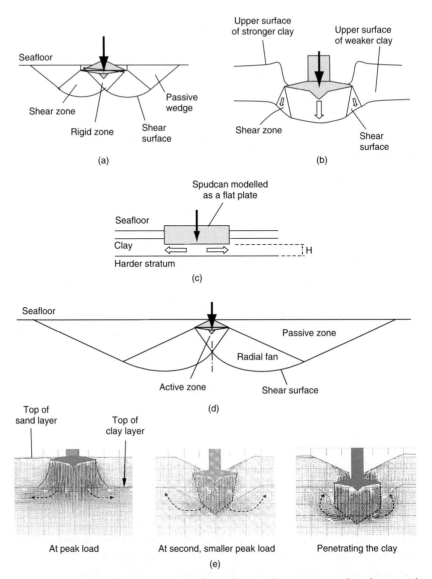

Fig. 4.9 Failure mechanisms. (a) Uniform clay: mechanism assumed in the general bearing capacity equation. The mechanism that actually occurs varies from surface failure to flow failure (see Fig. 5.6 and Menzies and Roper, 2008). (b) Clay over weaker clay: mechanism observed experimentally and confirmed in finite element analyses by Hossain et al. (2005a). (c) Clay over stronger clay: solution adapted from Meyerhof and Chaplin (1953). (d) Uniform sand: mechanism in the general bearing capacity equation assumed. (e) Sand over clay: mechanisms observed by Teh et al. (2008) as a model spudcan penetrates a dense sand layer and penetrates an underlying soft clay layer

calculation proposed by Brown and Meyerhof (1969), based on a simpler mechanism with a vertical cylinder of soil below the footing punching downwards into the underlying weaker soil. Dean (2008) proposed an updated equation, equivalent to

$$q_{u,net} = q_{u,net,b} + 4\alpha s_u \frac{H}{B}$$
(4.6)

where $q_{u,net,b}$ is the net ultimate bearing capacity that would apply if the spudcan rested on the surface of the lower layer, and s_u is the average undrained shear strength over the height H. The second term accounts for shear stress on the curved surface of a vertical cylinder that is assumed to be pushed downwards below the spudcan. The factor α would be 1 if the full undrained shear strength of the upper clay layer was mobilised on the surface. For consistency with SNAME (2002), it would be taken as 3/4.

For a spudcan on clay overlying a harder soil layer, the harder layer will prevent the general shear mechanism from extending into it. A squeezing motion can develop (Fig. 4.9c), depending on the height H from the bearing area to the top of the underlying layer. SNAME (2002) adapts the clay squeezing calculation proposed by Meyerhof and Chaplin (1953). That calculation followed the work of Prandtl (1923) and Sokolovskii (1946), but was done before Meyerhof's (1963) subsequent development of the general bearing capacity equation, which is now widely accepted. Based on Meyerhof and Chaplin's (1953) equation 7, Dean (2008) proposed

$$q_{u,net} = \left(N_c F_{cs} F_{cd} + \frac{B}{3H} - 1\right) s_u$$
(4.7)

Squeezing occurs if (a) the net bearing capacity is greater than the capacity for the uniform clay, and (b) the underlying layer can support the implied stresses. The first condition occurs when $H = B/3$. An intermediate mechanism may develop before the spudcan gets as close as this to the underlying layer, but this is not normally a critical effect. For the second condition, SNAME (2002) specifies that the bearing capacity cannot exceed the value that would occur if the underlying stronger material extended to the level of the spudcan.

For a spudcan bearing on uniform sand, White *et al.* (2008b) found experimentally that the conical tip of a spudcan causes pre-shearing as the spudcan penetrates the soil, and that this can have a major effect on the bearing capacity. SNAME (2002a) uses the familiar

191

general bearing capacity equation, based on a mechanism of the type shown in Fig. 4.9d, with

$$q_{u,net} = \tfrac{1}{2}\gamma'BN_\gamma F_{\gamma s}F_{\gamma d} + q(N_q F_{qs}F_{qd} - 1) \tag{4.8}$$

where the factors are given in Table 3.2. The depth factor again produces a spurious prediction of punch-through at $D/B = 1$. However, this is not often an issue since a penetration of one spudcan diameter into sand would be very unusual.

SNAME (2002) considers both alternatives for N_γ, and cautions that both methods have led to overpredictions for bearing capacity in the past, and that to account for this for large spudcans, the friction angle should be taken as 5° less than the value measured in triaxial testing. Both formulae were for flat footings. Bearing capacity factors for conical footings were proposed by Cassidy and Houlsby (2002). However, the analysis of model test data by White *et al.* (2008) indicated that N_γ values for conical footings were about 1/2 of those for flat footings, due to the pre-shearing effect, and that Bolton's (1986) stress–dilatancy approach led to improved values of N_γ.

For a spudcan on sand overlying clay Fig. 4.9e shows part of a sequence of mechanisms observed by Teh *et al.* (2008) in centrifuge model tests. SNAME (2002) adapts a calculation by Meyerhof and Hanna (1978) and Hanna and Meyerhof (1980), in which a simple cylindrical plug of sand is pushed down into the clay. Other calculations are explored by Craig and Chua (1990) and Frydman and Burd (1997). The SNAME (2002) equation may be written as

$$q_{u,net} = q_{u,net,b} + 2\frac{H}{B}(\gamma'H + 2q)K_s \tan\phi' \tag{4.9}$$

where $q_{u,net,b}$ is the net ultimate bearing capacity at the surface of the lower layer. The second factor uses a coefficient of punching shear, K_s, with values given graphically in the original references. However, the graphs did not cover the full range of friction angles relevant offshore. SNAME (2002) suggested $K_s \tan\phi' \approx 3s_u/(\gamma'B)$ as a lower bound on the value at the onset on punch-through, where s_u is the undrained shear strength of the lower layer. This has the odd effect that the second term in equation (4.9), which represents friction on the side of the cylinder, does not contain any frictional sand properties. It may give significantly smaller capacities than are thought to be correct (Van der Zwaag, 2006).

SNAME (2002) suggests the use of the load-spreading method as an alternative for sand over clay. A fictitious foundation at depth H below the spudcan bearing area, and diameter $(B + 2H/n)$, is considered to support the leg load and the weight of soil above the fictitious foundation. The equations given are equivalent to

$$q_{u,net} = \left(1 + \frac{2H}{nB}\right)^2 q_{u,net,b} \tag{4.10}$$

Young and Focht (1981) recommended $n = 3$. Baglioni *et al.* (1982) used $n = 1/\tan\phi'$. SNAME (2002) recommends $n = 3$ to 5, with $n = 5$ providing a lower-bound estimate of the foundation load at failure.

4.3.6 Notes

The critical mechanism at a given spudcan penetration is usually the one that gives the lowest net bearing capacity. Exceptionally, clay squeezing occurs if the corresponding capacity is greater than would be calculated for a uniform clay. As a flat-based spudcan approaches a boundary between a clay and stronger material, the typical sequence of calculated mechanisms is:

(*a*) when the spudcan is far above the boundary, a conventional general shear failure is predicted
(*b*) when the spudcan is nearer, squeezing becomes possible
(*c*) when the spudcan is nearer still, a conventional, general shear calculation becomes the critical mechanism a little before the flat base of the spudcan reaches the boundary.

In reality, however, the spudcan is conical, and the pre-shearing effect observed by White *et al.* (2008b) may occur if the underlying layer is sand.

Some care is needed for thinly layered soil profiles. Except for the clay-squeezing mechanism, the heights of the volumes of soil participating in a mechanism are of the order of one-half to one spudcan diameter. Consequently, soil layers that are significantly thinner than this have relatively little effect on the actual leg penetration. SNAME (2002) recommends an averaging procedure if there are several sand layers in sequence, based on Meyerhof (1984).

All of the formulae assume that the spudcans behave independently during preloading, and this assumption is also made for the subsequent, operational phase. In practice, leg spacings are often small enough that the failure mechanisms of different spudcans intersect in the seabed.

193

4.4   Failure modes

During operations, environmental loads can come from any compass direction. Potential failure modes during operations include bearing failure, sliding failure, and overturning failure of the entire unit, or limited foundation failures at individual footings. Similar failure modes can be induced by earthquake loading, and all modes can be affected by a history of cyclic loading and the development of excess pore water pressures in sandy seabeds as well as clayey ones. Liquefaction and fluidisation can be issues for sandy seabeds. Excessive cyclic settlement can be particularly problematic in silty soils. Consolidation can be important in silts and clays.

P–Δ effects can be important contributions to failure (Hambly, 1985; Hambly *et al.*, 1990, 1991). In Fig. 4.10a, the bow spudcan has reached equilibrium at some point on its vertical load–penetration curve. It then penetrates a small distance δv in an uncontrolled fashion, as a result of some small perturbation. This results in an increase in the foundation resistance by $K\,\delta v$, where K is the slope of the load–penetration curve at the current load. As a result of the movement, the jackup takes on a small lean at an angle $\delta\theta$ related to $\delta v/S$, where S is the leg spacing. The centre of gravity of the weight W of the jackup shifts horizontally towards the spudcan by a distance $\delta x = nL_w\,\delta\theta \approx nL_w\,\delta v/S$, where L_w is the height of the centre of gravity above the spudcan and n is some factor that takes into account leg bending and dynamic effects. This increases the load on the spudcan by an amount $W(\delta x/S) \approx nWL_w\,\delta v/S^2$. If this increase in the load is more than $K\,\delta v$, the foundation will no longer be able to support the load, and a punching event will begin. Thus, a simple criterion to avoid a P–Δ failure is

$$K > nWL_w/S^2 \tag{4.11}$$

An assessment therefore requires a calculation of the vertical load–displacement stiffness of the foundations, both during preloading, and in subsequent operations where the foundation may be simultaneously subjected to horizontal loads, moments, and possibly torque.

For units located on a dense sandy seabed, the spudcan may not penetrate fully into the seabed. Scour can then produce serious problems (Sweeney *et al.*, 1988; Rudolph *et al.*, 2005). Stonor *et al.* (2003) describe a process sketched in Fig. 4.10c. A jackup was located upslope from a fixed platform. Scour from under the front of the spudcans removed support there, implying that the centroids of the vertical soil reactions could no longer align with the plan centroids of

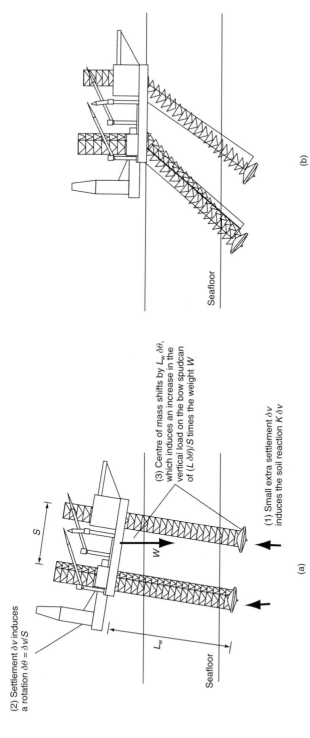

(2) Settlement δv induces
a rotation $\delta \theta = \delta v / S$

(3) Centre of mass shifts by $L_w \, \delta \theta$, which induces an increase in the vertical load on the bow spudcan of $(L \, \delta \theta)/S$ times the weight W

(1) Small extra settlement δv induces the soil reaction $K \delta v$

Seafloor

(a)

Seafloor

(b)

Fig. 4.10 *Some special potential failure modes for independent-legged jackups. (a)* P–Δ *failure (after Hambly, 1985). An instability can develop if the increase in the applied foundation on the deeper foundation is larger than the increased soil reaction. (b) Potential result of severe instability or punch-through: moments induced at the hull–leg connections bend the legs, and the movement does not stop until the hull has settled into the water. (c) Scour–hard-slope interaction (generalised from Stonor et al., 2003)*

195

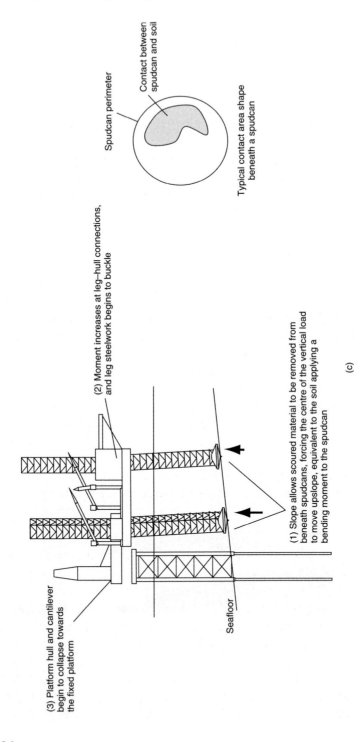

Spudcan perimeter

Contact between spudcan and soil

Typical contact area shape beneath a spudcan

(2) Moment increases at leg–hull connections, and leg steelwork begins to buckle

(3) Platform hull and cantilever begin to collapse towards the fixed platform

Seafloor

(1) Slope allows scoured material to be removed from beneath spudcans, forcing the centre of the vertical load to move upslope, equivalent to the soil applying a bending moment to the spudcan

(c)

Fig. 4.10 Continued

the spudcans. As a result, bending moments were induced in the legs, and the unit gradually moved towards the fixed platform. In this case, part of the connection system between the jackup legs and hull buckled.

Jackup motions due to wave loading depend critically on the stiffness characteristics of the foundation soils. For a jackup working over a fixed platform, cyclic wave loading will cause both structures to sway and surge cyclically. In severe sea states, the relative motions may cause drilling equipment to break, or may cause the upper parts of the two platforms to collide (Hunt, 1999). To avoid this danger, a weather watch is kept, and operations are suspended if the predicted sea state increases to a predetermined limit.

4.5   Dynamic analysis

4.5.1   Introduction

The objectives of a dynamic analysis are (1) to determine the forces and stresses in the jackup structure, (2) to verify that the structure is not overstressed, and (3) to verify that structural movements are not so large as to prevent drilling and other operations, or to cause the jackup hull to collide with a fixed platform when the jackup is situated close to that platform or working over it.

The environmental loads are typically calculated by a hydrodynamic or environmental engineer. Loads can come from any compass direction, and directions for wind, wave, and current loading can all be different. Wave spreading may apply, with individual waves arriving at a jackup from different compass directions (Brekke *et al.*, 1990; Smith *et al.*, 2006). Analyses are ideally done for a range of load directions.

4.5.2   Field data for dynamic jackup responses

Field data for jackup responses have been reported by Brekke *et al.* (1989, 1990), Hambly *et al.* (1990), Karunakaran *et al.* (1992, 1998, 1999), Bærheim (1993), Springett *et al.* (1994, 1996), Spidsøe and Karunakaran (1996), Karunakaran and Spidsøe (1997), Morandi *et al.* (1998), Hunt (1999), Temperton *et al.* (1999), Nelson *et al.* (2000, 2001), Hunt *et al.* (2001), MSL (2002b), Nataraja *et al.* (2003), Templeton (2006), and others.

Figure 4.11a shows the arrangement used by Brekke *et al.* (1990) in a measurement programme on the Maersk Guardian jackup in the 1988–1989 winter season in the North Sea. Accelerometers were attached to

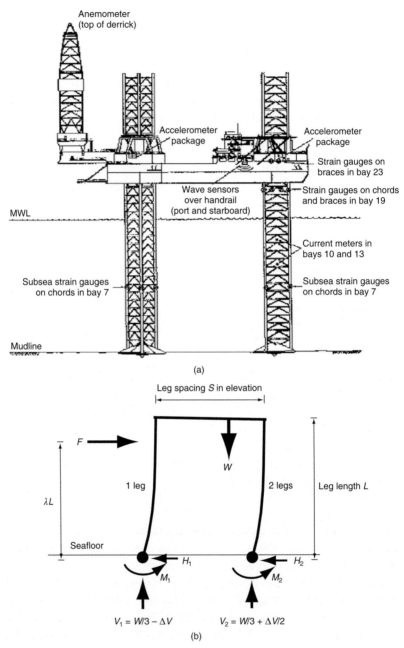

Fig. 4.11 *Examples of a field monitoring system and a simplified analysis model.* (a) *Example of a field monitoring system on a large jackup* (© 1990 *Offshore Technlogy Conference: Brekke et al., 1990*). (b) *Simplified analysis model* (© 2009 *Offshore Technology Conference: Dean and Metters, 2009*)

the jackup to measure the jackup response in terms of hull motions. Strain gauges were attached to the legs and the leg–hull connections to measure forces and moments in these elements. An anemometer was mounted at the top of the drilling derrick to measure wind speeds and direction. Two laser sensors were mounted on the hull to measure wave heights, and two current meters were mounted on the bow leg to measure water velocities at two different levels.

4.5.3 Simplified dynamic structural analysis

Sophisticated finite element models including detailed modelling of the legs, leg–hull connections, and hull and topsides structures are described by Martin (1994), Thompson (1996), Cassidy (1999), Howarth *et al.* (2003), and others. Simpler 'stick models' are also used, where the jackup legs are modelled as stick-beams and the hull is modelled as a plate-beam (Zentech, 2000).

Figure 4.11b shows an example of a simplified stick model of a three-legged jackup. The single bow leg is on the left, identified with a subscript '1'. The two aft legs are on the right (subscript '2'). The spud-cans are assumed to have penetrated a short distance into a flat seabed, with leg lengths L from the leg–hull connections to a 'seabed reaction point'. This is the point where the seabed reaction forces V_i, H_i and moments M_i are considered to act. It is usually taken at the level of the spudcan bearing area if the spudcan embedment into the seabed is small. The hull–leg connections are assumed to be rigid, and the hull is assumed to be rigid and have no rotational moment of inertia. The mass of the jackup is assumed to be dominated by the mass M_h of the hull, and the mass of the legs is ignored. The buoyant weight $W = M_h g$ is assumed to be applied at the plan centroid of the three legs.

In Dean and Metters's (2009) analysis, the legs were treated as simple beam-columns, subjected to bending and axial loads. The dynamic equations of motion of the hull were developed on the basis of Newton's laws of motion, with a simplified representation of wave and current loading. Provision was made for different vertical, lateral, and rotational stiffnesses for different foundations. Key parameters were found to include the ratio λ of the height f the line of action of the horizontal load above the seafloor to the leg length, the ratio S/L of leg spacing to leg length, and the following parameters:

$$\phi_{ri} = \frac{K_{3i}L}{K_{3i}L + EI} \tag{4.12}$$

$$\phi_{hi} = \frac{K_{2i}L^3}{K_{2i}L^3 + 3EI} \tag{4.13}$$

where K_{3i} is the rotational stiffness of the ith spudcan, K_{2i} is its horizontal stiffness, and EI is the flexural rigidity of the legs. The dimensionless parameters ϕ_{ri} and ϕ_{hi} are soil–structure interaction factors. The first is a measure of 'moment fixity'. It varies from zero, if the foundation is pinned with zero rotational stiffness, to 1, if the foundation is fixed and no rotation can occur. The second is a measure of horizontal fixity. It varies from zero, if the foundation slides under no horizontal load, to 1, if the foundation cannot move horizontally.

Under static conditions, if the vertical spudcan motions are small enough to be ignored and the horizontal fixities are 1, and if the rotational fixities are the same at all spudcans with $\phi_{r1} = \phi_{r2} = \phi_r$, the equations give the lateral hull deflection as

$$y = \frac{FL^3}{36EI}(4 - 3\phi_r) \tag{4.14}$$

This gives the well-known result that the displacement at hull level is four times as great under pinned conditions ($\phi_r = 0$) as under fixed conditions ($\phi_r = 1$). The loadpaths are plotted in Fig. 4.12a. If $\lambda = 1$, the change in the vertical load is twice as much when the rotational fixity is zero compared with when it is 1.

Figure 4.12b shows the relation between a normalised stiffness $K_h L^3/$ (36EI) at hull level, and the foundation fixity ϕ, for various conditions. For the case when $\beta = 0$ and the horizontal fixities are 1 and the moment fixities are all the same with $\phi_{r1} = \phi_{r2} = \phi$, the normalised stiffness varies from 1/4 if $\phi = 0$ to 1 if $\phi = 1$. For the case when $\beta = 0$ and the rotational fixities are all 1 and the horizontal fixities are all equal with $\phi_{h1} = \phi_{h2} = \phi$, the normalised stiffness varies from zero to 1. Normalised stiffness reduces if vertical spudcan displacements occur.

4.5.4 Dynamic responses

The wind, wave, and current loads on the jackup will in general contain steady and time-varying components at different frequencies and phases. For a lattice leg, the leg chords and braces are sufficiently small that the wave forces are drag-dominated, giving forces that are more complicated than a simple sinusoidal function. Consider a general

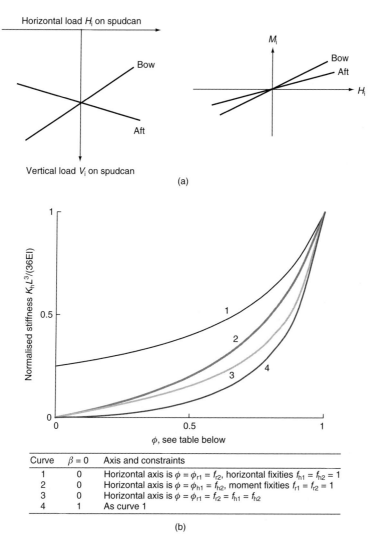

Fig. 4.12 Simplified stick model: some static analysis results. (a) Loadpaths. (b) Stiffness and fixities

wave spectrum expressed in the form

$$F = \int_{\omega=0}^{\infty} F_0 \sin(\omega t + \eta)\, d\omega \qquad (4.15)$$

where the Fourier amplitude F_0 is a function of the circular frequency ω, the phase η is also a function of ω, and the wave period $T = \omega/2\pi$. Equation (4.15) can also be expressed using complex coefficients in

Fourier analysis (e.g. Kreysig, 1999). Providing that the relevant dynamic constants are independent of the circular frequency, the lateral hull deflections y are given by

$$y = \int_{\omega=0}^{\infty} \frac{A'F_0}{K_h} \sin(\omega t + \eta - \varepsilon) \, d\omega \qquad (4.16)$$

where K_h is a measure of stiffness that depends on the foundation and hull stiffnesses, A' is an amplification factor, and ε is a phase lag. A' and ε depend on the ratio of the imposed frequency of loading to the resonant frequency of the jackup, and on the structural damping and foundation damping.

A large jackup will typically have a resonant period of the order of 6 seconds or so if the foundation fixities ϕ_r and ϕ_h are high, increasing to two or more times that value if the foundation fixities are smaller. A typical large wave has a period of 12–18 seconds. Hence, it is important to ensure that the foundation does not soften sufficiently to bring the jackup into resonance with the wave.

Figure 4.13a shows results for A' and the phase plotted against the ratio ω/ω_n of the applied frequency to the natural frequency of the stick model. Also shown is the phase lag of the hull displacement response behind the applied load. Because the vertical load is out of phase with the other two spudcan loads, the spudcan loadpaths are no longer straight lines, but ellipses. A measure $G(\omega)$ of the power spectral density for the displacements can be defined as

$$G(\omega) = \frac{1}{2} \left(\frac{A'F_0}{K_h} \right)^2 \qquad (4.17)$$

(e.g. Kramer, 1996). Figure 4.13b shows the form of the Fourier amplitude spectrum F_0 for a storm with energies focused around a circular frequency ω_s. Figure 4.13c shows the shape of the consequent power spectral density, calculated using the above equations. The first peak is due to the energy content of the storm, and the second to the resonant frequency of the jackup.

4.6   Bearing capacity and sliding checks

4.6.1   Introduction
The objective of a bearing capacity and sliding check is to verify that the loads experienced by the spudcans during the operational phase of the design life of the jackup will not exceed the capacity of the foundation to

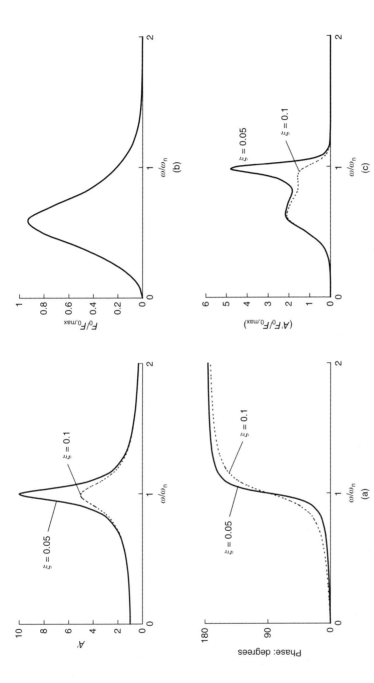

Fig. 4.13 Simplified stick model: some dynamic analysis results. (a) Amplitudes and phases. (b) Assumed Fourier amplitude spectrum for a storm. (c) Shapes of the power spectral density for hull displacements

support them, with an adequate margin of safety. In practice, checks are usually done for a range of soil conditions during the original jackup design. Additional checks for a site-specific assessment are done if the jackup fails the preload check for the site, or if there is some other reason to recheck. Examples would be if the environmental or soil conditions at a planned location fall outside of the range of conditions considered in the original design.

SNAME (2002) adopts the yield envelope formulation for the bearing capacity check. The location of the seabed reaction point is important in this formulation (see Section 4.6.2). Formulations for sand and clay are described in Section 4.6.3, and some applications are described subsequently. SNAME (2002) notes that additional considerations are required in the following cases:

- where there is deep penetration in silts or clays, and significant infill occurs during operations
- soils where the drained bearing capacity is less than the undrained bearing capacity
- where cyclic loading causes a reduction in strength over time
- where cyclic loading causes settlement in a situation where a punch-through potential exists
- where the foundation contains horizontal seams of weak soils.

4.6.2   Seabed reaction point

The seabed reaction point is the point on the spudcan where the vertical and horizontal force resultants and the spudcan moments are considered to be applied. For a flat spudcan that has not penetrated the seabed, one might guess that a suitable reaction point is at the centre of the flat bearing area. For a fully penetrated spudcan, some of the seabed reaction may come from the soil around the edges of the spudcan, and the seabed reaction point may be different. The choice is not arbitrary, as may be seen by the following calculation (Bell, 1991).

Consider two different candidate points for the seabed reaction point, P and Q in Figs 4.14a and 4.14b, separated by a height h. Let V_{iP}, H_{iP}, M_{iP} be the generalised foundation loads expressed as resultants at P, and let the corresponding resultants at Q be V_{iQ}, H_{iQ}, and M_{iQ}, respectively. If the two sets of resultants are to be equivalent, they must be in equilibrium, so

$$V_{iQ} = V_{iP} \tag{4.18a}$$

$$H_{iQ} = H_{iP} \tag{4.18b}$$

$$M_{iQ} = M_{iP} + hH_{iP} \tag{4.18c}$$

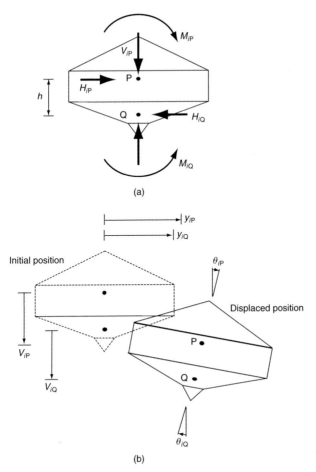

Fig. 4.14 Calculations for different selections P and Q for the seabed reaction point. (a) Equilibrium of force resultants. (b) Geometric relations for movements: spudcan assumed rigid

Consequently, the moments for the two reaction points are different. Moreover, these calculations have not accounted for the effects of displacements. If the structure between points P and Q is essentially rigid, then small displacements are related by

$$v_{iQ} = v_{iP} \tag{4.19a}$$

$$y_{iQ} = y_{iP} - h\theta_{iP} \tag{4.19b}$$

$$\theta_{iQ} = \theta_{iP} \tag{4.19c}$$

205

Assume that the diameter of the bearing area is B, and that the stiffness relations are given as follows at point A, where Δ denotes 'change of':

$$\begin{bmatrix} \Delta V_{iP} \\ H_{iP} \\ M_{iP}/B \end{bmatrix} = \begin{bmatrix} K_{1,iP} & 0 & 0 \\ 0 & K_{2,iP} & 0 \\ 0 & 0 & K_{ri,P} \end{bmatrix} \begin{bmatrix} v_{iP} \\ y_{iP} \\ B\theta_{iP} \end{bmatrix} \qquad (4.20)$$

where B has been introduced so as to make all components in the matrix have the same units, and $K_{ri,P} = K_{3,iP}/B^2$. Using the above relations to express the quantities at P in terms of the quantities at Q gives

$$\begin{bmatrix} \Delta V_{iQ} \\ H_{iQ} \\ M_{iQ}/B \end{bmatrix} = \begin{bmatrix} K_{1,iP} & 0 & 0 \\ 0 & K_{2,iP} & hK_{2,iP} \\ 0 & hK_{2,iP} & K_{ri,P} + (h/B)^2 K_{2,iP} \end{bmatrix} \begin{bmatrix} v_{iQ} \\ y_{iQ} \\ B\theta_{iQ} \end{bmatrix} \quad (4.21)$$

Thus, the stiffness matrix is different at Q, and has off-diagonal components there as well as on-diagonal ones. It also follows that equations for limiting loads can appear to be different depending on whether point P or point Q is used as the seabed reaction point.

Guidance on how to select an appropriate seabed reaction point does not yet appear to be available. It seems likely to be around the average level of the bearing area for a spudcan that is only embedded to a shallow depth.

4.6.3 Bearing capacity

The idea of using a yield envelope to describe the bearing capacity under combined loading was suggested by Roscoe and Schofield (1956), and was further developed by Ticof (1977), Butterfield and Ticof (1979), Tanaka (1984), and others. Osborne *et al.* (1991) show how a yield envelope can be developed from a conventional bearing capacity analysis.

For simplicity, consider a flat square footing of size B (Fig. 4.15a), subjected to a vertical load V, horizontal load H, and overturning moment M. The load reference point is taken at the middle of the flat circular base in contact with the soil. The load inclination is $\beta = \tan^{-1}(H/V)$. The load eccentricity is $e = M/V$. As is well known, the applied loads may be equilibrated by uniform vertical and shear reaction stresses from the soil over a width B', and this can be represented by the equivalent loads in Fig. 4.15b, where the equivalent foundation width $B' = B - 2e$. The equivalent footing now serves as a

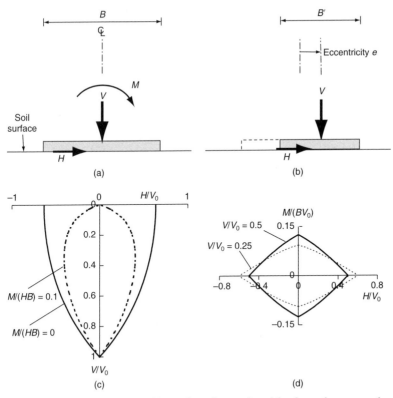

Fig. 4.15 Calculation for a yield envelope for combined loading of a square foot-ing on clay. (a) Actual loads for actual foundation of width B. (b) Equivalent loads for an equivalent foundation of width B'. (c) Yield envelope: elevation view. (d) Yield envelope: cross-sections at constant V/V_0

rectangular footing of width B' and length L. If the footing is on a uniform clay of undrained shear strength s_u, the ultimate vertical load V_{ult} is obtained from the general bearing capacity equation:

$$V_{ult} = B'Lq_{ult} = B'LN_cF_{cs}F_{cd}F_{cq}F_{ci}s_u \tag{4.22}$$

where N_c is the bearing capacity factor for cohesion, F_{cx} are modifying factors, and F_{ci} is the modifying factor for load inclination. Using Meyerhof's (1963) inclination factor $F_{ci} = 1 - \beta/90°$ gives

$$V_{ult} = V_0\left(1 - \frac{2M}{VB}\right)\left[1 - \frac{2}{\pi}\tan^{-1}\left(\frac{H}{V}\right)\right] \tag{4.23}$$

$$V_0 = BLN_cF_{cs}F_{cd}F_{cq}s_u \tag{4.24}$$

207

For any given value of V_0, equation (4.23) can be used to construct a surface in $\{V, H, M/B\}$ loadspace. The surface is sketched in Figs 4.15c and 4.15d. It is a limiting load envelope according to bearing capacity theory. In other words, it identifies the load combinations where large settlements or other deformations may be expected to start to occur. V_0 is the bearing capacity when $H = 0$ and $M = 0$. It is analogous to the preload for a jackup spudcan.

Similar calculations can be done for a circular spudcan, and for sand foundations, and for any embedment (e.g. Cassidy, 1999). The load inclination factors for self-weight loading on sand are different from the factors for the cohesion and surcharge terms in the bearing capacity equation, and the algebra becomes complicated. SNAME (2002) took the view that, given the inaccuracies involved anyway, a simple expression for the yield envelope would be adequate. Using the notation herein, its equation for a circular conical spudcan on sand can be expressed as

$$R_i^2 = \left(\frac{H_i}{H_{i0}}\right)^2 + \left(\frac{M_i}{M_{i0}}\right)^2 = 16\left(\frac{V_i}{V_{i0}}\right)^2 \left(1 - \frac{V_i}{V_{i0}}\right)^2 \tag{4.25}$$

where H_{i0} and M_{i0} are described below. Figures 4.16a and 4.16b show the shape of the yield envelope. It is sometimes described as a cigar-shaped surface. It is rotationally symmetric about the vertical load axis if the other axes are normalised by H_{i0} and M_{i0}. It has zero width at the preload point $V_i = V_{i0}$, and when the vertical load is zero, implying that no shear or moment load can be supported for those two conditions. H_{i0} is the magnitude of the largest horizontal load that can be supported, and occurs when $M_i = 0$ and V_i is half the preload. M_{i0} is the magnitude of the largest moment that can be supported, and occurs when $H_i = 0$ and V_i is half of the preload.

SNAME (2002) specifies $H_{i0} = 0.12V_{i0}$ and $M_{i0}/B = 0.075V_{i0}$ for a spudcan on siliceous sand. A possible issue is that these factors take no account of the friction angle or other properties of the sand, such as the relative density, silt content, compressibility, or other constitutive properties. The maximum horizontal load ratio H/V occurs at $V = 0$, and is $4H_0/V_0$, corresponding to a maximum load inclination of $\tan^{-1}(0.48) \approx 25.6°$. For sands with a spudcan–soil friction angle δ' less than this, an additional sliding limit $|H/V| < \tan\delta'$ might sensibly be applied, but perhaps depending on cone angle as well as embedment.

For spudcans on clay, the part of SNAME's (2002) envelope with $V_i/V_{i0} < 1/2$ is replaced by an expression that can take account of possible pull-out capacity for a spudcan embedded in clay soil.

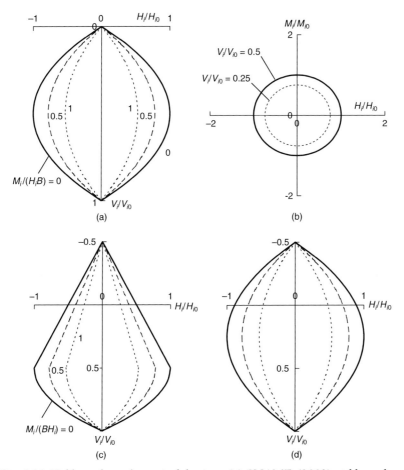

Fig. 4.16 Yield envelopes for conical footings. (a) SNAME (2002) yield envelope for sand: elevation view. (b) SNAME (2002) yield envelope for sand: cross-sections at constant V/V_0. (c) SNAME (2002) yield envelope for soft clay with reliable suction: elevation view. (d) Alternative yield envelope for clay with tension capacity $V_{it} = 0.5V_{i0}$: elevation view (after Murff, 1994)

Figure 4.16c shows the result for soft clay if the suction capacity is considered to be reliable. Martin (1994), Cassidy (1999), and others use expressions for the yield envelope shape that include factors that might conceivably be related to constitutive properties. One way to account for tension capacity for a deeply buried spudcan is to alter equation (4.25) to

$$\left(\frac{H_i}{H_{i0}}\right)^2 + \left(\frac{M_i}{M_{i0}}\right)^2 = 16\left(\frac{V_i + V_{it}}{V_{i0} + V_{it}}\right)^2\left(1 - \frac{V_i + V_{it}}{V_{i0} + V_{it}}\right)^2 \qquad (4.26)$$

209

where V_{it} is the magnitude of the foundation resistance to vertical uplift loading (Murff, 1994). Figure 4.16d shows this for a tension capacity equal to one-half of the compression capacity.

Because the size of the yield envelope depends on the penetration of the spudcan into the seabed, plasticity models can be developed that allow for these penetrations. Examples of such models are given by Schotman (1989), Nova and Montrasio (1991), Dean *et al.* (1997a,b), Van Langen *et al.* (1999), Martin and Houlsby (2001), Cassidy *et al.* (2004b), Bienen *et al.* (2006), and others.

4.6.4 Evidence for a yield envelope

Results of centrifuge model tests on footings and jackup models have been reported by Shi (1988), Tan (1990), Osborne *et al.* (1991), Murff *et al.* (1991, 1992), Kusakabe *et al.* (1991), Dean *et al.* (1993, 1995, 1997a,b, 1998), Wong *et al.* (1993), Tsukamoto (1994), Hsu (1998), Stewart *et al.* (1998), Ng and Lee (2002), Hossain *et al.* (2003), Cassidy *et al.* (2004a,b), Cassidy (2007), White *et al.* (2008), and others. Results of single-gravity, laboratory floor tests on model footings have been reported by Ticof (1977), Georgiadis and Butterfield (1988), Nova and Montrasio (1991), Martin (1994), Butterfield and Gottardi (1994), Gottardi *et al.* (1999), Martin and Houlsby (2000), Byrne and Houlsby (2001), Vlahos *et al.* (2005), Bienen *et al.* (2006), and others.

Figure 4.17a shows the results for a flat footing on sand (Butterfield and Gottardi, 1994). The horizontal load at yield, normalised by the maximum vertical load previously applied to the footing, is plotted versus the normalised moment load M/B, also normalised by the maximum vertical load. The data presentation uses an opposite sign convention for moments. The data show that the yield envelope in this view has a 'negative' eccentricity. A possible explanation is as follows. A horizontal load H at the level of the spudcan base will induce changes in the vertical stress in the soil at some depth below the level of the load. These vertical stresses will add to the vertical stresses due to a positive moment, but subtract from those due to a negative moment. It seems arguable, therefore, that yield will begin in the foundation soil at a lower value of moment if the moment is acting with the horizontal load as opposed to against it.

The result is important, because it suggests that the assumption of a yield envelope that is symmetric about the horizontal load and moment axes may be unconservative. However, Martin (1994) found that the

210

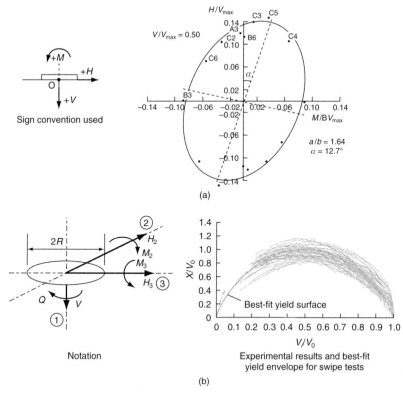

Fig. 4.17 *Experimental support for yield envelopes in first loading. (a) Results for a footing on sand (Butterfield and Gottardi, 1994). (b) Results for 6D loading of footing on sand (Bienen et al., 2006)*

opposite inclination applied for a yield envelope measured in tests on a conical spudcan.

Tan (1990) argued that, if a spudcan is dragged or 'swiped' across the seabed at a constant vertical position, the loads experienced by the spudcan would follow a path in loadspace that closely resembled the yield envelope. Figure 4.17b shows some results of 'swipe' tests by Bienen *et al.* (2006). These tests are believed to be the first to thoroughly explore multi-axial spudcan loading. They are important because jackups are subject to environmental loads from all directions, producing spudcan loadpaths that are more complex than is considered by the three-dimensional {V, H, M/B} loadspace. The results confirmed that the yield envelope concept is valid for first loading under these more complex conditions. The possible significance of torsional loading was identified, and is a subject of ongoing research.

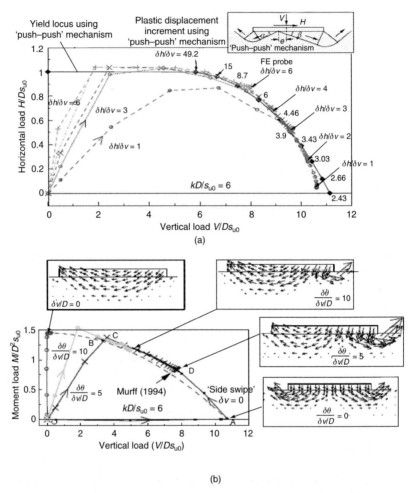

Fig. 4.18 *Numerical results for strip footings on clays (Bransby and Randolph, 1997). (a) Yield envelope and displacement mechanisms under V, H loading. (b) Yield envelope and displacement mechanisms under V, M loading*

Finite element analysis is also a valid way of exploring a concept such as the yield envelope, provided that a constitutive model is used that includes the yield behaviour for soil elements. Figure 4.18 shows finite element results by Bransby and Randolph (1997) for the yield envelope and associated displacement mechanisms for a two-dimensional footing on clay. The results show a clear relationship between the failure mode and position on the yield envelope. Further finite element results are presented by Templeton (2006), Gourvenec (2007a; 2007b), and others.

212

4.6.5   Effects of cyclic loading

Under cyclic loading, soil mechanics theory leads to an expectation of at least three behaviours. First, settlements would be expected to accumulate over many cycles. Second, excess pore pressures might be expected to develop in the soil as a result of the cyclic stresses induced by the loads, and these would be expected to dissipate in accordance with the theory of consolidation. If they are large enough, liquefaction or fluidisation of the soil may follow. Third, simple elastic–plastic load–displacement relations would be expected to be replaced by relations involving cyclic hysteresis.

Figure 4.19a shows results by Dean *et al.* (1995) for centrifuge model tests of a skirted spudcan on sand. Viscous oil was used as the model pore fluid, so as to correctly scale pore pressure generation and dissipation rates. Pore pressures were measured at several places in the sand. Results showed rather complex cyclic pore pressure responses that were different under the bow and aft spudcans.

Figure 4.19b shows data by Dean *et al.* (1998) for centrifuge tests of cyclic loading of a three-legged jackup model on clay. The time records show that a steady increase in settlement occurred at all three spudcans. Ng and Lee (2002) found that cumulative settlements also occurred in tests of a footing on dry sand (Fig. 4.19c). This showed that settlements are not wholly associated with pore pressure generation.

Figure 4.19d shows data by Dean *et al.* (1998) of the cyclic loading responses of a spudcan footing of a model jackup platform on clay. Three cycles are shown, of increasing amplitude. The data are complicated by zero offsets – caused by loads that have been locked-in to the jackup structure due to previous cycling and slip, and by digitisation effects in the data acquisition system. The results show the familiar cyclic loading response of a stable but inelastic system. Vlahos *et al.* (2005) interpreted clay responses in terms of Masing's (1926) rule, and developed a theoretical hyper-plasticity.

4.6.6   Stiffness and stiffness degradation

If the seabed reaction point is chosen such that the stiffness matrix is indeed diagonal, then application of the equations requires a knowledge of the soil shear modulus G and Poisson's ratio μ. Poisson's ratio is usually taken as 0.5 for an undrained analysis. The value in drained analysis can depend on the cyclic strain amplitude. A typical value for small strains is around 0.1–0.2 (Bienen *et al.*, 2007). The shear modulus also depends on the strain amplitude. Its values may be measured in

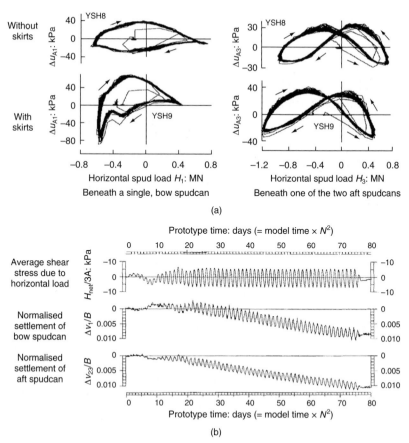

Fig. 4.19 *Some effects of cyclic loading. (a) Pore pressure responses about one-half of one spudcan diameter beneath the centrelines of skirted and non-skirted spudcans on sand (Dean et al., 1995). (b) Settlement responses for a spudcan on clay (Dean et al., 1998). (c) Cumulative settlements for models of 10 m diameter spudcans on dry dense sand (Ng and Lee, 2002). (d) Cyclic loading results for cyclic loading of a spudcan foundation of a model jackup on clay (Dean et al., 1998)*

laboratory tests such as the resonant column test, triaxial test, or simple shear test.

SNAME (2002) gives formulae for the shear modulus that may be dropped from the upcoming standard ISO 19905. The original equations for sand were based on preliminary analyses of centrifuge model test data. However, Wong *et al.* (1993) analysed more centrifuge data, and obtained much larger soil moduli. Field monitoring programmes gave values up to seven times higher than SNAME's

214

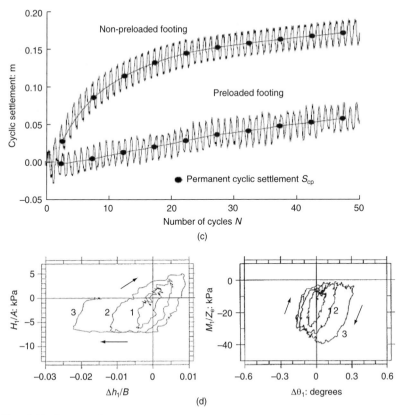

Fig. 4.19 Continued

values (e.g. Springett *et al.*, 1994, 1996; Morandi *et al.*, 1998; Temperton *et al.*, 1999; Nelson *et al.*, 2000, 2001; Nataraja *et al.*, 2003).

Cassidy *et al.* (2002a) analysed field data from three large jackups at eight locations in the North Sea. Significant wave heights during monitoring were in the range 4.1–9.85 m, with mean crossing periods of about 6.8–9 seconds. Based on the results, the small strain shear modulus for clay was considered in terms of the definition of the dimensionless rigidity index $I_r = G/s_u$, where s_u is the undrained shear strength at a depth of 0.15 spudcan diameter below the first level of maximum diameter above the spudcan tip. I_r is the inverse of the strain that would occur at shear failure if the soil retained its initial shear modulus throughout the loading process. Values of I_r of between 300 and 600 fitted the data at the three clay locations. Cassidy *et al.* (2002a) proposed an updated formula: $I_r = 600/\text{OCR}^{0.25}$. For sands, the small strain shear modulus was proposed as $G = g\sqrt{\gamma' B p_a}$, where

215

g is a dimensionless factor, p_a is atmospheric pressure, B is the maximum embedded spudcan diameter (which can be smaller than the maximum diameter), and γ' is the submerged unit weight. Values of g of between 300 and 400 were found at two locations with confidence. A value as high as 2000 was inferred from the data from one site, but there was uncertainty there. Cassidy *et al.* (2004b) proposed $g = 230$ $[0.9 + (RD/50)]$ where RD is the in-situ relative density of the sand as a percentage.

For more severe loading, the secant shear modulus reduces significantly. To address this in the context of the yield envelope, SNAME (2002) proposes that the shear modulus depends on the relation between the load state and the yield envelope. The approach is explained by Templeton (2007), and explored in detail by Dean and Metters (2009).

4.7   Mat-supported jackups

4.7.1   *General aspects*

Mat-supported jackups (see Fig. 4.1b) use a steel mat foundation to achieve low foundation bearing pressures. They are particularly suited to the many soft clay sites in the Mississippi delta, but are also used on sandy sites and worldwide. Typically, the mat is constructed from beams, plates, and box sections, and has a central cut-out, producing an A-shaped foundation. Its overall plan dimensions may be larger than the deck that it supports.

Specific geotechnical aspects of mat foundations are reviewed by Hirst *et al.* (1976), Young *et al.* (1981), Cox *et al.* (1990), and others, and include:

- site investigation issues
- bearing capacity and settlement on set down
- bearing capacity and horizontal sliding capacity during operations
- overturning stability
- cyclic loading effects
- clay consolidation and creep
- seafloor instability.

A typical maximum foundation bearing pressure during preloading is of the order of 30 kPa, which is about 10–20 times smaller than for an independent-legged jackup.

Turner *et al.* (1987) state that the most important soils data come from the upper 6 m or so of the seabed. Mats can be used on seabeds where the undrained shear strength at the seafloor is less than 2 kPa.

216

Precise identification of the level of the seafloor can sometimes be difficult, and the use of a seabed frame during the site investigation can render data in this soft material unreliable. Because the mat is wide but not high, lateral soil variability can be important. An uneven, hard seabed can produce concentrated pressures with the potential to overstress the mat locally.

A mat-supported jackup is subject to potential sliding, bearing, and overturning failures. Wave loading effects on the mat must be taken into account. Because of the width of the mat, modes similar to those for gravity platforms are also considered (see Chapter 7).

4.7.2   Case history

Stewart (2007) and Ooley and Stewart (2008) describe the Maleo Producer jackup (Fig. 4.20a). The unit that has been converted from drilling to production operations, and used at a clay site, offshore Indonesia, in a water depth of 57 m. The deck is supported by three tubular pipe legs, each of 12 feet (3.66 m) outside diameter and with wall thicknesses varying between 1.75 and 3 inches (38 and 75 mm). The mat is a steel box structure, 3.05 m thick, with multiple internal compartments, and with skirts of height 2 feet (0.6 m).

Soil conditions at the site are described by Audibert *et al.* (2008). The initial site investigation included one 100 m deep sampling boring, one 100 m-deep piezocone cone penetration test (PCPT) hole, four 20 m-deep PCPT holes, and associated laboratory testing. A problem arose during installation, and the classification society required further data. A second site investigation was carried out to obtain soil samples, and CPT and T-bar data particularly in the zone up to 18 m around the edge of the mat. The upper stratum consisted of clay with an undrained shear strength increasing from 2 kPa at the seafloor, linearly increasing at 1.22 kPa/m to a depth of about 14 m, where a slightly stronger clay was encountered.

For purposes of preload calculations, the mat was considered to consist of several strip footings. The unit experienced a tilt of about 2.5° during preloading, occurring in a period of about 10 seconds, producing a differential settlement of about 3 m between the bow and stern parts of the mat. The tilt was corrected by shifting weight over a period of about 45 minutes. The final average penetration was about 2.7 m. Soil heave around the edge of the mat was about 1.3 m at the edges of the mat, and the heave mound extended about 13 m from the edge of the mat.

(a)

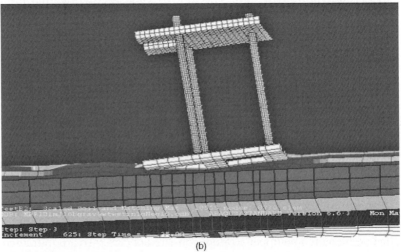

(b)

Fig. 4.20 Aspects of the geotechnical analyses for the Maleo Producer (© 2008 Offshore Technlogy Conference: Templeton, 2008). (a) Meleo Producer mat-supported jackup. (b) Geotechnical earthquake finite element analysis, deformations magnified 40 times, computed for an earthquake 10 times more severe than the design earthquake

Murff and Young (2008) describe the analysis of overturing stability. The critical loading direction was at 90° to the axis of symmetry of the mat. The mat was considered to consist of independent strip footings that would induce vertical and horizontal soil reactions. The uplift capacity was considered to be zero. The connections to the legs were

218

considered to be pinned. The analysis started by assuming the position of an axis of rotation during overturning. The position was then varied to determine the position that gave the lowest moment resistance of the foundation.

Seismic design criteria are described by Nissar (2008), and the analysis is described by Templeton (2008) for the foundations, and by Jacob and Stewart (2008) for the structure. The finite element model for the soil consisted of a disk about 50 m deep and 800 m wide, with nine soil layers. Figure 4.20b shows the deformed mesh for an analysis for an earthquake 10 times more severe than one of several design earthquakes. The deformations are magnified by 40 in this plot, producing an impression of severe tilt and heave of the seabed. Soil strains have reached 10% in parts of the foundation. Much smaller values were obtained for the design earthquakes, and the Maleo Producer met SLE (strength level earthquake) and DLE (ductility level earthquake) requirements with adequate margins.

4.8   Site departure

At the end of the deployment of an independent-legged jackup, the jackup legs are lifted out of the seabed, and the jackup is moved to another location. The main geotechnical issues are:

- *Leg extraction forces and times*. During operations at a location where the foundation consists of clay, the clay will have experienced consolidation. As a result, its strength may have increased. The pull-out or break-out force needed to extract a spudcan foundation from a deep penetration may be larger than the force needed to insert the spudcan to that depth in the first place.

    Data for pull-out and calculations for footings in clay are described by Vesic (1971), Dean *et al.* (1998), Cassidy and Byrne (2001), Purwana *et al.* (2005a,b), Lehane *et al.* (2008), Zhou *et al.* (2009), and others.

    Jetting can be tried in order to release a spudcan from the surrounding clay, but this tends to damage the soil to the extent that a subsequent deployment of a different jackup at the location may become impossible. Instances have occurred where jackups have been stuck for several months before the soil releases the spudcans.

- *Effect on nearby piled foundations*. As the spudcans come out of the seabed, soil flows around them in the opposite direction to that during installation. This motion can damage the piles, or the conductors of an adjacent fixed platform, either immediately or in terms of reducing the ultimate pile capacity.

Some similar issues can arise for mat-supported units. Also, if the mat has settled beyond its vertical thickness, surrounding soil may have flowed onto its upper surface, adding to the uplift resistance. Jetting would be expected to be an effective remedial action.

5

Jacket platforms

Jacket platforms are the most common type of offshore structure in the offshore hydrocarbons industry. Chapter 5 covers the principal geotechnical issues for these structures, and how to approach calculations for mudmat capacity, pile drivability, ultimate axial and lateral pile capacity, axial and lateral pile performance, and cyclic and group effects.

5.1   Introduction

5.1.1   Jacket platforms

Figure 5.1 shows typical features of a piled jacket platform. The jacket consists of an open-framed steel structure made of tubular leg chords, horizontal bracing, and diagonal bracing. It supports a deck and topside modules, usually including a helideck for access, and a drilling rig. Larger jackets may include accommodation and office modules. For some locations, two or more jackets may be used, one for drilling and production, and another for accommodation.

Stability against lateral loading is normally provided by piles driven into the seabed. The piles may pass through leg chords, or through external pile sleeves. A jacket is sometimes called a 'template' because it acts as the template for the piles. Exceptionally, the Europipe 16/11-E jacket used suction caissons instead of piles (Tjelta, 1994, 1995).

A jacket may support steel conductor pipes which pass down into the seabed and act as a conduit for oil and gas from the reservoir several kilometres below or laterally. The hydrocarbons are processed and then pumped along an export pipeline to another destination. Some jackets are used simply as pumping stations along a pipeline.

5.1.2   Construction and installation

Descriptions of the installation of jacket structures are given by Bærheim et al. (1990), Harris and Stone (1990), Palmer et al. (1990),

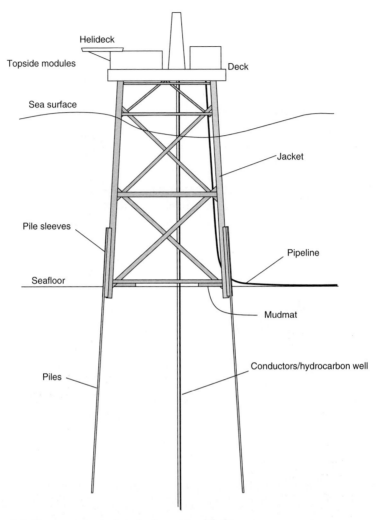

Fig. 5.1 Features of a jacket platform (simplified)

Serpas *et al.* (1990), White and Drake (1994), Sims *et al.* (2004), and others.

Figure 5.2 illustrates the principal operations. The jacket is constructed in a dry area in a coastal construction yard. The jacket is then skidded onto a barge for transport to the offshore location. On arrival, the jacket is skidded off the barge and into the sea, where it rights itself under the control of temporary buoyancy tanks. It is then pulled into position, the buoyancy tanks are flooded, and the jacket settles onto the seafloor.

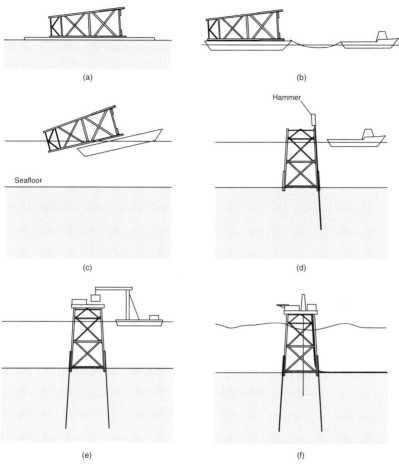

Fig. 5.2 Construction and installation of a large jacket. (a) Fabrication onshore. (b) Transport to an offshore location. (c) Upending. (d) Pile installation. (e) Assembly of the deck and topsides. (f) Pipeline attached: drilling hydrocarbon wells

Variations on this theme are also common. The jacket may be constructed on a barge in the dry yard; the yard is then flooded and the jacket is transported to its final offshore location. A smaller jacket may be lifted onto a barge, transported to its final offshore location, and lifted off and placed on the seafloor by crane.

Immediately after set-down, the jacket is supported temporarily by mudmats, which are essentially flat plates attached to legs or the lower braces. For some jackets, the lower bracing bears on the seafloor and provides some support. Jacket leg extensions protruding into the seafloor can also provide temporary on-bottom support.

The seabed will have been surveyed for debris and cleared, and may have been levelled by shallow dredging. Even so, the jacket may not set down level. Ballasting or jacking systems are used to bring it level. Ballasting redistributes the self-weight of the jacket, inducing the required differential settlements at different mudmats. If necessary, piles may first be driven a short distance into the seabed (Kitney and Penman, 2008). Levelling cannot normally be done after piling is completed because it can then cause high stress to be locked into the steel frame structure.

The piles are then driven either through the leg chords or through external pile sleeves. The order in which piles are driven at different legs may need to be planned so as to avoid excessive differential settlement. The driven piles are shimmed and grouted into the chords or sleeves to provide a shear connection between the jacket and the pile.

The deck is lifted onto the top of the jacket and fixed in place. The topside modules are then lifted onto the deck and fixed in place, by welding or bolts. A pipeline is attached. Everything is checked and tested, and the platform is then ready for operations.

5.1.3 Design life and environmental loads

The design life of a jacket depends primarily on its function and the time required to extract all extractable hydrocarbons. Typical design lives are in the region of 20 years, but shorter or longer lives are also common.

The design of a jacket is often centred on a structural engineering analysis that uses information and calculations from other specialists, including geotechnical engineers, hydrodynamic engineers, corrosion engineers, fatigue engineers, and seismic engineers. The design typically proceeds iteratively. This is particular so for geotechnical aspects, because many soil properties depend on load magnitudes and the loading history; the properties will affect the structural analysis results, and those results will normally affect the geotechnical properties. Several iterations may be needed to converge.

The principal environmental loads during the design life are due to wind, waves, and currents. Ice forces may be dominant in some locations (Blenkarn, 1970). Extreme and operating loads are typically calculated by meteorological and oceanographic (metocean) or hydrodynamic engineers, based on statistical metocean data for the location or region (Chakrabarti, 2003). Wind loads occur above sea level, and wave and current loads occur primarily in the upper part of the water column. Consequently, these loads create significant overturning

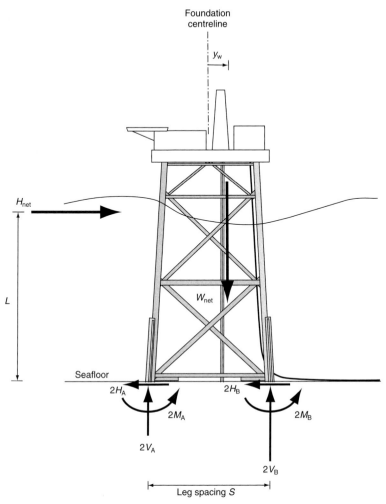

Fig. 5.3 Analysis of foundation loads for a four-legged jacket (simplified)

moments on the jacket, which are resisted by differential changes in the vertical loads on the piles. Earthquake loading may be significant in seismically active areas, including the Gulf of Mexico and many other offshore regions (Kramer, 1996). Accidental loading can come from boat impacts, dropped objects, and other accidents (Foss and Edvardsen, 1982; Gidwani and Renault, 1990; Ronalds, 2001).

Calculations of foundation loads will normally be done as part of the structural analysis. Figure 5.3 shows a simplified analysis for a four-legged jacket. The platform is seen end-on, and there are two legs on

225

the left and two on the right. The net horizontal load H_{net} is due to the wind, wave, and current load, and is time-varying. The net vertical load W_{net} is due to the buoyant weight of the structure, the weight of the equipment it supports, and vertical components of the wind, wave, and current load. The loads act at lever arms L and y_w, which are also time-varying. The foundations on the left react with the vertical reaction V_A, the horizontal reaction H_A, and the moment M_A. Those on the right react with V_B, H_B, and M_B. Ignoring dynamic effects, the vertical and horizontal equilibria give

$$W_{net} = 2V_A + 2V_B \tag{5.1}$$

$$H_{net} = 2H_A + 2H_B \tag{5.2}$$

Taking moments about the intersection of the centreline with the seafloor gives

$$W_{net}\,y_w + H_{net}L = 2M_A + 2M_B + (V_B - V_A)S \tag{5.3}$$

where S is the leg spacing at the seafloor. If the simplistic assumption is made that $H_A = H_B$ and $M_A = M_B = M$, say, the equations can be solved to give

$$V_A = \frac{W_{net}}{4}\left(1 - \frac{2y_w}{S}\right) - \left(\frac{H_{net}L - 4M}{2S}\right) \tag{5.4}$$

$$V_B = \frac{W_{net}}{4}\left(1 + \frac{2y_w}{S}\right) + \left(\frac{H_{net}L - 4M}{2S}\right) \tag{5.5}$$

and $H_A = H_B = H_{net}/4$. This shows that the horizontal loads cause changes in the vertical load on the piles, as well as lateral pile loads. In general, the moments M_A and M_B will be quite small in comparison with $H_{net}L$. The assumptions $H_A = H_B$ and $M_A = M_B$ are not normally correct because the foundation stiffnesses may depend on the magnitudes of the loads, which are different for the A and B loads. However, the above equations are reasonable first approximations.

5.1.4 Special hazards
Figure 5.4a illustrates the scour hazard for jacket platforms. Water movements over the seabed can cause cohesionless or very soft cohesive material there to be scoured away over time, particularly in association with high currents and with storm waves (Niedoroda *et al.*, 1981; Hoffmans and Verheij, 1997; Soulsby, 1998; Whitehouse, 1998). Global scour, occurs over the whole foundation footprint. It reduces the effective

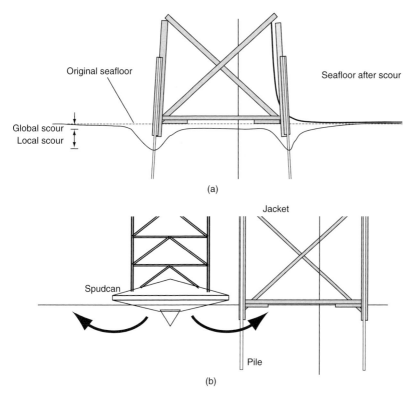

Fig. 5.4 *Special hazards for jackets. (a) Global and local scour (Soulsby, 1998; Whitehouse, 1998). (b) Soil pushed past piles during jackup deployment close by. (c) Seafloor instability, due to a sloping site or flowslide/debris flow/turbidity current. (d) Shallow gas and hydrocarbon drilling operations*

stresses in the soil, and this is accounted for in foundation design. Added to this, local scour develops in the immediate vicinity of objects that protrude from the seabed, including piles. Scour protection can be achieved by graded rock dumping, concrete mats, or other devices.

Figure 5.4b illustrates one of the hazards if a jackup platform is installed close to the platform. This is done, for example, to allow the jackup to extend a drilling rig over a small jacket and use it to drill wells into the seafloor, through a template on the jacket. Installation and removal of the jackup may cause significant soil movements past the jacket piles, changing the lateral stress conditions and, potentially, breaking piles (Mirza *et al.*, 1988; Siciliano *et al.*, 1990; Tan *et al.*, 2006).

Figure 5.4c illustrates hazards from seafloor instability. A jacket may sometimes be placed on or near a slope, giving rise to the possibility that the slope may fail. The failure may take place at the location of the

227

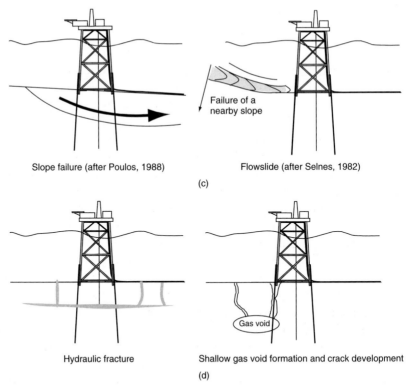

Slope failure (after Poulos, 1988) Flowslide (after Selnes, 1982)

(c)

Hydraulic fracture Shallow gas void formation and crack development

(d)

Fig. 5.4 Continued

jacket, or nearby. If the soil at the seabed and for a short depth below is very soft, it can be feasible to design a jacket to withstand significant lateral movements of that soil. The geotechnical task is to predict the lateral loads applied by the soil to the piles.

Figure 5.4d shows two foundation integrity hazards. The conductor pipes extend only a certain distance below the seabed. Below that depth, the hydrocarbon well is normally uncased. High fluid pressures may be used in the well drilling operation. This can potentially cause hydraulic fracture, reducing the structural integrity of the foundation soil mass (e.g. Schotman and Hospers, 1992; Andersen and Lunne, 1994). Additional hazards from drilling operations include vibrations that can cause cyclic settlements, particularly in silts.

Other hazards include shallow gas and gas hydrates. If there is gas in the soil, heat from recovered hydrocarbons, and other effects, can result in gas movements that can collect in large voids in the foundation, or collect around piles and move upwards, reducing the lateral and vertical pile capacity.

5.2   Temporary on-bottom support during installation

5.2.1   *Structural arrangements*

The total ultimate vertical resistance from the seafloor immediately after set-down is the sum of soil resistances from jacket leg extensions, mudmats, and any lower bracing that may be bearing on the seafloor. Some elements on the platform may not tolerate large differences between design and installed levels, such as boat landings. It is, therefore, important to estimate this resistance well, and to know whether an estimate is lower-bound, best-middle, or upper-bound.

A mudmat is essentially a flat stiffened plate that bears directly on the seabed and supports the jacket during piling (Fig. 5.5). Triangular, square, rectangular, and even circular shapes may be considered. Mudmats may be installed at the level of the lowest horizontal bracing, so that the bracing also rests on the seabed and provides some bearing capacity. Or they may be installed below this, possibly with jacks between the mudmat and the lower bracing, for platform levelling. Mudmats may be fitted with short skirts to better resist lateral forces and to improve the bearing capacity on soft soils (Digre *et al.*, 1989; Lieng and Bjørgen, 1995).

Jacket leg extensions are the parts of a jacket leg that extend below the lowest level of bracing, typically by about 1–3 m (Helfrich *et al.*, 1980). They act as the lower part of the structural joint between the leg chord and horizontal and inclined bracing. They can provide useful components of temporary bearing capacity, but can also prevent a jacket from seating properly, if the near-mudline soil is dense sand or hardpan. Jacket leg extensions up to 10 m or so in length can also be useful as long-term foundation elements, if the near-surface sediments are soft clays.

5.2.2   *Geotechnical calculations: mudmats*

For preliminary design, the geotechnical engineer will need to provide curves of ultimate mudmat capacity versus mudmat dimension, for various penetrations into the seabed. Several graphs may be needed, for different mudmat shapes and also to account for expected lateral loading during piling. The platform designer will use these curves, together with other considerations, to select the mudmat dimensions (Stockard, 1981).

For a seabed consisting of uniform soil to a depth equal to or greater than the largest envisioned lateral dimension of the mudmats, simple shallow foundation bearing capacity calculations may be all that is

229

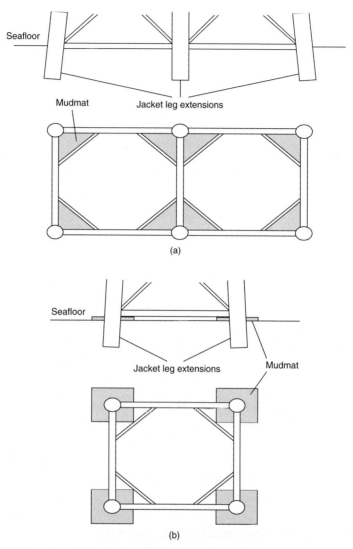

Fig. 5.5 Examples of elevation and plan views for mudmats and jacket leg extensions. (a) Triangular mudmats at the level of the lower braces on a two-bay jacket. (b) Square mudmats fitted below the lowest bracing on a single-bay jacket

needed. In this case, the mudmat capacity Q under pure vertical load can be calculated using the familiar bearing capacity equation:

for clays: $\quad Q = A\{s_u N_c F_{cs} F_{cd} + \gamma' z [-\gamma' z]\}$ \hfill (5.6)

for sands: $\quad Q = A\{\frac{1}{2}\gamma' B N_\gamma F_{\gamma s} F_{\gamma d} + \gamma' z N_q F_{qs} F_{qd} [-\gamma' z]\}$ \hfill (5.7) where A is the mudmat bearing area, s_u is the undrained shear strength for clays, z is the mudmat penetration below the mudline, and the other symbols are familiar from the general bearing capacity equation (see Chapter 4). The term $-\gamma' z$ represents an effect of soil flowing onto the top of the mudmat. Helfrich *et al.* (1980) include this term as part of the N_q component for calculations on granular soils. It should be considered if backflow may occur during the period of temporary support.

For right-angled triangular mudmats, Helfrich *et al.* (1980) recommend shape factors calculated for the following equivalent foundations (Fig. 5.6a):

- for clay (undrained) soils, calculate L/B using L as the length of the hypotenuse and B as the least altitude, e.g. $B/L = 0.5$ for a 90°/45°/45° triangle
- for granular (drained) soils, consider the triangle as equivalent to a circle of equal area, so $B/L = 1$.

For layered soil profiles, it is normal to adapt the bearing capacity calculations used for jackups, replacing the aforementioned shape factors with shape factors for the shape of mudmat being considered.

Figure 5.6b shows an example of a design chart of ultimate vertical mudmat capacity versus mudmat breadth, for various mudmat embedments into the seabed. If the period of temporary support is long enough to include significant risk of storms, the effect of lateral loading on the mudmat capacity will also need to be considered. From the chart, the structural designer can select a mudmat size and design penetration. For instance, in Fig. 5.6b, if the factored structural load is 8 MN, the designer has the choice of installing mudmats of breadth 7.6 m, which will penetrate 4 m into the seabed, or mats of breadth 9 m, which will not penetrate, or some breadth between these.

5.2.3   Geotechnical calculations: jacket leg extensions

Figure 5.7 shows the soil movements around a jacket leg extension when it is pushed into the seabed, and the consequent soil resistances. When the extension penetrates the soil vertically, some soil is pushed upwards in a passive wedge. Some soil falls or forms an active wedge. Deeper soil moves around the extension as the extension pushes through. The movements give rise to a complicated set of resisting forces, estimates for which can be made:

231

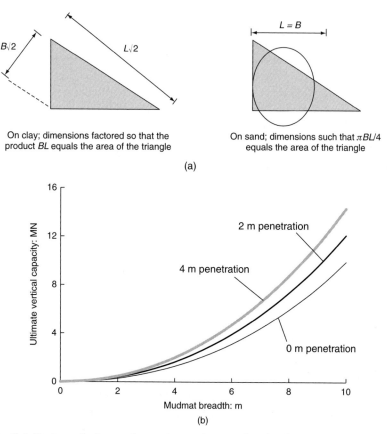

Fig. 5.6 *Design calculations for mudmats. (a) L and B for shape factors: mudmat plan view (based on Helfrich et al., 1980). (b) Example of a site-specific design chart for size selection*

- using ultimate axial pile capacity calculations for the shaft friction resistance Q_S acting on the outside of the leg extension, and the end bearing Q_P
- using ultimate lateral pile capacity calculations for the lateral resistance Q_L.

These calculations are described later. In reality, the actual ultimate shaft resistances are affected by the lateral load, and the ultimate lateral load is affected by the shaft load. Q_S and Q_L also mutually affect Q_P for short piles and extensions. It is usually satisfactory to assume that each soil reaction can be calculated independently of the other, and to apply appropriate judgement when combining the results.

232

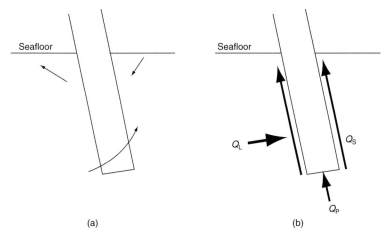

Fig. 5.7 Soil resistance components for jacket leg extension (after Helfrich et al., 1980). (a) Soil movements as the leg moves vertically downwards into the seabed. (b) Components of soil resistance

5.2.4 Special hazards for temporary support during installation

If the near-surface soils are clays and the period of piling is long, assessments may be needed of possible drainage, consolidation settlements, consequent strength gain, and cyclic strength degradation. Immediate settlements on medium-dense to dense granular seabeds are generally small enough to be ignored. Helfrich *et al.* (1980) recommend the procedure of D'Appolonia *et al.* (1971) for calculating immediate settlements for clay soils.

Helfrich *et al.* (1980) gave examples of possible problems, including:

- Excessive penetration into the seafloor, due to an under-estimated load or an over-estimated seafloor resistance. An extreme example was attributed to a 7 inch-thick layer of very soft clay squeezing out from under a mudmat.
- Inadequate penetration into the seafloor, for instance due to under-estimated soil strengths or underestimated effects of jacket leg extensions. An extreme example was due to scattered sand layers and lenses providing an unexpectedly high end bearing on a jacket leg extensions.
- Unequal penetration and/or settlement at different legs, leading to excessive tilting of the jacket, due to non-uniform loading of the jacket or to lateral soil variability.

If these problems occur, the jacket may need to be refloated, returned to land, and fitted with different temporary support systems. This is expensive, but the main cost can result from the programme delay.

5.3   Pile installation

5.3.1   *Types of offshore pile*

The most common type of offshore pile is a pipe pile (Fig. 5.8a), which is typically driven into the seabed by a hammer. The dimensions are specified by a diameter D or D_0, which is the outside diameter, and a wall thickness, t or w. The internal diameter is $D_i = D - 2t$. Diameters are available in multiples of 6 inches, and wall thickness at $\frac{1}{4}$-inch intervals. Typical D/t ratios are between 20 and 60. The lower value represents the greatest curvature that can normally be achieved in a steel rolling machine. The highest value represents a curvature beyond which wall-buckling or ovalisation effects can be common (Barbour and Erbrich, 1994; MSL, 2001; Aldridge *et al.*, 2005).

Pile make-up consists of the detailed design of wall thickness and other features of pile sections. There may be a driving shoe at the lower end, tapered for easier driving, and with a thicker wall section to cater for stress concentrations and non-uniformities in the soils and rocks encountered. The central sections may have a thinner wall because they will support less load during the operational phase of the platform design life. The upper sections may have a thicker wall because of the larger stresses there during operations.

The pile is driven through the jacket leg, or through a pile sleeve, which is a cylinder attached to a leg. After driving to the required tip penetration below the seafloor, shims may be inserted to hold the pile in place in the leg or conductor. Excess pile is cut away, and the annular space between the pile and the jacket leg or sleeve is grouted so as to provide a good structural joint that can transfer the required loads between the jacket and the pile.

In some designs, a two-stage pile is used (Fig. 5.8b). This can be useful, for example, where there is a cemented layer, where pile driving equipment may have difficulty with a large-diameter pile. The large-diameter pile is driven first to the top of the cemented layer. The soil plug inside the pile is then drilled out, and a smaller-diameter insert pile is driven through into the soil below. The annulus between the two piles is then grouted to give a good structural connection.

234

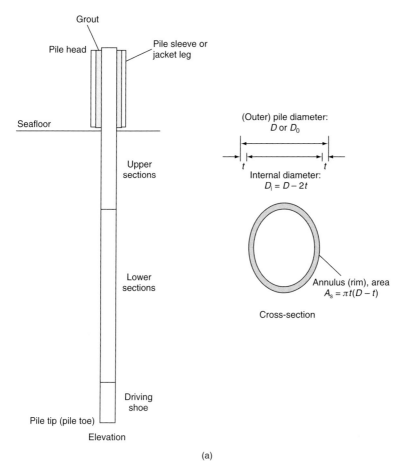

(a)

Fig. 5.8 Some types of offshore pile. (a) Commonly used steel cylindrical pipe pile: fabricated and installed in sections, typically driven, may be drilled-and-grouted or driven-and-grouted, then shimmed and grouted for connection to the jacket. (b) Two-stage pile: the large-diameter upper section is installed first, then the soil is drilled out, and the insert pile drilled or driven deeper, and the annulus grouted. (c) Belled pile: the pipe pile is driven, the shaft drilled ahead of the driven pile, an under-reamer installed and the cavity under-reamed, the under-reamer removed, reinforcement installed, and concrete installed by a tremie pipe. (Based on an original figure. © 1989 Offshore Technology Conference: Berner et al., 1989)

For piling in carbonate sands or in rock seabed, drilled and grouted piles are generally preferable. Carbonate sands develop very low pile–soil friction, and so give low ultimate capacities. Rocks are difficult to drive through and also develop low friction. Full-displacement

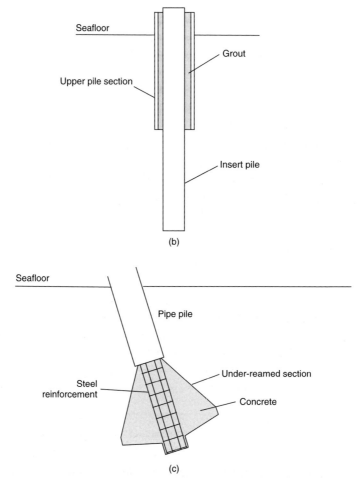

Fig. 5.8 *Continued*

reinforced concrete piles are also used. Driven and grouted pipes can be another useful alternative (Randolph *et al.*, 2005).

Figure 5.8c illustrates a belled pile, which can be used to spread vertical loads onto a wide area at the bottom of the pile, and to provide extra pull-out resistance. The concept and technology is the same as for onshore belled piles (George and Shaw, 1976). Berner *et al.* (1989) describe an application where bells were constructed 250 m below sea level as part of a foundation rehabilitation of the North Rankine A platform. A pipe pile is first drilled or driven to a certain depth. The spoil is then drilled out of the pipe, and a pilot hole is drilled below the bottom of the pipe. An under-reamer is then lowered into the pipe and rotated, expanding as it does so, cutting out the bell-shaped hole. Cuttings are extracted using drilling mud. The under-reamer is then removed, and the bell is inspected by a camera. A steel reinforcement cage is lowered into the bell, together with a tremie pipe, and concrete is poured through the tremie pipe.

5.3.2 Pile driving offshore

The principal methods of installing an offshore driven pile are described by Toolan and Fox (1977) (see also Gerwick, 2007).

Figure 5.9a illustrates the driving operation for a pile that is installed through a jacket leg. With the jacket supported by mudmats, the first few sections of pile are lowered to the seabed and allowed to break through a grout seal, if present. A hammer is installed on the stack, and is used to drive a segment of the pile into the seabed. When one segment has been driven to the limit of travel, the piling equipment is lifted off and another pile segment is lifted on and welded in place, The weld is normally subjected to non-destructive testing, after which the piling equipment is lifted back on. The operation is repeated until the required pile penetration below the seafloor has been achieved. The hammer is then removed, and shims may be welded in the annulus between the pile and the leg. Grout is injected into the annular space. Once set, the grout provides the structural connection between the pile and the jacket.

Figure 5.9b illustrates the operation if more than one pile is required per leg. Pile sleeves may be attached to the jacket around the base of each leg before loadout. Pile guides will be fitted at intervals above the sleeves. For each pile in the group, the pile is lowered through the guides and into a sleeve. Piling is then done in the same way as for a leg pile, with each pile installed in several segments, if necessary. If an over-water hammer is used, the last segment is installed using a follower, which is then removed once the target pile penetration is achieved.

5.3.3 Pile-driving hammers

Piles are driven by over-water or underwater hammers. Hammer manufacturers are keen to provide technical data for their products, and some provide software, design guides, and other services.

Figure 5.10 shows typical elements of an offshore hammer. The hammer has a driving system, drop weight or ram, anvil, one or more cushions, and a temporary pile cap or cage or helmet. The ram may

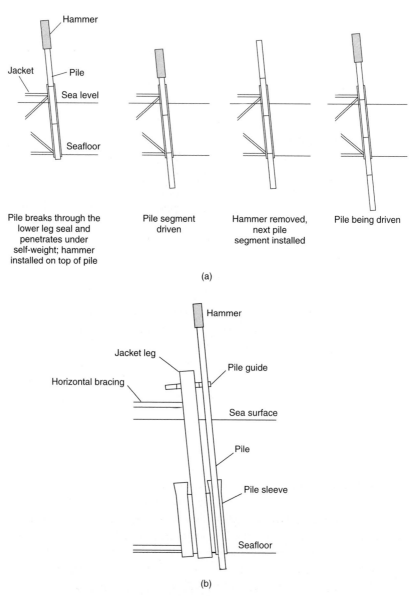

Fig. 5.9 Methods of pile driving. (a) Pile driving through a jacket leg. (b) Sleeve arrangement for pile group around a leg

be guided as a piston in a chamber, or by a central rod. The working fluid may be air, steam, oil, or a diesel–air mixture. The driving system may be an external generator of fluid under pressure (external combustion systems), or may be integral with the ram chamber (diesel hammers).

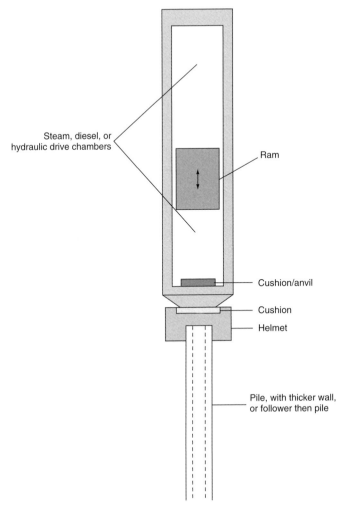

Steam, diesel, or
hydraulic drive chambers

Ram

Cushion/anvil

Cushion

Helmet

Pile, with thicker wall,
or follower then pile

Fig. 5.10 Typical elements of an offshore pile-driving hammer (see also Heerema, 1980)

In single-acting hammers, high pressure is used to drive the ram upwards in each stroke, with gravity used to drop the ram onto the anvil. In double-acting hammers, high pressure is used to move the ram in both directions.

The driving system lifts the ram and drops it onto an anvil or striker plate, or onto a cushion or capblock. The cushion absorbs some of the damaging high-frequency components of the blow, and helps to spread the stress evenly across the width of the element beneath it. Special cushion materials are used, such as Bongossi wood. They occasionally catch fire due to the energy they absorb. The stress from the blow passes into a pile helmet and then into the pile head. If a pile extension or follower is fitted, the wave passes into and down that, through a gravity connector or chaser, to the pile.

5.3.4   Effects of a hammer blow

When the hammer hits the anvil, stress is transmitted through the cushioning systems into the top of the pile. The top of the pile moves downwards, and a compressive stress–strain wave starts to travel down the pile (Fig. 5.11).

The wave travels at the speed of sound in steel, about 5100 m/s. Energy is transmitted into the ground through frictional slip at the soil–pile interfaces. This causes a shear wave to travel outwards from the pile into the soil. The consequent loss of energy reduces the energy of the stress wave travelling down the pile, an effect that can be modelled as radiation damping.

A partial reflection occurs when the wave reaches the seafloor, although this is minor except for a very stiff seafloor. Partial reflections also occur whenever the stress wave reaches a boundary between soil layers with different shear stiffnesses, and at imperfections and changes in the section properties of the pile. This can be advantageous because equipment can be installed to measure and analyse the reflected wave received at the pile head. This allows problems to be identified early. The information can also be used to assess the ultimate axial capacity of the pile (Wright *et al.*, 1982; Likins *et al.*, 2008; Webster *et al.*, 2008).

When the compressive stress wave reaches the pile tip, the pile shoe moves rapidly into the ground, transmitting energy into the ground by

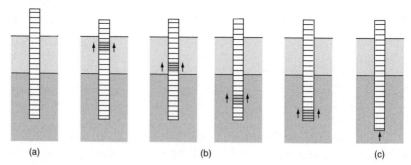

(a)   (b)   (c)

Fig. 5.11 *Passage of a stress wave from a hammer blow. (a) Unstressed. (b) Top of pile moves down, blow travels down pile, inducing soil resistance (vertical arrows). (c) Pile tip moves into soil, over-coming end bearing resistance*

normal stress. The ground does not fully spring back: instead, there is some permanent set there. This uses up more energy. The remaining energy is reflected and travels upwards into the pile, sometimes as a tensile wave which produces some elastic rebound in the upper parts of the pile. The overall elastic rebound may be fully dissipated by soil–pile friction, before the wave reaches the pile top.

One result of these events is a permanent set at the top of the pile. The inverse of this is the blowcount, typically expressed in blows per foot or quarter of a metre. Easy driving corresponds to blowcounts of around 10 blows/foot. Hard driving is above 50 blows/foot. Refusal is generally defined in a contract, and is taken to have occurred if the blowcount reaches 200300 blows/foot.

5.3.5 A practical example

Figure 5.12a shows the piling arrangement described by Hirsch *et al.* (1975) for one of the pile installations in the North Sea Forties Field. The steel pipe pile was 54 inches in diameter with 2 inch walls. It was installed in segments of 150, 110, and 120 foot lengths. A 13 ton chaser was attached to the upper segment, and a pile extension in three 90 foot lengths was above the chaser. The chaser ensures that there is a positive stress between the extension and the pile, and allows the extension to be lifted away at the end of the piling operation. A Menck 7000 hammer was fitted atop the extension.

Data for the present-day Menck MRBS 7000 are given in PDI (2003) and elsewhere. It uses a 685 kN ram with height 3.15 m, breadth 1.42 m, and a maximum stroke of 1.25 m. This is an order of magnitude more powerful than some onshore hammers. The Menck delivers a blow with a rated energy of 860 kJ about once every 2 seconds. The estimated energy efficiency is 67%. The ram impact velocity is around 4 m/s.

Strain gauges were installed in the pile head to measure the stresses as the compressive stress wave passed. Figure 5.12b shows typical results. A typical duration of the main part of the stress wave was about 10 ms. If the wave velocity in steel is 5100 m/s, the compression wave will have extended along a length of pile of about 51 m, which is considerably less than the height of the hammer above the seabed. This suggests there was no time for interaction between the soil and the driving system. If an average compression strain in the steel was 0.1%, the displacement of the top of the 51 m wave packet would have been about 5 cm relative to the bottom.

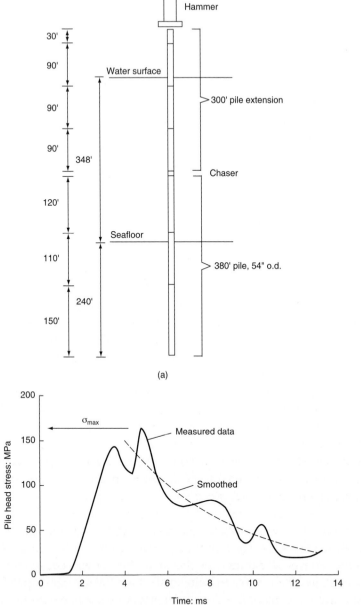

(a)

(b)

Fig. 5.12 Piling arrangement and stress wave measurements for a North Sea platform. (a) Typical pile arrangement. (b) Typical stress wave at the pile head. (c) Typical driving record. (Replotted from original figures. © 1975 Offshore Technology Conference: Hirsch et al., 1975).

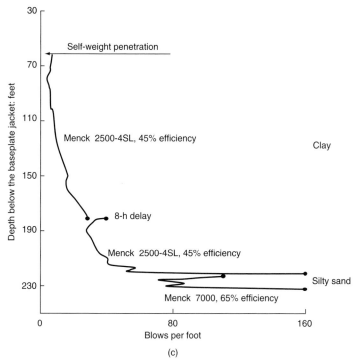

Fig. 5.12 *Continued*

The area under the stress–time graph is about 1 MPa.s. If this is multiplied by the pile cross-sectional area, it gives the impulse imparted to the pile. If all of the impulse was converted into pile momentum for the length of the pile and the attachments below the measurement point, the pile would have a velocity equal to the impulse divided by the mass of these objects. With reasonable assumptions, the velocity is around 1 m/s for the data shown.

Figure 5.12c shows one of the driving records for the Forties field work. The blowcount is plotted versus the pile tip position relative to a reference level of the jacket. A smaller hammer, the Menck 2500-4SL, was used in the upper clay, where driving was not expected to be difficult. There was an 8 hour delay at a penetration of 185 feet. The delay allowed time for the soil around the pile to recover some strength (lost due to excess pore pressures induced by driving), so that the blowcounts after driving re-started were larger. Silty sand was encountered at about 225 feet, as predicted from the site investigation, and the hammer was changed to the Menck 7000. This was able to penetrate some way into the silty sand.

5.3.6 Pile driveability methodology

In a pile drivability study, upper and lower bound predictions are made of the numbers of hammer blows per foot of penetration needed to drive the pile into the seabed, and of the maximum compressive and tensile stresses induced in the pile during driving. Predictions depend on the characteristics of the hammer and the associated equipment, the pile dimensions, the soil properties, and how far the pile has penetrated into the seabed. The following strategy is usually used, sketched in Fig. 5.13:

(a) For a given pile diameter and wall, estimate the upper and lower bounds on the soil resistance to driving (SRD). This is the ultimate axial pile capacity that would occur under static loading conditions. The estimates are plotted as a graph of the SRD versus pile tip penetration into the seabed. The calculation is described in Section 5.4.6.

(b) For a given pile-driving hammer and required final pile tip penetration, calculate the relation between the SRD and hammer blows required to drive the pile per foot or per quarter of a metre of movement. This is done using a wave equation analysis described in Section 5.3.7. It gives a 'bearing graph'. Upper and lower bound

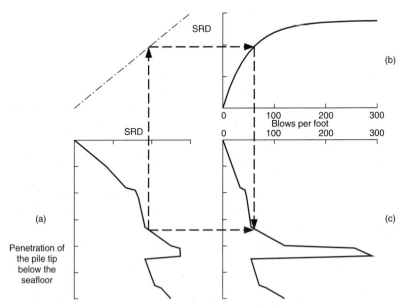

Fig. 5.13 *Method of calculating blowcounts versus depth*

graphs may be needed, but a single graph can be used if the bounds are close.

(c) For each pile penetration and bound, the SRD is read from the SRD profile, the corresponding blowcount is determined from the relevant (upper or lower bound) bearing graph, and the result is plotted on the blowcount–penetration graph.

As well as blowcount data, maximum compressive and tensile stresses will be available from the computer output in step (b). The pile designer will estimate the fatigue damage caused to the pile by combining this information with results from step (c). For some pile installations, stress cycles during driving can use up to 70% or more of the fatigue life.

A disadvantage of the three-step strategy is that, in reality, the bearing graph for a given hammer depends on the length of pile that has been installed. However, if computing power and time are limited, it is normally acceptable to calculate bearing graphs for the design pile penetration, or for the pile penetration at the largest SRD if this is different. Accurate prediction of pile drivability remains an uncertain art, and ongoing experience is often written up in the technical literature (e.g. Dutt *et al.*, 1995). ISO 19902 (ISO, 2007) recommends that driving stresses should be monitored for all offshore pile-driving operations, and results should be compared with predictions. Causes and implications of any differences should be assessed. Remedial measures should be taken, if necessary, such as the installation of extra piles.

5.3.7 *The one-dimensional wave equation*

A wave equation analysis is a calculation that takes account of the dynamic response of the pile and soil during driving. Such an analysis is generally required for offshore pile driving (see API RP2A (API, 2000) and ISO 19902). Energy methods that are sometimes used onshore and not generally regarded as sufficiently reliable for offshore use (Bender *et al.*, 1969).

Figure 5.14a shows a pile of cross-sectional area A_p and mass density ρ_p in a notional, unstressed static condition before a hammer blow and without gravity. Figure 5.14b shows the gravity of the pile earth, at some time t after the hammer hits the anvil. Consider a coordinate axis z along the pile, and a segment of pile that was between the coordinates z and $z + \delta z$ in the unstressed condition, where δz is a small distance. The top and bottom of the segment have moved downwards by distances w and $w + \delta w$, respectively, so the axial extension here is

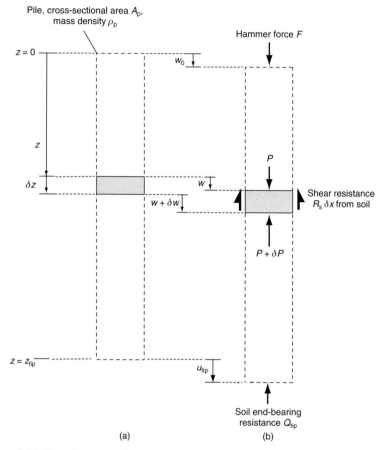

Fig. 5.14 One-dimensional wave equation. (a) Notional state before blow sand without gravity, pile unstressed. (b) At time t after hammer contacts anvil

$\delta w/\delta z$. If Young's modulus of the material is E_p, the compressive axial force in the pile is the initial force plus $E_p A_p$ times $-\delta w/\delta z$. Taking the limit as δz tends to zero gives

$$P = -E_p A_p \frac{\partial w}{\partial z} \tag{5.8}$$

The net force downwards on the segment is the segment weight $\rho_p A_p \, \delta z g$, where g is the acceleration due to gravity, less δP, less the resistance $R \, \delta z$ from the soil, where R is the resistance per unit length. This causes the mass of the segment, $\rho_p A_p \, \delta z$ to accelerate downwards with an acceleration of $\partial^2 w/\partial t^2$. Applying Newton's laws of motion,

246

dividing by δz, and taking the limit as δz tends to zero, gives

$$\frac{\partial P}{\partial z} + R = \rho_p A_p \left(g - \frac{\partial^2 w}{\partial t^2} \right) \tag{5.9}$$

Using equation (5.8) to substitute for P, and re-arranging the result, gives

$$\frac{\partial^2 w}{\partial z^2} = \frac{1}{c^2} \left(\frac{\partial^2 w}{\partial t^2} - g \right) + \frac{R}{E_p A_p} \tag{5.10}$$

where $c^2 = E_p / \rho_p$. This is the one-dimensional wave equation taking account of gravity. If it is assumed that the pile is in static equilibrium at the start and end of a blow, the dynamic part of the response can be obtained by removing the factor g.

Forms of the wave equation are applicable in many subject areas, such as the telegraph equation in telecommunications, and the Klein–Gordon equation in physics (Polyanin, 2002). More generally, the equation can be solved by the method of separation of variables (Kreysig, 1999), if the soil resistance function R is of a suitably simple algebraic form. If $R = 0$, Warrington (1997) shows that d'Alembert's principle can be used to infer that the solution consists of a sum of incident waves travelling in the $+z$ direction at speed c, and reflected waves travelling in the $-z$ direction, also at speed c.

5.3.8   Smith's approach

In practice, closed-form solutions are difficult to find for realistic expressions and profiles of soil resistance (Deeks, 1992; Warrington, 1997). Numerical methods are used instead, and are implemented in commercial software such as GRLWEAP (PDI, 2003), TNOWAVE, and others.

Figure 5.15a illustrates Smith's (1960, 1962) proposals for a general numerical solution method. The hammer and pile system are discretised into a number of distinct elements, and springs and dashpots are used to represent the stiffness of the pile, and the frictional resistance from the soil, and the point resistance from the soil below the pile toe. It is found to be important to model several distinct components of the hammer system.

PDI (1998) summarises several approaches for calculating dynamic soil resistance. Figure 5.15b illustrates Smith's proposals. The frictional soil resistance R per unit pile length, at a position z and time t, is plotted vertically versus the pile displacement w. The dynamic resistance R is

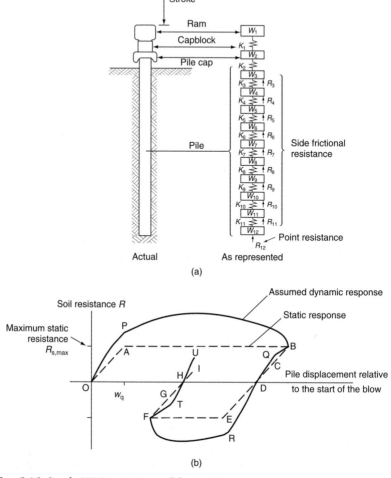

Fig. 5.15 Smith (1960, 1962) model. (a) Wave transmission model (reproduced with permission from the ASCE). (b) Soil resistance model

obtained by factoring the static resistance R_s, which is represented by the curve OABCDEFGHI. The initial loading OA is assumed to be linear, reaching a maximum $R_{s,max}$ at a displacement $w = w_q$, called the 'quake'. A further displacement w is assumed to occur at constant resistance $R_{s,max}$. On unloading from point B, an elastic response is assumed with the same slope $R_{s,max}/w_q$ as the initial loading OA. When the maximum resistance is reached in the reverse direction, the perfectly plastic response FG is assumed. On reloading, the assumed response is again linear, with the same slope as before.

248

The dynamic resistance R follows curve OPBQDRFTHU, and is computed from the static resistance R_s and the local pile wall velocity $\partial w / \partial t$ as

$$R = R_s \left(1 + J_s \left| \frac{\partial w}{\partial t} \right| \right) \tag{5.11}$$

where J_s is the Smith damping coefficient for frictional resistance. A similar approach is used for the resistance of the soil beneath the pile toe. However, this equation produces an anomaly, as follows. Along OP and to just before B, the pile velocity is positive, so the dynamic resistance is larger than the static resistance. At B, the pile velocity is zero, so the dynamic resistance equals the static resistance. Along BCD, the pile velocity is negative, so equation (5.11) again makes the dynamic resistance greater. At D, both resistances are zero, since the static resistance is zero. The anomaly does not normally have a large effect on the permanent set, which is usually achieved at D. It can be readily removed by replacing the unloading curve using Masing's rules, described in Chapter 3.

For open-ended pipe piles, PDI (1998) recommends shaft and toe quakes of 2.5 mm for all soils. The Smith damping coefficient is the inverse of the pile velocity that would double the soil resistance. Shaft damping is recommended as 0.16 s/m for non-cohesive soils, and as 0.65 s/m for cohesive soils. Toe damping is recommended as 0.5 s/m for all soil types.

5.3.9   Set-up, compaction, and friction fatigue

Set-up is the increase in soil resistance that can develop after a pause in driving through strong clay soils (Aurora, 1980; Colliat *et al.*, 1993; Xu *et al.*, 2006). The high cyclic stresses in the soil close to the pile can cause excess pore pressures to build up in clayey soils, usually resulting in easier driving than would otherwise be the case. For this reason, soil resistance during driving can be less than the ultimate axial capacity of the pile. Pore pressures dissipate quickly during a pause in driving, resulting in increased frictional resistance when driving restarts. PDI (1998) gives set-up factors of 1 for sand, 1.5 for silt, and 2 for clay, indicating that the driving resistance can double for clay as a result of set-up. Pauses are inevitable due to the need to add pile sections as the installed pile length increases. Set-up effects can be avoided by careful planning to minimise the delays once a strong clay stratum has been reached.

An opposite effect can occur in driving through loose sands, which can be compacted by the stress wave in the soil, resulting in increased friction as the pile penetrates further into the seabed.

Friction fatigue can develop due to large pile displacements relative to the soil (Heerema, 1978). It reduces soil–pile friction, and is greatest in the upper part of the soil profile where the cumulative movement of pile past a particular soil layer is greatest. Friction fatigue effects are considered in new cone penetration test (CPT)-based calculation methods for ultimate pile capacity (White and Bolton, 2004; White, 2005).

5.3.10 *Problems and remedial actions*

Refusal occurs if the number of blows needed to drive the pile per foot of penetration becomes so high that it is practically impossible to complete driving in the available time. Judgement of when this occurs can be contentious: project delays are expensive, and remedial measures are expensive, but continued driving of a pile at refusal can damage the hammer. A blowcount of 300 blows per foot would often be considered as refusal.

Section 22.5.7 of ISO 19902 recommends that the definition of refusal be specified in advance. Section 22.5.8 describes remedial actions in the event that refusal occurs. One is to review the hammer performance to check that it is working at its best efficiency. If it is, then:

- The soil plug can be drilled out, reducing the internal soil resistance.
- An undersized pilot hole can be drilled ahead of the driven pile, reducing the external and internal soil resistance when the pile is subsequently driven. Driving then recommences.
- A hole can be drilled to the full internal diameter, or can be created by jetting.
- An insert pile can be used to continue the driving.

These methods require a re-evaluation of the adequacy of all of the pile design calculations because they reduce the ultimate pile capacity once the pile has been installed.

If high blowcounts are expected, it is usually wise to have equipment on hand for remedial actions. Drilling and jetting equipment can be on board the piling support vessel in case of need.

5.3.11 Further aspects of pile drivability

Pile drivability prediction using the wave equation is more accurate than by energy formulae, but is still an art that requires the use of judgement and experience. There is also considerable research in the area. Litkouhi and Poskitt (1980) and Heerema (1981) provide alternative approaches for damping. Field data from pile-driving experiences have been reported by Hirsch *et al.* (1975), Aurora (1980, 1984), Wright *et al.* (1982), Stockard (1986), Dutt *et al.* (1995), Alm and Hamre (1998), Doyle (1999), and others.

Wu *et al.* (1989) carried out finite element analyses, and found that Smith's damping coefficient is not, in general, a constant. However, their results may have depended on the constitutive model used for the soil. Randolph and Simons (1986) proposed a new type of soil model. De Nicola and Randolph (1997) investigated the plugging behaviour that sometimes occurs in dense sand and can cause refusal during driving. Danzinger *et al.* (1999) used an improved soil model to back-analyse field data. Broere and van Tol (2006) found several issues in using finite elements to model pile driving. Paikowsky and Chernauskas (2008) used a finite difference method to further investigate plugging of pipe piles. Alves *et al.* (2008) explored the dimensionless variables governing pile drivability.

A problem occurred in piling through carbonate soils at the North Rankin A platform site off Western Australia (Jewell and Khorshid, 2000). The first pile fell 64 m into the seabed under its own weight. Subsequent piles also showed much lower soil resistances than predicted. Costs of subsequent research and remedial works were around A\$340 million. This led to major changes in the engineering of piles in carbonate sands (Murff, 1987; Kolk, 2000; Randolph *et al.*, 2005).

5.4   Ultimate axial pile capacity

5.4.1   Introduction

Figure 5.16 illustrates the concept of an ultimate axial pile capacity in compression. A pile has been installed to some penetration below the seafloor. Its buoyant weight is W', taking account of buoyancy in water above the seafloor and in soil below it. A vertical load V is applied to the pile at the level of the seafloor, resulting in a settlement there of magnitude s. If a graph of the total buoyant load $Q = V + W'$ is plotted versus s, the result might look like curve A or curve B:

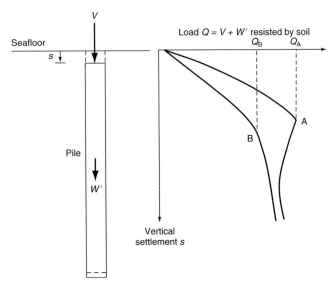

Fig. 5.16 *Vertical load–displacement curves for installed piles*

- for curve A, the peak load Q_A is the ultimate axial pile capacity Q_{ult} in compression
- for curve B, the load Q_B is the ultimate axial pile capacity Q_{ult} in compression, where there is a marked increase in the slope.

In some soils, the change in the slope of the load–displacement curve is so gradual that a clear yield point at B cannot be uniquely determined. In this case, Q_{ult} is determined at the largest value of settlement that the platform can tolerate in an ultimate limit state.

For piles that are subjected to tension, a similar approach applies. If an upwards force T is applied to the pile head, the net force that is resisted by soil is $T - W'$. The maximum value of this net force, or the value at large upwards displacements, is the tension capacity. It is determined by the pile dimensions and soil layering and properties.

The ultimate axial pile capacity depends on many factors, one being the penetration of the pile tip beneath the seafloor just before the vertical load V is applied. An axial capacity curve is a graph of the ultimate axial capacity plotted versus this pile tip penetration. Figure 5.17 shows an example, where the capacity in both tension and compression are shown. When using working stress design (WSD), the curves will not have had any safety factors applied. The platform designer will use the curves by:

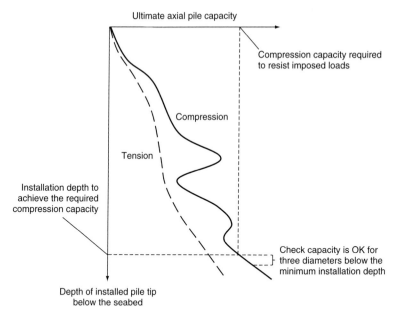

Ultimate axial pile capacity

Compression capacity required
to resist imposed loads

Compression

Tension

Installation depth to
achieve the required
compression capacity

Check capacity is OK for
three diameters below the
minimum installation depth

Depth of installed pile tip
below the seabed

Fig. 5.17 Ultimate axial capacity curves

(a) calculating, on the basis of structural analysis and predicted platform loadings, the smallest ultimate capacity that will satisfy the code requirements
(b) entering the diagram at that ultimate load and reading off the corresponding pile penetration
(c) checking that the capacity does not reduce below the required value for three pile diameters below that penetration.

Step (c) is done so as to avoid a punch-through of the pile tip from a strong stratum into a weaker one.

Recommended calculation methods for the ultimate axial pile capacity have changed over the years. A major change occurred for pile capacity in clay in the early 1980s, when previous API provisions were replaced after a review of the API pile load test database (Randolph and Murphy, 1985). Changes to the methods for sands are currently under way. ISO 19902 contains four CPT-based calculations methods that are optional alternatives to the API method for sand. These methods are compared with the API method in Section 5.4.5. API and other methods are reviewed by Le Tirant (1992), including the λ and β methods for clays (Vijayvergiya and Focht, 1972; Burland, 1973).

Section 6.3.4 of API RP2A details the safety factors to be used for working stress design: essentially 1.5 for extreme conditions and 2.0 for operating conditions. Sections 8.2.4 and 17.3.4 of ISO 19902 specify load factors in the range 0.9–1.35 for different components and situations, and partial resistance factors of 1.25 for extreme events, and 1.5 for operating conditions.

5.4.2 Overview of calculation

Figure 5.18a shows a pipe pile immediately after installation. Subsequently, some global and local scour will occur, reducing the support available from the soil. During subsequent loading, the vertical compressive bearing capacity of the pile is the sum of a frictional resistance force Q_{sx} between the pile and the soil on the external surface of the pile, and a point resistance Q_P at the pile tip:

$$Q_{ult(compression)} = Q_{sx} + Q_P \tag{5.12}$$

If the pile fails in the coring mode (Fig. 5.18b), the pile cuts through the soil, and the soil plug inside the pile stays where it is, and the point resistance is the sum of the internal shaft friction Q_{si} between the soil plug and the inner wall of the pile, and the end bearing resistance Q_a of the soil immediately below the steel annulus of the pile. In the plugged mode (Fig. 5.18c), the soil plug remains fixed in position relative to the pile as the pile moves downwards. The point resistance is the sum of the end bearing resistance Q_e from the soil beneath the soil plug, and the resistance Q_a below the annulus. The critical failure mode is the one that gives the lower value of capacity. It may be different at different pile penetrations for a given soil profile.

In both modes, shaft resistance is calculated by integrating a unit skin friction, f, over the area of the pile in contact with the external soil:

$$Q_{sx} = \int_{z=z_s}^{z} \pi D f \, dz \tag{5.13}$$

where D is the outside diameter. The integral is taken from the depth of the local plus global scour below the mudline, z_s, to the depth z of pile tip penetration. In the coring mode, the point resistance is calculated as

$$Q_{P(coring)} = \pi(D - t)tq = \int_0^z \pi(D - 2t)f \, dz \tag{5.14}$$

where t is the wall thickness. The first term is the end bearing resistance Q_a. The second is the internal soil–pile friction. The integral is taken from the seafloor (or the assumed level of the soil surface inside the

254

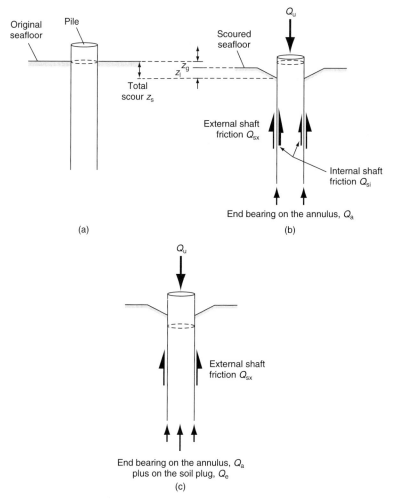

Fig. 5.18 Ultimate axial capacity and soil resistance components for coring and plugged conditions. (a) Installed pile before loading. (b) Coring: pile cuts through soil. Total resistance $= Q_{sx} + Q_{si} + Q_a$. (c) Plugged: soil plug pulled down by pile. Total resistance $= Q_{sx} + Q_e + Q_a$. (d) Failure mechanisms in the soil

pile) to the pile tip depth. If the assumed level is lower than the seafloor, account is taken of the difference in levels of soil strata inside and outside of the pile. In the plugged mode, the end bearing or point resistance is the product of a unit end bearing q and the overall cross-sectional area of the pile:

$$Q_{P(\text{plugged})} = \frac{\pi D^2}{4} q \tag{5.15}$$

Pile wall, thickness
exaggerated for clarity

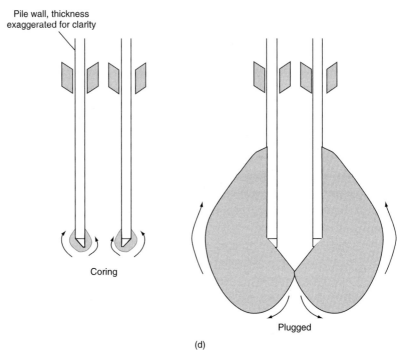

Coring

Plugged

(d)

Fig. 5.18 Continued

The same value of the unit end bearing is used in both modes, although the failure mechanisms are different (Fig. 5.18d). The mechanism for coring is almost a plane strain one, because the circumference of the pile is much longer than the wall thickness. The plugged mechanism is axi-symmetric.

The ultimate axial pile capacity in tension is considered to be composed of just the external shaft resistance Q_S. However, the designer is allowed to take account of the weight of the soil plug in computing the net load on the pile, if this can be justified.

5.4.3   Unit parameters

Table 5.1 summarises the unit parameters recommended by API RP2A and ISO 19902, and also gives some data for carbonate sands.

For granular materials, drained conditions are assumed to apply. For siliceous granular materials, API RP2A parameters are based on relative density and silt content. Unit shaft friction is calculated as the smaller of $K\sigma_v' \tan \delta'$ and f_{lim}, where K is a coefficient of lateral earth pressure (inside and outside of a pile), σ'_v is the vertical effective stress, δ' is the soil–pile friction angle, and f_{lim} is a limiting unit skin friction. The vertical effective stress is calculated assuming that it is reduced by the effect of global scour. API recommends $K = 0.8$ for open-ended, driven pipe piles in tension or compression. Other recommendations are made for closed-end piles and for drilled piles. The unit end bearing is taken as the smaller of $N_q\sigma'_v$ and q_{lim}, where N_q is a bearing capacity factor from Table 5.1, and q_{lim} is a limiting unit end bearing.

For cohesive materials, axial pile failure is assumed to take place sufficiently rapidly that undrained conditions apply. API (2003) recommends that the unit shaft friction f be calculated as a multiple α of the undrained shear strength s_u. The multiplier α depends on the ratio $\psi = s_u/\sigma'_v$ of the undrained shear strength to the vertical effective stress, as given in the first two columns of Table 5.1. Columns 3 and 4 interpret the API recommendations in terms of the over-consolidation ratio (OCR), using Semple and Gemeinhardt's (1983) relation. API RP2A recommends that the unit end bearing be taken as $9s_u$ in clay.

Following the experience at North Rankin A, a major review was carried out of methods of calculating the shaft friction and the end bearing in calcareous and carbonate sands (Jewell and Khorshid, 2000). It is now recommended that grouted piles are better suited to soil profiles consisting primarily of calcareous and carbonate materials (Kolk, 2000). For soil profiles that contain relatively thin layers of calcareous and carbonate sands, driven piles may still be feasible. A brief summary of Kolk's (2000) recommendations for open-ended pipe piles is as follows:

- If the calcium carbonate content (CC) is less than 20%, treat the material as a siliceous sand at the same relative density and silt content.
- If the CC is between 20 and 80%, unit parameters can be estimated by a semi-log interpretation involving the parameter KCC in Table 5.1b, where f_{si} and q_{si} are the values for a siliceous sand, and f_{ca} and q_{ca} are values for carbonate sand. Kolk (2000) noted that judgement had to be applied in developing this formulation, due to the relative scarsity of data for the CC between 20 and 80%.
- If the CC is 80% or more, the unit shaft friction $f = f_{\text{ca}}$ can be calculated as $0.14\sigma'_v$, limited to $f_{\text{lim}} = 15\,\text{kPa}$, based on Dutt and Cheng (1984) and Datta *et al.* (1980), respectively. The unit end bearing $q = q_{\text{ca}}$ can be assessed from CPT data, if available. A unit end bearing of 70% of the CPT cone resistance was suggested for the coring mode, and 30% for the plugged mode.

Table 5.1 Summary of some recommendations for unit parameters

(a) Siliceous sands, API RP2A

Soil description	δ': degrees	f_{lim}: kPa	N_q	q_{lim}: kPa	Notes
Very loose sand* Loose sand–silt* Medium silt*	(15)	(47.8)	(8)	(1900)	The 2005 update of API RP2A, and ISO 19902, state that previous API recommendations for soils (marked here with an asterisk) can be unconservative, and recommend the use of CPT-based methods for these soils. ISO 19902 does not give values for dense gravel
Loose sand* Medium sand–silt* Dense silt	20	67	12	2900	The 2005 API update and ISO 19902 use a skin friction factor β that is the same as 0.8 tan δ' here. ISO 19902 f_{lim} values are the same as here but rounded to the nearest integer. ISO 19902 q_{lim} values are the same but rounded to the nearest MPa
Medium sand Dense sand–silt	25	81.3	20	4800	
Dense sand Very dense sand–silt	30	95.7	40	9600	
Dense gravel* Very dense sand	35	114.8	50	12000	

(b) Carbonate sands, simplified based on Kolk (2000)

Range of carbonate contents: CC	Unit shaft friction	Unit end bearing	Notes
CC ≤ 20%	As API siliceous sand	As API siliceous sand	–
20% ≤ CC ≤ 80%	$f = f_{si} - K_{CC}(f_{si} - f_{ca})$	$q = q_{si} - K_{CC}(q_s - q_{ca})$ $K_{CC} = \dfrac{\log(CC/20)}{\log(4)}$	
80% ≤ CC	$f = \min(0.14\sigma'_v, 15\text{ kPa})$	Determined from CPT cone resistance q_c $q = 0.7q_c$ for coring, $q = 0.3q_c$ for plugged	Use $N_q = 10$ and $q_{lim} = 3$ MPa if no CPT data available

Based on Kolk's Figures 6 and 10, $N_q = 10$ might be used in the absence of CPT data. A limit of $q_{lim} = 3$ MPa would seem to be appropriate. It remains advisable for a designer today to check for any recent literature that may apply, particularly if the calcareous or carbonate sand layers are

Table 5.1 Continued

(c) Clays

API RP2A and ISO 19902		Interpreted in terms of OCR[*]	
Range of ψ	α	Approx range of OCR	α
$\psi \leq 0.25$	$\alpha = 1$	OCR ≤ 1.3	$\alpha = 1$
$0.25 \leq \psi \leq 1$	$\alpha = 0.5/\psi^{0.5}$	$1.3 \leq$ OCR ≤ 6.6	$\alpha \approx 1.11/OCR^{0.425}$
$1 \leq \psi$	$\alpha = 0.5/\psi^{0.25}$	$6.6 \leq$ OCR	$\alpha \approx 0.74/OCR^{0.213}$

[*] Interpretation based on Semple and Gemeinhardt's (1981) relation $s_u = 0.2\sigma'_v \times OCR^{0.85}$. Clay end bearing taken as $9s_u$.

found to provide a significant contribution to the ultimate axial capacity. Further aspects of calcareous and carbonate sands are described by Le Tirant *et al.* (1994).

Other materials include micaceous sands, glauconitic sands, volcanic soils, corals, cemented soils, and rocks. Local experience is often necessary to determine unit parameters for these materials (e.g. Stevens and Al-Shafei, 1996). This is often available from engineers in national oil companies, and will typically be related to the relative density for sands, and rock quality designation (RQD) for cemented materials. Stevens *et al.* (1982) argued that weak rocks would be broken into granular material by pile driving, so that the unit shaft friction could be assessed as a sand or gravel, or a sand–silt for rocks containing significant silt or clay seams. The unit end bearing was estimated as three times the unconfined compressive strength for an intact rock layer.

Kolk (2000) cites pile load test data by Puech *et al.* (1990), and argues that pile design in coral or highly fractured rock requires site-specific load tests in view of the difficulty in characterising these materials from site investigation data. Toume and Sadiq (2000) discuss the use of driven cast-in-place and bored cast-in-place concrete piles in corals.

API RP2A indicates that special tests may be required to determine shaft friction parameters for soils with weak grains, or containing significant quantities of mica or volcanic materials.

5.4.4 Effects of layer boundaries

The unit parameters described above apply where the relevant depth is well away from a boundary between two soil layers. Where this is not the case, unit skin friction values in the stronger layer are reduced, because the weaker layer cannot provide the required complementary shears.

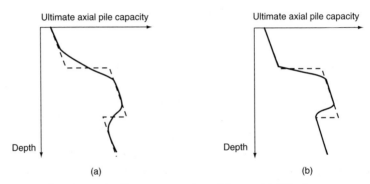

Fig. 5.19 Adjustments for the presence of a soil layer. (a) Weighting or averaging method. (b) Method retaining minimum values

Unit end bearing values grade gradually between the strong and weak layers, because the end bearing failure mechanism will be partly in one layer and partly in another.

API RP2A recommends that account be taken of this if the pile tip is within two to three diameters of a layer boundary. However, a specific procedure was not provided, and different engineers use different ones. For instance, simple averaging over depths between two or three diameters form the boundary; weighted averaging, depending on the distance from the position of interest; or graphical smoothing arranged to pass through the minimum capacity points. Figure 5.19 shows examples.

5.4.5   CPT-based methods
The API method for pile capacity takes no account of the detailed stress history of the soil around the pile. Piles used offshore are larger than piles onshore, and a programme of pile testing for large-diameter piles was initiated in the late 1980s, for the Magnus platform in the North Sea (Clarke, 1993). The tests were carried out onshore at Pentre and Tilbrook Grange in the UK. More tests were carried out there and elsewhere in the UK and France. Tests were also conducted under the EURIPEDES joint industry project, on very-large-diameter piles in dense silica sands (Zuidberg and Vergobbi, 1996; Kolk *et al.*, 2005).

Partly as a result of these efforts, a new calculation method was developed at Imperial College London (Jardine and Chow, 1996). The new method was also motivated by the desire to take proper account of stress history effects on the soil, and by the observation that data from CPTs could be used directly in pile capacity calculations, rather than indirectly through the estimation of soil strength parameters followed by the use of these parameters to calculate the unit skin friction and the end-bearing. The new method is now referred to as the MTD method or the ICP method. Clausen and Aas (2001) compared the ICP method with API methods and data, and found that the API approach over-predicts the capacity in normally consolidated clays of low plasticity.

Several other organisations have developed similar methods, and ISO 19902 contains four of these 'CPT-based' methods in its commentary. The methods are used for calculations of unit parameters for granular materials, and are considered to be alternatives to the API method that is given in the main text. CPT-based methods are mandatory for loose sands, because ISO 19902 considers the API method for these materials to be unconservative.

The four methods provided in the ISO 19902 commentary are simplified versions of the full methods published in the literature. Figure 5.20a shows comparisons between the API and simplified methods for the case of a 60×2 inch pile in medium-dense siliceous sand. The diagram on the left shows the assumed cone penetration resistance, calculated from equation A.17.4-21 of ISO 19902, which is based on Ticino sand data (Baldi *et al.*, 1986; Jamiolkowski *et al.*, 1988). The next diagram shows the unit shaft friction. Values of the unit skin friction for the API calculation do not depend on the installed length of the pile. They do in the CPT-based methods, as part of the way stress-history effects are accounted for, and the values plotted are for a 100 m installed pile length. The third diagram compares unit end bearing values. For the ICP-05 method, the unit end-bearing was applied over the pile annulus only.

The fourth diagram shows the relation between the ultimate axial pile capacity and the installed pile length. The API method gives the largest value at an installed length of 100 m. The UWA-05 (plugged) method gives a capacity of a little over one-half of the API value.

Figure 5.20b shows a comparison for the same pile in dense sand, with a relative density of 80%. Except for the ICP-05 method, unit end bearings are in good agreement. All methods give good agreement for the ultimate axial pile capacities. The NGI-05 method gives values that are about 50% larger than the API method at 100 m pile penetration.

5.4.6 Calculations for the SRD

The SRD is the ultimate axial pile capacity that is experienced during the dynamic conditions of pile driving. Predictions of the SRD are

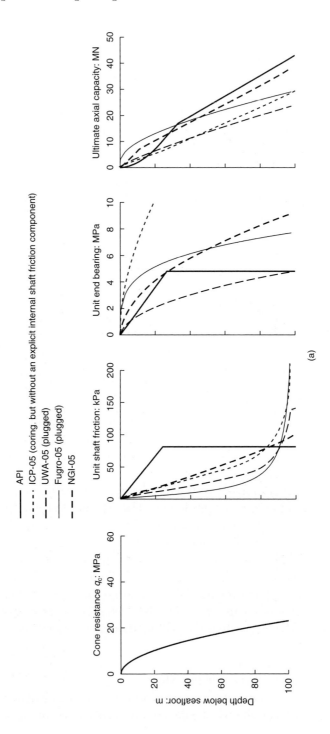

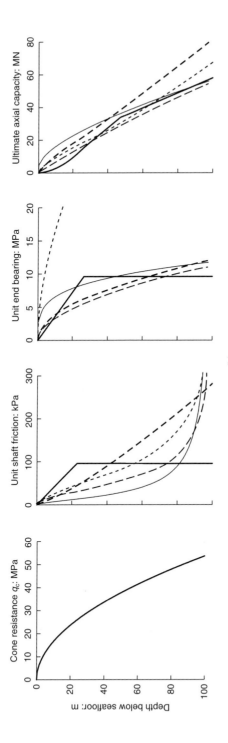

(b)

Fig. 5.20 Comparisons for a 100 m long pipe pile, 60 inch diameter, 2 inch wall thickness, in non-silty sand, particle size $D_{50} = 0.2 \, mm$, submerged unit weight 9 kPa/m. (a) Medium-dense sand, relative density (RD) = 50%. API parameters: $\delta' = 25°$, $f_{lim} = 81.3 \, kPa$. CPT-based parameters: $\delta_{cv} = 28°$, $q_{lim} = 4800 \, kPa$. (b) Dense sand, RD = 80%. API parameters: $\delta' = 30°$, $f_{lim} = 95.7 \, kPa$, $N_q = 40$, $q_{lim} = 9600 \, kPa$. CPT-based parameters: $\delta_{cv} = 28°$

usually calculated by modifying the calculation for the ultimate static axial pile capacity in compression. API RP2A and ISO 19002 refer to several methods proposed in the literature.

The recommendations Stevens *et al.* (1982) are widely used. The recommendations were based on 58 case histories of installations of large-diameter pipe piles at 15 sites in the Gulf of Mexico. The case histories were analysed using $K = 0.7$ for sand (API RP2A now uses 0.8), and with the 1981 API RP2A method for clay. This is now superseded (Randolph and Murphy, 1985), but is given in the API commentary. Some alternatives for hard soils are proposed by Colliat *et al.* (1993). The approach for carbonate sands is very different now (Kolk, 2000; Rausche and Hussein, 2000).

A designer using Stevens *et al.* is recommended to start from the 1981 calculation for the ultimate axial pile capacity. This is then modified, to obtain four curves of the SRD versus depth:

- upper bound, pile assumed plugged
- upper bound, pile assumed coring
- lower bound, pile assumed plugged
- lower bound, pile assumed coring.

The lower bounds are estimates for the case of continuous driving. The upper bounds may go some way towards accounting for set-up and for uncertainties in soils data or hammer performance.

Table 5.2 Simplified summary of Stevens et al. (1982) factors for the upper- and lower-bound SRD

Mode	Lower bound	Upper bound
Coring	Assume the skin friction on the inside surface of the pile is 50% of the external friction.[*][†] Use the unfactored unit end bearing	Assume the skin friction on the inside surface of the pile equals the external friction[*][†]
Plugged		Increase the unit skin friction by 30% in sand, use the static value in clay; increase the unit end bearing by 50% in sand, 67% in clay. Assume corresponding increases in f_{lim} and q_{lim}

[*] Values of 0 for the lower bound and 50% for the upper bound may be relevant for clay (see Stevens, 1988).
[†] Puech *et al.* (1990) report that the SRD in dense sands is always far in excess of API static resistance; for these materials, they recommend using the static capacity as the lower bound, and CPT cone resistance for the unit end bearing in the upper-bound coring case.

The modified curves are determined using soil properties determined from site investigation data in a way that would give a reasonable upper bound on static capacity, rather than a reasonable lower bound that is used in a capacity calculation. The unit skin friction for continuous driving through clay is obtained by multiplying the 1981 values by a pile capacity factor F_p:

$$F_p = 0.5 \times OCR^{0.3} \tag{5.16}$$

Shaft resistances Q_S and point resistances Q_P are then factored as indicated in Table 5.2.

5.5   Axial pile performance

5.5.1   *Introduction*

ISO 19902 defines axial pile performance as axial pile behaviour aimed at meeting service requirements. This involves the relations between axial loads applied to an installed pile, axial deflections of the pile, and the axial stresses in the pile along the pile length. Axial loads include self-weight effects of the piles and jacket, plus the effects of environmental loading, calculated in Section 5.1.3. Performance is important in determining settlements, tilt, and second-order stress effects in the jacket structure; in determining foundation stiffness and damping values to be used in dynamic analysis of the structure; and in pile make-up design, through calculations of stresses in the pile, stress concentrations, and fatigue life.

Load transfer from the pile to the soil occurs through shear stress at the internal and external pile–soil interfaces, and through normal stress at the pile tip. Shear and normal stress are therefore induced in the soil surrounding the pile. In a simplified analysis, settlements of the soil around the pile are assumed to depend primarily on the radius from the pile, so that concentric cylinders can be considered to settle, as sketched in Fig. 5.21a. Kraft *et al.* (1981a) estimated that the zone of influence around the pile would have a radius r_m of about

$$r_m = 2.5L(1 - \mu)\rho \tag{5.17}$$

where L is the pile length, μ is Poisson's ratio of the soil, and ρ is the ratio of the soil shear moduli at the mid-depth divided by the modulus at the pile tip. Typically, μ will be in the range 0–0.5, and ρ may be 0.5 or so, implying that the radius of influence is of the order of one-half to one times the pile length. Soil around the pile is assumed to deform essentially in simple shear, as sketched in Fig. 5.21b. Effects of stresses

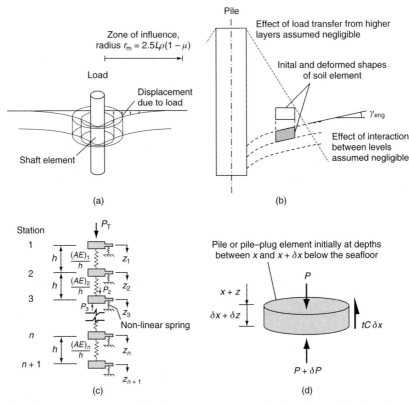

Fig. 5.21 *Concepts for axial pile performance. (a) Settlement modelled as shearing of concentric cylinders (after Kraft et al., 1981a, with permission from the ASCE). (b) Soil in simple shear, assumption of little interaction between levels, and primarily vertical movements. (c) Calculations model (Kraft et al., 1981, with permission from the ASCE). (d) Continuum model: derivation of differential equation for the axial load–deflection response*

induced by load transfer from higher levels are usually considered to be of second order.

Seed and Reese (1957) suggested a subgrade modulus approach, in which the shear stress t at position x on the pile is assumed to be related uniquely to the relative vertical displacement of the pile relative to the soil at that position. Similarly, the end-bearing resistance Q of the soil beneath the pile toe is assumed to be related solely to the vertical movement z of the pile into the soil there. API RP2A and ISO 19902 both adopt this t–z and Q–z approach. At a particular depth x below the seafloor, the shear stress t on the external soil–pile interface is assumed to be related solely to the vertical movement z of the pile at that depth x.

An advantage of the simplified approach is that it leads to the simple numerical calculation model in Fig. 5.21c. The pile is discretised into segments. Springs between each segment represent the axial stiffness of the pile. Non-linear springs and other elements between the pile and assumed fixed stations represent the response of the soil.

5.5.2 The components of pile head settlement

Elastic solutions for pile settlement are published by Randolph and Wroth (1978), Randolph (1985), Castelli and Motta (2003, 2005), and others. Das (2004) describes the separation of pile head settlement, relative to some fixed system far from the pile, into three components: (1) the compression of the pile, (2) the settlement of the pile tip into the ground beneath the pile tip, and (3) the settlement of the ground beneath the pile tip.

For onshore piles, which are often much shorter than offshore piles, Vesic (1977) proposed the following expression for the third component of settlement, z_3:

$$z_3 = \frac{Q_{ws}C_s}{Lq_p} \tag{5.18}$$

where Q_{ws} is the frictional shaft resistance under working load conditions, L is the pile length below the ground surface, q_p is the ultimate unit point resistance or end bearing, and C_s is a dimensionless coefficient given by

$$C_s = (0.93 + 0.16\sqrt{L/D})C_{(p)} \tag{5.19}$$

where $C_{(p)}$ is another dimensionless coefficient with typical values of 0.02–0.04 in siliceous sand, 0.03–0.05 in silt, and 0.02–0.03 in clay.

$Q_{ws}/L\pi D$ is the average skin friction along the pile. For offshore piles, this is typically smaller than q_p. Hence, z_3 is typically smaller than $C_s\pi D$. If $L/D = 100$, say, then C_s evaluates to between 0.05 and 0.13, depending on the soil type, so that s_3/D evaluates to less than 0.15–0.45.

5.5.3 Differential equation governing compression of the pile and pile tip settlement

One of the historical problems for the analysis of pile performance is that the symbol z is used to denote the pile deflection downwards, associated with the first two components of settlement described above. This symbol is usually used for vertical position in other soil mechanics calculations. The following development follows the historical method.

Figure 5.21d shows a segment of a pile that was initially between the vertical positions x and $x + \delta x$ below some reference level, where δx is a small distance. On application of a pile load, the top of the segment moves downwards by a distance z, and the bottom moves down by a distance $z + \delta z$. This gives a compressive strain of $-\delta z / \delta x$. If the pile behaves elastically with a cross-sectional area A and Young's modulus E, then taking the limit as δx tends to zero gives

$$P = EA \frac{\partial z}{\partial x} \tag{5.20}$$

This is just the same as equation (5.8) but with different notation. The parameter EA represents the axial stiffness of the pile. Two choices are available for this. One is to consider that P is the force in the steel of the pile. In this case, E would be the Young's modulus of the steel, and A would be its cross-sectional area. Alternatively, P may be taken as the axial force in the pile and the soil plug. In this case, EA would be a combined stiffness value for the pile and the soil plug together.

Under static conditions, forces acting on the element in Fig. 5.21d are the net axial force δP upwards, the shear resistance from the soil, and the weight of the element. The shear resistance is the shear stress t at the soil–pile interface, multiplied by a circumference C and height δx. If P is the force in the steel, then tC is the sum of the products of the shear stress and the circumferences at the inner and outer soil–pile interfaces. If P is the axial force in the steel and the soil plug, C is the external circumference only. Equating forces and resistances, dividing by δx, and taking the limit as δx tends to zero, gives

$$\frac{\partial P}{\partial x} = \rho A g - tC \tag{5.21}$$

where ρ is the density of the pile if P is the axial force in the steel alone, or a weighted average density of the pile and the soil plug if P is the axial force in the steel and the plug, and $g = 9.81 \text{ m/s}^2$ is the acceleration of gravity. Using equation (5.20) to substitute for P, and re-arranging, gives

$$\frac{\partial^2 z}{\partial x^2} = \frac{Ct}{EA} - \frac{g}{v^2} \tag{5.22}$$

where $v^2 = E / \rho$. The effects of axial load on the pile can be determined by solving a reduced equation without the gravitational term.

5.5.4 *Solutions*

A solution of equation (5.22) would need to involve consideration of the relation between the pile displacement z at a particular position x on the pile, and the stresses, strains, and displacements in the soil, which can give rise to stresses t over the entire pile length. Approximate closed-form solutions for an elastic soil have been developed by Randolph and Wroth (1978). Solutions for a soil with the elastic modulus increasing with depth are described by Poulos (1979, 1988).

For a simple linear relation $t = kz$, where k is a constant along the pile, it can readily be shown that the results depend on the relative stiffnesses of the pile, soil in shear, and soil in the end bearing, and that the following dimensionless parameter characterises the solutions:

$$\psi_0 = \frac{(K_{tip}/|\sqrt{CkEA}|) - 1}{(K_{tip}/|\sqrt{CkEA}|) + 1} \tag{5.23}$$

where the axial load at the pile toe $(x = L)$ is assumed to be related to the displacements there by $P = K_{tip}z$. ψ_0 runs from -1, if the pile tip stiffness is zero, to $+1$, if the pile tip stiffness is infinite.

Figure 5.22a shows results for the linear analysis. The pile displacement reduces exponentially down the pile shaft, and the load in the pile also reduces exponentially. In reality, there would be two limitations. First, the stiffness parameter k would likely increase with depth below the seafloor, and would be different for different soil layers. Second, limiting skin frictions would apply at sufficiently large loads, in accordance with the calculations described in Section 5.4. This can give the more complex results shown in Fig. 5.22b. At low loads, the displacements may again reduce exponentially with depth. At larger loads, the limiting skin frictions are likely to be reached first in the upper parts of the pile, where the movements are largest. Consequently, as the load increases further, the depth of the zone where this has occurred will gradually increase. It is usually the case that the tip displacement needed to mobilise limiting end bearing is larger than the displacement needed to mobilise limiting skin friction.

5.5.5 *Practical t–z and Q–z curves*

In practice, relations between shear stress and soil displacements (t–z relations) and between end bearing force and end displacement (Q–z) are used in finite element or finite difference programs to analyse the pile performance. API RP2A and ISO 19902 give shapes for the t–z

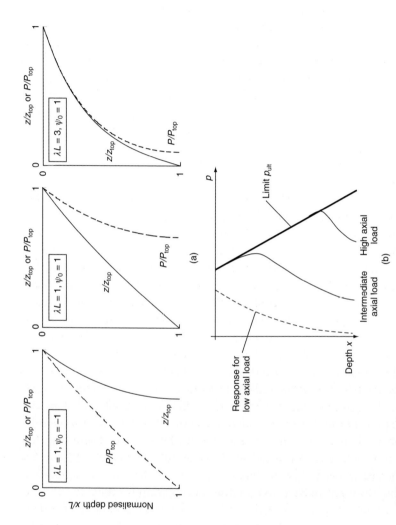

Fig. 5.22 *Examples of solutions for axial pile performance. (a) Elastic solution for constant lateral stiffness with depth. (b) More realistic expected development of the lateral resistance profile, for lateral stiffness and limiting resistance increasing with depth*

and Q–z curves that can be used in design for driven piles. Explicit guidance on how to calculate cyclic t–z responses does not seem to be given. However, data for such responses for silty clay are given by Pelletier and Sgouros (1987) and others. The shapes have been coded into several commercial software packages, and so are often the ones that are used in design. Their origins, some other shapes, and shapes for piles installed by other methods, are discussed by Reese *et al.* (2006).

For siliceous sands, the standard shape for the case of an increasing shear stress is a linear-elastic, perfectly plastic response (Fig. 5.23a). The shear stress rises from zero at a relative displacement of 0, to $t = t_{\max}$ at a relative displacement of 2.5 mm, followed by a constant value $t = t_{\max}$ for larger deflections. For clays (Fig. 5.23b), the initial part of the standard response is slightly curved, and is specified as a function of $t/t_{\max}$ versus the displacement z divided by the pile diameter. The maximum $t_{\max}$ is reached at a displacement of 1% of the pile diameter, after which the shear stress is assumed to reduce, reaching a residual value at a further displacement of 1% of the pile diameter. The residual value is specified as between 70 and 90% of the maximum. Vijayvergiya (1977) indicates that the ratio decreases with increasing OCR.

Figure 5.23c shows a t–z response for a carbonate sand, described by Wiltsie *et al.* (1988), in agreement with the finding by Bea *et al.* (1986) that residual friction for piles in calcareous soils could be very significantly less than the peak friction. Figure 5.23d shows the recommended Q–z curve for siliceous sand and a clay, and a curve for a carbonate sand (Wiltsie *et al.*, 1988).

The shear stress in these curves is the total shear stress due to the sum of the initial shear stresses after installation plus the changes in the shear stresses that occurred after that time. Consequently, the zero point represents a notional zero: the actual start of the curves after installation occurs at some value of shear stress that is, in general, not zero. The maximum values of shear stress in the recommended curves are presumed to be the same as the values calculated for unit shaft friction used in calculations for ultimate axial pile capacity. The tip displacement required to mobilise full end bearing resistance is usually larger than the tip displacement needed to reach the maximum frictional stress. Consequently, there is a mismatch between the displacements required to achieve peak shear stress in clays and carbonate sands, and those required to achieve maximum end bearing.

For most offshore sites, the soil is layered. Different t–z and Q–z curves apply for different layers. For an interpretative report following

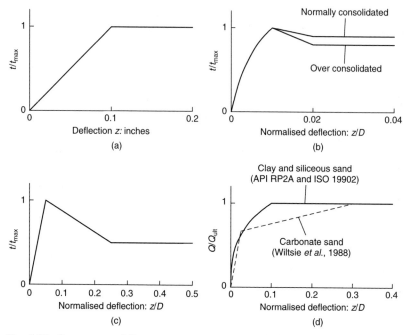

Fig. 5.23 *Some t–z and Q–z curves. (a) t–z curves for siliceous sand (API RP2A and ISO 19902). (b) t–z curves for clay (API RP2A and ISO 19902). (c) t–z curve for carbonate sand (Wiltsie* et al., *1988). (d) Q–z curves*

an offshore geotechnical site investigation, a typical requirement is for a tabulation of t–z and Q–z data at various depths below the seafloor. The depths required will typically include the top and bottom of each soil layer, and intermediate depths for deep layers. The tabulated values will typically be used to calculate equivalent soil springs to be used in a software programme running a finite difference or other numerical analysis of the structure.

5.5.6 Limitations

Some of the simplifying assumptions involved are discussed by Randolph and Wroth (1978), Kraft *et al.* (1981a), Reese *et al.* (2006), and others. The subgrade modulus approach is inconsistent with simple elastic theory, as may be verified by using Mindlin's (1936) approach and other solutions quoted by Davis and Selvadurai (1996). Consequently, it is unlikely to be consistent with a full analysis taking account of the elastoplastic behaviours of soils.

Pile performance can be affected by any events that occur in the zone of influence. For example, if a jackup spudcan is installed there, its presence may have a general stiffening effect, but the soil may be remoulded and the pile performance may be less stiff after the spudcan is removed. Pile performance after pile installation can be affected by residual stresses remaining in the pile and soil as a result of pile driving (Holloway *et al.*, 1978). It is also affected by post-installation settlements associated with consolidation of clay layers, and with related changes in the strength and redistribution of stress in the soil and structure. The soil response is also affected by the cyclic loading history that develops during the design life of a structure, so that pile performance changes over that lifetime.

Axial pile performance can also be affected by lateral pile loading and performance. In particular, the limiting shear stress at the external soil–pile interface may be affected by combined loading, and the lateral pile deflections can give rise to $P-\Delta$ effects that can increase the potential for a pile to buckle (Bhattacharya *et al.*, 2005).

5.6   Lateral pile performance

5.6.1   Introduction

Lateral pile performance is pile behaviour aimed at meeting service requirements. It is the lateral analogue of axial performance. Lateral deflections are important if there are relatively rigid connections between a piled structure and another object, such as between a jacket and a pipeline. The deflections are limited as a result of lateral soil resistance. This also limits the bending moments experienced by a pile. Lateral soil stiffness and damping characteristics affect the dynamic response of the whole structure (Bea, 1991; El Naggar and Novak, 1995, 1996).

The principal method used in practice is the p–y method, in which the lateral resistance p of the soil at a given depth below the seafloor is related to the lateral displacement y of the pile relative to the soil at that depth. This is a subgrade reaction method, and was pioneered for offshore applications by Reese and Matlock (1956), Matlock (1970), Reese *et al.* (1974), and others. In Fig. 5.24a, the pile has deflected laterally by a distance y at a depth x. The resistance from the soil, from active, shear, and passive components, is represented as a force p per unit pile length. The ratio $E_{py} = p/y$ is termed the reaction modulus for a pile under lateral loading, and can depend on a variety of factors, including the lateral load p. The p–y approach assumes that the

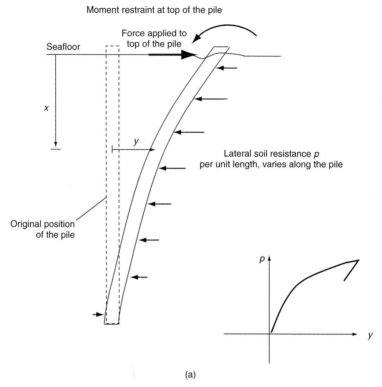

Fig. 5.24 *Concepts for lateral pile performance. (a) Conceptual model. (b) Discrete element model for numerical calculations. (c) Analytical element model for algebraic calculations*

values of changes in p at a given depth below the ground surface are related to the values and changes in y at that depth, and are independent of events at other depths. The pile is analysed as a beam subjected to a distributed load p.

Several commercial software programs are available for the p–y analysis of piles. Figure 5.24b shows a typical analysis (e.g. Fleming *et al.*, 1992; Kitiyodom *et al.*, 2005). The pile is discretised into elements. Each has bending stiffness, and can have shear and axial stiffness. The soil response is represented by a number of discrete springs, whose characteristics are generally non-linear and are calculated from soil p–y relations. In static loading calculations, the reference stops are considered to be fixed in position. In dynamic wave loading and seismic analyses, these stops can be allowed to move laterally by amounts that are determined by a separate analysis of the earthquake-induced ground motions. Damping elements can be incorporated in addition to non-linear springs.

274

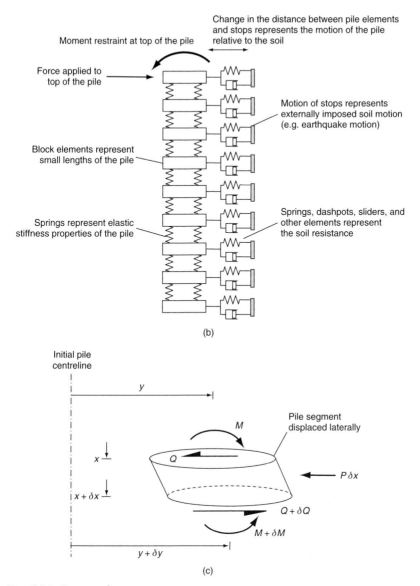

Change in the distance between pile elements and stops represents the motion of the pile relative to the soil

Moment restraint at top of the pile

Force applied to top of the pile

Motion of stops represents externally imposed soil motion (e.g. earthquake motion)

Block elements represent small lengths of the pile

Springs represent elastic stiffness properties of the pile

Springs, dashpots, sliders, and other elements represent the soil resistance

(b)

Initial pile centreline

y

M

Pile segment displaced laterally

x

Q

$x + \delta x$

$P \, \delta x$

$Q + \delta Q$

$M + \delta M$

$y + \delta y$

(c)

Fig. 5.24 *Continued*

5.6.2 *Governing differential equation*

Figure 5.24c shows a segment of a uniform circular pile subject to some lateral loading process. Consider a thin element of the pile at depths x and $x + \delta x$ below the seafloor, where δx is a small distance. Suppose that, as a result of lateral loading, the top and base of the element moves laterally by distances y and $y + \delta y$, respectively. Let the consequent lateral soil resistance force be p per unit length.

Let Q be the net shear force in the pile and the soil plug at position x, and let M be the moment there. The corresponding quantities at the base of the element are $Q + \delta Q$ and $M + \delta M$. Let $\rho A\, \delta x$ be the mass of the element, where ρ is the weighted mass density of the pile steel and the soil plug, and A is the cross-sectional area of the pile. The net lateral force on the element is $\delta Q - p\, \delta x$. The lateral acceleration of the element is $\partial^2 y / \partial t^2$, where t represents time. Applying Newton's laws, and dividing both sides of the result by δx, taking the limit as δx tends to zero, gives

$$\frac{\partial Q}{\partial x} - p = \rho A \frac{\partial^2 y}{\partial t^2} \tag{5.24}$$

Taking moments about the level of the top of the element, the net moment on the element is found to be $\delta M + Q\, \delta x$, plus a component proportional to the product of the reaction force $p\, \delta x$ and a part of the element height δx. Equating the net moment to zero, dividing the result by δx, and taking the limit as δx tends to zero, gives $\partial M / \partial x = -Q$, which is just the same as in beam bending theory. If the pile behaves as a simple elastic beam, then the moment is given by $M = EI\, \partial^2 y / \partial x^2$, where EI represents the combined flexural rigidity of the pile and the soil plug. In practice, the soil plug will usually contribute a negligible moment. Using these relations, and assuming EI does not change with position x, gives

$$\frac{\partial^4 y}{\partial x^4} + \frac{p}{EI} = -\frac{1}{r^2 c^2} \frac{\partial^2 y}{\partial t^2} \tag{5.25}$$

where $c^2 = E / \rho$ is the weighted average speed of a compression wave along the pile, including the wave in the soil plug, and $r^2 = I / A$ is the weighted average radius of gyration of the pile.

5.6.3 Static solutions

Static solutions to equation (5.25) is one for which the acceleration term is zero. Solutions depend on the relation between p, y, and x. Solutions are developed by Reese and Matlock (1956), Reese and Van Impe (2001), and others. Consider the case of a linear relation $p = E_{py}\, y$, where E_{py} is a constant, independent of x, with units of stress. Putting the acceleration term zero in equation (5.25) then gives

$$\frac{\partial^4 y}{\partial x^4} + 4\beta^4 y = 0 \tag{5.26}$$

$$\beta = \sqrt{\frac{1}{2}} \sqrt[4]{\frac{E_{py}}{EI}} \qquad (5.27)$$

This show that the pile responses are determined partly by the pile stiffness EI and partly by the soil stiffness E_{py}. Reese and Van Impe (2001) express the general solution in the form

$$y = \{\chi_1 \cos \beta x + \chi_2 \sin \beta x\} \exp(\beta x)$$
$$+ \{\chi_3 \cos \beta x + \chi_4 \sin \beta x\} \exp(-\beta x) \qquad (5.28)$$

where χ_i are constants to be determined from the boundary conditions. The corresponding inclinations, moments, and shear loads can be deduced by differentiation and use of the above equations.

For instance, consider the case of a jacket pile that is loaded laterally by a force H_0 at the seafloor, $x = 0$, and suppose that the jacket itself provides a sufficiently stiff rotational constraint that the pile head rotation there can be assumed to be zero. The boundary conditions at $x = 0$ are that $dy/dx = 0$ at $x = 0$ and $Q = -H_0$. The boundary conditions at $x = L$ are that $Q = 0$ and $M = 0$ there. The four conditions allow the found constants χ_i to be determined.

Figure 5.25 shows results for four values of the dimensionless parameter βL. In each case, the ratio y/y_0 of pile deflection to pile head deflection has been plotted on the left, then the inclination dy/dx to an arbitrary scale, then the shear load ratio Q/Q_{top} and the moment ratio M/M_{top}, where Q_{top} and M_{top} are the values of Q and M at $x = 0$. The results show that, for a sufficiently long pile, the pile length has no additional effect on the shear load and moments near the top of the pile. This is one reason why a pile make-up can be designed with a thinner wall thickness below a certain depth.

Figure 5.26 illustrates the concept of a 'critical pile length' (Reese and van Impe, 2001). The graph shows the relations between the normalised parameter βL and two ratios. The deflection ratio is the ratio of the pile head deflection, at a given load H_0, divided by the deflection that would be computed for an infinitely long pile at that same load. The moment ratio is the ratio of the pile head moment that is required to prevent rotation, divided by the moment computed for an infinite pile. The computations depend on the p–y curves that are assumed. In general, the results show that the pile length has relatively little effect for piles longer than about $1/\beta$.

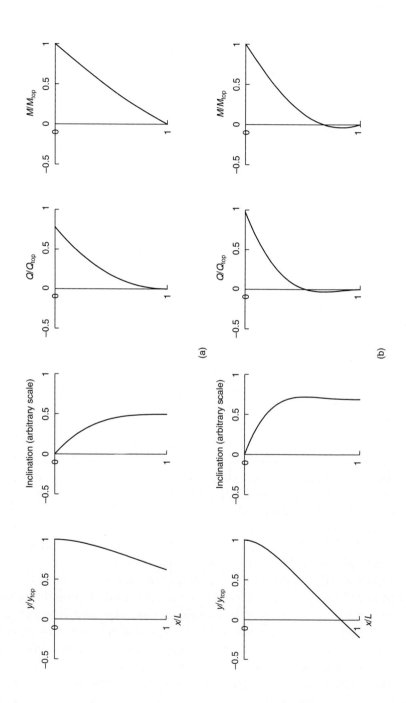

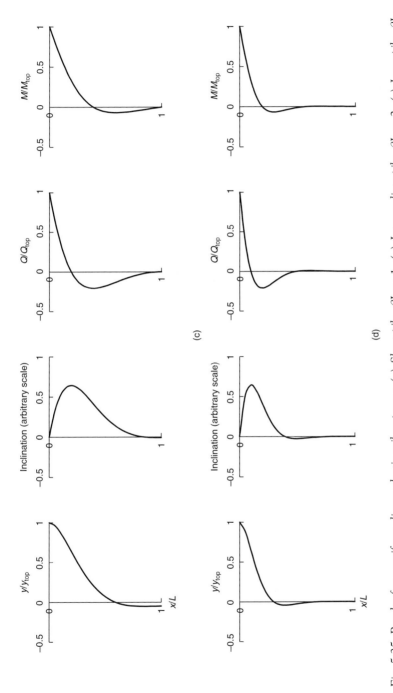

Fig. 5.25 *Results for a uniform, linear-elastic soil response. (a) Short pile, $\beta L = 1$. (a) Intermediate pile, $\beta L = 2$. (c) Long pile, $\beta L = 4$. (d) Very long pile, $\beta L = 8$*

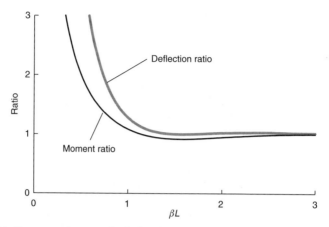

Fig. 5.26 *Concept of a critical pile length (after Reese and Van Impe, 2001)*

5.6.4 Practical p–y curves

Figure 5.27 shows the relation between lateral load and displacement at the pile head, measured in small-scale field tests on a pile in clay. The loops in the centre of the diagram are approximately simple hysteresis

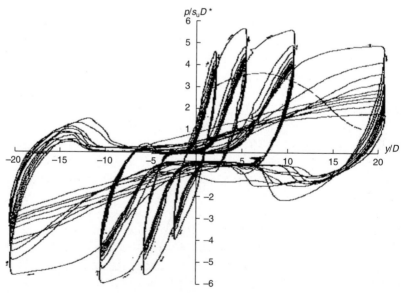

* Original graph labelled the vertical axis (*p/cdL*)

Fig. 5.27 *Measured p–y curves: displacement-controlled laboratory cyclic loading test with free water on a clay surface. (© 1970 Offshore Technology Conference: Matlock, 1970)*

loops. However, with relatively little increase in load, the loops develop into shapes that have relatively little stiffness over a central range of displacements, with a recovery of resistance at larger displacements. This phenomenon is believed to occur as a result of severe softening of the soil immediately around the pile. Significant softening was also observed in centrifuge model tests by Doyle *et al.* (2004), extending about three pile diameters in front of and behind a cyclically loaded pile in clay.

API RP2A and ISO 19902 give shapes for the p–y curves that can be used in design for driven piles driven into layered soils consisting of soft clays or siliceous sand. The API used the symbol 'p' to represent a stress in recommendations for clay, but used the same symbol to represent a force per unit length in sand. ISO 19902 has adapted the clay recommendations, so that 'p' is now used as force per unit length for both sand and clay.

Figure 5.28a illustrates the recommendations for soft clays. The vertical axes represent the ratio of lateral soil resistance to the ultimate lateral resistance p_{ult}. The horizontal axis is the ratio of the lateral deflection y divided by a reference deflection $y_c = 2.5\varepsilon_c D$, where D is the pile diameter and ε_c is the axial strain measured in an undrained triaxial compression test when the deviator stress in that test has reached 50% of the ultimate deviator stress. Rees and Van Impe (2001) recommend the values listed in Fig. 5.28e for normally consolidated clays, depending on shear strength. API RP2A and ISO 19902 provide several p–y curves. For short-term static loading, the full representative resistance is mobilised at larger lateral deflections. For equilibrium conditions of cyclic loading, the curve depends on whether the clay is within the zone of reduced resistance.

Figure 5.28b shows characteristic shapes recommended by Reese and Van Impe (2001) for soft clay after cyclic loading. Zero resistance is assumed up to a lateral deflection that was achieved in the history of cyclic loading, after which the curve returns to the API curve for cyclic loading. For stiff clay, defined as clay with an undrained shear strength greater than 96 kPa, it is noted that stiff clays may be more brittle than soft ones, and may experience more severe cyclic degradation.

Figure 5.28c illustrates the recommendations for siliceous sands. The curves are based on the hyperbolic tangent function. The constant k is the rate of increase in the initial subgrade reaction modulus with depth in the sand, and is assumed to depend on the angle of internal friction of the soil as given in Fig. 5.28e. The parameter A is given by $A = \max\{3 - 0.8(x/D), 0.9\}$ for static conditions, or as $A = 0.9$ for

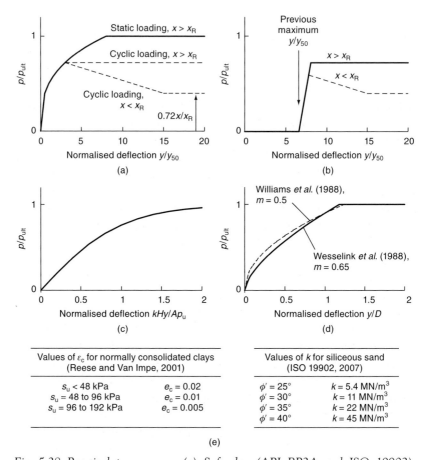

Fig. 5.28 Practical p–y curves. (a) Soft clay (API RP2A and ISO 19902). (b) Soft clay after cyclic loading (Matlock, 1970; Reese and Van Impe, 2001). (c) Siliceous sand (API RP2A and ISO 19902). (d) Carbonate sands, static loading, shown for $p_{ult}/p_{ref} = 0.9$, using Novello's (2000) equation

equilibrium cyclic conditions, where x is depth below seafloor. For static loading conditions, A is such that the lateral resistance at large displacement in sand can be as much as three times the representative resistance. However, the multiplier reduces rapidly with x, and is 0.9 for depths greater than 2.625 times the pile diameter. For cyclic loading, the multiplier is 0.9 at all depths.

Figure 5.28d shows p–y curves by Williams et al. (1988) and Wesselink et al. (1988) for calcareous and carbonate sands. Further aspects of these materials are discussed by Le Tirant et al. (1994).

5.6.5   Limitations

Like the *t–z* method for axial performance, the *p–y* assumption is that load–deflection behaviour at one level in the soil is unaffected by loads or deflections at another level. However, the implied lateral movements of soil are different at different levels, so shear stress must develop in the soil to correct this displacement incompatibility in the analysis. Nevertheless, the *p–y* method has the advantage of being usable with presently available software and hardware.

Kramer (1988) reviewed pile design methods for the lateral loading of onshore piles, and concluded that the *p–y* method is reliable when used with appropriate judgement. Reese and Van Impe (2001) stated that the results of finite element analysis for lateral loading can be instructive, but that analytical difficulties limit its practical contribution. The problem is essentially three-dimensional, and will normally require considerable computer resources (Klar and Frydman, 2002). Erbrich (2004) describes how theory, finite element analysis, and centrifuge modelling can be combined in an effective design process (see also Templeton, 2009; Jeanjean, 2009). Field tests for offshore applications were conducted by Cox et al. (1974), Reese et al. (1975), and others. Doyle et al. (2004) describe the results of centrifuge model tests which confirmed the accuracy of the *p–y* method in soft clay. Templeton (2009) and Jeanjean (2009) describe the use of finite element analysis and centrifuge model tests to determine *p–y* curves in clay.

The lateral pile performance can be affected by residual stresses remaining in the pile and the soil as a result of pile driving, and by changes in the strength and redistribution of stress in the soil as a result of the post-installation consolidation settlements of clay layers. The lateral performance and the capacity can also be affected by axial pile loading and performance (Darr et al., 1990; Guo and Ghee, 2005). In particular the stresses in the soil and the limiting shear stress at the external soil–pile interface can be affected by combined loading.

5.7   Ultimate lateral pile capacity

5.7.1   Introduction

The ultimate lateral capacity of a pile is a measure of the maximum horizontal load that the pile can support at some defined point. For jacket platforms, the point of interest may be at a level representing the connection between the pile and the jacket, or at the level of the lowest horizontal bracing on the jacket.

Unlike axial capacity, the calculation of the ultimate lateral capacity of a pile almost always involves consideration of plastic failure in the pile as well as in the soil. The soil at a given depth x below the seafloor is considered to provide a maximum lateral resistance p_{ult}, expressed as a force per unit length of the pile. Two possible failure mechanisms are considered in calculating p_{ult}, depending on the depth. The lowest value at a given depth is assumed to be the value that applies at that depth.

Various failure mechanisms are then considered, with most involving one or more plastic hinges developing in the pile. The lateral capacity is taken as the smallest capacity calculated for all of these mechanisms.

5.7.2 Failure mechanisms in the soil

Figure 5.29a shows a shallow failure mechanism for the soil just below the seafloor. When the pile moves from left to right, it pushes a passive wedge of soil up in front of it. Ground heave in front of a laterally loaded pile can extend for several diameters in front of the pile (Reese and Van Impe, 2001). Soil is also pushed around the sides of the pile. An active failure or a gap develops behind the pile. Figure 5.29b illustrates a different failure mechanism that can occur at depths where the overburden is able to restrict the ability of the soil to move vertically. The soil moves around the pile as the pile moves, but stays in the same horizontal plane throughout the motion.

Methods of determining the ultimate lateral resistances p_{ult} for the two mechanisms are given in API RP2A and ISO 19902, and are briefly described below. Figure 5.29c shows a typical plot of the results for a uniform soil profile. The shallow failure mechanism will normally give the lower value of resistance above a certain depth, termed the depth of reduced resistance, x_R. The deep failure mechanism is assumed below this depth. For layered soils, the graph can have several intersections. ISO 19902 suggests that the depth of reduced resistance is the depth at the first intersection.

The API used the symbol 'p' to represent a stress in recommendations for clay, but used the same symbol to represent a force per unit length in sand. ISO 19902 adapted the clay recommendations, so that 'p' is now used as force per unit length for both sand and clay. For soft clay soils subject to static loading conditions, the ultimate force per unit length, p_{ult}, at a depth x is computed as

clay, shallow mechanism: $\quad p_{ult} = 3s_u D + \sigma'_v D + Jxs_u$ $\qquad$ (5.29)

clay, deep mechanism: $\quad p_{ult} = 9s_u D$ $\qquad$ (5.30)

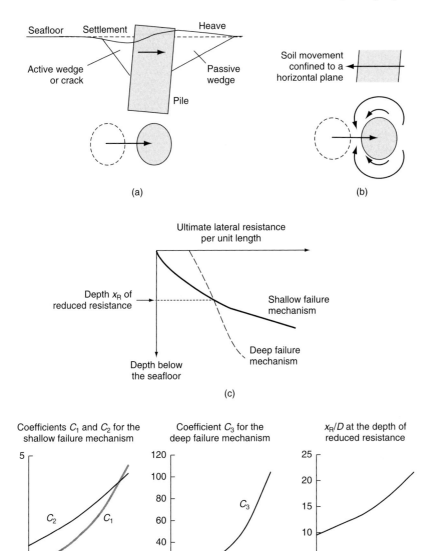

Fig. 5.29 Soil failure mechanisms for lateral loading. (a) Shallow soil failure mode: elevation (top) and plan view (bottom). (b) Deep soil failure mode: elevation (top) and plan view (bottom) (after Fleming et al., 1992). (c) Calculation for the depth of reduced resistance. (d) Parameters for siliceous sand (after API RP2A and ISO 19902) and H/D ratios for the depth of reduced resistance

where s_u is the undrained shear strength at depth x, D is the pile diameter, σ'_v is the vertical effective stress at depth x, and J is an empirical constant in the range 0.25–0.5. J is usually taken as 0.5 if there is no data indicating otherwise. In underconsolidated soils, the calculation of σ'_v needs to take account of actual pore pressures in the soil. In general, the depth of reduced resistance (x_R) is given by

$$6s_uD = \sigma'_vD + Jx_R s_u \tag{5.31}$$

For normally consolidated soils, s_u is approximately $0.2\sigma'_v$ (Semple and Gemeinhardt, 1981), so the depth of reduced resistance is about $6D/J$, or about 12 pile diameters if $J = 0.5$. For over-consolidated soils, s_u is larger, resulting in smaller depths x_R.

For siliceous sands subject to static loading conditions, the API and ISO calculations for the ultimate force per unit length, p_{ult}, at a depth x can be written as:

siliceous sand, shallow mechanism: $p_{ult} = C_1x + C_2D\sigma'_v$ (5.32)

siliceous sand, deep mechanism: $p_{ult} = C_3D\sigma'_v$ (5.33)

where the coefficients are obtained from a graph. The first two graphs in Fig. 5.29c shows the constants depending on the angle of internal friction ϕ' of the soil. The depth of reduced resistance is

$$x_R = \frac{C_3 - C_2}{C_1}D \tag{5.34}$$

The third graph in Fig. 5.29c shows the implied depth ratios x_R/D. The depth varies from about 10 pile diameters, if $\phi' = 20°$, to about 22 diameters, if $\phi' = 40°$.

5.7.3 Soil–pile failure mechanisms with the jacket loading the soil

Three commonly considered failure mechanisms are shown in Fig. 5.30. They resemble mechanisms considered by Broms (1964a,b; 1965) that are commonly used for onshore calculations, as also described by Fleming *et al.* (1992), Das (2004), and others. In all cases, the top of the pile is assumed to be connected to the jacket platform, and the connection is assumed to be capable of providing moment restraint.

In the translational mode (Fig. 5.30a), the pile is short and strong. It is pushed through the soil under a lateral load H, with a restraining moment M provided by the jacket. Considering the equilibrium of the horizontal forces acting on the pile, and taking moments about the

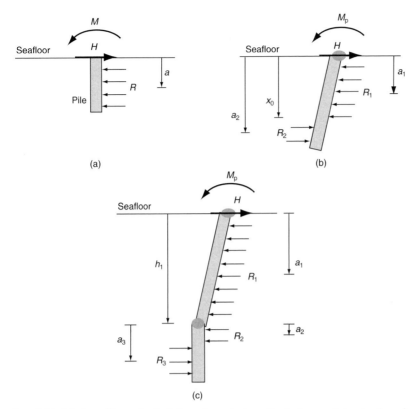

Fig. 5.30 Modes of lateral pile failure for a jacket pile: jacket applying load to the pile. (a) Translational failure mode. (b) Short-pile mode: plastic hinge in the pile. (c) Long-pile mode: two plastic hinges in the pile

top of the pile, gives

$$H = R \tag{5.35}$$

$$M = Ra \tag{5.36}$$

where R is the ultimate soil reaction force, calculated by integrating p_{ult} along the whole pile length, and a is the lever arm of its line of action below the seafloor. This mechanism can occur if the moment M computed in equation (5.36) is less than the plastic moment of the pile, provided that the implied moments at any depth x in the pile are lower than the plastic moment of the pile at that depth.

In the short-pile mode (Fig. 5.30b), a plastic hinge develops at the top of the pile, and the pile rotates about some point a depth x_0 below the seafloor. Below that point, the pile pushes back against the soil, and the soil provides a forwards-acting resistance R_2 that is computed by integrating p_{ult} over the length of the pile below the rotation point. No account is taken of the relation between p and y, so that the ultimate resistance per unit length is p_{ult} leftwards immediately above the rotation point, and p_{ult} rightwards immediately below it. Considering horizontal force equilibrium and taking moments about the hinge gives

$$H = R_1 - R_2 \tag{5.37}$$

$$M_p = R_1 a_1 - R_2 a_2 \tag{5.38}$$

where a_1 and a_2 are the lever arms of the soil reactions about the level of the top of the pile. In practice, the values of a_1 and a_2 are determined by iterating to find the value of x_0 that allows equations (5.37) and (5.38) to both be satisfied.

In the long-pile mode (Fig. 5.30c), a second plastic hinge develops at some depth h_1, and the pile below that does not move. Soil resistances R_1, R_2, and R_3 develop as shown, with lever arms a_1, a_2, and a_3. R_1 and R_2 are calculated by integrating p_{ult} over the relevant depths, but R_3 can be less than the corresponding integral for the lower part of the pile, because the soil is not failing there. If the pile section is uniform, the plastic hinge will start to develop during the loading process at a point where the moment is greatest. Hence, from the beam bending equation, the shear force in the pile at that point is zero. Considering horizontal force equilibrium of the upper part of the pile, and taking moments about the hinge at the top of the pile, gives

$$H = R_1 \tag{5.39}$$

$$M_p + M_{p1} = R_1 a_1 \tag{5.40}$$

where M_{p1} is the plastic moment in the pile at the lower hinge. In practice, the moment equation can be solved for any given hinge depth h_1, and the horizontal load H for that hinge depth can then be inferred. An iteration is needed to find the hinge depth that gives the smallest value of H. In addition, a check has to be made that the lower part of the pile is long enough to support the plastic moment M_{p1}. Considering horizontal force equilibrium and taking moments about the top of the lower part gives

$$R_3 = R_2 \tag{5.41}$$

$$M_{p1} = R_3 a_3 - R_2 a_2 \tag{5.42}$$

Equation (5.41) allows the level to be determined at which the soil reaction changes from being leftwards to being rightwards. A check can then be made that the values of R_2 and R_3 required to satisfy the second equation do not exceed the maximum values available from the soil.

5.7.4   Other soil–pile failure mechanisms

The mechanisms in Figs 5.31a–5.31c may be relevant to the jackup hazard situation of Fig. 5.4b, where soil is being pushed past one of the piles or pile groups of a jacket. The soil is moving from left to right, and the top of the pile is being held in place by the jacket. The jacket is not moving because it is being held in place by other piles that are unaffected by the spudcan. Figure 5.31a shows the mechanism

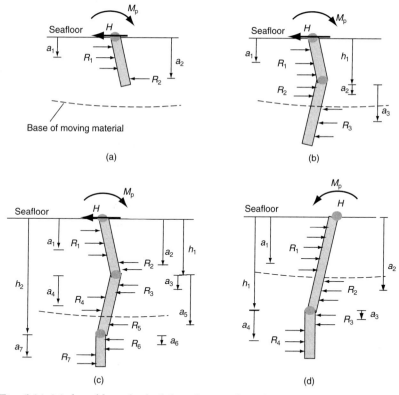

Fig. 5.31 Modes of lateral pile failure for a jacket pile: soil applying load to pile, moving from left to right. (a) Short-pile mode: connection to a leg held in a fixed position. (b) Deeper mode: connection to a leg held in a fixed position. (c) Long-pile mode: three plastic hinges in a pile, with connection to a leg held in a fixed position. (d) Seabed instability: two plastic hinges in pile, with the platform translating too

for a very short pile. It is similar to the short-pile mechanism of Fig. 5.30b, and has the same equations. Figure 5.31b shows a mechanism for a longer pile. The motion is different from the motions of Fig. 5.30. Figure 5.31c shows a third mechanism, which has similarities to Fig. 5.30b.

Figure 5.31d shows a mechanism for the case of a landslide in the seabed soil. This corresponds to the special hazard on the left of Fig. 5.4c. The soil is moving rightwards in Fig. 5.31d. The whole jacket will translate that way too, and will provide no lateral restraining force on the pile. The aim of design in this case would normally be to provide a pile that is sufficiently long and strong that it can withstand the lateral forces acting on it without the development of the plastic hinges.

5.7.5   *Limitations*

ISO 19902 notes that these empirical relationships for the ultimate lateral resistance p_{ult} do not necessarily apply where strength variations are erratic. Some guidance is given on how to modify the equations to account for the effects of scour. It is also noted that the equations for sand can be unconservative in the case of a sand layer that is overlain by soft clay. The reason is that the failure mechanism in the sand requires that certain values of stress can develop in the overlying material, and this is not necessarily the case for soft clay.

The lateral pile capacity can certainly be affected by an axial load in the pile (Darr *et al.*, 1990; Guo and Ghee, 2005). The axial load will transfer stress into the soil, but the lateral failure mechanisms already assume that the soil is at yield and that the soil–pile friction is fully mobilised where the soil is moving past the pile. Consequently, the lateral capacity in the presence of an axial load may be expected to be lower than values computed without an axial load.

5.8   Cyclic loading of piles

As mentioned above, the API RP2A and ISO 19902 standards take account of cyclic loading effects by using factors and adjustments in the provisions for unit shaft friction and the end bearing, limiting values of these, and in the specifications of standard p–y, t–z, and Q–z curves. While these provisions are likely to be adequate, they may also be over-conservative in some cases. There is a considerable literature exploring further aspects of the cyclic loading of piles.

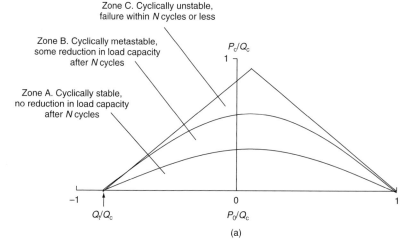

Zone C. Cyclically unstable,
failure within *N* cycles or less

Zone B. Cyclically metastable,
some reduction in load capacity
after *N* cycles

Zone A. Cyclically stable,
no reduction in load capacity
after *N* cycles

P_c/Q_c

-1

Q_t/Q_c

0

P_0/Q_c

1

(a)

Tentative values of degradation parameters

Pile type	Soil type	D_{lim}	$\lambda^{\dagger}$
Driven or jacked	Clay	0.4–0.6	0.2–0.4
	Silica sand	0.5–0.7	0.2–0.4
	Calcareous sand*	0.2–0.6	0.3–0.6
Bored	Clay	–	–
	Silica sand	0.2–0.4	0.3–0.5
	Calcareous sand	0.05–0.1	0.4–0.6

* Values highly dependent on particle characteristics
$\dagger$ Values of λ very approximate

(b)

Fig. 5.32 Concepts for cyclic loading for piles (after Poulos, 1988). (a) Cyclic stability diagram. (b) Tentative values of degradation parameters: Matlock and Foo's (1979) model

Figure 5.32a shows Poulos's (1988) concept of a cyclic stability diagram for the cyclic axial loading of piles. The horizontal axis represents the average axial load P_0 applied to the pile head divided by the ultimate axial capacity Q_c. The vertical axis represents the cyclic component P_c of the axial load divided by Q_c, so that the cyclic load is between the limits $P_0 \pm P_c$. The limiting conditions for a single cycle are

$$-Q_t < P_0 \pm P_c < Q_c \qquad (5.43)$$

where Q_t is the magnitude of the ultimate pile capacity in tension. The limits plot as two lines at 45°. Poulos postulated the existence of three zones below the lines. In zone A, no reduction in the soil stiffness would occur in a given number of cycles. In zone B, some reduction would

291

occur. Cycling in zone C would cause failure in that number of cycles. The zone boundaries would depend on the number of cycles.

Poulos (1988) also discusses the degradation of the ultimate shear resistance on the external surface of a pile due to cyclic loading. In Section 5.5, it was shown that the depth over which limiting shear stresses develop increases with the axial pile load. Under cyclic loading, there will be stress reversals. Matlock and Foo (1979) proposed that the cyclic degradation of the ultimate skin friction would occur wherever the soil was subjected to reverse slip, and that each reverse slip imposes an additional degradation until a lower limit is reached. The model could be expressed in terms of a degradation parameter D with

$$D_N = (1 - \lambda)D_{N-1} + \lambda D_{lim} \tag{5.44}$$

where D_N is the ratio of the ultimate skin friction after N slips to the ultimate skin friction before degradation, D_{N-1} is the value after $N - 1$ reverse slips, and D_{lim} is a lowest value. Since $D_0 - 1$, the model gives

$$D_N = (1 - \lambda)^N + \lambda D_{lim} \tag{5.45}$$

which is a logarithmic-type degradation law that is very straightforward to apply in practice. Poulos's (1988) proposals for some tentative values of the parameters λ and D_{lim} are given in Fig. 5.32b.

Poulos (1988) concluded that it is difficult to come to simple general conclusions regarding the ability of piles to withstand cyclic loading. His investigations indicated that long piles may exhibit a ductile type of cyclic response, while short piles exhibit brittle cyclic responses. Randolph (1983) developed a way of estimating the boundary between the stable and metastable regions in the stability diagram, based on measures of the pile and soil compressibilities and pile geometry.

5.9   Pile groups

A single pile depends for support and stiffness on the surrounding and underlying soil. When piles are installed in groups or close together, some of the soil around each of the piles will have been affected by the presence of the other piles and by the load, displacements, and installation events for those other piles. Consequently, a pile group has properties and behaviours that are different from the sum or average of the properties and behaviours of the individual piles in the group.

Pile groups or clusters are commonly used offshore. For example, several piles may be needed to support a jacket leg, rather than a

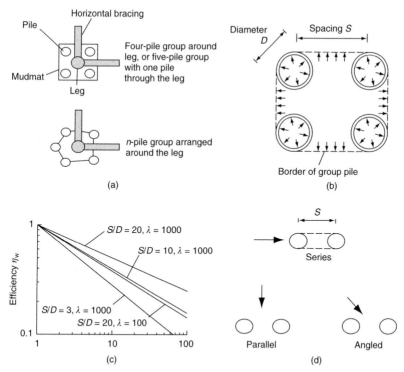

Fig. 5.33 *Some concepts for pile groups. (a) Some offshore pile groups: plan view.
(b) Plan view of a group pile formed from four piles arranged on a square: the
circumference of the group pile is $\pi D + 4S$, compared with the sum of $4\pi D$ for
individual piles. (c) Stiffness efficiencies of square pile groups, computed for
$L/D = 25$: stiffness increasing with depth ($\rho = 0.75$), Poisson's ratio $= 0.3$ (after
Butterfield and Douglas, 1981; Fleming et al., 1992). (d) Lateral loading of a
two-pile group in series, parallel, and angled modes*

single large pile (Fig. 5.33a). Section 6.9.1 of API RP2A states that pile
group effects may have to be evaluated if the spacing-to-diameter ratio
of neighbouring piles is less than about 8. Group effects are discussed by
Poulos and Randolph (1983), Focht and Kocht (1973), Matlock et al.
(1980), O'Neill and Ha (1982), O'Neill (1983), Randolph (2003),
Doyle et al. (2004), and others.

Group effects can apply to all of the geotechnical issues for piles. The
following are some examples of the considerations needed:

- *Installation.* The driving of one pile will affect the ground that the
next pile in a group is to be driven into, both compressing it and
by cyclic loading. Fleming et al. (1992) mention that piles may

wander off line considerably below ground, and that closely spaced slender piles may collide.

- *Scour.* Scour around pile groups can be different to scour around an individual pile or leg chord (Whitehouse, 1998; Sumer *et al.*, 2005). Local scours at neighbouring members of a pile group can coalesce into a wider scour that will affect the effective stresses in the soil to a greater depth.

- *Ultimate axial capacity.* Group effects on the pile capacity are theoretically addressed by comparing the capacity of individual piles acting separately with the capacity of a group pile. An example of the construction of a group pile is shown in Fig. 5.33b. For the group, several modes of failure are possible, depending on whether individual piles are coring or plugged, and on whether the infill material behaves in a coring or plugged mode. For the plugged mode, consideration is needed of whether the surrounding soil can support lateral bursting pressures imposed on it by the infill material.

One way to characterise the result of a group pile calculation is by a group efficiency E_g, defined as the ratio of the capacity of the group pile divided by the sum of the capacities of the individual piles calculated as if they were isolated from one another. However, this parameter has limited utility: it does not assist design since individual and group calculations must anyway be done.

Different piles in a group may support different loads (Randolph, 2003b; Poulos, 2006). Vesic (1969) found that E_g values for the shaft resistance of group piles in sands may be as high as 3. By contrast, De Mello (1969) and O'Neill (1983) reported group capacities in clays with E_g in the region of 0.7–0.9 at spacing/diameter ratios of 4. The Converse–Labarre equation, described by Moorhouse and Sheehan (1968), is given by

$$E_g = 1 - \left(\frac{n-1}{m} + \frac{m-1}{n} \right) \frac{\tan^{-1}(D/S)}{90°} \qquad (5.46)$$

for a rectangular group of $m \times n$ piles of diameter D with a centre-to-centre spacing of S. For a 2×2 group, this gives an efficiency of 70% if $S/D = 2$, and 92% if $S/D = 8$. The equation gives a rough idea of efficiency, but is less used nowadays (Bowles, 1996).

- *Axial pile performance.* Elastic settlements caused by different piles in a group add together, and stresses due to each pile add. Consequently, the settlement of a pile group can be much larger than for individual piles loaded to the same average load. The stiffness of one pile is not normally compatible with the soil displacements due to the loading of another (Mylonakis and Gazetas, 1998). Computer programs for large pile groups include PGROUP (Banerjee and Driscoll, 1978), DEFPIG (Poulos, 1980), and PIGLET (Randolph, 2003a), and SPLINTER and GROUP, available on the Internet.

One way to quantify the results is by a stiffness efficiency η_w, relating the stiffness K of a pile group (load divided by average settlement) divided by the sum of the stiffnesses k of the N isolated piles (Butterfield and Douglas, 1981). Fleming *et al.* (1992) present calculations indicating that η_w is approximately proportional to $1/N^e$ in large groups, where N is the number of piles in the group and the exponent e is between 0.4 and 0.6. Figure 5.33c shows some examples.

- *Lateral pile performance and capacity.* Lateral capacity effects can depend on the direction of loading, as indicated in Fig. 5.33d. Data and analyses of lateral group effects are presented by Focht and Kocht (1973), Matlock *et al.* (1980), Bogard and Matlock (1983), Brown *et al.* (1987), Lieng, (1989), Horsnell *et al.* (1990), Doyle *et al.* (2004), Reese *et al.* (2006), and others.
- *Cyclic and dynamic effects.* Studies by Sheta and Novak (1982), Kaynia and Kausel (1982), and others indicated that the dynamic stiffness and the damping of pile groups can vary significantly with the frequency of loading. The group stiffness and damping may be reduced or increased by interaction, depending on the frequency, spacing, and other factors (Poulos, 1988).

5.10   De-commissioning

Deconstruction or decommissioning of a jacket platform at the end of its useful life is, in principle, straightforward. Equipment and modules are removed from the deck, and the deck itself is cut away from the jacket. Depending on regulatory requirements, piles may be cut a short distance below the seafloor, using special tools, and the jacket is then removed. In practice, there can be many unknowns at this stage in the life of the platform, including the amount of corrosion of steel and grout that has occurred, and the strength of the components of the platform. The planning and safe execution of deconstruction can therefore be a major engineering task (CDOP, 1985).

6

Gravity platforms

Chapter 6 describes gravity platforms and the key geotechnical issues involved, providing a few simple models of how these platforms perform. This chapter covers the uses and types of gravity platform, site investigation and laboratory testing requirements, the main design issues, and the main soil behaviours and their impact on platform design.

6.1   Types of gravity platform

A gravity platform, or gravity-base structure (GBS), uses its weight to maintain stability against environmental actions. This type of platform has been installed in up to 300 m water depth. Figure 6.1 shows several configurations.

In the Condeep and Seatank types of platform, the deck and topsides are supported on one or more concrete legs that transfer loads to a cellular caisson base (Young *et al.*, 1975; Mo, 1976; Andersen, 1991). A platform of this type, installed in 100 m water depth, will typically have a caisson with a width of around 100 m and a height of 20–40 m. The hollow concrete legs might typically be 20 m in diameter. Oilwells and gas wells can be drilled through them and through the base of the caisson and into the seabed. The legs may be tapered to reduce wave loads in the splash zone.

The caisson provides oil storage and weight. It can be equipped with short vertical steel or concrete piles, called dowels, protruding below the base of the caisson. During installation, these penetrate the seabed before any other part of the structure, and help hold the structure in position. There may also be vertical walls called skirts that penetrate a soft seabed and transfer load to a more competent underlying soil layer. Skirts also function as shear keys, and help to prevent scour-induced loss of ground around the edges of the platform. The compartments they form are used as suction and pressure pads to control the platform during installation.

296

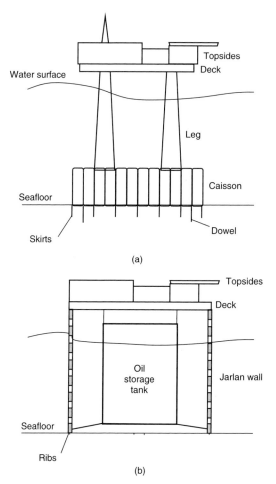

Fig. 6.1 *Types of gravity structure. (a) Condeep and Seatank types (adapted from Poulos, 1988). (b) Surface-piercing Ekofisk tank with a force-reducing wall (Clausen et al., 1975; Gibson and Dowse, 1981). (c) Concept used on the Maureen platform installed over a pre-installed template (adapted from Berthin et al., 1985). (d) GBS concept for windfarm structures (adapted from Staff, 2003). (e) GBS concepts for LNG storage and processing (adapted from Raine et al., 2007)*

Variations on this theme include the Troll East Gas Platform, installed in over 300 m of water, with skirts penetrating 36 m into the soft clay seabed. It is one of the world's tallest concrete structures (Andenæs et al., 1996; Huslid, 2001). For the Ravenspurn A platform, large-volume hydrocarbon storage was not required, and a partially open cellular structure was used instead of a closed caisson. The open cells were filled

297

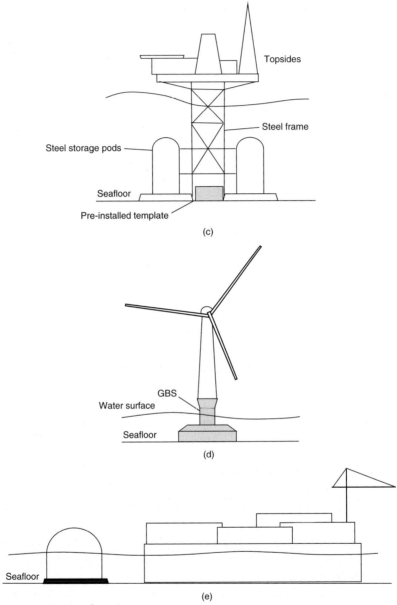

Steel storage pods ———

Topsides

Steel frame

Seafloor

Pre-installed template

(c)

GBS

Water surface

Seafloor

(d)

Seafloor

(e)

Fig. 6.1 Continued

with heavy solids after the structure was installed (Jackson and Bell, 1990; Roberts, 1990). For the Brage platform, in 136 m of water, the caisson is reduced to a reinforced concrete slab (Helland *et al.*, 1991). Small gravity platforms have also been highly successful for wind farms (Staff, 2003).

298

For the Ekofisk tank, installed in 70 m of water in 1973, the principal function was to provide oil storage. The caisson pierced the water surface and was protected by a reinforced concrete 'Jarlan wall' containing many holes (Clausen *et al.*, 1975; Andersen, 1991). When a wave arrives at the wall, some of the kinetic energy is dissipated in turbulent flow as water passes through the holes. This reduces the net horizontal wave load on the structure. The Hibernia GBS includes an outer wall that is shaped in a way that initiates cracks in ice sheets that press against the structure in winter months, thereby reducing the ice forces (Huynh *et al.*, 1997; Ugaz *et al.*, 1997). Gravity platforms with LNG storage and processing facilities have been developed for shallow water, resembling boxes and circular domes resting on the seabed (Raine *et al.*, 2007).

In the Maureen Technomare platform, three steel pods were used instead of a concrete base (Berthin *et al.*, 1985; Broughton *et al.*, 2002). To reduce the time needed to bring the oilfield into production, wells were drilled through a template that was installed prior to the installation of the main platform.

6.2   Construction and installation

A typical construction and installation sequence for a gravity platform is illustrated in Fig. 6.2.

The caisson is partially or completely constructed in a coastal construction yard or dry dock. On completion, the yard is flooded. The caisson floats, and is towed to a nearshore sheltered deepwater location. The remainder of the caisson and the legs are constructed by slip-forming, with formwork used at one level and then raised to construct the next level. As this occurs, the caisson can be sunk into the water, so that the height of the slipforming operations above the water line is not excessive. On completion, a deck may be floated over and connected. Alternatively, the deck may be installed later. The platform is then raised and towed to the offshore location (Reppe and Helsø, 1994).

The seabed will be prepared. Any obstacles and unsuitable foundation materials are removed, and the seafloor may be levelled by dredging and/or placement of granular material (Gerwick, 1974, 2007).

On arrival of the platform, seawater is pumped into the caisson, and the structure is lowered to the seabed. In parallel descent (Fig. 6.2f), the platform is lowered with the base parallel to the seafloor. As the caisson base approaches the seabed, water is pushed out of the way. This creates

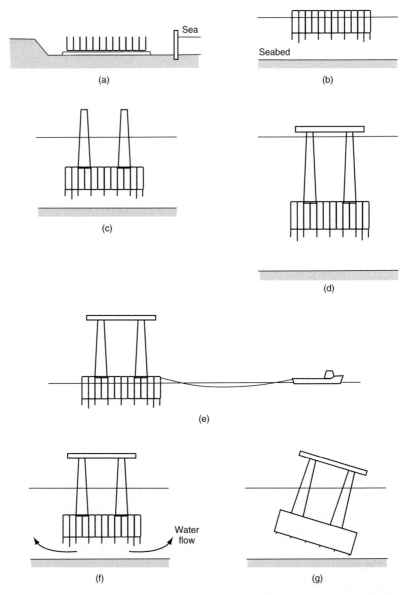

Fig. 6.2 Construction and installation of a large gravity structure (after Mo, 1976; Andersen, 1991). (a) Construction of caisson in dry dock. (b) Caisson walls slipformed in sheltered water, with skirts and dowels attached. (c) Legs slipformed. (d) Deck mating at a deep water site. (e) Towing to the final location. (f) Parallel descent. (g) Inclined descent (adapted from O'Riordan and Clare, 1990)

a potential hydrodynamic skidding instability that increases as the caisson nears the seabed. To prevent this, the projecting dowels penetrate the seabed and pin the caisson in place.

As the caisson is further lowered, the skirts penetrate the seabed, and form watertight compartments. The initial penetration rate is typically around 150 mm/h to avoid overpressurising the water in these compartments and washing out the soil. Water is pumped out, and the base of the caisson is set down on the seabed. The final penetration rate may be up to 1 m/h or so. Differential pumping rates between different compartments can be used to ensure that the platform sets down level, and a relative suction can be used, if necessary, to achieve the required penetration into the seabed.

Once the full weight of the platform is supported on the seabed, cement grout is pumped into the spaces between the underside of the caisson and the seabed (Boon *et al.*, 1977). Once set, the grout helps to redistribute the foundation stresses more evenly. The deck is floated over, if it has not already been attached, and the topsides are installed. Additional scour protection may be laid on the seafloor around the edges of the caisson. Connections are made to pipelines and cables, everything is inspected and checked, and the platform is ready for use.

Inclined descent is possible for some types of platforms (Fig. 6.2g). This tends to reduce the hydrodynamic skidding effect as the caisson base nears the seabed, but can result in one corner or edge of the caisson digging into the seabed and damaging it in touchdown.

For smaller caissons such as those for some wind farm structures, one or more caissons may be constructed on a barge (Staff, 2003). The barge is then towed to the offshore site. The caissons are lifted by crane and placed on the seafloor. They can then be installed using the same pumping, levelling, and grouting operations as for a larger structure. Connections are made to electrical and control cables that have been pre-laid on the seafloor. The wind tower is lifted on and attached to the platform, the turbine is lifted and installed onto the tower, and everything is checked and inspected.

6.3   Design codes and issues

Gravity platforms are addressed by the ISO 19903 (ISO, 2006) code of practice. Foundation issues are also covered in API RP2A (API, 2000) and by Det Norske Veritas (DNV, 1992).

Gravity foundations are often considered to be more complicated than jackets because soil behaviours must be considered in a three-dimensional volume that stretches one or more caisson diameters below the caisson, and several diameters either side. The principal geotechnical design questions are:

- How wide does the foundation need to be?
- What skirt depth and spacing is needed?

The answers depend on soil properties, and on iterations with the structural and hydrodynamic engineers and others. There are many detailed questions to be addressed. The principal issues are described by Young *et al.* (1975), Eide and Andersen (1984), Andersen (1991), and others, and include:

- installation
- scour
- effects of cumulative cyclic loading
- dynamics
- bearing capacity and sliding capacity in extreme loading events
- liquefaction of sandy soils
- consolidation
- immediate and long-term settlements
- subsidence.

Regional geohazards must also be addressed, such as the possibility of a turbidity current strike if a landslide is feasible nearby. In seismically active zones, earthquake loading can be a significant design consideration (Watt *et al.*, 1976; Penzien and Tseng, 1976).

6.4   Environmental conditions

A gravity platform typically experiences environmental loads that are far more severe than a comparable onshore structure. Average base pressures imposed on a strong seafloor by a GBS can be of the order of 200–300 kN/m^2 (Lunne *et al.*, 1981). Horizontal environmental loads can be 25% of the buoyant weight of the structure. Because the legs can be of a relatively large diameter, wave and current forces on them can be inertia-dominated, which is different to the drag-dominated forces for steel platforms (Newman, 1977; Chakrabarti, 2003). Because the caisson breadth is a significant fraction of the wavelength for a large caisson (typically one-third to one-half of the wavelength of the extreme wave), wave and current forces on the caisson require special analysis using diffraction theory (Loken and Olsen, 1976; Garrison and Stacey, 1977; Isaacson and Cheung, 1992). These forces can include significant vertical components, which may be up to 90° out of phase with the horizontal loads. Also, as water must accelerate and travel faster around the caisson, scour action can be severe around the edges of the caisson, and scour protection may be needed.

Cyclic loading occurs continuously, and has cumulative effects that are different at different parts of the three-dimensional volume of soil. The effects include the development of excess pore pressures, and changes in the soil stiffness and soil strength. For platforms on layered sands and overconsolidated clays, primary and secondary consolidation settlements may be of the order of a few tens of centimetres. Immediate and consolidation settlements can be very much larger if the platform is founded in normally or lightly overconsolidated clay. Over time, the edges of the platform can settle differentially compared with the centre, which can induce damaging bending stresses in the caisson. However, a benefit of consolidation is that the strength of the foundation increases with time. Sand drains and other systems can be used to accelerate the process (Tjelta *et al.*, 1990; Leung and Shen, 2008).

6.5   Site investigations for gravity platforms

For the purposes of stability analysis, failure mechanisms will be examined that extend into the seabed about the same depth as the caisson width, and extend laterally by about one caisson diameter from the edge of the caisson if the soil is mainly clay, or several diameters if the soil is mainly sand. Thus, for a gravity caisson of 100 m breadth, an area of several hundred metres square would be investigated, to a depth of at least 100 m below the seafloor. Deeper investigations may be needed, depending on the foundation design. For example, the skirt walls of the Troll A GBS, installed in 303 m water depth, were designed to penetrate 36 m into the soft and firm clay soils at the site (Huslid, 2001). The total base area was $16\,596\,\text{m}^2$, equivalent to a circle with a diameter of 145 m. Primary consolidation was expected to take 1000 years. Soil conditions and samples were investigated to 220 m below the seafloor.

A practical approach is to start with an extensive geophysical survey centred on the planned location of the GBS. If the location has not been determined at the time of surveying, a larger area will need to be surveyed, covering all the available options. The survey will normally be followed by an assessment of the lateral variability of soil strata at the planned location, and a plan for a geotechnical investigation.

For a small GBS in shallow water, one sampling borehole might be satisfactory, provided there is good confidence in the geophysical results and that they show lateral uniformity of the soil strata. For a larger GBS, Hitchings *et al.* (1976) described an investigation that involved one deep boring to 100 m below the seafloor, between four and eight shallow borings to 30 m below the sea floor, and 13 cone penetration tests (CPTs) of the upper few metres of seabed. Lunne *et al.* (1981) gave a site plan for the Brent B GBS that included over 20 holes over a plan area of 225 × 225 m. George and Shaw (1976) show a plan including 24 borings and CPT holes for two structures, a jacket and gravity platform.

Because of the importance of consolidation of clays, both for settlement calculations and for the estimation of pore water pressures and the evolution of strengths, a good knowledge of compressibility characteristics, permeability, and consolidation parameters will be needed for each clay layer in the soil profile. This requires extensive oedometer testing, which may need to go to relatively high values of the vertical effective stress. In-situ CPT dissipation tests can assist in verifying design assumptions and parameters for fluid flow and consolidation rates.

Because relatively complex failure mechanisms will be examined in design, laboratory tests can include triaxial extension as well as compression tests, direct shear, and possibly other tests including simple shear, hollow cylinder, and even true triaxial tests. Because of the major influence of cyclic loading, many tests will be needed to determine the cyclic behaviours of the various soil layers, and the effects of cycling on stiffness and strength parameters. Specific test requirements and conditions may be a function of the ongoing design process.

Assessment of the design soil profile is also different. It can be crucially important to identify thin soil layers and lenses, particularly in the upper part of the soil profile which will be penetrated by skirts and dowels. For instance, thin layers of soft clay can provide preferential slip surfaces that can significantly reduce the sliding resistance of the foundation. Lenses of loose sand surrounded by clay can trap excess pore pressures, leading to a reduction in the sliding resistance, and/or cracking or piping phenomena if the excess pore pressures are sufficient to break through the enclosing soil. Unexpected lenses and layers of sand can redistribute excess pore pressures and so dramatically alter the effective stresses in the foundation soil, and can lead to difficulties in applying differential under-base pressures in skirt compartments during installation. Unexpectedly hard layers or lenses, or the presence of boulders in other materials, can prevent the full penetration of dowels and skirts during installation. Variations of strata over the planned area of caisson foundation can lead to non-uniform settlements, which can induce bending stresses in the caisson, and excessive settlement and/or tilt of the structure as a whole.

6.6   Geotechnical design for installation

Most gravity platforms are kept level as they are lowered to the seabed. This allows the dowels to start to penetrate the seabed more or less simultaneously. Similarly, the skirts will penetrate simultaneously, and may not need to be designed to sustain large lateral loads at this time. The principal design issues for parallel descent are sketched in Fig. 6.3 and discussed below. O'Riordan and Clare (1990) examined issues associated with inclined descent, with the platform being lowered at an angle. One corner or edge will contact the seabed first. The platform will then rotate as further water ballast is added, until the base comes to the horizontal. The additional design issues include how far the struc-ture will embed at the touchdown point, whether the skirts can sustain bending stresses during the rotation, and what damage is done to the seabed during the process.

The dowels are typically vertical steel piles up to about 2 m in diameter (Gerwick, 2007). They contact the seabed first and pin the

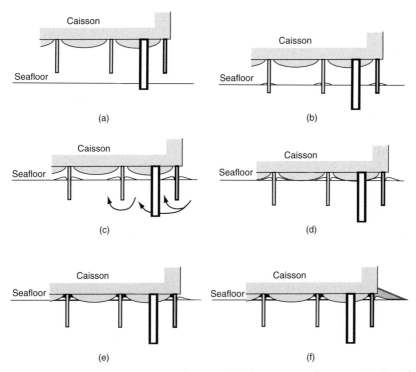

Fig. 6.3 Principal design issues for parallel descent installation. (a) Dowel penetration. (b) Skirt penetration. (c) Base suction or pressure. (d) Dome contact stresses. (e) Grouting pressures and density. (f) Scour protection

platform to the seabed. They project typically a few metres below the lowest level of other parts of the foundation. Steel skirts may be several millimetres thick, while concrete skirts may be a metre or so thick. Their height is determined by the need to transfer vertical load to competent strata below the seafloor, and by the need to provide a shear key against horizontal loading. Ribs are very short projections below the base of the caisson, and may similarly be of steel or concrete. The platform designer will need to know the maximum vertical forces that these elements will apply to the caisson, and the maximum lateral forces and bending moments. This information is needed for the structural design of the elements themselves, and for the design of caisson details in the vicinity. The installation manager may also need to know the least lateral resistance that the dowels will provide.

Geotechnical calculations for the vertical resistance of these elements are described specifically in Section 6 of DNV (1992). Two different calculations are recommended, one for the most probable soil resistance, the other for the highest expected resistance. Dowels are designed essentially as piles, except that special considerations are required if friction reducers are used. Skirts and ribs are also designed as piles, so that the general equation for all three elements is

$$R = R_s + R_p \tag{6.1}$$

where R is the net soil resistance to penetration, R_s is the skin friction on the inside and outside of a dowel, or the wall of a skirt, and R_p is the end bearing of the dowel or skirt. The coefficients involved in the detailed calculations for unit skin friction and unit end bearing can be different to those in other pile calculations, and are different for the most probable resistance and highest expected resistance.

Geotechnical calculations for the lateral resistance of dowels can be done using the same methods as for the lateral pile capacity. The lateral resistance of skirts and ribs is discussed in Section 6.10. A designer may choose to base calculations on different estimates of soil strength, one being the most probable and the other being the highest. If the foundation soils contain boulders or other heterogeneities, the consequent soil resistance will need to be calculated, and the skirts will need to be designed to push them aside during the installation process.

Under-base suction can be used to increase the skirt penetration during installation. Differential suctions or pressures between different skirt compartments can be used to force the skirts on one side of the caisson to penetrate more than another, which may be needed to restore a foundation to verticality. The suction or pressure can affect the penetration resistance, and excessive suctions or pressures can result in the soil being damaged by fluidisation or reverse-bearing capacity failure. The geotechnical calculations for resistance, and for the maximum allowable differential pressure between neighbouring skirt compartments, can be done using the methods for suction caissons described in Chapter 9.

For some gravity platforms, the bases of the cells in the caisson are hemispherical domes. These are efficient structurally for resisting uniform pressures, but they contact the soil non-uniformly during installation. The soil resistance to penetration can normally be calculated by modelling the contact area between the dome and the soil as a shallow foundation, and using familiar bearing capacity theory. The resistance may increase above this value, however, once the general shear failure mechanism becomes sufficiently extensive that it starts to be confined by the inside edges of a skirt compartment.

Bearing capacity calculations are essentially the same as for jackups, except that the foundation breadth is much larger for a large gravity platform. This means that deeper soil layers are affected, and the width of the failure zone is larger. One consequence is that many more soil layers may need to be considered. A profile of strong sand over weaker clay can be hazardous for gravity platforms, and the designer may elect to use skirts to transfer the bearing load to the underlying stronger layers. Calculations for immediate settlements during installation are described in Section 6.11.

Once the platform has reached its final penetration and has been levelled, weak cement grout is normally pumped into the space remaining between the underside of the caisson and the soil in the skirt compartments. Once set, the grout will help to distribute the bearing stress and so reduce stress concentrations in the caisson. Low grout pressures are used to avoid fluidising the soil beneath the skirts, or reversing the installation and pulling the skirts out of the soil (Gerwick, 2007). Scour protection is normally installed.

6.7   Hydrodynamic loads

The loads acting on the foundation are usually calculated by a structural engineer, based on environmental loads obtained from a hydrodynamic calculation. The hydrodynamic calculation is based partly on a meteorological and oceanographic (metocean) assessment, which typically includes a probabilistic or stochastic element.

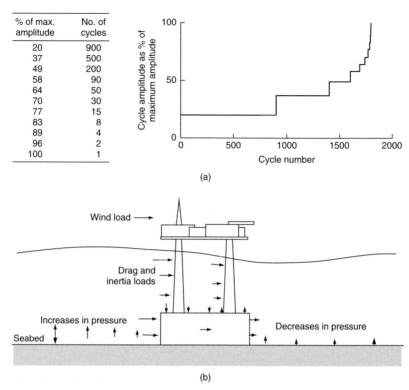

% of max. amplitude	No. of cycles
20	900
37	500
49	200
58	90
64	50
70	30
77	15
83	8
89	4
96	2
100	1

(a)

(b)

Fig. 6.4 Hydrodynamic loads. (a) Example of a pseudo-static storm specification, simplified (after Andersen, 1991). (b) Components of loads due to wind, waves and current

The results of the metocean assessment may be presented in the form of one or more design storms, which will include wind speeds, wave heights and periods, and current speeds. Figure 6.4a illustrates part of one such storm. The storm is characterised by a maximum wave height at some time during the storm, with a build-up that is simplified as a sequence of sets of uniform waves of given amplitudes, and with another sequence occurring after the peak of the storm. The dominant wave period tends to increase with wave height. A typical 100 year extreme design wave for the severest parts of the North Sea may have a wave height of 100 feet (30.48 m), and a wave period of 16 s. This means that the largest loads are acting on the structure over a period that may be only five seconds or less. Although this duration is short, sufficient movements may occur that the platform is considered to have reached an ultimate limit state rather than simply a serviceability limit.

Figure 6.4b shows typical changes in the water pressures applied to the structure and seabed resulting from a wave cycle (DNV, 1992). The changes result in changes in the net vertical loads on the caisson, and through it onto the foundation soil. The lateral water pressures occur above the level of the base of the caisson, and so have a component of overturning moment on the foundation bearing area. Vertical water pressures on the top of the caisson also produce a component of overturning moment that is out of phase with other loads. Changes in the water pressures also act directly on the open seabed surrounding the caisson. These changes act as surcharge loads in undrained analyses of foundation responses, and as boundary conditions on pore pressures in drained analyses. The changes in the water pressure are different on different sides of the caisson, due to wave phase effects. As a result, water pressures can apply a component of net lateral load to the skirts in drained analysis cases (DNV, 1992).

One of the factors that needs to be determined during the design process is the time at which an extreme wave can have the greatest effect. In some designs, the worst case scenario will occur with an extreme wave occurring early in the design life, before consolidation strengthens the soil. The worst case may occur towards the end of a design storm, after damaging excess pore pressures have been generated in the early part of the storm. In other cases, the worst case scenario may occur later in the design life or earlier in a storm.

For pseudo-static analyses, the loads are not sensitive to foundation responses. However, local details of the stresses applied to different regions in the foundation soil are indeed sensitive to soil behaviours. Consequently, the stresses in the caisson can be sensitive to local effects. Foundation stiffness is also an important parameter input into dynamic analyses of the platform.

6.8   Geotechnical design for cyclic and dynamic loading

6.8.1   *Keeping track: the stress path method*

The effects of cyclic loading tend to dominate the design process for gravity platforms. Cyclic loads cause excess pore pressures to develop in clays, silts, and even sandy soils beneath a wide caisson. These, and strain–history effects, can change the stiffness and strength of a soil. For less permeable soils, the effects can persist for many weeks and months, and accumulate with each successive storm. Different parts of the foundation soil experience different magnitudes and phases of cyclic loads, and the behaviour of the foundation can change gradually over time.

One way to keep track of what is happening is illustrated in Fig. 6.5, based on the stress path method described by Bonin *et al.* (1976), Foss *et al.* (1978), and others. First, a number of key locations in the soil are identified. The locations will, in general, be selected as a result of analyses, as described later. Figure 6.5a shows six locations A–F which might be related to potential failure surface in the soil for example. More points will normally be involved, and software can help to keep track of the experiences at these points.

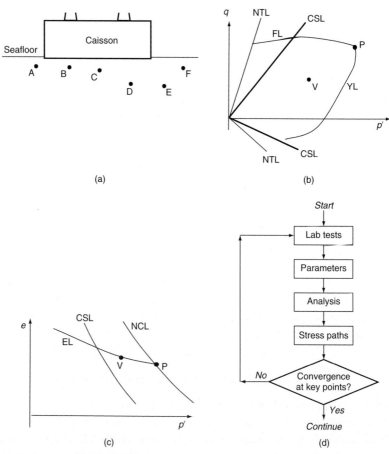

Fig. 6.5 Stress–path interactive approach with analysis and laboratory testing. (a) Identifying key points. (b) Stress space plot (NTL, no tension line; FL, failure line; CSL, critical state line; YL, yield locus; V, in-situ state; P, pre-consolidated state). (c) Stress–volume plot, with the volume represented by the void ratio (NCL, one-dimensional compression line; EL, elastic line). (d) Interactive analysis and laboratory testing

For each key point, the initial soil state prior to platform installation is plotted on two diagrams. The state will be updated as design events are considered. The first diagram shows an average effective stress plotted versus a shear or deviator stress. In Fig. 6.5b, the triaxial parameters p', q are plotted. For some key points it may be more appropriate to plot the vertical effective stress versus the shear stress on a horizontal plane, or to use a Mohr's circle diagram. The in-situ vertical effective stress $\sigma'_{v, \text{in situ}}$ at some point a depth z below the seafloor, and the initial horizontal effective stress $\sigma'_{h, \text{in situ}}$, can normally be estimated from

$$\sigma'_{v, \text{in situ}} = \int_{\zeta = 0}^{z} \gamma' \, d\zeta \qquad (6.2)$$

$$\sigma'_{h, \text{in situ}} = K_0 \sigma'_{v, \text{in situ}} \qquad (6.3)$$

where γ' is the submerged unit weight of the soil at a depth ζ below the seafloor, and K_0 is the in-situ coefficient of the lateral earth pressure at the depth z. The stress ratio at a critical (CSL) or steady state can then be sketched in, based on drained triaxial test data. For clays, an estimate of the initial yield envelope may be plotted. The stress state at point P on the yield envelope can be estimated from the vertical and horizontal stresses σ'_{vp}, σ'_{hp} there, with

$$\sigma'_{vp} = \text{OCR} \, \sigma'_{v, \text{in situ}} \qquad (6.4)$$

$$\sigma'_{hp} = K_{0,\text{nc}} \sigma'_{vp} = K_{0,\text{nc}} \, \text{OCR} \, \sigma'_{v, \text{in situ}} \qquad (6.5)$$

where $K_{0,\text{nc}}$ is the coefficient of the lateral earth pressure for the clay when normally consolidated. The yield envelope shape can then be sketched in, either from specific laboratory tests designed to probe the envelope, or through judgement by comparison with published data for similar clays (e.g. see Graham *et al.*, 1988; Diaz-Rodriguez *et al.*, 1992; Terzaghi *et al.*, 1996).

The second diagram for a key point includes a measure of volume. In Fig. 6.5c, the mean normal effective stress is plotted versus the void ratio. For clays, the one-dimensional asymptotic compression line (NCL) and elastic swelling or recompression lines (EL) can be drawn in from the measurements made in an oedometer test. The critical states line (CSL) can be drawn by plotting the critical states from triaxial tests on this diagram, and by then sketching in a line or curve that mimics the shape of the one-dimensional compression curve. For sands, a steady state line can be drawn if there are drained triaxial tests that achieved steady states at different void ratios.

The design process then proceeds as indicated by the flow diagram in Fig. 6.5d. Analyses are carried out for all the events that will affect the foundation soil during the design lifetime of the platform. Stress paths at each key point are calculated from the analyses, and laboratory tests are then carried out to determine the response of the soil to those stress paths. The laboratory results are used to extract engineering parameters, which are then used in a re-analysis of all relevant events. The iterative process continues until a reasonable convergence is obtained between the predicted and the measured responses.

6.8.2   Stress paths for mild events

DNV (1992) describes several methods for estimating stress paths. For mild sea states, the theories of linear isotropic or anisotropic linear elasticity may be used. Although the stress cycles may be small, they occur in large numbers. For example, a 20 year design life can include over 50 million cycles of small waves with a 10 second period. The cumulative effect of this number of cycles may be noticeable.

Computer programs to estimate stress paths for elastic materials are readily available commercially. They require estimates of Young's modulus E or the shear modulus G, Poisson's ratio μ, and one or more anisotropic moduli where anisotropic elasticity is used. These parameters depend on the stress level, the stress history, and the cyclic stress or strain amplitude, and are affected by the cyclic strain accumulation and the accumulation of excess pore pressures.

Davis and Selvadurai (1996) summarise and explore several solutions for stresses induced in a uniform isotropic linear-elastic half-space by loads acting on the surface or interior. Figure 6.6 shows some of these solutions for a circular gravity platform of diameter $B = 2a$ and area $A = \pi B^2/4$, subjected to a load P. The algebra is shown in Table 6.1, and explained as follows.

Figure 6.6a shows contours of the ratio ψ_{bv} of the change in the vertical stress in the soil, induced by a point load $P = \gamma'AB/4$ at the centre of the foundation, divided by the in-situ vertical effective stress $\gamma'z$. The effect of the vertical load is significant to at least one caisson diameter below the caisson, but reduces considerably below that, with the ratio reaching 0.1 at about two diameters below the caisson.

Figure 6.6b shows the ratio of the contact vertical stress induced on the bearing area immediately below a rigid caisson, divided by the average vertical stress on the area. Relatively large changes in the

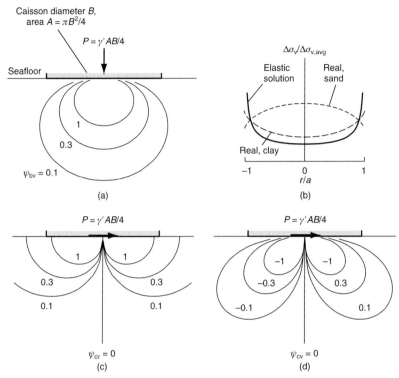

Fig. 6.6 Aspects of some elastic stress distributions beneath a circular footing. (a) Changes in the normalised vertical stress due to a vertical point load (Boussinesq's solution). (b) Vertical contact stresses immediately beneath a rigid circular footing. (c) Normalised shear stresses due to a horizontal point load (Cerruti's solution). (d) Normalised vertical stresses due to a horizontal point load (Cerruti's solution)

vertical effective stress are induced at the edges of the foundation. This indicates that the soil reaches its limiting stresses in those areas, and the elastic solutions do not apply (Davis and Selvadurai, 1996). The actual contact stresses tend to be larger at the edges for a rigid footing on clay, but smaller at the edges for a rigid footing on sand (Craig, 2004).

Figure 6.6c shows contours of the ratio $\psi_{c\tau}$ of the shear stress on the horizontal planes in the soil, induced by a horizontal point load $P = \gamma' AB/4$ at the centre of the foundation, divided by the in-situ vertical effective stress $\gamma' z$. The largest ratio occurs at the contact point below the centreline, but the ratio is zero on the centreline below that. Large ratios occur some distance below the edges of the caisson, and also some distance either side.

313

Table 6.1 Some solutions for a uniform, isotropic, linear-elastic half-space

Figure 6.6	Elastic solution[*]	Ratio plotted	Reference
(a)	$\Delta\sigma_v = \dfrac{3Pz^3}{2\pi R^5}$, with $R^2 = r^2 + z^2$	$\psi_{bv} = \dfrac{\Delta\sigma_v}{\gamma'z}$	Boussinesq (1878)
(b)	$\Delta\sigma_v = \dfrac{P}{2\pi a\sqrt{a^2 - r^2}}$, with $r^2 = x^2 + y^2$	$\dfrac{\Delta\sigma_v}{P/A} = \dfrac{1}{\sqrt{1 - (r/a)^2}}$	Boussinesq (1878)
(c)	$\tau = \dfrac{3Px^2z}{2\pi R^5}$, with $R^2 = x^2 + y^2 + z^2$	$\psi_{c\tau} = \dfrac{\tau}{\gamma'z}$	Cerruti (1884)
(d)	$\Delta\sigma_v = \dfrac{3Pxz^2}{2\pi R^5}$, with $R^2 = x^2 + y^2 + z^2$	$\psi_{cv} = \dfrac{\Delta\sigma_v}{\gamma'z}$	Cerruti (1884)

[*] $\{x, y, z\}$ coordinate system with the origin at the centre of the caisson, x horizontal in the direction of horizontal loading, y horizontal normal to the direction of loading, and z vertically downwards. See Davis and Selvadurai (1996) for complete solutions.

Figure 6.6d shows contours of the ratio ψ_{cv} of the vertical stress in the soil, induced on a central plane in the soil ($y = 0$) by a horizontal point load $P = \gamma'AB/8$ in the direction $+x$ at the centre of the foundation, divided by the in-situ vertical effective stress $\gamma'z$. The ratio is zero on the centreline, positive on the side towards which the shear load is acting, and negative on the other side.

As mentioned earlier, several computer programs are commercially available to do elastic calculations. Most can produce contour plots of many different parameters in addition to the vertical stress and the friction ratio, and some can apply limiting stresses. By examining the program results in detail, an assessment can be made of the key positions in the three-dimensional volume of soil, and of the types of soil tests that are needed to mimic the stress paths at these points, and so determine:

- the elastic parameters to be used in a reanalysis
- the cumulative effects of cyclic loading in terms of the development of excess pore pressures and the change in the void ratio.

Different types of laboratory tests may be needed at different key points. For example, triaxial tests can be appropriate where the analysis indicates that the changes in stress are mainly in the vertical and horizontal normal stresses. Direct shear or simple shear tests may be appropriate where the analysis indicates that cyclic shear stresses dominate the results.

6.8.3 Finite element analyses for moderately severe events

Figure 6.7 shows some of results of a finite element analysis by Rahman *et al.* (1977) of the Ekofisk tank in a 6 hour storm. The tank was 305 feet (93 m) in diameter, and was installed at a water depth of 230 feet

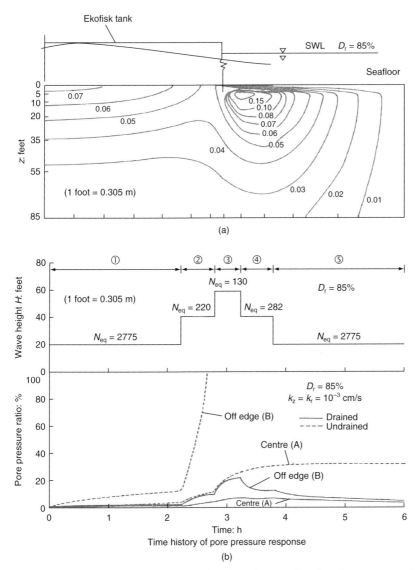

Fig. 6.7 *Finite element analyses of the Ekofisk tank (reproduced with permission of the ASCE from Rahman et al., 1977). (a) Ratios of excess pore pressures to initial stresses due to a 41 foot (12.5 m)-high wave occurring 3.5 hours into a 6 hour storm. (b) Comparison of predictions for undrained and drained calculations*

(70 m), on 85 feet (26 m) of dense to very dense sand overlying clay. The permeability of the sand was about $k = 10^{-3}$ cm/s and the coefficient of volume change was about $m_v = 1.73 \times 10^{-5}$ m^2/kN. The coefficient of consolidation was about $c_v = k/(\gamma_w m_v) = 3.5$ m^2/min.

Cyclic stress ratios in the soil were calculated due to loading from a 12.5 m-high wave. The results were combined with cyclic strength curves for the soil to determine the component of build-up of pore water pressures due to the wave. The analysis is repeated for many waves in the storm. Figure 6.7a shows contours of the calculated pore pressure ratios at the peak of the storm 3.2 hours after the start. A ratio of 1 would correspond to liquefaction. For the present analysis, the largest ratio was about 0.2, which occurred just outside the edge of the tank.

Figure 6.7b shows the pore pressure build-up and decay calculated for the 6 hour storm. The dashed curves were calculated assuming fully undrained conditions. The solid curves show that much smaller pore pressure increases would be expected if drainage is accounted for. The peak of the storm occurred after about 3 hours. Using the above soil parameters and the radial consolidation parameters in Section 6.11.3, the time factor at a time of 3 hours is $T_v = 4c_v t/B^2 = 4 \times 3.5 \times 3 \times 60/90^2 = 0.3$, which confirms that excess pore pressures essentially dissipate almost fully over 3 hours. This is why the pore pressures for the drained calculations are much smaller than for the undrained ones.

Observed soil responses of the tank were reported by Clausen *et al.* (1975). Pore pressure rises of the order of 20 kPa were recorded in the sand under the centre of the tank, for a 24 hour storm with significant wave heights up to about 11 metres. The data also confirmed dissipation of pore pressures during the period of the storm.

6.8.4 Modes of shallow sliding failure

Young *et al.* (1975) identified several modes of shallow sliding failure (Fig. 6.8). The modes are analysed assuming that the skirts are strong enough to support the implied loads. Each will need to be examined in design, usually by adapting a sliding block analysis, plasticity method, or slope stability analysis using limit equilibrium (e.g. Chen and Liu, 1990). The skirts are then designed structurally to support these loads:

(a) In passive wedge failure, the skirt pushes a passive wedge upwards as the caisson and skirts move laterally. An active failure may

316

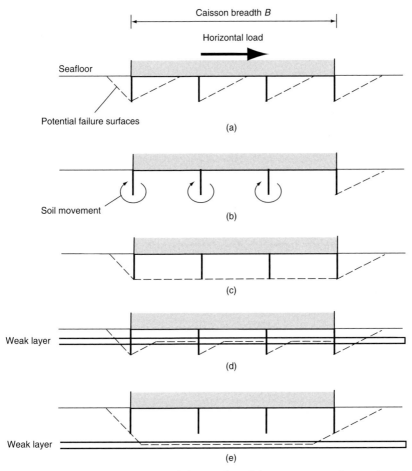

Fig. 6.8 Modes of shallow sliding failure (adapted from Young et al., 1975). (a) Passive wedge failure. (b) Deep passive failure. (c) Sliding base failure. (d) Sliding failure in a shallow weak zone with widely spaced skirts can be prevented by reducing the skirt spacing sufficiently. (e) Sliding failure in a deep weak zone can be prevented by increasing the skirt length sufficiently

develop behind the trailing skirt, or a crack may open there. A variation can include an active failure within each skirt compartment.

(b) In the deep passive failure mode, soil flows around the skirts as the caisson moves laterally. Shear resistance develops as a result of the plastic work needed to cause the associated shear deformations, which is manifested as changes in the normal stress on the skirts, and as a result of sliding on the base of the caisson.

317

(c) Sliding base failure involves a simple flat shear plane at the level of the skirt tips. A passive wedge develops ahead of the leading skirt. An active failure or crack develops behind the trailing skirt.

(d) If a weak soil layer exists and skirts do not penetrate far into it, a combined passive failure and sliding failure mode can develop. One way to prevent this is to make the skirts longer. Another way is to space the skirts close together, so that they interfere with the passive and active failure mechanisms within the skirt compartments.

(e) If a weak soil layer exists a short distance below the skirt tips, the failure surface can be diverted into the weak layer, with a passive wedge developing in front of the leading skirt and an active wedge or crack behind the trailing skirt.

The critical mode depends on the skirt length and spacing, and on the soil properties, and can be affected by relatively thin layers or lenses of weaker or stronger materials. For this reason, it is not always appropriate to optimise the skirt design: a robust design that is insensitive to thin layers can be better.

For the one or two most critical modes, key points can be identified, and stress paths experienced at these points can be determined from the analysis. These paths can then be applied to a soil sample in the laboratory, and the results can then be used in a further analysis.

6.8.5 Deep-seated failures

Deep-seated failures can result from adverse combinations of vertical, horizontal, and moment loading on the caisson, together with the water pressure loads on the surrounding seafloor and the buoyant weight of the caisson. Classical vertical bearing capacity failure can occur at a phase in the wave loading cycle when the horizontal loads are small. At this time, there may be some moment due to the variation in the water pressure across the top of the caisson. Figure 6.9 shows other deep failure modes:

(a) Deep-seated bearing failure: this is analysed by first replacing the actual foundation area with a reduced area over which only vertical and horizontal loads are assumed to act (Lauritzen and Schjetne, 1976).

(b) CARL and CARV failures (Andersen, 1991). In the CARL mode, the structure experiences a combined translation and forward rotation in the direction of the horizontal load, and the soil

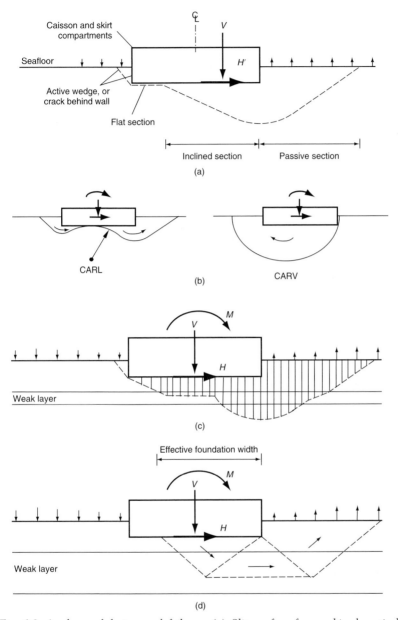

Fig. 6.9 Analyses of deep-seated failures. (a) Slip surface for combined vertical, horizontal, and moment loading (adapted from Lauritzen and Schjetne, 1976). (b) CARL and CARV failure surfaces (after Andersen, 1991). (c) Generalised failure surface through a weak zone, analysed using the method of slices (adapted from Young et al., 1975). (d) Sliding block analysis (adapted from Georgiadis and Michalopoulos, 1985)

moves in the same direction, with a passive failure in front of the motion and an active failure combined with a reverse bearing capacity failure at the trailing skirt and underneath the caisson. In the CARV mode, the structure rotates about a centre that is above the bearing area, with the soil moving in the opposite direction to the horizontal load on the structure.

(c) Distorted CARL-type failure (Young *et al.*, 1975): here, part of the CARL failure surface passes preferentially through a weak soil at some depth beneath the skirt tips.

(d) Sliding block mode (Georgiadis and Michalpoulos, 1985): a simplified analysis in which the caisson translates rightwards and downwards, with blocks of soil developing as shown.

In all cases, the three-dimensional nature of the failure surface must be accounted for. Depending on the soils present, these modes can be analysed using plasticity theory, or by adapting the method of slices used in slope stability problems. Different depths of slip surface and different centres and radii for the curved parts are tried until the mode with the lowest factor of safety is found.

Alternatively, a finite element analysis using an elasto-plastic constitutive model for the soil may be used, coupled with a realistic failure criterion. Further laboratory tests may be carried out based on stress paths inferred from the analyses, and the structural analysis may then be repeated in an iteration cycle. A typical arrangement of tests is shown in Fig. 6.10:

- cyclic triaxial extension and compression tests may be carried out for soils in the active and passive regions of a failure surface, where the principal changes in the stress during the critical failure mode are changes in the vertical and horizontal stress

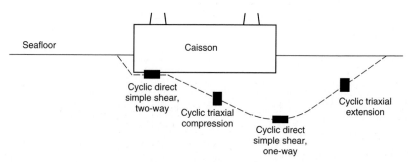

Fig. 6.10 Example of the relationship between analysis results and laboratory tests

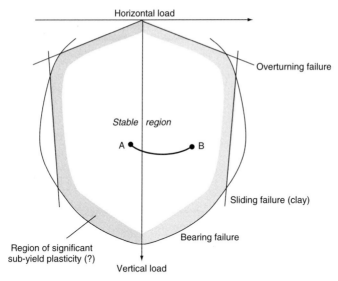

Fig. 6.11 Concept of a stability diagram (adapted from Young et al., 1975), and an example of a cyclic load path AB, including an offset due to steady current

- cyclic direct shear tests, simple shear tests, or hollow cylinder tests may be carried out for soils in the regions where shear motions dominate.

The cyclic stress magnitudes in the tests are typically modelled on the design storm. For example, if a simple storm consists of N_1 cycles at 33% of the maximum wave load, N_2 at 66%, and N_3 at 100%, then the cyclic load magnitudes applied in the laboratory tests may be N_1 cycles at 33% of the cyclic stresses calculated for the worst-case failure mode, N_2 at 66%, and N_3 at 100% of these stresses.

6.8.6   *Stability diagram*

Young *et al.* (1975) describe the concept of a stability diagram, in which limiting combinations of horizontal and vertical load on the platform are plotted for various failure scenarios. An example is sketched in Fig. 6.11. They recommend that such diagrams be used with some care, owing to the complexities of variable strength profiles and cyclic loading effects. Probabilistic studies such as those by Kraft and Murff (1975) and Wu *et al.* (1983, 1989b) can be of substantial assistance in assessing the reliability of the field data and of the analytical procedures on which the diagram is based.

6.9   Geotechnical design for dynamic and seismic loading

Seismic analysis of a gravity structure is a soil–structure interaction problem because the presence of the heavy structure can have a major effect on the earthquake accelerations experienced by the soil. This, in turn, has a major effect on the soil stiffness and damping responses, which affect the accelerations transmitted from the ground into the structure (Veletsos and Boaz, 1979; Svein and Andreasson, 1982). An additional complication is that earthquake-induced motion of the large volume of the concrete base through the water induces an additional resistance, sometimes modelled as an 'added-mass' effect.

An earthquake typically lasts between a few seconds and a minute or so. The soil is usually modelled as undrained during this period. Excess pore pressures generated during the earthquake are considered to dissipate after the shaking stops.

Penzien and Tseng (1976) describe the lumped-mass approach. As shown in Fig. 6.12a, the structure is modelled by a number of discrete masses connected by springs and dampers. The earthquake shaking is applied to one end of a system of three or four springs and dampers modelling the soil. The other end of the system is connected to the structure. Table 3.1 of this book lists stiffnesses for a rigid circular foundation on a uniform isotropic elastic half-space. A lumped mass approach has the advantage that, except for the caisson, the structural model can be quite sophisticated, the calculation can include added mass effects from the water, and the motions include effects of rocking as well as shear.

A more sophisticated approach is to model both the structure and the soil in a dynamic finite element analysis (Shaw *et al.*, 1977; Prevost and Hughes, 1978). This is costly in terms of requirements for computer calculation speed and memory, but can, in principle, fully represent all relevant aspects of behaviour. The method can be used for the dynamic analysis of wave loading as well as dynamic seismic loads. A sophisticated constitutive model can be employed to represent the soils.

A practical preliminary approach for seismic analysis is to use a one-dimensional wave propagation analysis, such as SHAKE/EERA described in Chapter 4, but with two different calculations (Fig. 6.12b). One calculation is for the soil response without a structure. In the second, a material layer is added to represent the mass of the structure per unit area of foundation. The calculated responses give two estimates of how the structure interacts with the soil. For example, the mode shapes for resonance will be different depending on whether the structure is included. The effects of prior cyclic loading can be addressed, and the

322

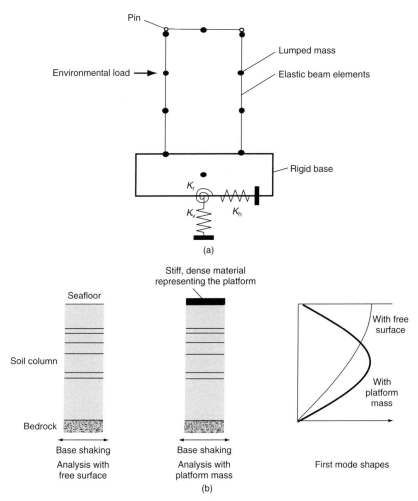

Fig. 6.12 Examples of simplified approaches to dynamic analysis. (a) Discrete parameter model for a gravity platform (after Penzien and Tseng, 1976). (b) One-dimensional approach for seismic analysis: effect of the structure weight on mode shapes. (c) Example of an extended iterative procedure when geotechnical and structural analyses are done separately

effects of cyclic strain amplitude can be included iteratively for the soil. A disadvantage is that the rocking motions are not included. In principle, however, the results can be used to specify the input accelerations for a simple lumped mass model, and the rocking motions that are outputs from that model can finally be applied in a finite element analysis of just the soil. This procedure has the disadvantage of being rather time-consuming, but it resolves problems of computer performance and can

323

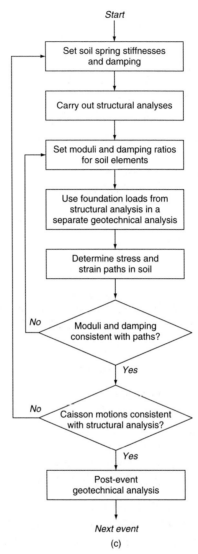

Start

Set soil spring stiffnesses and damping

Carry out structural analyses

Set moduli and damping ratios for soil elements

Use foundation loads from structural analysis in a separate geotechnical analysis

Determine stress and strain paths in soil

Moduli and damping consistent with paths?

No

Yes

Caisson motions consistent with structural analysis?

No

Yes

Post-event geotechnical analysis

Next event

(c)

Fig. 6.12 Continued

provide the engineer with a very good understanding of what happens in the soil during an earthquake.

As is the case for jackups and jackets, cyclic strain amplitudes and rate effects should normally be accounted for in the assessment of soil properties. One iterative approach is sketched in Fig. 6.12c. A separate, pseudo-static finite element analysis is carried out for the foundation soils, based on the outputs from the structural analysis. Within the

324

foundation analysis, elastic properties are determined iteratively, depending on the strain and other factors. An assessment of cyclic stiffness degradation and a liquefaction assessment may be needed. Once convergence is achieved, equivalent spring stiffnesses and damping values are calculated and compared with those used in the original structural analysis. If necessary, a further structural analysis is done using these new parameters, and the process continues until convergence between structural response, soil parameters, and soil responses is obtained.

A consolidation analysis is carried out to determine how the excess pore pressures in sand layers dissipate in association with fluid flow towards the edges of the foundation. The hydraulic gradients are calculated to determine whether fluidisation may occur; if so, its effects are assessed, and mitigation measures may be employed, such as the placement of a gravel or rock pile. It is also feasible that liquefaction may develop as a result of movements of pore pressure in the ground after an earthquake. The excess pore pressures generated in the clay layers add to the history of those layers, and will affect their subsequent response in terms of wave loading responses and of consolidation.

6.10   Geotechnical design of skirts

6.10.1 Design considerations

The principal geotechnical calculations with respect to skirt design are the calculations to determine skirt length and spacing, and the calculations for soil reaction forces that are used as inputs to the detailed structural design of the skirts and their connections to the underside of the caisson (Lacasse and D'Orazio, 1988). Skirt lengths and spacing must be sufficient to:

- force the critical failure mechanisms in the soil to be deep enough to provide an adequate margin of safety against global failure under the design actions
- provide the required installation functions
- transfer the implied load from the structure into the soil
- limit settlements, scour, fluidisation, and other effects.

It can happen that a platform location is changed during design. Because some of the foundation failure modes are sensitive to the presence of weak layers, robust skirt design choices should be insensitive to this. Some of the considerations involved are sketched in Fig. 6.13, and discussed below.

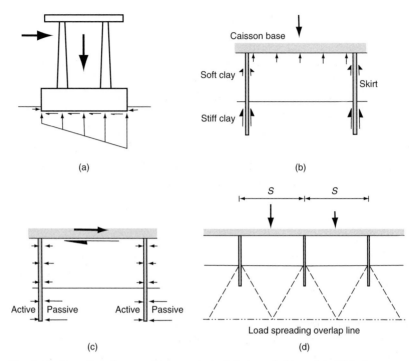

(a)

(b)

(c)

(d)

Fig. 6.13 *Considerations in the geotechnical design of skirts. (a) Global assumption for soil reaction stresses. (b) Details of vertical load transfer within a skirt compartment. (c) Lateral load transfer. (d) Load spreading into the soil*

6.10.2 Vertical load transfer

Figure 6.13a illustrates a common assumption for the overall changes in the bearing stress on a foundation due to lateral loading including overturning moment. A linear stress distribution is assumed as an overall trend, and active and passive shear resistances can develop around the edges. However, detailed load transfer for a skirted foundation occurs partly through concentrated loads on the skirts themselves. Larger skirt loads will occur at the edges of the caisson compared with the centre. The detailed structural analysis is different compared with a small onshore shallow foundation.

Figure 6.13b shows aspects of the vertical load transfer from the caisson and into the skirt and the soil in a skirt compartment. In this case, the skirt has penetrated through soft clay into stiffer material. There are two possible routes for vertical load transfer:

- from the caisson into the skirt walls, then via shear stress and end bearing into the soil

- directly by vertical bearing on the soil in contact with the roof of the skirt compartment.

During installation, only the first route is mobilised initially, until the soil comes into contact with the roof. Consequently, the main part of the platform weight may be carried by the walls. Grouting effectively establishes the second route as a possibility for cyclic components of vertical load. Under low-level cyclic loading, both routes may be partially mobilised, provided there is no gas in the skirt compartment or the soil. During a global bearing failure, the second route will be mobilised once the skin friction on the skirts has been overcome.

6.10.3 Lateral load transfer

Figure 6.13c illustrates the lateral load transfer between the caisson and the underlying soil. The same two routes are again available, except that the load transfer from the roof into the soil will require a relative motion between the soil and the caisson that is constrained by the skirt wall. Consequently the principal route will often be via the walls. This means that the soil resistance will consist of passive pressure on one side of each skirt wall, and a reduction from initial to active pressures on the trailing side.

The state of the soil in a skirt compartment can be analysed using a simple commercially available finite element package. For closely spaced skirts, the passive wedge can interfere with the active wedge, resulting in a rather complicated stress distribution in the soil.

For relatively widely spaced skirts, Murff and Miller (1977) analysed the mechanism shown in Fig. 6.8a, in which a triangular wedge of material is pushed forwards by the skirt, and moved upwards on an inclined slip surface. The mechanism acts against the downwards force on the soil from the caisson, and can prevent the full shear stress being mobilised on the plane through the skirt tips. An approximate relation was developed for the vertical stress required to prevent the mechanism from occurring and so ensure that the skirt system acted as an effective shear key.

6.10.4 Local effects on consolidation and settlement

Consolidation and settlement effects associated with the soils in and just below skirt compartments are also affected by the route taken by the vertical and lateral loads.

For vertical load transfer via the skirts, a load spreading approach sketched in Figure 6.13d might be considered. In this case the contribution of the soft clay has been ignored, and all of the vertical load is taken by friction and end bearing in the stiffer clay. Settlements arise as a result of compression of the triangular wedges of material, and can be calculated by adapting the textbook calculation for load-spreading (e.g. Das, 2004; see also Section 6.11).

If a load spreading factor of n is used, the wedges meet at a distance $nS/2$ below the top of the stiffer layer, where S is the skirt spacing. By choosing a skirt length to penetrate at least this distance into the stiffer clay, an efficient design is achieved in which a reasonably uniform distribution of vertical stress is applied to a bearing area at the level of the skirt tips, in line with the assumption of Fig. 6.13a.

6.10.5 Scour and fluidisation issues

The potential for scour around the edges of a gravity platform is increased because the caisson forces flowing water to increase in speed as it passes around the caisson (Fig. 6.14a). Edge skirts allow

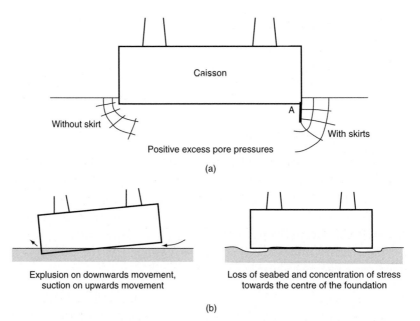

Fig. 6.14 Some aspects of fluidisation and scour/erosion. (a) Effect of the skirt in changing the flownet near the edge of the bearing area. The flownet with skirts has an increased flowpath length and a decreased hydraulic gradient there, helping to reduce the possibility of piping or erosion there. (b) Pumping action with tension and no skirts

scour to occur outside the bearing area, but prevent material from being lost from underneath the caisson edges.

The possibility of fluidisation near the edges of the caisson arises because of excess pore pressure generated in sandy soils beneath the centre of the caisson, as a result of storm or earthquake loading. The pore pressures induce fluid flows which can be conceptualised in terms of a flownet. The flowlines tend to converge at the edge of the caisson, indicating higher flow velocities here. Depending on the magnitudes of the excess pore pressures, the gradients may become sufficiently high that the effective stresses in the soil at the edge of the caisson reduce to near zero, and the soil loses almost all strength.

The possibility of fluidisation and erosion is increased dramatically if the vertical stress at the caisson edges reaches zero during cyclic loading (Lacasse *et al.*, 1991). In the absence of skirts, the process shown in Fig. 6.14b can develop. The caisson lifts slightly away from the soil during part of a wave cycle, sucking water into the gap. When the gap closes, the water is pushed out, taking some of the soil with it. The process then repeats in the next cycle.

6.11   Geotechnical design for consolidation and settlement

6.11.1 *Types of settlement*
Offshore structures experience immediate settlements, gradual settlements due to the effects of cyclic loading and changes of load condition over time, and long-term settlements associated with primary and secondary consolidation and with regional subsidence. Settlement limits are determined by limits on:

- Differential settlement between a platform and its hydrocarbon conductors, and between it and its connections to sub-sea pipelines and cables. Excess settlement can overstress and possibly fail these items.
- Absolute settlement with respect to sea level. This can affect the usability of a boat landing deck attached to the platform, and can reduce an inadequately sized air gap to such an extent that a large wave may impact the deck.
- Absolute tilt, which can affect serviceability by affecting the industrial systems on the deck and the ability of people to work on the platform.

Eide and Andersen's (1984) taxonomy classified settlements according to the type of load (static or cyclic), time (immediate or long term), and

329

type of strain (volumetric or combined volumetric and shear). Static load effects in this taxonomy include:

(1*a*) immediate settlements, essentially undrained for clays
(1*b*) creep settlements at constant volume, also called secondary compression
(2) primary consolidation settlement, considering only the volumetric components of strain
(3) secondary settlement – the redistribution of stresses due to the effect of primary consolidation.

Settlements due to cyclic loading were classified as resulting from:

(4*a*) local plastic yielding and stress redistribution under undrained conditions
(4*b*) cyclically induced pore pressures and changes in the effective stress and soil stiffness
(5) volumetric strains due to the dissipation of cyclically induced pore pressures.

The processes are somewhat interactive. For example, type (5) is a consolidation process, and leads to secondary effects of type (3) due to redistribution of effective stress, and the changes in the stress and density lead to changes in the soil stiffness, which affect the original consolidation process.

Bowles (1996) found that, for onshore structures not subjected to extensive cyclic loading, immediate and long-term consolidation settlements could be estimated quite accurately, but estimates of the rate of consolidation settlement were often inaccurate. He notes that structural problems can sometimes be induced by settlements that are more rapid than predicted. It can be wise to ensure that a robust design is not sensitive to the rate of settlement.

6.11.2 Immediate settlements

Immediate settlements occur almost simultaneously with the application of the load that causes them. For gravity platforms these settlements occur during installation. They can be elastic or elasto-plastic. They can be estimated using a finite element program incorporating an appropriate elasto-plastic constitute model, or by the methods of settlement calculation for shallow foundations described in standard textbooks (e.g. Bowles, 1996; Das, 2005).

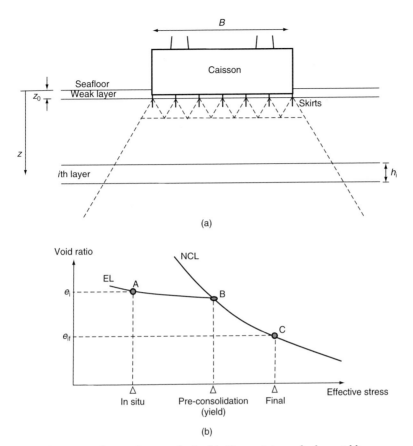

Fig. 6.15 (a) Load-spreading method. (b) Determining whether yielding occurs
for one-dimensional compression

One such standard method, the load-spreading method, is illustrated
for a gravity platform in Fig. 6.15a. The net change in the vertical load
on the foundation bearing area consists of the buoyant weight W' of
the platform. This net change is assumed to be supported, at a depth
z beneath the seafloor, by an effective foundation whose lateral
dimensions have been increased by spreading, through a spreading
factor n. If the foundation bearing area is A at the reference level, at
depth z_0 below the seafloor, the average increase $\Delta\sigma_v$ in the vertical
stress beneath the centreline at z below the seafloor is estimated as

$$\Delta\sigma_v = \frac{W'/A}{(1 + 2z - z_0/nB)^2} \tag{6.6}$$

It may be satisfactory and conservative to include the full buoyant weight in this calculation, and to ignore the shear resistance on the outside of the edge skirts. For sufficiently long skirts, the reference level will be the level of the skirt tips. The settlements calculated below will be added to the local settlements due to stress concentrations around the skirt walls.

A drained analysis is done for sand layers, and to compute the long-term settlements in silts and clays. The imposed changes in the stress are assumed to be taken up entirely by changes in the effective stress. The net settlement is calculated by summing the settlement contributions for all of the sub-layers. One way to calculate for a cohesive layer is to plot the effective stress state during the loading on a stress–volume diagram (Fig. 6.15b). If the stress does not reach yield, the response is determined by the elastic line EL. If the stress goes beyond yield, the response is determined by the normal compression line (NCL). The net settlement s of the sub-layers can then be estimated as

$$s = \left(\sum_i h_i \frac{\Delta\sigma_v}{D_i}\right)_{\text{granular sub-layers}} + \left(\sum_i h_i \frac{e_i - e_{if}}{1 + e_i}\right)_{\text{cohesive sub-layers}}$$

(6.7)

where h_i is the height of the ith sub-layer, D_i is the constrained modulus of the soil in a granular layer, and e_i and e_{if} are, respectively, the initial and final void ratios of the soil in a cohesive layer.

DNV (1992) provides several empirical equations relating constrained modulus to effective stress and other parameters, based on Janbu (1967). A simplified summary of the recommendations is given in Table 6.2. The constrained modulus for a linear, isotropic elastic soil is given by

$$D = \frac{(1 - \mu)E}{(1 + \mu)(1 - 2\mu)} = \frac{2 - 2\mu}{1 - 2\mu}G$$

(6.8)

where E is the drained Young's modulus, G is the shear modulus, and μ is Poisson's ratio. These properties can be measured in a drained triaxial test, and depend on the stresses in the test, the density of the soil, the change in the stress that is applied, and other factors.

For undrained loading, Poisson's ratio is sometimes considered to be 1/2, which gives an infinite constrained modulus and no strain. While this is a good estimate for one-dimensional conditions in an oedometer, these conditions are not applied in reality. One simple practical approach for undrained settlement is to replace the drained constrained

Table 6.2 Constrained moduli (DNV, 1992)

Type	Equation	Parameters and notes
EL (elastic)	$D = mp_a$	Norwegian overconsolidated clays: m in the range 20–150
EP (elastic–plastic)	$D = m\sqrt{p_a \sigma'_v}$	Inorganic sands: m in the range 80–400. Inorganic silts: m in the range 40 to >80
PL (plastic)	$D = m\sigma'_v$	Normally consolidated clays: m between about 10 for soft clays to greater than 20 for stiff clays

$p_a = 100\,\text{kN/m}^2$ represents atmospheric pressure. σ'_v is the vertical effective stress.

modulus in the settlement calculation with the drained Young's modulus. In effect, this assumes that no change occurs in the horizontal effective stress. Provided no yielding occurs, this can overestimate the undrained settlements, but can be adequate if the results satisfy the limiting settlement criteria.

6.11.3 Primary consolidation

Terzaghi's theory of consolidation was briefly reviewed in Chapter 3. The one-dimensional theory is often used as a first approximation for the consolidation settlements of type 2 in Eide and Andersen's (1984) taxonomy. Figure 6.16a shows a situation in which this approximation is reasonably accurate. The gravity base rests on a relatively thin layer of clay of height H, overlying a sand layer that can serve as an effective drain. Because H is much smaller than the caisson breadth B, the principal flow of water will be vertical, into the sand layer. Figure 6.16b shows an alternative situation where the radial consolidation equation is more appropriate. The gravity base rests on a thin compressible layer overlying relatively impermeable soil or rock. The flow of water is primarily radial.

The initial increase in the pore water pressure for the one-dimensional case equals the average stress W'/A applied by the buoyant weight of the platform. This is fairly uniform across the base, but there will be some relatively rapid drainage at the edges of the caisson. For the radial consolidation case, the equal-strain analysis gives a parabolic initial pore pressure distribution (Fig. 6.16c), with the largest pressure being twice the imposed vertical stress (Olson, 1977; Olson and Li, 2002). The effective stresses do not change immediately, so the caisson is bent upwards at the centre due to the greater support there.

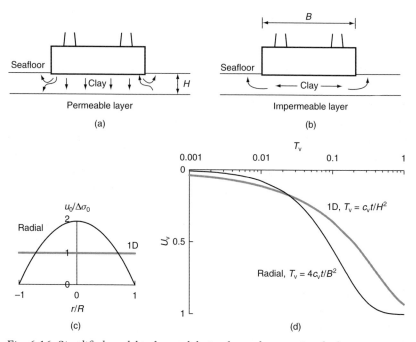

Fig. 6.16 Simplified models of consolidation beneath a gravity platform resting on a relatively thin layer of relatively compressible clay. (a) Approximately one-dimensional consolidation of a thin clay layer over a relatively permeable layer. (b) Approximately radial consolidation of a thin clay layer over a relatively impermeable layer. (c) Initial vertical total stress beneath the caisson base. (d) The degree of consolidation U_v versus the time factor T_v

Figure 6.16d shows degree of consolidation U_v plotted against time factor T_v for the two analyses. For the one-dimensional case, $T_v = c_v t / H^2$, where c_v is the coefficient of consolidation of the clay layer and t is time from loading. c_v is obtained from an oedometer test between relevant stress levels. For example, for a gravity platform resting on a 10 m-deep clay layer with a coefficient of consolidation of 1 m²/year, nearly all the long-term settlement will have occurred when $T_v = 1$, corresponding to a duration of $1 \times 10^2 / 1 = 100$ years. For the radial case, using the equal-strain theory for a rigid base, $T_v = 4c_v t / B^2$. Nearly all the consolidation is completed when $T_v \approx 0.4$. For a gravity platform with a 100 m-wide caisson on clay layer with a coefficient of consolidation of 1 m²/year, this corresponds to a duration of $0.4 \times 100^2 / (4 \times 1) = 1600$ years.

Excess pore pressures also develop as a result of cyclic loading during the lifetime of the structure. These are considered in relation to type 4 settlements in Eide and Andersen's (1984) taxonomy, and their dissipation is considered as type 5. Because different parts of the foundation soil experience different cyclic stresses, the excess pore pressures are different, and a more complex pattern of fluid flow and volumetric compression develops in the three-dimensional soil body. An additional issue is that the changes due to these effects can also change the coefficient of consolidation of the soil, hence affecting the type 2 analyses. In principle, a finite element program should be able to handle this complexity. In practice, sound engineering judgement is required. The effects also alter the bearing stresses beneath the caisson, and so affect the structural analysis of the caisson and platform as a whole.

Consolidation settlements can be reduced in clays using preinstalled sand drains and other systems (Tjelta *et al.*, 1990; Leung and Shen, 2008).

6.11.4 Secondary consolidation
The theory of secondary consolidation was reviewed in Chapter 3. The evidence for practical effects of this and for ageing is described by Bjerrum (1973). The process appears to be one in which fluid flow is driven by a gradient that is not associated with excess pore pressures (Mesri and Vardhanabhuti, 2005). It can be significant particularly for silty soils, and can be identified in the results of oedometer tests.

6.11.5 Regional subsidence
Regional subsidence can be caused by the removal of hydrocarbons from a deep reservoir. If the hydrocarbons are not replaced by water injection, the removal reduces the pore oil pressure in the reservoir, and so increases the effective stress on the solids in the reservoir. This leads to settlement of the sand or rock skeleton, leading to regional settlement at the ground surface.

For example, about 4 m of subsidence occurred in the first 20 years or so of field development around Ekofisk in the North Sea (Sulak and Danielsen, 1988; Johnson *et al.*, 1988). The principal oil-bearing stratum is a chalk. Application of soil mechanics principles, applied in a finite element analysis, appears to provide a straightforward explanation (Boade *et al.*, 1988). Expected subsidence in 2011 is between 6 and 11 m.

Regional subsidence can be monitored using GPS (Mes *et al.*, 1995). It can be controlled by appropriate control of well pressures. Camp and Langley (1991) discuss the design of offshore structures to withstand severe subsidence.

Small amounts of regional subsidence can also, in principle, be caused by changes in the pore water pressure in soil layers that are confined between impermeable layers and under non-hydrostatic pressure before field development. Such changes can occur as a result of various holes and cracks that may be made in the confining layers as part of the field development process, such as site investigation boreholes and hydrocarbon wells. The estimation of the potential settlement from this case requires a good knowledge of the initial in-situ pore water pressure, and of the compressibility of the soil layer.

6.12   Monitoring and validation

Gerwick (2007) lists the following instrumentation that is typically used for controlling the installation of a gravity platform:

- echo sounders to show the bottom clearance
- pressure transducers to read the draft
- pressure transducers to read the internal ballast in each caisson cell
- strain gauges to read axial forces and moments in dowels and selected skirts
- differential pressure transducers to monitor water pressures in skirt compartments
- biaxial inclinometers to read the tilt
- earth pressure transducers for contact pressures in the base slab of the caisson
- strain gauge transducers to measure stresses in the base slab and the domes
- pressure transducers to monitor skirt penetration.

Many of these systems will continue in operation after installation. Additionally, remotely operated vehicles (ROVs) can be used to monitor the penetration of the skirts into the seabed, and to inspect the edges of the foundation during service.

Much of the installation monitoring system will continue to be of service during the lifetime of the structure. Instrumentation will also normally be installed to measure settlements, pore water pressures in the soil, subsidence, accelerations, and, sometimes, the total stress in the soil. A data management system on board the platform will record the information and may transmit it onshore for analysis. Huslid (2001) describes the use of pore water pressure transducers installed at 10 m intervals in a predrilled borehole to 60 m below the seabed. Settlements of the platform relative to the seabed were measured with a cased and tensioned tell-tale rod anchored to a cement grout body located at the bottom of a borehole. Lunne *et al.* (1981) describe a short-term settlement measurement system employing a hydraulic reservoir fixed to the platform and connected to a pressure transducer located on the seabed about one caisson diameter from the edge of the caisson. Spidsoe and Hilmarsen (1983) describe acceleration data and analyses of three concrete gravity platforms subjected to one of the most severe hurricanes ever recorded in the North Sea. More data are presented by Spidsoe and Skjastad (1986, 1987). Mes *et al.* (1995) describe the use of GPS to measure the subsidence of the seafloor, essentially relative to the nearly static mean sea level. Total stress cells can also be installed in the soil.

Centrifuge model testing has been used to validate design proposals prior to construction, and to prove concepts (Rowe and Craig, 1976; Finn *et al.*, 1985; Allard *et al.*, 1994; Andersen *et al.*, 1994; Taylor, 1995; Springman, 2002).

6.13 Decommissioning

Decommissioning occurs at the end of the design lifetime of a gravity platform, when its function has been achieved. A platform may alternatively be reused, after appropriate inspection and renovation if necessary. Pliskin (1979), CDOP (1985), Broughton *et al.* (2002), OGP (2003), and others describe the issues that can arise. In some cases, the requirement for safety during removal can be a critical factor in the original design of the platform, or in determining its design life.

After 20 years or so, the soil will have experienced a large number of severe environmental loading events, and may be denser and stronger than during installation, but also with stress histories that may be noticeably different in different parts of the three-dimensional volume of soil. A new site investigation may be required in order to plan the platform removal.

In principle, the removal may be simply done by removing all heavy weights from the platform, pumping ballast out of the caisson, and pumping air into the skirt compartments below the caisson. The induced buoyancy may pop the structure out of the soil. In practice, this is an unstable event that can severely stress the caisson. ISO 19903 recommends that the possibility of uneven separation from the seabed, and drop off of soil or under-base grout shortly after separation, should be considered, and that the structural and motion response of the platform should be evaluated.

337

7

Pipelines, flowlines, cables, and risers

Chapter 7 describes the various types of offshore pipeline, flowline, cable, and riser, covering pipeline and cable route selection, design and execution of a survey for a pipeline or cable, selection of appropriate installation methods and technologies, assessment of pipeline–seabed and riser–seabed interactions, and planning of shore approaches.

7.1   Introduction

7.1.1   General

Offshore pipelines and flowlines are pipes that are laid on or below the seabed to carry oil, gas or other fluids from one place to another. They are described as the 'arteries' of the oil and gas industry (Palmer and King, 2006). Several long pipelines stretch the length or breadth of the North Sea (Berge, 2005). Europipe 1 carries offshore gas 660 km from the Draupner East riser platform, west of Stavanger in Norway, to Emden in North Germany. The Langeled gas export pipeline is 1200 km long, running from Nyhamna on the west coast of Norway via Sleipner in the North Sea to Easington in the UK (Solberg and Gjertveit, 2007). Pipelines can be laid in deep water (Palmer, 1994; Randolph and White, 2008a): the Independence Trail Pipeline in the Gulf of Mexico reaches a depth of 2412 m (Al-Sharif, 2007).

Figure 7.1a shows some of the terminology involved for oil and gas pipelines (Bai and Bai, 2005; Guo et al., 2005). 'Export pipelines' transport hydrocarbons from production facilities to shore. Within a particular offshore field development, 'flowlines' transport oil or gas from satellite wells to sub-sea manifolds, or from manifolds to tie-ins with risers, which transport the fluids up to the systems on the deck of a platform. Flowlines also transport water or other chemicals from production facilities, via sub-sea manifolds, to injection wellheads.

338

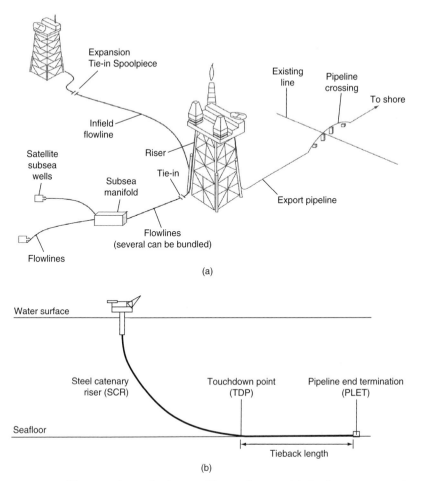

Fig. 7.1 Offshore pipelines, flowlines, cables, and risers. (a) Pipelines, risers, and associated systems (© 2005 Elsevier: Guo et al., 2005). (b) Steel catenary riser for a floating platform (© 2006 Offshore Technology Conference: adapted from Brunner et al., 2006)

'Infield flowlines' transport oil or gas between production facilities. In deep water (Fig. 7.1b), steel catenary riser (SCR) pipes hang from a floating platform and are connected to sub-sea wellheads or to a pipeline termination (Gosse and Barksdale, 1969; Coker, 1991; Bai and Bai, 2005; Antani et al., 2008).

Pipeline and flowline diameters range from about 10 cm for gas flowlines up to about 2 m for lines transporting large quantities of oil or gas. Their contents can be at high temperature (HT) and high pressure (HP). Wall designs range from simple steel pipes to sophisticated designs with separate layers for internal and external corrosion and abrasion control, structural strength, and thermal insulation (Palmer and King, 2006). In pipe-in-pipe (PIP) pipelines, an inner pipe is contained within an outer pipe, with heated water being pumped through the annulus between them (Harrison *et al.*, 2003; Jukes *et al.*, 2008). Some pipelines include electrical heating along their length. The condensation of paraffin waxes, hydrates, and other solids can be a problem. Robot systems called 'pigs' are used to clean pipelines periodically. These are inserted at one access point and travel many kilometres under their own power, removing obstructions and carrying out minor repairs (Haugen *et al.*, 1983; Guo *et al.*, 2005).

Sub-sea cables carry electrical or optical signals, or electrical power between platforms, and carry telephone, telegraph, and Internet traffic across seas. The transatlantic telegraph cables are over 4000 km long. The first was attempted in 1857, and the first successful one was completed in 1866 (Hearn, 2004). Noad (1993) lists 16 sub-sea fibre-optic cables between the UK and Europe. Sub-sea power cables carry electrical power between windfarm platforms, and from offshore to land.

Pipelines and cables can be installed directly on the seafloor, or in trenches, or be buried below the seafloor. Many flowlines are simply laid on the seabed. A trench has the advantage that it helps to keep the pipeline in place laterally (TJA, 1999). Burial can provide good thermal insulation as well as protection against seafloor hazards including fishing gear and debris flows (Morrow and Larkin, 2007). Trenching and burial are done using specialised sub-sea jetting or ploughing systems.

7.1.2 Pipeline projects

Large pipeline projects are multidisciplinary and often international in character. Pipelines typically pass through areas with different ecologies, environmental loading characteristics, and geohazard settings. Geotechnical design tasks can include installation design, provision of systems to stabilise pipelines on or in the seabed, and shore approach designs which take the pipeline into shallow water and across the wave zone.

Arthur *et al.* (1994) describe a project involving the installation of over 300 km miles of high-pressure pipes, power lines, and fibre-optic control cables in the environmentally sensitive area of Mobile Bay, Alabama. Features of the project are illustrated in Fig. 7.2, and included

- use of PIP technology to transport and insulate high-temperature gas at pressures of up to 70 MPa

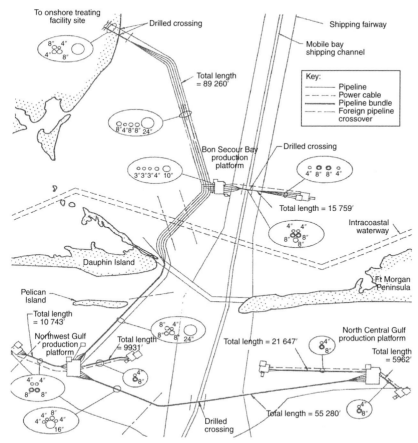

Fig. 7.2 Mobile Bay Pipeline Project. (© 1994 Offshore Technology Conference: Arthur et al., 1994)

- water depths ranging from less than a metre to 15 m
- soils ranging from an extremely soft clay to a very hard sand
- two directionally drilled shore crossings
- two directionally drilled water-to-water borings under the shipping channel
- crossing of the 900 m-wide natural sandbar 'Pelican Island'
- construction of 58 risers
- return of the bottom contour to within 1 foot of the original position.

Over 50 contractors were involved with an in-place procurement budget of US$82 million. Design studies started in early 1986. Construction took place in the 1991 and 1992 summer seasons, when weather windows allowed. The work was completed on time and within budget, with no lost-time safety accidents and no significant environmental incidents.

7.1.3   Pipeline geotechnics

The intimate contact between the pipeline and the seabed over long distances means that geotechnics plays a major role in pipeline design. Cathie *et al.* (2005) define 'pipeline geotechnics' as a specialty in which geotechnical knowledge and methodologies are applied in systematic ways to the engineering of cables and pipelines.

Pipelines and cables encounter many different terrains and geohazards along their length. They have little longitudinal buckling strength, and even a 1 m steel pipe behaves like a floppy string at a length scale of kilometres. Installation and performance are strongly affected by the upper few metres of seabed. These upper few metres are affected by scour and marine life. In-situ effective stresses are low, and undisturbed sampling and laboratory testing can be difficult. Some of the phenomena involve particle size effects, and may lie outside the range of many continuum constitutive models.

7.2   Pipeline and cable route selection

7.2.1   Factors determining route selection

The start and end points of a cable or pipeline are usually determined by production or delivery locations. The route in between is usually selectable. The difference in cost between a well-selected route and a poorly selected one can amount to many millions of dollars.

The aim of route selection is to find a route that provides security, allows the asset to be installed in a practical and cost-effective way, and allows it to be operated, inspected, maintained, and repaired if necessary. Palmer and King (2006) describe the principal factors to be considered, including:

- politics and regulatory requirements
- environmental impact
- physical factors
- interactions with other uses of the seabed.

The assessment of environmental impact, physical factors, and interactions with other users of the seabed normally includes:

342

- an assessment of the geological setting
- an oceanographic survey
- a bathymetric and geophysical survey, usually including seafloor imaging
- a geohazard assessment, including seismic risk assessment in earthquake-prone regions
- a geotechnical survey
- a borrow search.

Several case histories are available in the literature, including a survey for a gas pipeline between Oman and India (Mullee, 1995), the Malampaya gas pipeline in the Philippines (Macara, 2002), the Ormen Lange gas pipeline off Norway (Eklund *et al.*, 2007; Eiksund *et al.*, 2008), and the Gaza pipeline in the Eastern Mediterranean (Willis *et al.*, 2008).

7.2.2   Hazards for pipelines

Figure 7.3 shows some common hazards for offshore pipelines. Commercial fishing is one of the major hazards in some regions (Fig. 7.3a). Large trawlers use heavy weighted nets that are pulled along the bottom of the sea, and which stretch several kilometres behind the trawler. These nets and their attachments can snag as they go over an unburied pipeline, potentially leading to pipeline damage as well as to damage to the fishing gear and the trawler too (TJA, 1999).

Vessels that set anchors down on the seabed are also a hazard, through their weight as well as by catching and dragging. Dropped objects are a hazard too. Some areas of the seabed are used for military purposes, such as for submarine exercises. These areas can contain mines, wrecks, munitions, and other dumped material, and should obviously be avoided.

Uneven seabeds can lead to free spans (Fig. 7.3b), where a pipeline spans two high points. This subjects the pipeline to additional bending and axial stresses in the free span, and can lead to pipeline flow-induced vibration caused by vortex shedding as water flows over and under the pipe (Wallingford, 1992). Where necessary, berms can be built by rock dumping or gravel dumping to smooth out a seafloor and so allow a pipeline to pass (Eklund *et al.*, 2007; McClure and Dixon, 2008). The materials used in the dump will often be from the area of the dump, and will be found in a borrow search of the area involving geophysical exploration to find potential suitable materials, followed by sampling to verify properties.

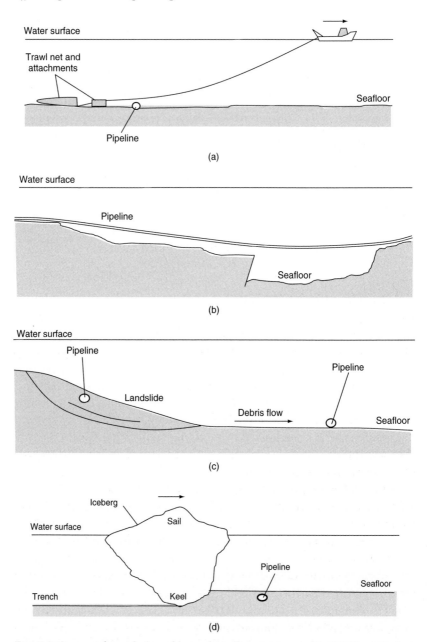

Fig. 7.3 Some geohazards for cables and pipelines (not to scale). (a) Hazards from fishing vessels and anchoring vessels. (b) Free span created by an uneven seabed, sand dunes, rock outcrops, or movement on a geological fault. (c) Submarine landslides and debris flows. (d) Trenching action of an iceberg keel. (e) Fluid expulsion features in the seafloor, and other pipelines or seabed debris

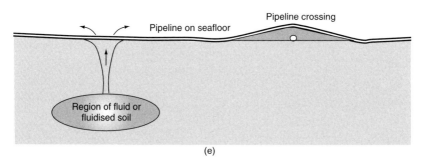

Fig. 7.3 *Continued*

Geological faults are hazards because they are places where significant ground movement can occur (Willis *et al.*, 2008). A long pipeline may pass through areas of different seismic risk, and of different hydro-dynamic climates. Cyclic pressures from earthquakes and water waves can potentially lead to a liquefaction of a sandy seabed, allowing a light pipeline to rise from a buried depth, or a heavy one to sink in. However, wave pressures can also lead to densification of trench fill material (Clukey *et al.*, 1980b).

Hard, rocky seabeds can abrade a pipe or cable, and do not provide easy ways to fix the pipe in position. Very soft seabeds allow a pipeline to sink in, which can create difficulties for maintenance. Seabeds containing boulders or rock outcrops can result in severe bending of the pipeline, and can be a cause of construction delays for pipelines or cables that are to be buried.

Some seafloor regions are hilly and even mountainous, posing a risk of submarine landslides (Fig. 7.3c). Mudslides can be triggered by hurricanes, earthquakes, or simply the accumulation of deposited material over time (Mirza *et al.*, 2006; Gilbert *et al.*, 2007). Seafloor valleys can channel debris flows or turbidity currents from landslides that are far away, providing a potential threat to pipelines and cables that pass through valleys (Parker *et al.*, 2008; Zakeri and Nadim, 2008). 'Furrow fields' are large-scale variations in the seafloor topography which, amongst other effects, can channel sub-sea currents in a way that increases scour around pipelines (Clukey *et al.*, 2007).

In cold regions, icebergs can pose a significant threat to pipelines. About 80% of an iceberg exists underwater (Fig. 7.3d). If the keel is too deep, the iceberg will ground on the seafloor, and will be held until it breaks unto smaller pieces or melts. If the keel is not so deep, just a few metres deeper than the water depth, the iceberg will gouge out a channel in the seabed as it is pushed along by wind and currents. The channel depth can be calculated using geotechnical methods, and pipelines can be constructed in these hazard regions by burying them deeper than this depth (Palmer *et al.*, 1990b; Kenny *et al.*, 2007).

Some areas of the seabed contain fluid expulsion features such as pock marks and mud volcanoes. These pose a hazard because they remove support from a pipeline, as well as applying forces to it. Existing cables and pipelines also create difficulties for a new cable or pipeline. A bridging structure will normally be needed. One method involves placing gravel and rock fill over the existing pipeline, and placing the new pipe on the fill (Fig. 7.3e).

Shorelines are hazardous because the relatively shallow water depth means that water movements associated with waves and currents can be significant at the level of the seafloor, potentially leading to scour around the pipeline. Geomorphologic and environmental factors include wave breaking, longshore currents, rip currents, wave refraction, variable seabed geology, and complex sediment transport issues (Herbich, 2000a; Reeve *et al.*, 2004). Shorelines are also utilised by many other users.

7.2.3 Route surveys

Bathymetry is a major determinant of pipeline design and of the installation technologies that will be needed. Mullee (1995) describes a preliminary reconnaissance with approximate bathymetry over an 8–10 km-wide swathe, followed by more accurate bathymetry over a 1 km-wide corridor. OSIF (1999) recommends that a bathymetric and geophysical survey be conducted on a corridor with a width of between 500 m and 1 km centred around the planned route of a pipeline or cable.

For shore approaches, OSIF (1999) recommends three geotechnical boreholes and/or in-situ test locations per kilometre. A typical programme further offshore would involve sampling and in-situ testing at kilometre points (KP) along the entire pipeline route, with additional investigations where there are geohazards or where special structures are required such as span-supports or pipeline crossings. Borehole depths will normally depend on the size of the cable or pipeline, the nature of the seafloor features and the geohazards, and the decision on whether to lay it on the seabed, place it in an open trench, or bury it. Recommended minimum borehole depths are 1–2 m in untrenched sections, the trench depth plus 1 m in trenched section, up to 5 m or more in a soil transition zone or at a pipeline crossing, and deeper if needed to investigate seafloor hazards such as pock marks and scours.

Specialised geotechnical tests can also be done at little extra cost. OSIF (1999) recommends that consideration be given to in-situ model ploughing and/or jetting tests (Noad, 1993), small-scale model pipeline settlement tests, plate bearing tests, and tests of the thermal conductivity of the seafloor. Laboratory investigations of strain–rate effects on the soil strength can assist in planning installation. Electrical resistivity, geochemical, and bacteriological tests assist the corrosion engineer to estimate pipeline corrosion rates and select counter-measures.

7.3   Installation

7.3.1   Pipe-laying operations

Pipelines, flowlines, and cables may be laid on the seabed or in a pre-cut trench by one of four methods, called tow/pull, S-lay, J-lay, and reel-lay (Gerwick, 2007).

In the tow/pull method, a pipeline is fabricated in a coastal construction yard. Brown (2006) describes two types of assembly site, either parallel to the coast or perpendicular to it. In the former case, several kilometres of pipeline can be constructed on a long beach. The pipe will be fitted with buoyancy modules, and small blimps or balloons may be attached as markers, and then the pipe is carefully pulled out to sea. In a perpendicular site, a relatively short section of pipeline is constructed, and then a tug pulls part of it out to sea, at right angles to the coastline. Sections of pipe are welded on, with buoyancy tanks and blimps, and the tug pulls moves a little more out to sea.

Pipelines may be towed to their final location in several configurations. Figure 7.4a shows the surface tow mode, where the pipeline travels at the water surface and is therefore subject to wave action. Pipelines can be towed at some intermediate water depth by attaching heavy chains to them at intervals along their length. The chains pull the pipeline down until they contact the seafloor, whereupon some of the weight is taken by the seafloor. By careful design of chain weights and lengths, it is possible to keep the buoyant pipeline at a controlled depth. Pipelines can also be pulled along the seafloor. The longest single length of pipeline installed in this way is believed to be 30 km (Palmer and King, 2006). A typical coefficient of roughness is 1, so that the pull force applied by the tug has to be as much as the weight of the pipeline on the seafloor. Consequently, accurate weight control

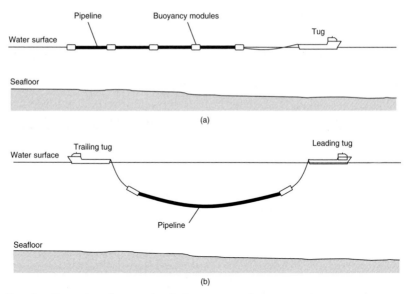

Fig. 7.4 *Examples of towing methods (not to scale). (a) Surface tow. (b) Controlled depth or catenary tow*

is essential. Shorter lengths of pipeline can also be transported by the catenary method shown in Fig. 7.4b.

Figure 7.5a illustrates the S-lay method of installation. A lay barge is pulled along the pipeline route, feeding pipe down onto the seabed. The pipeline is made up from straight sections of up to about 30 m in length. Each section is welded on in a horizontal position, painted, coated, and inspected, and the vessel then moves forward on anchors by one section length, paying pipe out over a stinger and into the water. The stinger supports the pipe and limits the amount of overbending that it experiences. The pipe experiences a sag bend when it bends back onto the seafloor, and a smaller bend just behind the touch down point in the seafloor. A diver or remotely operated vehicle (ROV) will normally watch the seafloor contact to help verify that the pipe is installed in the correct position and does not encounter any unexpected seafloor hazards.

In J-lay operations (Fig. 7.5b), pipe sections are welded in the vertical position. This eliminates the overbend, but may increase the sag bend. S-lay and J-lay systems are suitable for all pipe diameters, and S-lay can be used in all water depths. J-lay cannot be used in shallow water because of the need to limit the pipe bending. Lay rates are typically up to several kilometres per day. The lay barges are kept supplied

348

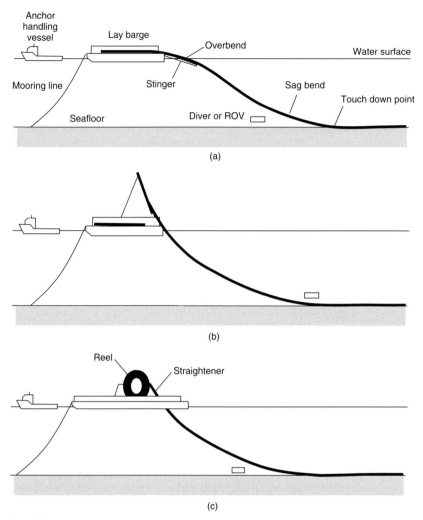

Fig. 7.5 Pipe-laying operations (not to scale). (a) S-lay system. (b) J-lay system. (c) Reel system

with pipe by supply boats, or by tugs which tow sealed pipe bundles from shore. In a reel strip (Fig. 7.5c), pipe or cable is first threaded onto a reel, onshore. The reel is then transferred to the lay ship, or to a supply vessel which takes it to the lay ship. As the ship moves along, the pipe or cable is slowly unwound off the reel, and is plastically straightened before it passes into the water. Reel ships are suitable for cable-laying, and can be used for pipes up to about 0.5 m or so in diameter.

Zhang *et al.* (1999) describe 'overpenetration' during the pipe-laying process. Because the pipe is bent to lay flat on the seabed, it must apply additional stress to the soil just behind the touchdown point. Wave action causes the pipeline barge to move up and down, causing cyclic lift-off and re-touchdown of the pipe on the seabed. This can result in the pipe digging itself into the seabed.

7.3.2 Riser construction

Figure 7.6a illustrates one method for connecting a pipeline to a platform. A J-tube is pre-installed on the jacket platform. A cable is passed down the tube and brought out at the bottom and pulled onto a lay barge. Straight sections of pipe are attached at the jacket end. Sections of pipe are then passed down into the J-tube, welded, inspected, and coated. As this happens, the lay barge pulls on the

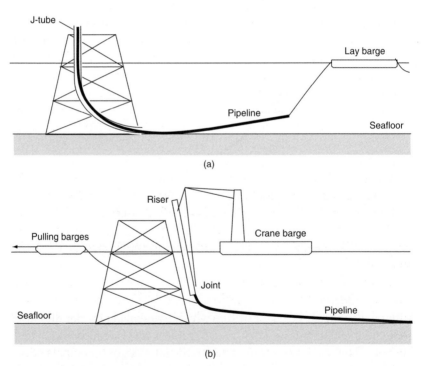

Fig. 7.6 Examples of methods of installing a riser on a fixed platform (not to scale). (a) J-tube system: may be used to pull the pipe from the platform, or in reverse to pull the pipe into the tube and up to the deck. (b) Tension installation method

cable, and so pulls the pipeline around the bend in the J-tube and out at the bottom of the tube. For a short flowline, this operation can continue until the pipe has been pulled to its destination, where the reverse operation can be done if required, with the pipe being pulled into a J-tube and up to the deck of another jacket platform. For long pipelines, the section that comes out from the bottom of the J-tube on a jacket can be welded underwater to a pipeline that has already been laid on the seafloor up to that point.

Figure 7.6b illustrates another method. A pipeline is laid up to a certain position relative to the platform. The riser pipe has been constructed onshore and transported to the location separately. A crane lifts the riser and brings its bottom end to the pipeline. Divers weld the pipeline to the riser. The crane then lowers the riser into guides on the side of the platform, and the riser is welded in place.

7.3.3   Trenching and burial technologies

Offshore pipelines can be laid on the seabed, or in pre-formed trenches, or in trenches formed during the laying operation, or in trenches formed after the pipeline is laid on the seabed. In the last case, a ship pulls a trenching machine along the seabed. The machine rides over the pipeline, cutting a trench below it or to the side of it, and guiding the pipeline into the trench. The process is controlled by an operator on the ship who is able to monitor seabed operations via closed-circuit TV cameras and other devices on the trencher. Spoil from the cutting operation may be placed back over the pipeline by the trenching device, or by a second device that follows some way behind the trencher, or the trench may be left open and allowed to fill by the natural process of sediment transport and deposition (Ochtman and den Boer, 1980; Cathie and Wintgens, 2001; Hettinger and Machin, 2005; Voldsund, 2007). For clay soils, time may be needed for reconsolidated of the remoulded backfill material.

Figure 7.7a shows an end view of a jet trencher. The machine straddles the pipeline. It is attached to a ship via a towing cable and an umbilical for data and control signals and power. The trencher slides of skids as the ship pulls it along. Water jets cut into the soil or fluidise the soil at the front of the machine, and air/water eductors suck the cuttings and fluidised soil up. As the machine moves forwards, the pipeline bends downwards until it lies at the bottom of the trench. If a simple trench is to be cut, the suspended solids are discharged to the side. If the trench is to be backfilled, the solids may be discharged over

351

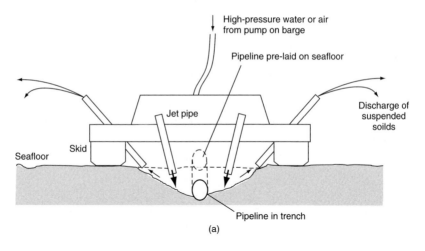

High-pressure water or air
from pump on barge

Pipeline pre-laid on seafloor

Discharge of
suspended
soilds

Jet pipe

Skid

Seafloor

Pipeline in trench

(a)

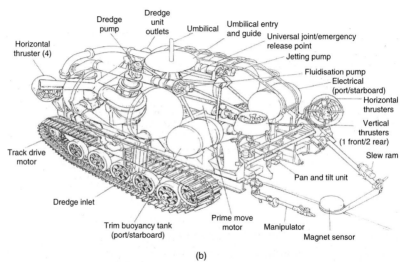

Dredge
unit
outlets

Dredge
pump

Umbilical

Umbilical entry
and guide

Universal joint/emergency
release point

Horizontal
thruster (4)

Jetting pump

Fluidisation pump
Electrical
(port/starboard)

Horizontal
thrusters

Vertical
thrusters
(1 front/2 rear)

Track drive
motor

Slew ram

Pan and tilt unit

Dredge inlet

Trim buoyancy tank
(port/starboard)

Prime move
motor

Manipulator

Magnet sensor

(b)

Fig. 7.7 Jet trenching systems. (a) Principle of the jet trenching operation: the system is being pulled towards the reader. (b) Jet trencher on tracks with an onboard drive system (reproduced with permission, from Noad, 1993. © Springer Science and Business Media)

the top of the laid pipe, or a second machine may follow, pushing the discharged solids back into the trench.

Figure 7.7b shows a jet trenching system that incorporates an on-board drive system that drives the unit along the seabed on tracks.

Figure 7.8a shows an offshore plough. The machine runs on front and rear skids. This system neatly opens a slot in clay seabed, lays a cable or small pipeline into the slot, and lets the soil fall back down

352

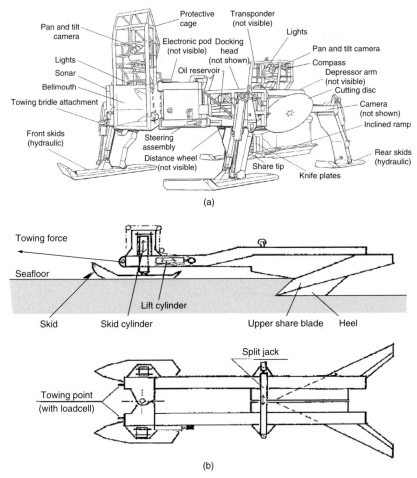

Fig. 7.8 Offshore ploughs. (a) Subsea plough and burial device (Noad, 1993). (b) Submarine plough (© 1980 Offshore Technology Conference: Ochtman and den Booer, 1980). (c) Depth control, elevation view (after Brown and Palmer, 1985); see also model tests by Bransby et al. (2005) and Hatherley et al. (2008)

into the pipeline. Figure 7.8b shows another type of plough, with ploughshares and mouldboards that are positioned well behind the front skids and towing point. Large machines weigh up to 30 tonnes or so, and are 10–30 m long. As the plough is pulled along, the share blades cut and lift the soil, and the mouldboards push it sideways. Figure 7.8c illustrates the system of depth control. The beams between the towing point and the share blade are arranged so that, if the share

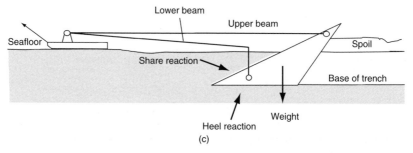

Fig. 7.8 *Continued*

rotates and its front moves upwards, the force in the lower beam reduces and the force in the upper one increases, so that a restoring moment is applied to the share blades. If the share digs in at the front, the opposite occurs, and a moment is created that causes the blade to rotate backwards. Very good cutting depth control can be achieved by this means, even in a relatively uneven seabed.

Figure 7.9 shows one type of submarine rock cutter. The machine moves along the seabed on tracks, using a conventional rock-cutting system to cut a trench in the rock. Systems exist using teethed wheels, chain saws, and other devices. Spoil can be removed by water jets and eductors.

7.3.4 Burial assessment

Burial assessments are carried out prior to commencing a project in order to determine the ease or difficulty with which a pipeline may be

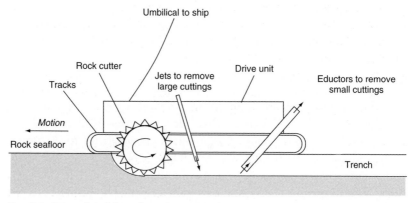

Fig. 7.9 *Principle of the submarine rock cutter*

trenched or buried in a seabed, and to determine the technologies required and the timescales, and costs. Burial assessment can include:

- *Trenchability*: the ease with which a trench may be dug in the seabed.
- *Ploughability*: the ease with which a seabed may be ploughed.
- *Rippability*: the ease with which a rock seabed can be broken.

Different assessments may be needed in different areas along a pipeline (Cathie, 2001; Puech and Tuenter, 2002). Examples are given by CSLC (2009).

Trenchability and ploughability analyses are typically qualitative, partly because research is still ongoing into factors that control the effectiveness of these operations. Considerations include:

- *Bearing capacity.* Jetting systems, ploughs, and some mechanical cutters require vertical support from the seabed. This is assessed in terms of the undrained shear strength for clays and the relative density for sands. High strength is good for bearing capacity.
- *Cuttability.* This also depends on the soil strength, but high strength indicates difficult cuttability. Cuttability is also affected by inclusions in the soil, such as lenses, boulders, and cemented layers.
- *Mouldability.* Cutting and ploughing machines apply plastic deformations to soil. A low shear strength and a low over-consolidation ratio (OCR) give good mouldable clays, but very low shear strength gives a clay that is so mouldable that it cannot be handled easily.
- *Erodability.* Jets move sands by erosion. Erodability is a complex function of grain size, soil density, water velocity, and time. Clays tend to be less erodable than sands. The water jet velocity puts an upper limit on the grain size that it can erode.
- *Sedimentation.* The rate at which the eroded material settles back onto the seafloor is an important issue for jet trenchers. Large particles settle faster than smaller ones.
- *Trench side stability.* This is a function of grain size, strength, and time. A trench in soft clay may stand unsupported for several months, while the stable slope angles for a sand may be as low as only 10° or so.
- *Density, permeability, and dilation.* These properties can control rate effects in granular soils. A dense sand may be relatively easy to trench slowly, but relatively difficult to trench fast. The trenching operation induces shear stresses in the sand, and those induce suctions in the pore water, which increase the strength of the

sand. The effect is reduced by drainage, and the time required for this is determined by the permeability and the compressibility.

Rock rippability depends on the strength of rock, its degree of fracturing in situ, the thickness of the rock stratum, and other factors (Weaver, 1975; Basarir *et al.*, 2007).

7.3.5 Cable and pipeline inspections

McLean and Cairns (2003) describe some of the quality control and inspection processes for pipelines and cables. Inspections are normally carried out shortly after a pipeline or cable has been installed, and at regular intervals afterwards. Inspections can be carried out by ROV or an autonomous underwater vehicle (AUV), or by devices that are pulled along the seabed by a ship.

7.4 Positional instabilities of pipelines

7.4.1 Introduction

A pipeline is installed under ambient temperature and pressure, and is usually under tension in order to prevent buckling failure during installation. Subsequently, when a hot fluid under high pressure is then passed through the pipeline, thermal expansion and pressure-induced straining occur. These can cause the initial tension to reduce, and even put the pipe into compression. Figure 7.10 shows three phenomena that can then occur and which can result in the pipeline moving in position:

- *Lateral buckling.* The pipeline moves laterally across the seabed, so that an initially straight pipeline will become curved. Movements can be up to 20 or more pipeline diameters, and can affect pipeline lengths of several hundred metres. The pipeline moves into a shape whose length is longer than in the unbuckled position; this relieves the induced stresses.
- *Upheaval buckling* (Guijt, 1990). A buried pipeline curves up, and may break out above the seafloor, creating a free span that can extend several metres above the seabed. The curve is longer than the original shape, so the axial stresses are relieved. The breakout defeats the objective of burial, which was to protect the pipeline against hazards above the seafloor.
- *Walking* (Carr *et al.*, 2006). Because the internal fluids carry the temperature and pressure in the pipe, changes in the temperature

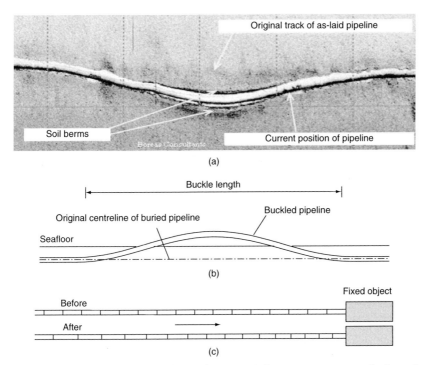

Fig. 7.10 *Positional instabilities for pipelines. (a) Side-scan sonar image of a lateral buckle (lateral scale exaggerated for clarity) (© 2008 Offshore Technology Conference: Bruton et al., 2008). (b) Uplift buckling (after Guijt, 1990). (c) Pipeline walking towards a fixed object*

and pressure progress axially along the pipe. Repeated changes cause a cyclic effect, in which a pipeline on the seafloor expands, moves a small distance axially, then contracts and moves back; but not all the way due to soil friction. Over many cycles, the pipeline moves along its length.

The mechanisms also interact. Pipeline walking can be a cause of buckling because it compresses the pipe ahead of the walking part, and feeds into the buckle when it occurs. Conversely, walking can be induced by a buckle. The buckle reduces the axial load in the buckled section, thereby allowing pipe to feed in to the buckle from continuous sections of unbuckled pipe.

These phenomena also occur for onshore pipelines (Hobbs, 1984; Palmer and Williams, 2003). Although buckling relieves the axial stress, bending stresses are increased. This may cause cyclic fatigue, plastic failure in bending, local buckling of the pile wall, rupture of thermal insulation, cracking or tearing, water ingress, serviceability failure from loss of flow capacity and loss of piggability, loss of contained fluids, and contamination of a local environment. The consequences of unrelieved stresses in a region that has walked towards a fixed connection such as a manifold or riser can also damage those structures.

7.4.2 Mechanics of buckling and walking

Figure 7.11a shows the proposal by Palmer *et al.* (1990a) that the initiation and development of upheaval buckling could be explained by imperfections in the as-laid position of the pipeline. These could be caused by unevenness of a seafloor, or of the base of a trench in which the pipe is laid. When the pipeline is started up, the changing temperature and pressure cause axial compressive stress to develop, and the pipe tends to move upwards where the soil resistance is least, usually at a place where there is an upwards overbend in the pipeline due to the imperfections, The upwards movement there relieves some of the axial compression in the pipe, and nearby sections of the pipe stretch longitudinally and feed pipe into the bend. At some point the pipe breaks out of the seafloor, creating the visible evidence of buckling and exposing the pipe to the hazards that burial was intended to avoid.

Figure 7.11b shows a concept for lateral buckling of a pipeline laid over a seabed. The axial compression in the pipe may be partly relieved by a torsional motion along part of the pipe length, allowing the pipe to roll and increase its length along a section. At some stage, the torsion will be sufficient to cause the frictional resistance to reach the limiting resistance, and the pipe will slip laterally over the seabed in the affected section. As observed by Baker *et al.* (2006) and others, the slip can push material in front of the pipe, creating a small berm. Under cyclic change in the internal temperature and pressure, berms can be created each side of the pipeline, as seen in Fig. 7.10a.

Figure 7.11c shows the effects of a typical thermal cycle analysed for a buried, free-ended pipeline using the t–z concept of pile performance from API (2000) and ISO 19902 (ISO, 2007). As the pipeline heats up, it expands and begins to move longitudinally. This induces longitudinal resistance in the magnitude t per unit length. At a certain small displacement, the maximum axial resistance is mobilised, and the resistance reduces. An unstable expansion and movement then occurs as the soil resistance reduces to its residual value and the compressive force in the pipe reduces due to the expansion. On further heating, the pipeline will extend without further change in the soil

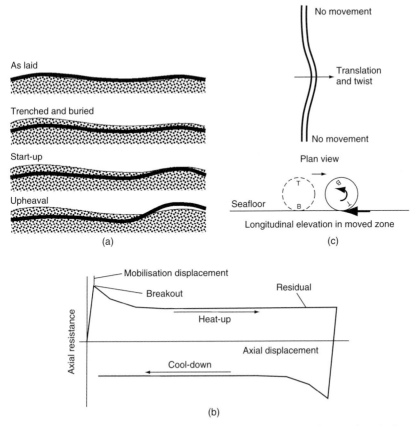

Fig. 7.11 *Concepts for buckling and axial walking. (a) Pipeline and seabed in side elevation: concept of an overbend initiating an upwards buckle and break-out (© 1990 Offshore Technology Conference: Palmer et al., 1990a). (b) Flowline walking and ratchetting: axial soil resistance under a cycle of full heatup and cooling (© 2006 Offshore Technology Conference: Brunner et al., 2006). (c) Pipeline in plan and longtitudinal section: concept of friction and torque as resistances to lateral buckling of a pipeline on a seafloor*

resistance. On cooling, the reverse occurs. The axial soil resistance reduces and reverses, and some part of the expansion of the pipe is recovered.

Calculations for pipeline buckling have been developed by Hobbs (1984), Palmer and King (2006), and others, and several software products are able to predict when pipeline buckling problems are likely to occur. One way of preventing buckling is to dump rock over a pipeline at intervals along the line. Research into this and other methods is ongoing (see Section 7.4.4).

359

7.4.3 Geotechnical analysis

One way to manage the analysis of pipeline processes is to use the yield locus concept (Schotman, 1987). Figure 7.12 shows an adaptation by Zhang *et al.* (2002). The vertical load on the soil supporting a pipeline, per unit length of pipeline, is plotted versus the horizontal force applied to the soil, per unit length of pipeline. A yield envelope joins load-states at which some form of large displacement starts. The nature of the mechanism involved is related to the size of the envelope and to position around it. Vertical embedment mechanisms occur where the downwards vertical force dominates. Lateral displacement mechanisms dominate where there is a large lateral load. Uplift mechanisms dominate where the vertical load is negative.

Randolph and White (2008a) identify three driving mechanisms for pipeline embedment during pipe-laying: self-weight, force concentration during installation, and cyclic motions. Additional embedment will occur during pipe-laying. These mechanisms, and the subsequent backfilling and possible reconsolidation of the soil, determine the size

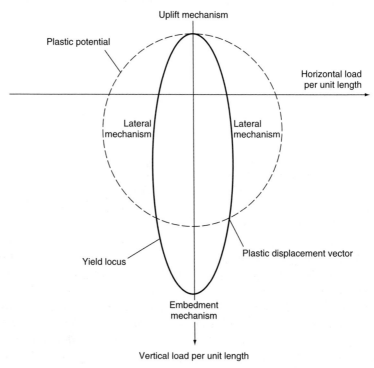

Fig. 7.12 Concepts of yield locus and plastic potential (adapted from Zhang et al., 2002)

of the yield envelope, measured by the maximum vertical load on the envelope, and the tension limit.

Figure 7.13 shows some simplified embedment mechanisms. A conventional bearing capacity mechanism for a pipeline on clay is shown in Fig. 7.13a. The pipeline is considered to be a strip footing.

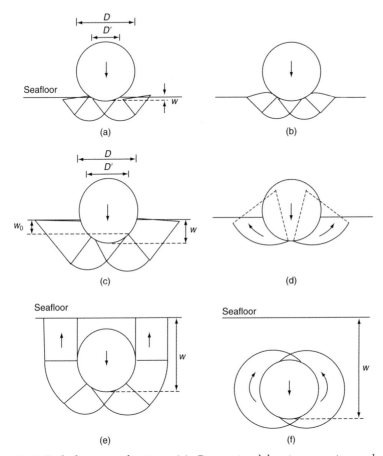

Fig. 7.13 Embedment mechanisms. (a) Conventional bearing capacity mechanism, 'wished in place' at a shallow embedment D. (b) Likely heave and berm formation, confirmed by finite element analysis (after Clukey et al., 2008). (c) Conventional Prandtl-type bearing capacity mechanism (after White and Randolph, 2007). (d) Martin's mechanism (after Martin and Randolph, 2006). (e) Potential intermediate flow mechanism. (f) Deep flow mechanism. (g) Deformation pattern at $w/D = 0.5$, and penetration curves from large-deformation finite element analysis (© 2008 Offshore Technology Conference: Randolph and White, 2008a). (h) Comparison of some solutions for the case of shear strength constant with depth

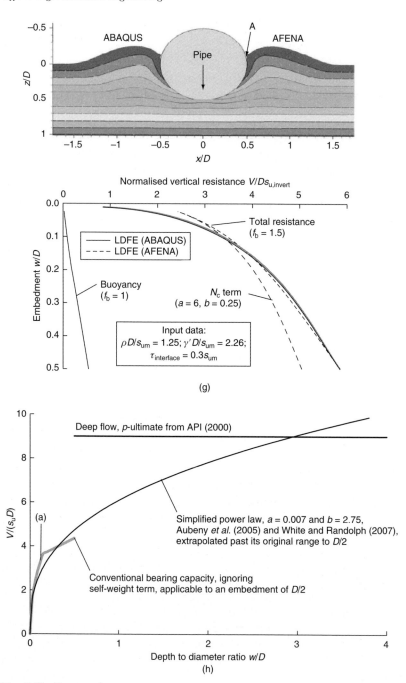

Fig. 7.13 Continued

At a penetration distance of w, the width D' of the strip footing can be calculated by geometry, and is $2\sqrt{w(D-w)}$. Using the general bearing capacity equation, the vertical bearing capacity V per unit length of a strip footing of this width on the surface of a clay of uniform shear strength s_u is

$$V = (\pi + 2)s_u 2\sqrt{w(D-w)} \tag{7.1}$$

An issue with this calculation is that the penetration of the pipeline will cause heave, shown in Fig. 7.13b. However, this can be accounted for in large-strain finite element analysis (Clukey *et al.*, 2008). Figure 7.13c shows the conventional mechanism at an embedment deeper than w_0, given by

$$w_0 = \frac{D}{2}\left(1 - \frac{1}{\sqrt{2}}\right) \tag{7.2}$$

It is convenient to consider the pipe as a strip footing at this depth with a width of $D/\sqrt{2}$. The general bearing capacity equation gives

$$V = \frac{D}{\sqrt{2}}\left[(\pi + 2)s_u\left(1 + 0.4\frac{w - w_0}{D/\sqrt{2}}\right) + \gamma'z\right] \tag{7.3}$$

where the second part of the expression in brackets is Hansen's (1970) depth factor. An inverse tangent function would apply at footing depths $w - w_0$ greater than $D/\sqrt{2}$. Martin and Randolph (2006) proposed a different mechanism, shown in Fig. 7.13d, but this may involve rotation of rigid blocks, which does not seem to fit exactly with the kinematics. Figure 7.13e shows another potential mechanism at deeper embedments. At very deep embedments, the pipe will act simply as a pile, so that the deep failure mechanism for lateral loading of a pile can be applied (Fig. 7.13f).

Figure 7.13g shows analyses by Randolph and White (2008a) taking account of the large deformations involved. Analyses were carried out with the ABAQUS and AFENA finite element programs, with good agreement between the two results. Figure 7.13h shows comparisons between various mechanisms, plotted in terms of the normalised vertical load parameter V/s_uD. The power law has been the subject of some controversy and change, and has been expressed as

$$\text{Bruton } et\ al.\ (2006): \quad \frac{w}{D} = \frac{S_t}{45}\left(\frac{V}{Ds_{u,invert}}\right)^2 \tag{7.4a}$$

White and Randolph (2007): $\quad \dfrac{w}{D} = A\left(\dfrac{V}{s_u D}\right)^B$ $\qquad$ (7.4b)

Randolph and White (2008a): $\quad \dfrac{V}{s_{u,\text{invert}} D} = a\left(\dfrac{w}{D}\right)^b$ $\qquad$ (7.4c)

where the constants are related by $b = 1/B$ and $a = 1/A^b$. The mechanisms are the subject of ongoing research. If the soil sensitivity S_t is unity, the equation (7.4a) gives $a = 6.7$ and $b = 0.5$. Thusyanthan (2009) recommends the equation (7.4c), and provides the following comment:

> Touchdown effects and cyclic laying effects can significantly increase the embedment in the field. This increase is captured in design by a touchdown factor and dynamic embedment factor (Bruton et al., 2008). The touchdown effect is captured by multiplying the pipe weight by a touchdown lay factor to account for the stress concentration at the touchdown (on soft clay this is typically 2–3). The dynamic effect is captured by multiplying the embedment calculated (with touchdown lay factor) by a dynamic embedment factor. In soft clays (s_u 2–4 kPa), the typical dynamic embedment factor is in the order of 1 to 3. But on stiff clay seabed with shear strength exceeding 100 kPa, the factor can be about 5 to 8 (Bruton et al., 2008).

Table 7.1 lists some parameters for equation (7.4c). In Fig. 7.13h, the constants have been taken as $A = 1/a = 0.007$ and $B = 1/b = 2.75$, as quoted in White and Randolph (2007) for smooth pipes at shallow embedment, equivalent to $a = 6.08$ and $b = 0.36$. The actual mechanism that occurs for a given penetration will be the one that

Table 7.1 Pipeline embedment parameters a and b, equation (7.4c)

		a	b	
Upper-bound numerical analysis	Rough pipe	7.40	0.4	Merifield et al. (2008)
	Rough pipe	7.41	0.37	Aubeny et al. (2005)
	Smooth pipe	5.66	0.32	Merifield et al. (2008)
	Smooth pipe	5.42	0.29	Aubeny et al. (2005)
Experimental, full scale and centrifuge	Upper estimate for embedment	5.65	0.5	Cheuk (2005)
	Lower estimate for embedment	8	0.5	Cheuk (2005)

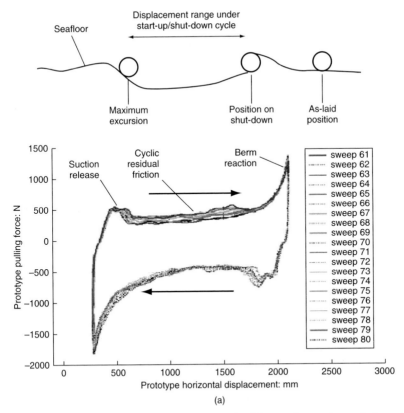

Fig. 7.14 Lateral mechanisms. (a) Creation of soil berms due to the cyclic lateral movement of a pipeline on the seafloor (Baker et al., 2006; Bruton et al.; 2006). (b) Mechanisms and upper bound solutions for the lateral break-out of rough pipes in clay (Merifield et al., 2008)

gives the lowest bearing resistance, but will be modified by the large-displacement effects mentioned above.

Mechanisms for the creation of the berms in lateral buckling are described by Baker *et al.* (2006) and Bruton *et al.* (2006). Figure 7.14a shows the lateral load–displacement relations that develop once the berms have formed. Figure 7.14b shows mechanisms analysed by Merifield *et al.* (2008) for the break-out of a pipe that is partially embedded in clay. Several directions of motion were analysed, giving different flow mechanisms in the soil.

Figure 7.15 shows concepts and results for vertical break-out. Preliminary calculations by Schaminée *et al.* (1990) assumed that a buried pipeline would lift a vertical-sided wedge of soil (Fig. 7.15a).

365

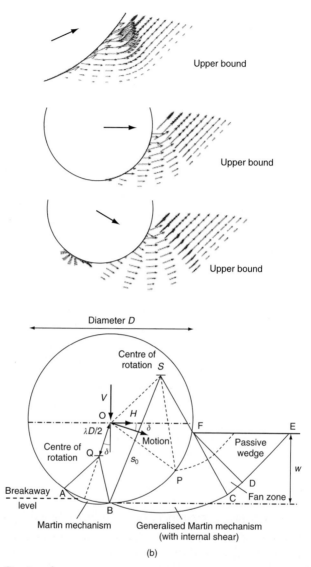

Fig. 7.14 *Continued*

For a pipe of diameter D installed in a trench and covered by soil to a depth H:

for clays: $w = w_p + \gamma' HD + 2Hs_u$ (7.5)

for sands: $w = w_p + \gamma' HD + \gamma' KH^2 \tan \phi'$ (7.6)

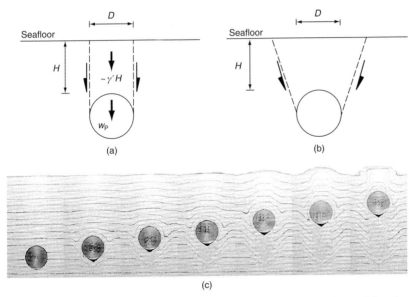

Fig. 7.15 Uplift/break-out mechanisms. (a) Forces resisting the uplift of a straight-sided plug (after Schaminée et al., 1990). (b) Uplift wedge failure mechanism in sand (White et al., 2001, 2008a). (c) Photographs showing various stages of a pipeline being lifted upwards through loose sand. The initially horizontal lines are thin, coloured sand layers used to show how the sand moves around the pipeline as the pipeline is being lifted (© of the ASME 2006: Shupp et al., 2006)

where γ' is the submerged unit weight of the soil, s_u is the undrained shear strength of the clay, ϕ' is the angle of internal friction of the sand, and K is a lateral earth pressure coefficient. Bruton *et al.* (1998) proposed an adjusted equation for sand.

However, White *et al.* (2001, 2008a) found that a wider wedge would develop (Fig. 7.15b). This is very similar to a mechanism that develops in the uplifting of horizontal plate anchors (Das, 2007). Figure 7.15c shows photographs taken of an experiment in which a model pipe was installed in sand in a glass-ended box. Thin layers of coloured sand were placed at regular intervals during the model preparation. The first photograph on the left shows the pipe and sand after installation. The next six photos show various stages of lifting. The photographs show that sand grains at the top of the pipeline initially move upwards, but subsequently move around the pipeline and fall into the space below it. The mechanism changes in character as the soil surface is approached.

7.4.4 *Preventative and remedial measures*

Measures to prevent buckling and walking can involve decreasing the driving forces, increasing the resisting forces, or both. The driving forces can be reducing the axial compression force or increasing the bending resistance. This can be done by increasing installation tension, or by reducing the wall thickness, the stiffness, the thermal expansion coefficient, the temperature change, or the internal pressure. However, the temperature and the pressure are determined by the need to ensure that the line can transport given fluids (i.e. by 'flow assurance' requirements).

Figure 7.16 illustrates some measures that can be effective for lateral buckling. Soil or rock cover increases friction and prevents movement

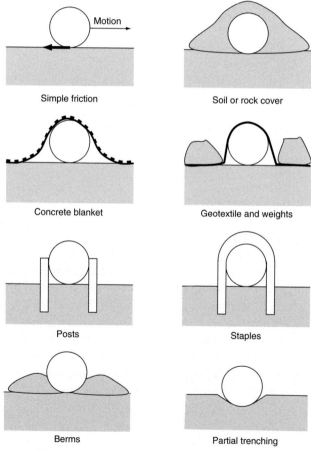

Fig. 7.16 Concepts for the prevention of buckling (not to scale)

368

by its bulk. A concrete blanket is a textile that is sewn with pockets containing concrete blocks or rocks. An alternative is to lay a geotextile on top of the pile, and place weights on the geotextile. Posts and staples can hold a pipe in position, but special attention is needed to ensure that stress concentrations are not induced in the pipe. Small berms or partial trenching may be effective if the driving forces are small.

Ellinas *et al.* (1990) describe the use of periodic rock dumps to stabilise a pipeline against lateral or upheaval buckling. For a 10 cm diameter flowline installed in an open trench in the North Sea Cormorant field, 40 m-long rock dumps were placed to a height of about 0.8 m above the pipe at intervals of about 150 m. After a period of carrying fluids at 75–85°C, an ROV inspection showed that the lines snaked in the shallow trench, without yielding or uncontrolled buckling having occurred.

Harrison *et al.* (2003) found that, where the clay strengths required in backfill must be achieved by consolidation, the time required for the consolidation process can be impractically long. For that reason, it can be better to use sand to backfill a trench in clay. They also review proposals for snake-laying and controlled buckle initiation, so that buckles can be controlled in a way that avoids overstressing the pipe. The following methods are sketched in Fig 7.17:

- *Counteracts.* The pipeline is laid on the seafloor in a snake pattern that passes the pipe around large, cylindrical weights placed on the

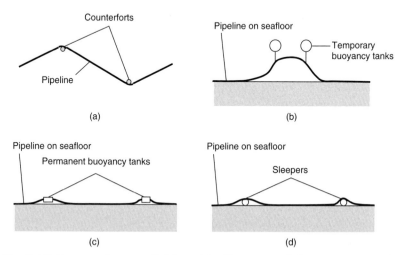

Fig. 7.17 Concepts for controlled lateral buckling to avoid damage (not to scale) (after Harrison et al., 2003). (a) Counteracts: plan view. (b) Slack loop: elevation. (c) Permanent buoyancy: elevation. (d) Sleepers: elevation

seafloor. The counteracts have a tight radius and are designed to bend the pipe during installation if the pipe moves at that time. They are removed after installation, leaving a pipe that will buckle preferentially at the bends.

- *Slack-loops.* These are constructed by attaching temporary buoyancy at intervals along a pipe during laying, sufficient to lift the pipe off the seabed locally. After installation, the buoyancy is removed. The pipe falls over sideways, forming a slack-loop that might act rather like a dogleg.
- *Permanent buoyancy.* Segments of permanent buoyancy are added at intervals along the pipeline during laying. By providing uplift forces, these segments tend to act as buckle initiation sites. Also, frictional resistance from the seafloor is reduced, producing a gentler buckle.
- *Sleepers.* Large-diameter pipes are pre-laid on the seafloor at right angles to the intended path of the pipeline. If the pipeline walks between the sleepers, the walk feeds into a controlled buckle in which the pipeline moves laterally along a sleeper.

The review was part of the design process for two PIP lines, of diameters 8 and 12 inches, to be laid on the seafloor as separate flowlines in 5000 feet water depth. The final choice was to install 29 sleepers of diameter 32 inches and lengths 80 m, at intervals varying from 900 m at the hot end of the pipeline to 2500 m at the cool end.

7.5   Riser–seabed interactions

For deepwater structures, risers are often designed to hang as catenaries (see Fig. 7.1b), sometimes with additional fixed buoyancy at intermediate depths. The method induces motions on the seafloor because the vessel may move up and down or from side to side due to wind, waves, or currents, and because the riser itself is subjected to significant wave and current forces over its length.

Figure 7.18a shows the concept of a touchdown zone. The flowline on the seabed is just a continuation of the riser pipe. The riser applies a tension T to the flowline, and a moment M, and the pipe can move up and down, creating a zone where the flowline is sometimes in contact with the seafloor and sometimes not. A complex riser–seabed interaction therefore develops, with soil motions that may be three-dimensional below the laydown area. The interaction can have a major effect on stresses in the riser, and so on the fatigue life of the riser.

All of the research on the yield envelope and on the mechanisms of embedment is relevant. Figure 7.18b shows a summary of some concepts

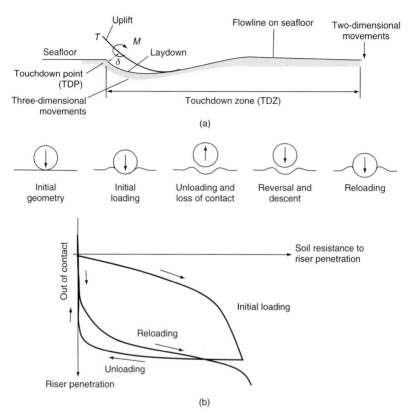

Fig. 7.18 Riser–seabed interactions. (a) Geometry and processes in the touch-down zone (© 2008 Offshore Technology Conference: Aubeny and Biscontin, 2008). (b) Loading sequence in a riser–soil interaction (adapted from Clukey et al., 2008)

and results by Clukey *et al.* (2008). In initial loading, the riser pushes into the soil, expanding the yield envelope and creating a settlement furrow. In the initial unloading, loss of contact can occur, and water is sucked into the space between the riser and the seabed, causing some scour. On reversal and descent, the water is expelled, taking some of the soil with it. An equilibrium may develop over time, but this will also change when different motions are applied, for instance during storms.

7.6   Shore approaches
Shore approaches present special technical challenges for offshore pipelines (Palmer and King, 2006). Environmental conditions include

breaking waves and longshore currents that can apply forces to pipelines that are significantly larger than for pipelines on a seafloor. Scour conditions are also severe. Shorelines are also utilised by many other users. The principles and practice of coastal engineering apply (Herbich, 2000a; Reeve *et al.*, 2004). There are essentially two methods. One is to pre-cut a trench, then either pull the pipe into the trench from an assembly point onshore or pull it in from the sea to the shore. Another is to drill a tunnel beneath the surf zone.

8

Artificial islands

Chapter 8 describes the types of offshore artificial island that have been constructed, the methods of construction, and the key geotechnical issues involved.

8.1 Introduction

8.1.1 General

An artificial island is an earth structure that is constructed in a lake, sea, or ocean by human actions rather than other natural processes.

The history of artificial islands is probably as old as human history. In ancient Scotland, loch-dwelling families built island homes, probably for safety. The city of Tenochtitlan, the Aztec predecessor of Mexico City, stood on a natural island in Lake Texcoco, and was surrounded by numerous artificial islands made of mud and reeds. The islands were partially for agricultural purposes, but also served to house an expanding population (McClellan and Dorn, 2006).

Artificial islands today are used or proposed for industrial, housing, transportation, and leisure purposes. Section 8.1.2 briefly reviews some of these structures, which are primarily coastal rather than offshore structures. Artificial islands have also been used as temporary or permanent platforms for hydrocarbon exploration and production, particularly in the Canadian Beaufort Sea. Some of these islands are described in Section 8.1.3 and discussed further in the main body of this chapter.

Islands can also offer attractive foundation solutions for wind farms, as the surface area provides an ability to access wind turbines above water, and can be useful for other purposes.

8.1.2 Coastal artificial islands

Spriggs (1971) proposed constructing a small artificial island off Southern California to house a desalination plant to provide for an expanding supply of water for California farmers. The plant required considerable power, and so a nuclear power plant was also part of the planned development. The island was to be in a water depth of about 10 m, and with a surface area of about $150\,000\,\text{m}^2$. The design study identified the importance of local geology, ecological and environmental considerations, seismic risk, access, deep geotechnical site investigation, slope design, sea defences, and sourcing and compaction of fill material.

Many artificial islands have been constructed for port structures. Soros and Koman (1974) describe an artificial island trans-shipment terminal 8 miles off the coast of Brazil. The terminal allows shallow-draught coastal freighters to bring salt to a facility where it could be loaded onto a deep-draught ocean-going ship for export. It was built in 23 feet of water at the edge of a 55 foot-deep natural channel, and was connected by a 400 m long conveyor to a shiploader in that channel. Bottom soundings, seismic survey, and geotechnical borings were carried out as part of the site selection and design works.

Treasure Island is a 162 hectare $(1.62\,\text{km}^2)$ artificial island constructed in 1936–37 as the site of the 1939 Golden Gate Exhibition (Seed *et al.*, 1990). Dean *et al.* (2008) examined oceanographic, environmental, and engineering aspects of a 1400 hectare industrial island, including a post-Panamax port off Trinidad and Tobago. The large area meant that the proposed coastal island might significantly change the pattern of water movement along the coast. The transport of suspended solids along the coast could be affected, so changing the established pattern of coastal erosion and deposition. In general, the environmental, coastal morphological, and social issues associated with a large coastal island are often complex and sometimes contentious.

Kansai International Airport is an artificial island off Kobe, Japan. The island is about 4 km long and 1.2 km wide. It is notable for its very large settlements, thought to be due to secondary consolidation of Pleistocene clays deep beneath the seafloor (Mimura and Yang, 2003). Other offshore airports include Hong Kong International, which was constructed on reclaimed land around two small natural islands, and Macao International. HKI was voted one of the top 10 construction achievements of the 20th century (Marsden and Whiteman, 1999).

The Palm Islands are off the coast of the Arabian Sea, and are arranged to form the shape of a palm tree in plan view. They provide many miles of new beach, with residential properties, marinas, shopping, and sports facilities. Special care was taken to ensure that civil engineering works were conducive to local marine ecosystems. As a result, the project has a very beneficial environmental impact.

8.1.3 Artificial islands for hydrocarbon exploration and production

Artificial islands are particularly useful for resisting horizontal forces from ice sheets. Islands can be built in one or two seasons, so it can be cost-effective to construct one as an exploration platform with a design life of only a year or so (Agerton, 1983). A design life of 20 years or so would be typical where hydrocarbons are found. Arctic islands are covered by the ISO 19906 standard (ISO, 2009).

The Arctic Beaufort Sea is covered by ice for most of the year. An ice sheet is moved by wind shear, and can apply very large cyclic loads to a structure, typically with a sawtooth waveform (Bjerkas, 2004; Jefferies and Been, 2006). This can produce a rather violent shaking of a structure, such as an island, that stands in the sheet. Temperatures fall to below −40°C, and onshore soils may be permanently frozen as 'permafrost'. The soil contains many lenses of pure ice, and collapses when unfrozen (Chamberlain, 1983; Phillips *et al.*, 2003). Road traffic can also disrupt the permafrost. Even where the soil is not frozen, temperature control can be important because of the effect of temperature on pore water pressures, pore water movements, and associated ground settlement or heave.

In Fig. 8.1a, the artificial island consists of hydraulic fill that is placed on a prepared seabed (Lucas *et al.*, 2008). The fill is obtained by dredging from a borrow source that is not normally more than 10–30 km away. The side slopes may be sacrificial if the design life of the island is short, or may be armoured or protected for a more permanent island. After placement, the fill is normally compacted to achieve a soil that is strong enough to support buildings and other structures on the island. The island will be roughly circular or square in plan view. Access may be by a causeway, bridge, or via a harbour built on the island, or by helicopter.

In Fig. 8.1b, the sides of the island have been constructed using caissons, in the same way that a coastal breakwater can be constructed using caissons (Kamphuis, 2007). The example shown is Tarsuit caisson-retained island, which was constructed in the Canadian Beaufort Sea as an exploration and production platform for hydrocarbons. Four caissons were used. They were floated onto a pre-prepared berm on the seafloor, and set down in the form of a square in plan view.

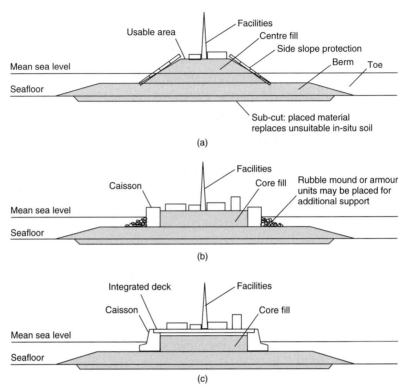

Fig. 8.1 Artificial islands (not to scale). (a) Key features of a small earth island in elevation. Note: vertical and horizontal scales are different in this sketch – the actual island would appear much wider using equal scales. Typical toe berm gradients are 1:15. Typical side slope gradients are 1:6 to 1:15. (b) Caisson-retained island. (c) Mobile caisson seated on a prelaid berm

The joints between neighbouring caissons were closed off. The centre was then filled with sand to provide resistance to ice forces that were later applied to the island once the sea froze over.

Figure 8.1c shows features of the Molikpaq mobile arctic caisson, which was originally used in the Canadian Beaufort Sea, and is now in use in the Sakhalin developments off the east coast of Russia (Weiss *et al.*, 2001). It is an approximately square steel box in plan view, with the box essentially being four caissons that together form a single structural unit. The unit was floated onto a pre-installed berm, and set down onto the berm. Sand fill was then placed inside the central area, again to provide horizontal resistance against ice forces that would ensue when the sea froze over.

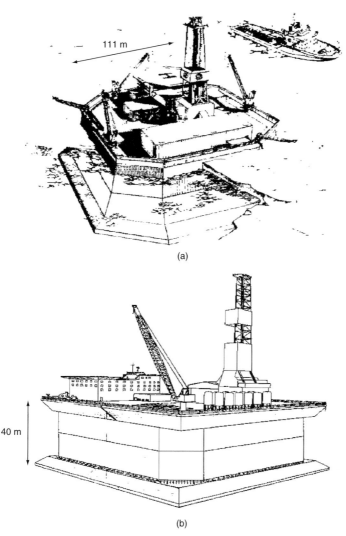

(a)

(b)

Fig. 8.2 Examples of mobile islands. (a) Gulf mobile arctic caisson. The plan dimensions of the deck are approximately 111 m square. The sand core fill is approximately 200 000 tonnes (© 1983 Offshore Technology Conference: Stewart et al., 1983). (b) Concrete island drilling system (© 1984 Offshore Technology Conference: Wetmore, 1984)

Figure 8.2a shows an artist's impression of the Molikpaq. Overall plan dimensions were 111×111 m. Wetmore (1984) describes the mobile concrete island drilling system (CIDS), shown in Fig. 8.2b. The foundations included 5 foot-deep skirts arranged in a grid pattern.

The structure between the deck level and the foundation was constructed of concrete cells in a honeycomb arrangement, allowing oil and/or water ballast storage. The platform was equipped with a rubble generation system capable of creating a 100 m-wide grounded ice berm encircling the structure in about two weeks.

Another concept for an island is simply a large, flat-bottomed ship that is floated over a prepared seafloor and then sunk onto the seafloor. This concept was employed in Dome Petroleum's SSDC (single steel drilling caisson). It consists of a converted supertanker that is 162 m long, 53 m wide at the stern (38 m at the bow), and 25 m high, with vertical sides at the waterline. After some initial drilling, it was fitted with a widened base to provide extra stability against overturning (Johnston and Timco, 2003).

8.1.4 Grounded ice islands

Islands made of ice form naturally (Breslau *et al.*, 1970). The island may have started as a tabular iceberg that broke naturally from part of a glacier that extended over water. It is moved by wind and current forces, and happens to pass into an area of shallow water, where it grounds on the seafloor. In 1968, an island of several square kilometres grounded off Alaska, scattering smaller fragments along 150 km of coastline. Grounded ice islands can be stable for many years, and have been used for scientific research stations.

Figure 8.3a shows the results of an exploration by Breslau *et al.* (1970) of a small grounded ice island off Prudhoe Bay, Alaska. The island was a little over 120 m long. Sonar profiling revealed that the cross-sectional shape of the island was like a flattened hourglass, wider at the top and bottom, and narrower at mid depths. This kind of island can be stabilised by the process sketched in Fig. 8.3b. A water pump is installed on a temporarily grounded ice island or an ice sheet. The pump lifts water from below the ice, and pours or sprays it onto the top of the ice, where it freezes rapidly and adds to the weight of the island. The weight keeps the island grounded for longer than would otherwise be the case. Ice islands of half a kilometre in diameter can be constructed relatively quickly in this way (Lucas *et al.*, 2008).

Figure 8.3c shows another use of this technology. Water is sprayed over a moving ice sheet to ground it around a fixed structure. The grounded ice then acts to protect the fixed structure from ice forces from the surrounding ice sheet.

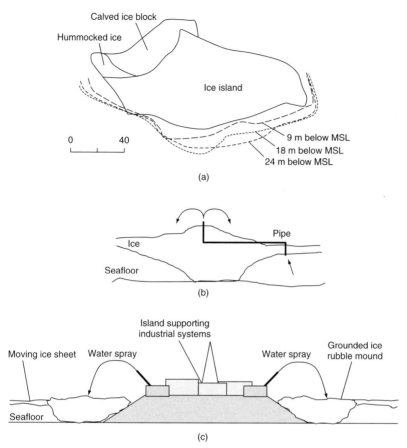

Fig. 8.3 Grounded ice islands. (a) Exploration results for a grounded ice island off Prudhoe Bay, Alaska (MSL, mean sea level) (© 1970 Offshore Technology Conference: Breslau et al., 1970). (b) Technique for maintaining an ice island (Reimnitz et al., 1982). (c) Use of ice to protect an island structure (adapted from Boone, 1980)

8.2 Geotechnics of artificial islands

8.2.1 Objectives and scales of geotechnical design

Geotechnical design for an island proceeds at two scales. The first is the design of the island itself, the second is the design of foundations of structures to be placed on the island.

For the first scale, the objectives are to ensure that the island can be constructed, that the short- and long-term settlements will be

379

acceptable, and that the island will have an adequate margin of safety against short- and long-term failure. For these purposes, an estimate will be required of the weights of materials to be placed on the island. For large islands, it is sufficient to know the weights and layouts of structures near the edges, since the remainder will not often have a major impact on the settlement or the stability of the island itself. The island soil will be placed by filling, and a target density and target strength will need to be determined before construction, so that the designers of the structures to be placed on the island will know what soil properties to use in their designs.

For the second scale, the objectives apply to the structures on the island or associated with it. For small islands, the same designer may be involved at both scales, but it is useful to separate the tasks conceptually. Some interaction may be expected, since some of the choices made for the second scale may affect the settlement or stability of the entire island.

8.2.2   Feasibility and borrow search

Much of an artificial island is made of soil. The design of the island may start several years before construction, and the feasibility study will normally include an assessment of the volume of soil likely to be needed, and of where it might be obtained. A major part of the preliminary work will normally involve an environmental impact assessment. Several sites may need to be considered, including the proposed island site, the 'borrow' site or sites where the materials for this island construction are to be taken from, and dump sites where unsuitable, fine-grained soils will be dumped.

Mancini *et al.* (1983) describe a borrow search for a planned caisson-retained island in the Canadian arctic. The search covered over $100\,000\,\text{km}^2$ of seafloor, and was probably only cost-effective because several other islands were also being planned. A search of this size requires geographic, geological, and hydrodynamic predictions to help determine where best to look, and geophysical and geotechnical survey methods to find potentially dredgable materials and to measure their properties.

Good island-building material consists of clean sand or gravel, with little or no fines of silt or clay. Sand deposits that contain many thin seams or lenses of clay cannot be used, because the cost of separating out the clay fraction would be excessive.

8.2.3   Site investigation

Artificial islands can experience the same geohazards as other offshore structures. Additionally, because of their large size, islands have a significant effect on the movements of water around them, and of ice in cold regions. Islands located in estuaries may be subject to increased scour, with water velocities around the island different from values measured before construction. The large area also gives a larger chance that the island will cross a geological fault, and the weight of the island can alter the stresses on those faults, and so alter the likelihood of rupture under normal conditions or during an earthquake.

A comprehensive geophysical survey around a proposed island site is recommended, including a detailed survey of the island site itself. Local bathymetry can also be significant. The weight of an island that is close to the edge of submarine slope will significantly reduce the global stability of the slope.

Bowles (1996) recommends that the depth of boreholes in a geotechnical site investigation be at least as great as the depth at which the changes in the stress due to the imposed foundation loads have reduced to 10% of the imposed surface load. For a shallow foundation, this occurs at a depth about equal to twice the foundation width. However, this is only technically feasible for relatively small islands. A geotechnical borehole must reach a sufficiently deep and thick competent stratum, and is occasionally done to 400 m below the seafloor.

8.2.4   Dredging operations

Figure 8.4a shows a simple back-hoe dredging operation, in which a back-hoe mounted on a barge lifts material from the seafloor and places it either in the same barge or one alongside. In the clamshell dredger (Fig. 8.4b), a clamshell bucket is lowered by a crane to the seafloor. The jaws of the bucket are then closed by hydraulic rams or other means, and the material is lifted and placed in a barge. In a suction dredger (Fig. 8.4c), a suction eductor pipe is used to suck soil up to the barge or ship. Water jets may also be used to loosen the seabed soils. In the cutter suction dredger (Fig. 8.4d), the ship anchors itself using a spudpole pushed into the seabed. It turns on an arc about the spudpole, cutting soil from the seabed and sucking it up into the hold. In the trailer suction hopper dredger, the ship moves along a line, sucking soil up from the seabed. Cutting or water jet or jetting systems can be used to loosen the soil.

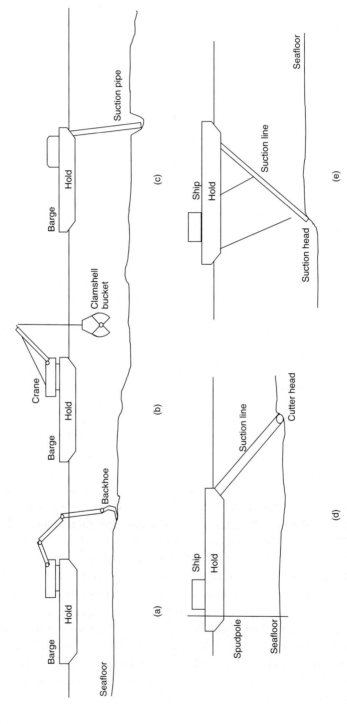

Fig. 8.4 Dredgers. (a) Backhoe dredger. (b) Clamshell dredger. (c) Suction dredger. (d) Cutter suction dredger. (e) Trailer suction hopper dredger

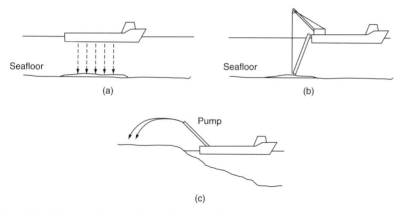

Fig. 8.5 *Delivery of dredged sand or gravel. (a) Uncontrolled dump from the hold. (b) Controlled piping onto the seafloor. (c) Rainbow technique*

Vigorous and clear quality control is required during dredging for construction materials. Clayey and silty materials are not wanted. Quality control is relatively easy for backhoe and clamshell dredgers, since a geotechnical engineer or technician can examine every load when it is brought up, and reject loads that are unsuitable. A second barge may need to be alongside so that rejected loads can be set aside and dumped elsewhere later.

Suction dredgers are continuous operations, and require a different approach. Stewart *et al.* (1983) describe a system in which two phases of sampling were carried out aboard the dredge vessel. In the first phase, material coming on board was inspected visually once every 5 minutes. The inspection was achieved by placing a cylinder beneath the inlet pipe on the ship. Where this showed that unsuitable material was being taken on board, the material was dumped over the side. The inspection was backed up by immediate particle gradation analysis. The second phase was carried out once the hopper was filled. A vibrocore was taken of the entire depth of fill recovered. The core was examined while the vessel was en route from the borrow site to the construction site. If unsuitable material was found, the entire load was discharged, and the ship returned to the borrow site.

Figure 8.5 illustrates three methods by which a suction dredger can discharge its load. In bottom dumping, the hull has doors underneath the hold. The doors are opened, and the dredged material falls rapidly to the seafloor. One alternative is to fluidise the soil in the hold, and pump fluidised soil along a flexible pipe that can be directed to a specific

383

place on the seafloor. This gives better control over where the material will be placed. In the third method, called the rainbow technique, fluidised sand and water are pumped out and sprayed over the area where the material is to be placed. This technique can be used when the material is to be placed at a location where the dredge ship cannot get to.

8.2.5 Construction

The first phase of island construction involves dredging out the unsuitable material. The material is taken into a dredger and dumped at some distance from the construction site. If necessary, gravel may be placed quickly around the edge of the excavated area to ensure that unsuitable material does not flow back into the area from outside. Stewart *et al.* (1983) describe a construction method in which an under-water bund was first constructed carefully around the edge of the area to be filled. The central area was then filled with bottom dumping. The next level of bund was then placed, and the operation repeated.

During construction it is usual to take regular bathymetric surveys, and to carry out cone penetration tests or geotechnical borings in the placed soils to determine the density and other parameters. It is feasible to compact material that has been placed. Gerwick (2007) describes an underwater vibrating plate system that is placed on top of the material to be compacted. Trials have been carried out of underwater compaction using rollers or a remote-controlled bulldozer. Vibroflotation is also feasible (Brown, 1977).

Once the island has reached a certain height, it will be levelled underwater if a caisson or other structure is to be placed on top. A caisson can reduce the volume of material required, and can provide some protection against erosion. It is installed by floating it over the island, pumping ballast in board, and setting it down onto the prepared ground (Gijzel *et al.*, 1985). Positioning of a single caisson within a few metres of the target position is feasible.

The core of the caisson is then filled. This can be done by piping fluidised soil from a dredger to a hopper. Gijzel *et al.* (1985) reported that core filling took 12 days for the Molikpaq. During this operation, excess water flows out under the caisson and through the berm. Once filled, a site investigation will normally be done to determine the density of the placed materials. If necessary, compaction can be carried out. Stewart and Hodge (1988) describe the use of explosives to compact sand for the Molikpaq.

8.2.6   Material properties

The material properties of the berm and fill material are determined by two factors. One is the particle size gradation that has been achieved as a result of the quality control operations during dredging. The second is the method used to place the materials at the construction site, and the methods of densification used, if any.

Hydraulic fill is not the same as in-situ soil. The dredging and placement operations will have destroyed any in-situ structure in the interparticle arrangements. Subsequent engineering properties including strength and stiffness depend on the method of placement, and therefore on the degree to which the placement is controlled (Berzins and Hewitt, 1984; Lee *et al.*, 1999). Air entrainment may also be an issue, since air bubbles will promote the placement of very loose fill, which may collapse later when the air dissolves in the water or rises out.

The properties of the dredged material will not be known exactly at the time of the initial design, so a conservative approach is appropriate, with design dimensions and, in particular, slope angles chosen in a way that allows subsequent change if the quality control and monitoring operations during construction reveal the need for changes.

8.3   Slope protection

8.3.1   *The need for slope protection*

The side slopes of an artificial island are typically constructed of sand or gravel, and so may be considered to be sand or gravel beaches. Established techniques in coastal engineering can therefore be used in their design.

Figure 8.6a shows some of the effects of a wave on a sloping beach. As a wave approaches a beach, it first pulls water towards it. The motion lifts some of the particles from the beach surface. As the wave comes close, the direction of the water motion changes, and water pushes up the beach. When the wave recedes, the water recedes too, and the soil may be redeposited. Because of the beach slope, there is a bias towards deposition at a lower elevation than where the sand was picked up from. Hence, over many waves there is a net scour of soil.

A breaking wave applies a shock pressure to a beach or a structure on the beach. Rather large pressures can be generated (Sorensen, 1997; Wolters *et al.*, 2005; Zhang *et al.*, 2009a,b). Beneath the beach surface, the changes in the water level and the slamming loads cause cyclic loading in the soil, and wetting/drying cycles to the soil near the average water level.

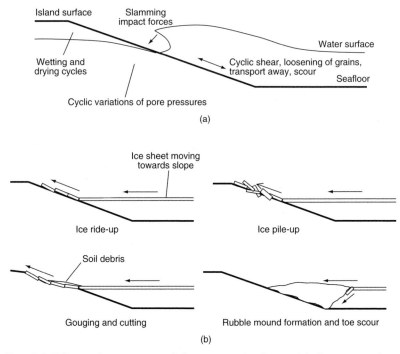

Fig. 8.6 Effects of environmental forces on side slopes. (a) Some geotechnical impacts of waves on a slope. (b) Some geotechnical interactions between an ice sheet and a slope (expanded from Abdelnour et al., 1982)

Figure 8.6b shows some of the events that can occur when an ice sheet moves towards a beach. In ride-up, the ice breaks in bending or compression, and is pushed up the beach, possibly reaching the top of the beach if there is no structure in the way. In pile-up, the ice piles up at some level on the beach. The force required to break an ice sheet depends on many factors, including its thickness and temperature. A strong enough ice sheet will be able to cut into a soil slope. A weak ice sheet may break or crush, and form into a rubble mound. As more ice is pushed into the mound, its keel moves downwards, potentially scoring the toe of the slope.

8.3.2 Methods of slope protection

The shoreline of a small artificial island can be protected from waves in the same ways as for coastal shorelines. Kamphuis (2002) describes a variety of conventional armour blocks placed on top of an underlayer above a filter layer on the slope (Fig. 8.7a). The blocks serve to dissipate

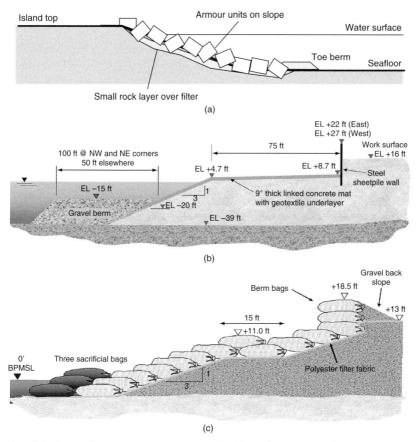

Fig. 8.7 Some slope protection options. (a) Use of conventional armour units. (b) Gravel berm, concrete mat with geotextile underlayer, and sheetpile wall (© 2008 Offshore Technology Conference: Gadd et al., 2001; Leidersdorf et al., 2008). (c) Sacrificial and permanent gravel bags (© 2008 Offshore Technology Conference: Ashford, 1984; Leidersdorf et al., 2008)

incoming wave energy. Depending on availability and environmental conditions, quarried rock can be sued for armour. Gabion baskets can be used as part of the upper slope protection in some circumstances (Townsend *et al.*, 1983).

Figure 8.7b shows a system used at BP's Northstar Production Island in the Alaskan Beaufort Sea. The island is located in a water depth of approximately 11.5 m, and is subjected to significant wave and ice loads. The protection includes a gravel berm to protect the toe of the slope, a system of lined concrete mats placed over a geotextile resting on the underlying material, and a steel sheet pile wall set back 25 m

387

from the top of the main slope, able to stop ice wave run-up and ice ride-up.

Figure 8.7c shows a system recommended for one of the beaches at the Oooguruk Offshore Drillsite, also in the Alaska Beaufort Sea. The armour system includes gravel bags placed on a permeable geotextile that serves to retain the underlying soil. The bags and the geotextile are composed of high-strength, UV-stabilised, woven polyester. The bags each contain 4 cubic yards of gravel, and weigh about 6 tonnes each. The lower sacrificial bags provide additional toe protection against ice scour; they are replaced when destroyed by the ice.

8.4   Calculations for ultimate limit states

8.4.1   *Global failure modes for sand and gravel islands*

Figure 8.8 shows some of the global failure modes that need to be considered in the design of a sand or gravel island. All of the modes can be analysed using modern slope stability software. For small islands, some of the global failure modes are three-dimensional, and will break the initial axi-symmetry of a circular island. Jefferies and Been (2006) describe the famous case of the Nerlerk berm that experienced four partial slides at different times during construction, and a fifth that was induced on purpose in an attempt to understand why the previous four occurred. Methodologies for three-dimensional slips are examined by Stark and Eid (1998), Griffith and Marquez (2007), Cheng and Lau (2008), and others.

A small island can be considered to be a footing that has some flexibility. Consequently, if the soil under the island is uniform, a straightforward bearing capacity calculation can provide a first estimate of vertical stability.

Figure 8.8a shows three possible modes of shallow slope failure. These are straightforward slope stability calculations. If the factor of safety is found to be too small, the principal remedial measure is to make the slope flatter, which requires making the lower parts of the island wider. Figures 8.8b and 8.8c shows failures involving a thin, weak layer at some depth below the seabed. A finite element analysis would be capable of showing this mode of deformation. Depending on the magnitudes of the settlements and the use of the island, this mode may sometimes be considered to be a serviceability limit state rather than an ultimate limit state.

Figure 8.8d illustrates complex sliding failures in which the slip surfaces may pass through several lenses of weak soil. If the failure

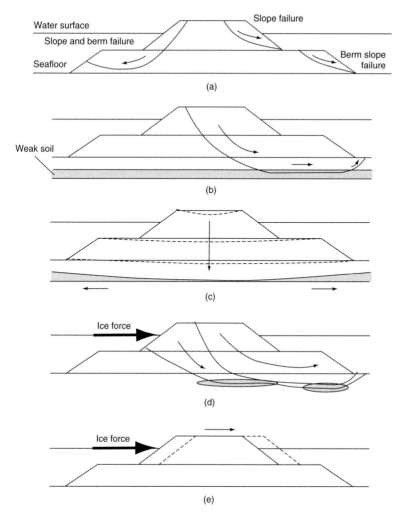

Fig. 8.8 Some failure modes for sand or gravel islands. (a) Shallow slip failures: can be promoted by progressive cumulative damage to slope protection. (b) Sliding failure in a thin, weak soil layer. (c) Squeezing a thin weak soil layer. (d) Failures connecting weak lenses. (e) Decapitation. (f) Base sliding. (g) Deep rotational slip. (h) Inducement of a landslide

surface intersects the side of the island below the water surface, then water pressures acting on the surface there will be involved in the analysis. Ice forces will affect the results if the island is in a region where they occur, and the effect of the weight of ice piled up on one side of the island may also be important. If weak soil layers reduce the factor of safety below an acceptable value, they will need to be

389

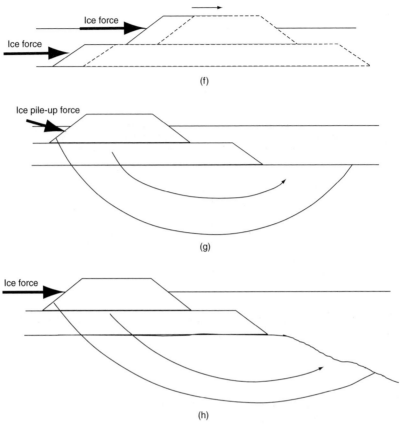

Ice force

Ice force

(f)

Ice pile-up force

(g)

Ice force

(h)

Fig. 8.8 Continued

removed, or the island may need to be widened. Chemical grouting or jet grouting may be an alternative solution in some situations (Ou, 2006).

Figure 8.8e shows a mode termed 'decapitation', in which the upper part of the island slides over the lower part. This may be feasible if significantly different materials are used in the two parts. Sliding may also be feasible at the interface between the island and the underlying soil, and if there is a weak layer there (Fig. 8.8f).

Figure 8.8g shows a deep rotational slip. This also will be affected by water or ice forces. The factor of safety will certainly be reduced if the arrangement in Fig. 8.8h is used, with the island placed near the edge of a slope or created by removing material from the immediate vicinity.

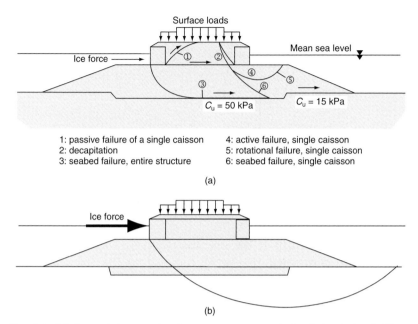

1: passive failure of a single caisson 4: active failure, single caisson
2: decapitation 5: rotational failure, single caisson
3: seabed failure, entire structure 6: seabed failure, single caisson

(a)

(b)

Fig. 8.9 (a) Some failure modes for a caisson retained island (© 1983 Offshore Technology Conference: Weaver and Berzins, 1983). (b) Deeper mode, if there is weaker underlying soil

8.4.2 Static failure modes for caisson-retained islands

Figure 8.9a shows some of the global failure modes for a caisson-retained island. In the case considered, the island was constructed from four separate caissons that were set down together in the form of a square in plan view.

Ice forces acting on one caisson could conceivably cause a passive failure in the soil in the core. Ice forces could also conceivably be transmitted around the square, moving the opposite caisson and causing an active failure in the soil there. If the width-to-height ratio of the core region is sufficiently small, the passive failure wedge will interfere with the active failure wedge, and create a more complex failure pattern. Even at large width-to-height ratios, the stress state of the soil in the core will be complex during horizontal environmental loading.

Decapitation is a more realistic mode for this geometry, due to the confining effect of the caissons. For this particular design, it was considered feasible for one caisson to experience a rotational failure that would be largely unrestrained by the attachments around the

391

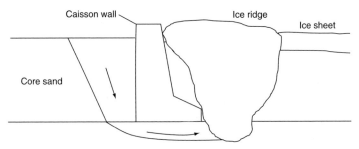

Fig. 8.10 *Loss of core fill from a caisson-retained island by scour-induced failure followed by hopper flow failure of partially liquefied sand (Jeyatharan, 1991)*

square. The in-situ soil at the site was relatively strong, and seabed failures were considered that were confined to the soil above the seafloor. Deeper modes of failure are feasible if this is not the case, such as the deep mode shown in Fig. 8.9b.

8.4.3   Other failure modes

Under cyclic environmental loading, the soil of a small artificial island is subjected to cyclic stresses that would be expected to result in the generation of excess pore pressures. Hicks and Smith (1988) carried out numerical calculations that demonstrated that liquefaction of the core fill of a caisson-retained island was a possible result. Depending on the width of the base of the caisson, it is then feasible for a piping failure to develop, with fluidised soil being lost by breaking out underneath the caisson.

Gerwick (2007) describes a failure of a joint between two independent caisson walls, involving liquefaction of sandy soil close to the joint, and piping underneath the caisson. Figure 8.10 shows another potential piping failure mode. An ice ridge or mound of ice rubble scours the sand from beneath the outer wall of the caisson. When the ice then moves, a depression is left in the seabed. A hopper-type flow failure may then become feasible, with soil flowing downwards in a conical depression, and out under the caisson. The factor of safety against this type of failure would be reduced if, in addition to the ice scour, prior cyclic loading had increased the excess pore pressures in the fill, so reducing its shear strength.

Figure 8.11 shows the data for a centrifuge test of earthquake effects on a simplified model island. The island was trapezoidal in elevation,

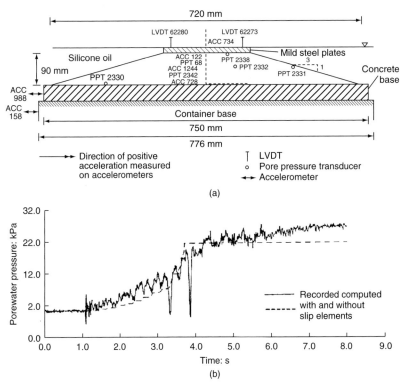

Fig. 8.11 Investigating the seismic response of an island (© 1984 Offshore Technology Conference: Finn et al., 1984). (a) Section through a 1/100th scale model of the submerged island. The model width of 720 mm corresponds to a prototype width of 72 m (ACC, accelerometer; PPT, pore pressure transducer; LVDT, displacement transducer). (b) Pore pressure response beneath the centre of the island, showing the pore pressure build-up as a result of an earthquake

with a 720 mm-wide footprint, representing 72 m at full scale. The island rested on a rigid concrete base for modelling purposes. The top area was subject to a surcharge load modelled by steel plates. Various transducers were attached to the container or in the model, including accelerometers, pore pressure transducers, and displacement transducers. The model was subjected to several episodes of severe horizontal base shaking. Figure 8.11b shows the pore pressure response in the soil immediately below the model centreline in line with the model earthquakes. The pore water pressure in the sand rose to about 20 kPa above its initial value. This was a significant value, possibly indicating local liquefaction of the sand.

393

8.5   Calculations for serviceability limit states

8.5.1   General

Estimates of settlement can be made using the familiar load-spreading method (e.g. Bowles, 1996; Das, 2004). However, finite element software capable of carrying out short-term (immediate) and long-term (consolidation) settlement calculations is readily available. Small islands are three-dimensional, so software with three-dimensional capability is desirable.

The settlement of a structure on an island can be considered to be the sum of three parts: (1) the settlement of the structure into the island soil, (2) the settlement of the island soil relative to the in-situ soil, associated with the self-weight of the island soil, and (3) the settlement of the underlying strata due to the weight of the island and the structures it supports. Settlements of all three types can arise from several causes, including self-weight effects and cyclic loading effects. The latter may include the effects of wave loads, wind gust loads, ice loads, and earthquake-induced loads, as well as long-period changes such as changes in the water level.

The primary consolidation settlement of an island can be accelerated in the same ways as for an onshore foundation, principally by preloading and/or drainage. Sand drains can be used to accelerate the consolidation of the clay, for example. Secondary compression is considered to be the main cause of the very large, unexpected settlements occurring at Kansai International Airport (Mesri and Vardhanabhuti, 2005). The potential for this can be assessed from a laboratory oedometer test.

8.5.2   Case example: Tarsuit N-44

Figure 8.12 illustrates results by Conlin *et al.* (1985) for Tarsuit N-44 caisson-retained island in the Beaufort Sea. The island profile is shown in the upper diagram, with different horizontal and vertical scales. The island applies a surcharge load of about 350 kPa to the foundation. The behaviours of the foundation clay and silt were of particular interest. The underlying frozen soil was assumed to be rigid, an assumption that was acceptable in this case because the near-surface soils were relatively very soft.

Figure 8.12b shows the finite element mesh. In this case it was judged to be unnecessary to continue the finite element mesh outside the toes of the slope. Figure 8.12c shows the predicted vertical and lateral displacements in the clay immediately after construction. Large

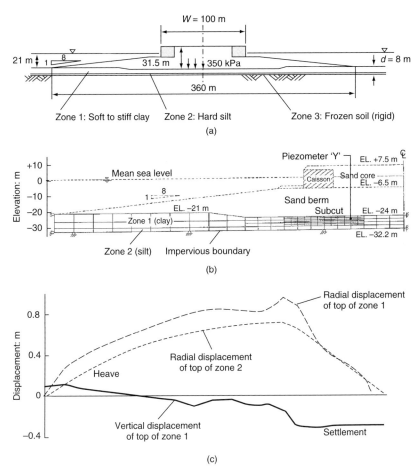

Fig. 8.12 Example of a finite element analysis for settlement: Tarsuit N-44 caisson-retained island (© 1985 Offshore Technology Conference: Conlin et al., (1985). (a) Geometry and loads. (b) Axisymmetric finite element mesh: the mesh is rotationally symmetric about the centreline. (c) Predicted movements

movements are indicated, with the clay being pushed downwards on the centreline, squeezing outwards at intermediate radii, and heaving upwards at the toe of the slope. As well as these results, excess pore pressures up to 240 kPa were predicted on the centreline immediately after construction, reducing to 180 kPa after 33 days.

The analyses would have been accompanied by short-term stability analyses taking account of the excess pore pressures, and analyses for long-term settlements and stability.

8.6   Instrumentation and monitoring

It is normal to install a range of instrumentation on a small island that is built for hydrocarbon exploration or production. The instrumentation can provide early warnings of problems, and can produce data that can help in developing experience and understanding of the environmental loads and soil responses. Witney and Muller (1986) describe the instrumentation and monitoring system installed on the Molikpaq mobile arctic caisson. The system was controlled and monitored by a central computer capable of interpreting the data and generating alarms. The sensors initially comprised:

- 282 strain gauge systems with water-blocking and low-temperature capability
- 40 total pressure cells
- 12 pore pressure transducers
- 10 extensometers on the structure
- 9 tilt meters on the structure
- 36 in-place inclinometers
- 30 electrical piezometers
- 31 ice load panels, measuring ice loads on the structure
- 8 resistance thermometers.

After initial experiences, a second high-speed data acquisition system was added to study the dynamics of the interactions between the structure and the ice.

8.7   Decommissioning

Decommissioning an island represents a second environmental change that may need to be the subject of an impact assessment. For an island that has been used for hydrocarbon exploration or production, decommissioning will normally include removing all of the structures that were there, removing contaminated soil if any, and removing the sea defences.

Anderson and Leidersdorf (1988) studied erosion on Mukluk Island, a gravel island that had been constructed for exploration purposes. Hydrocarbons were not found, and the island was cleared and sea defences removed. Wave action was found to reconfigure the island quickly, removing side slope material at a rate of 1 foot per hour, even though much of the gravel was frozen. The experience demonstrated the severe environmental forces that were at work.

9

Deep and ultra-deep water

Chapter 9 describes the challenges and principal solution concepts for deep water, covering how to plan and participate in a deepwater geotechnical site investigation, and use applicable standards and references to carry out calculations for the installation, capacity, and the removal of tension piles, anchor piles, suction caissons, and drag embedment anchors.

9.1   Introduction

9.1.1   General

Deep water is considered to be a water depth greater than about 200–300 m (Chakrabati et al., 2005; Campbell et al., 2008). Figure 9.1 shows the locations of some of the deepwater field developments around the globe. Deep water is commercially interesting partly because shallow-water fields were the first to be exploited and are therefore becoming depleted now, and partly because of the enormous volumes of hydrocarbons that are discovered at some deepwater locations.

The technical and operational complexity of developing in deep water is an order of magnitude greater than for shallower water. The pressure at a depth of 1000 m is about 100 MPa. Divers cannot survive or work under this pressure, so all seafloor operations are carried out remotely with control on the surface. If a tube of steel with a length $L = 1000$ m and submerged unit weight $\gamma' = 70 \, \text{kN/m}^3$ is hung vertically from a ship, the tension in the tube is about $70 \times 1000 \, \text{kPa} = 70 \, \text{MPa}$, which is a significant fraction of the yield stress of the steel. If a site investigation tool is lowered to the seafloor at a speed of about 1 m/s, it takes about 20 minutes to get there. If a bubble of gas exists in a seabed soil sample with a diameter of 1 mm in situ, it expands to a diameter of about 10 mm when the soil sample is brought to the surface. The reduction in the stress as the soil

Fig. 9.1 Locations of some current deepwater developments

sample is lifted to the surface can also contribute to significant sample damage.

Deep water also offers increased geohazard challenges. Many current deepwater developments are close to a continental rise, and so are subject to additional potential geohazards associated with possible landsliding. An example is provided by the Zaire Fan, created over millions of years from turbidite deposits from the Zaire River, together with debris flows from the collapse of sand bodies in the Zaire Canyon (Droz *et al.*, 2003). Heezen *et al.* (1964) reported breaks in telephone cables crossing the estuary at a rate of about 60 per 100 years, indicating significant present-day sub-sea landsliding. Another example is along the Sigsbee Escarpment in the Gulf of Mexico (Liedtke *et al.*, 2006; Berger *et al.*, 2006), with water depths plunging to 2 km. It is not uncommon to have to change the planned location of a structure due to existing seafloor hazards such as mud flows, mud mounds, expulsion features, and geological faults, or because of the potential for landsliding during the design lifetime of the structure.

9.1.2 *Platform concepts*

Figure 9.2 shows the elements of a tension leg platform (TLP). The platform consists of a number of large pontoons providing buoyancy, supporting columns that support the decks and topsides. The platform is pulled downwards below its free floating level by tendons that are held by tension foundations on or in the seabed. Even under the most

398

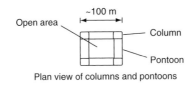

Plan view of columns and pontoons

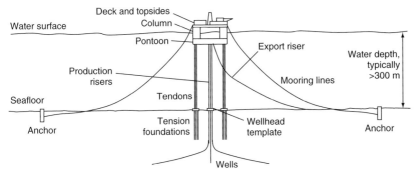

Fig. 9.2 Tension leg platform and foundation elements (not to scale)

adverse meteorological and oceanographic (metocean) conditions, tension is maintained in the tendons. As a result, the platform is held in an approximately constant vertical position as a wave passes. The stability of the lateral position is achieved by mooring lines connected to anchors in the seabed. The mooring lines may be several kilometres long. Hydrocarbon wells may be drilled from the platform, or pre-drilled before the platform is installed. The wellheads may be supported on a template, and are connected to the platform by production risers. There may also be several risers connected to import pipelines from other platforms or to export pipelines to shore. Control umbilicals connect the seabed systems to the TLP.

The first deepwater platform was the Hutton TLP, which was installed in 146 m of water in the North Sea in 1984 (Bradshaw *et al.*, 1984, 1985). Recent TLPs in the Gulf of Mexico include the Ursa, Mars, Brutus, and Ram Powell platforms in over 1000 m water (Doyle, 1999). In the Atlantia Deepstar TLP, pontoons are arranged as three spokes from a single, central column supporting relatively small topsides facilities (Harte *et al.*, 2006). In a spar platform, the platform consists of a vertical tube that incorporates buoyancy and oil storage (van Santen and de Werk, 1976). The tube may be 50 m or more in diameter and 200 m or so in height, and is typically fitted with spoilers to prevent vortex-shedding vibrations as water flows past it. Stability is provided by inertia and anchors rather than tension

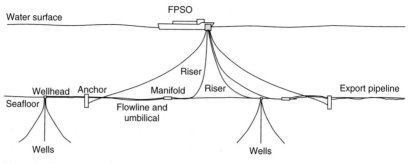

Fig. 9.3 *Floating production system (not to scale)*

legs. In the truss spar concept, the lower part of the spar is a steel truss (Chakrabarti *et al.*, 2005).

Figure 9.3 shows the concept of a floating production (FP) system, using a ship as the platform (Leghorn *et al.*, 1996; Bordieri *et al.*, 2008). The ship may be purpose-built or converted. A swivel may be at one end. It allows the ship to change direction and 'weather-vane', so as to take up the most advantageous orientation in relation to changing wind, wave, and current conditions. All the risers and umbilicals needed for the seabed production system pass through the swivel. In some designs, multiple anchor lines are arranged with different stiffnesses to allow partial weather-vaning without the use of a swivel. The seabed production system consists of wellheads that will have been pre-drilled from a semi-submersible, together with seabed manifolds, flowlines, and the associated umbilicals.

9.1.3 Foundation concepts and codes of practice
The foundation concepts for deep water consist primarily of tension systems for TLPs, anchoring systems for all types of deepwater platform, and wellheads, seabed manifolds, pipelines, and risers.

Foundation solutions for tension and anchoring systems are reviewed by Eltaher *et al.* (2003), Aubeny and Murff (2005), and others. The geotechnical aspects of these systems are covered in the API RP2T standard (API, 1997), for TLPs, and API RP2SK (API, 2005), for anchor foundations, which are considered to be part of the station-keeping system of the platform. The new ISO standards appear to be arranged differently: ISO 19904-2 (see Wichers *et al.*, 2007) will address TLPs. ISO 19901-7 (ISO, 2005) contains some valuable geotechnical guidance for station-keeping.

Some of the foundation components are covered by the general standard API RP2A (API, 2000). Wellhead templates and seabed manifolds are normally designed as simple shallow foundations.

9.2   Site investigations

API RP2T recommends that deepwater investigations include a geology survey to identify the processes occurring in the seabed and surrounding area, a geophysical survey including bathymetric and shallow seismic data to assess seafloor and seabed hazards, a geotechnical investigation, including sampling and in-situ testing, and a pre-installation survey to verify that conditions have not changed. The overall investigation will need to cover the entire area used by the seafloor production systems, and a sufficient surrounding area to be able to identify all relevant geohazards. Depending on the nature and variability of the area, sampling and in-situ testing will normally be done at a tension foundation site, at every anchor site, and at the sites of every other hardware item placed on the seafloor. Additional studies are done as relevant, including studies of scour, sand waves, liquefaction, and seafloor instabilities.

In a canyon or slope environment, slope stability assessments may be needed to verify that the proposed foundations are unlikely to become part of a submarine landslide, are unlikely to become a contributing factor to the initiation of a landslide, and are safe against debris flows from nearly slopes (Nowacki *et al.*, 2003). This can include a major predictive task since the slopes in an active deltaic environment may evolve significantly over a typical 20 year structure design life (Niedoroda *et al.*, 2003). Campbell *et al.* (2008) emphasise that deepwater investigations are an order of magnitude more complex than investigations in relatively shallow 100–200 m water depths. Careful advance planning and contracting activities are needed, since the global availability of the required specialist equipment and expertise is presently very limited.

Figure 9.4 illustrates some of the techniques available or in development. Conventional offshore site investigation with a drillstring stretching from a drillship or semi-submersible is feasible, but requires considerably upgraded equipment and procedures. The weight of the drillstring is an order-of-magnitude greater than for shallower water, and all of the drilling derrick, lifting equipment, deck foundations, and ship structure may need to be upgraded. At least one current system uses lightweight aluminium drillstrings instead of standard API

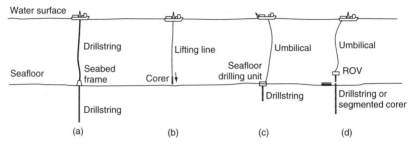

Fig. 9.4 *Site investigation technologies (not to scale)*

5 inch-diameter steel pipe (Borel *et al.*, 2005). The seabed frame and the control and actuation systems it supports may need to be upgraded to work under the higher water pressures involved. The drillstring may bend significantly over the distance from the ship to the seafloor, due to water currents at intermediate depths. Its twist at the level of the ship may be one revolution in advance of the twist at the seafloor, changing the nature of the control of the system during drilling.

For shallow sampling, a core barrel can be lowered from the ship and released at some height above the seafloor. The barrel drops and penetrates into the seafloor, collecting a sample. The current state-of-the-art sampler is the STACOR® sampler, which can, in principle, take a 30 m-long core sample (Borel *et al.*, 2005; Wong *et al.*, 2008). Sample quality is much improved compared with the familiar Kullenberg corer. However, the upper metre or so of a soft seabed may be 'blown by', creating a depth offset for a STACOR® core compared with one obtained using conventional drilling.

Drill operations can be carried out by systems deployed on the seafloor and controlled via an umbilical. In the portable remotely operated drill (PROD) system, up to 260 m of drilling tools are loaded into two magazines, including core barrels, in-situ testing tools, and casing. Hydraulic actuators load the required equipment into the drilling unit as required (Carter *et al.*, 1999). Seabed operations can be monitored visually using cameras fixed to the seafloor units or on remotely operated vehicles (ROV's). In principle, a seabed drilling system operated by an ROV may be practical.

9.3   Deepwater soils

Deepwater soils can be classified as either turbidites or pelagic deposits (Baudet and Ho, 2004). Turbidites are deposited by turbidity currents or debris flows, which are generally short-lived deposition episodes typically associated with a distant submarine landslide or other short-duration source. Pelagic sediments consist primarily of the carbonate remains of the skeletons of micro-organisms. The carbonate compensation depth (CCD) is the depth at which the supply of calcite from above equals its rate of dissolution in seawater (Murff, 1987). Kelly *et al.* (1974) reported data for fine-grained cemented carbonate sediments obtained from 3700 m water depth. The CCD is typically about 4500 m, depending on temperature factors. Carbonate soils below this depth are transported deposits rather than pelagic ones.

In many areas, the soil profile consists of alternating turbidite and pelagic layers. Turbidites can be deposited quickly, particularly in the fan zone from a major river. By contrast, pelagic deposition rates can be as slow as a fraction of a millimetre per year.

The majority of deepwater sites in the Gulf of Mexico appear to be normally consolidated clay sites with relatively thin sand layers. Figure 9.5 shows data from a site on the Sigsbee Escarpment. The undrained shear strength increases at a rate of about 0.2 times the vertical effective stress, consistent with normally consolidated clay. In some other deepwater areas the clays are significantly underconsolidated, suggesting that the rate of deposition has been faster than the rate of consolidation, and that the resulting excess pore pressures have not yet dissipated. Soil strengths for clays at these sites increase much slower with depth compared with elsewhere. Puech *et al.* (2004a) reported that submerged unit weights were smaller at some Gulf of Guinea sites compared with the Gulf of Mexico. The rate of increase in the shear strength with depth was also less for clays in the Gulf of Guinea, but were not as low as in the Mississippi delta, where deposition rates are very high (Quiros and Little, 2003).

Le *et al.* (2008) caution against the use of the SHANSEP testing procedure for sensitive structured clays. They found that reconsolidation significantly altered the clay microstructure, and that strengths measured after reconsolidation can be similar to remoulded shear strengths rather than undisturbed strengths. The clay they tested did not exhibit the same normalised behaviour as other clays.

Ehlers *et al.* (2005) reported the existence of near-seafloor crust zones in clays at deepwater sites, offshore Nigeria. The typical crust thickness was 1–2 m, with strengths up to 10 kPa, sufficient to affect pipeline design and shallow foundation penetrations. Their investigations suggested that the crusts were the result of intense bioturbation or reworking of deposited soil by small creatures.

403

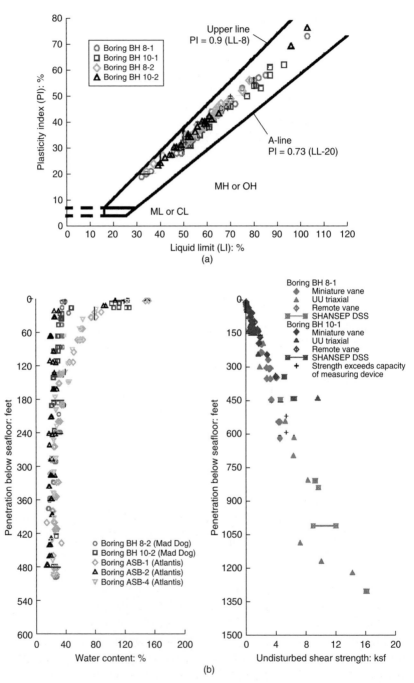

Fig. 9.5 *Data from a site on the Sigsbee Escarpment, Gulf of Mexico* (© 2003 *Offshore Technology Conference: Al-Khafaji et al., 2003b*)

9.4   Suction-installed foundations

9.4.1   *Overview*

A suction-installed foundation unit (Figs 9.6a–9.6c) consists of a cylinder that is open at its base and closed at its top, with a vent in

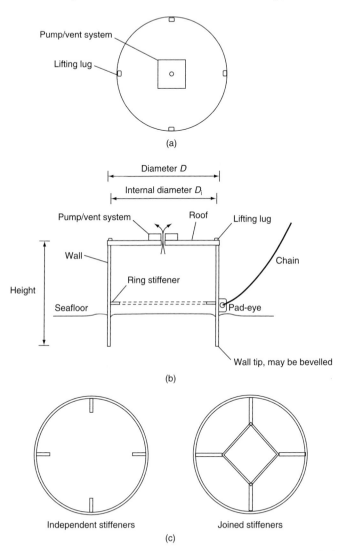

Fig. 9.6 Suction-installed foundation units. (a) Plan view. (b) Sectional elevation. (c) Plan sections of examples of arrangements for longtitudinal stiffeners. (d) Plan view of a three-caisson suction caisson cluster. (e) Elevation view of a multiple suction caisson foundation with installation using an ROV (© 2002 Offshore Technology Conference: Sparrevik, 2002)

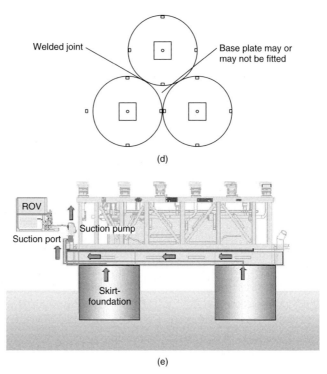

Fig. 9.6 *Continued*

the roof (Wang et al., 1977, 1978). There may be ring stiffeners and/or longitudinal stiffeners inside. The cylinder is lowered to the seabed and allowed to penetrate into the seabed due to self-weight. Water is then pumped out from the interior. The pumping lowers the water pressure inside the cylinder, creating a pressure differential across the caisson roof. This creates a force that pushes the unit into the seabed. During installation, it is vital to be able to apply enough suction to overcome the soil resistance, but not so much suction that the soil inside the caisson fluidises. Once installed, the roof vent may be closed off or left open. If closure can be guaranteed for the design lifetime, the suction caisson may be considered to act as a buried shallow-gravity foundation with a weight equal to the buoyant weight of the caisson and the material it encloses.

Suction units are also installed in clusters (Fig. 9.6d), where individual control of suction in the different units during installation permits some degree of directional control of the embedment process. Suction units can be fitted to the base of a sub-sea structure (Fig. 9.6), allowing good control of the verticality of the structure as it is emplaced on a soft seabed.

A suction-installed unit is called a suction pile if its height-to-diameter ratio is large, or a suction caisson if the ratio is about 1 or less. Suction caissons have also been called 'bucket foundations' because of their resemblance to an upturned bucket. They were successfully used in place of piles on the Europipe 16/11-E jacket platform in 70 m of water in the North Sea after extensive field trials (Tjelta and Haaland, 1993; Tjelta, 1994; Bye *et al.*, 1995). The caissons were 12 m in diameter, and penetrated 6 m into the sandy seafloor. Suction caissons are also feasible foundation solutions for offshore wind turbines (Houlsby *et al.*, 2005a).

A unit is called a suction anchor if it is to be used as an anchor. Suction anchors have been widely used for deepwater applications. Andersen *et al.* (2005) reviewed methodologies and data from 485 anchors installed at 50 sites in water depths approaching 200 m. Installation is almost always a successful operation, although, in a few instances, several attempts had to be made at different positions on the seabed before a successful installation was achieved. Very occasionally, the caisson wall buckles, but it is now straightforward to design against this. No performance problems were reported, indicating that actual capacities were generally not less than the values calculated in design.

9.4.2   Installation: overview

Installation calculation methods for sands and clays are described in API RP2SK, and by Andersen *et al.* (2005), Houlsby and Byrne (2005, 2006), and others. Essentially, the calculation involves balancing the downwards force due to suction inside the caisson with the resistance from the wall friction and the end bearing on the sides of the caisson. Additionally, the possibility of sand boiling or fluidisation inside the caisson must be considered.

Figure 9.7 shows a typical arrangement for installation. An installation vessel lowered the suction caisson to the seabed and carried out the main suction control operations. An ROV may be used to monitor the seabed processes, together with depth, tilt, and other instrumentation on and in the caisson. A rope-handling vessel manages a rope attached to a short segment of heavy anchor chain. After the caisson is installed, the rope-handling vessel will be involved in connecting the anchor chain to a chain to the TLP or floating structure.

Installation occurs in two phases. First, in the self-weight penetration phase, the roof vent is open, and the caisson is pushed into the seabed by

407

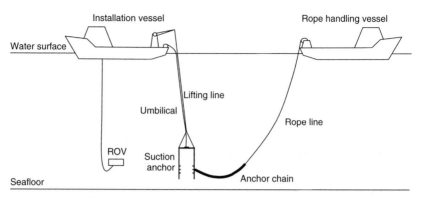

Fig. 9.7 Typical installation arrangement (Hagen et al., 1998; Sparrevik, 2002)

its buoyant self-weight W'. Next, in the suction-assisted phase, the roof vent is closed, and pumping reduces the internal water pressure by some amount Δp, creating a pressure differential (underpressure) Δp across the roof. The driving force F is

$$F = W' \frac{\pi D_i^2}{4} \Delta p \qquad (9.1)$$

where D_i is the internal diameter of the caisson. The equation applies with $\Delta p = 0$ for self-weight penetration. The penetration in each phase is determined by equating the driving force F to the resistance Q. The latter is determined by adapting the method for calculating ultimate axial pile capacity:

$$Q = Q_{side} + Q_{tip} \qquad (9.2)$$

where Q_{side} is the side resistance and Q_{tip} is the end bearing resistance. The resistances come from shear stresses along the inner and outer walls of the caisson, normal stresses on the base of the wall, and from stresses applied by the soil to protuberances such as the pad-eye, mooring chain, launching skids, and any change in the wall section thickness.

The factors used in the calculation are different to those for pile capacity calculations. For clays, Section E3.2 of API RP2SK recommends a shaft friction adhesion factor that is equivalent to assuming the wall shear stress is the remoulded undrained shear strength. This has been found to work well in practice, provided the steel surface is not smoothed or painted (Schroeder et al., 2006). Painting reduces the friction. The end bearing factor depends on the objective of the calculation. For sands, advice is provided by Houlsby and Byrne (2005), Andersen et al. (2008), and others. Wall friction is affected by:

- The negative excess pore pressures (suctions) in the soil induced by the reduction of pressure inside the caisson. These can be calculated using three-dimensional flownet software.
- The transfer of shear load from the wall to the soil, which increases the vertical effective stress in the soil, so increasing the horizontal effective stress, and increasing the skin friction.

The vertical effective stresses in the soil outside the caisson are increased by the suction, while those inside are decreased. The critical underpressure is the value of the pressure drop Δp that causes the soil plug inside the caisson to fail. In the case of sand, the failure is by fluidisation. It is important to ensure that this does not happen during installation, because the effect can be to significantly reduce the subsequent holding capacity of the unit. The allowable underpressure is obtained by dividing by a factor of safety, typically 1.5. Considerations of structural integrity of the roof, caisson walls, pipework, seals, and other details may reduce the allowable underpressure further.

9.4.3   Installation: experiences and complexities

Field trials of a 3.8 m-diameter suction pile installation in sand and clay are reported by Hogervorst (1980). Senpere and Auvergne (1982) describe an installation of suction anchor piles in soft-over-stiff clay in the North Sea. Hagen *et al.* (1998) describe an installation for the Schiehallion FPSO (floating production, storage, and offloading system), west of Shetland. Schroeder *et al.* (2006a; 2006b) reported installation data for caissons of diameters between 5.5 and 7.6 m and penetrations between 14.3 and 25.9 m into varied clays. Tran *et al.* (2007) reported centrifuge test data from an installation in sand with silt layers. The industry experience of the penetration of skirted foundations and anchors in sand was reviewed by Andersen *et al.* (2008).

Figure 9.8 shows some effects of ring stiffeners. In clay, a ring stiffener provides additional resistance to penetration, but also has the effect of pushing the clay away from the wall above it. Once the clay has passed a sufficient distance, it will collapse back against the wall, trapping water. This can be detrimental to the subsequent performance of the caisson, since the water provides no shear resistance and may soften the soil inside the caisson over time (Dendani, 2003). If there are several ring stiffeners in sequence, they can hold the soil away from the wall. For sand, the material that fails above the stiffeners may be in a loose

409

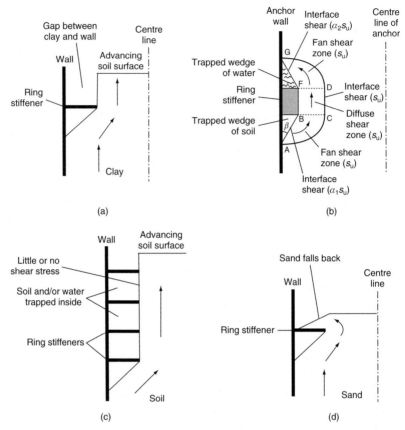

Fig. 9.8 Some considerations of internal ring stiffeners. (a) Clay squeezing past an internal ring stiffener, and not returning to the wall. (b) Clay squeezing past a ring stiffener, and collapsing onto the wall, trapping water (© 2002 Offshore Technology Conference: Erbrich and Hefer, 2002). (c) Dead zone with soil moving past a series of ring stiffeners (adapted from Erbrich and Hefer, 2002). (d) Sand moving past an internal ring stiffener, and falling back onto the stiffener

state, and so contribute less to wall friction. Its weight adds to the driving force.

For an unsymmetrically placed protuberance, such as pad-eye, the protuberance attracts extra resistance during installation. This causes a moment on the caisson, which must be equilibrated by changes in the normal stress on the caisson walls. If necessary to prevent tilting, a symmetric protuberance may need to be attached.

The amount of soil entering the caisson is thought to depend significantly on the detailed design of the base of the caisson wall (Lee *et al.*,

2005). If the wall tip is bevelled, some control is obtained over how much soil moves into the caisson, compared with how much passes outside. This affects soil heave inside the caisson, which can significantly effect the maximum penetration that can be achieved. For example, Clukey (2005) reported data for caissons of diameter 6.5 m, wall thickness up to 50.8 mm, and design embedments of 24 m in normally consolidated clay. The 50.8 mm caisson wall has a volume of about $\pi \times 6.5 \times 0.0508 \times 24 = 24.9\,\mathrm{m}^3$. If half of this moves inside the caisson, the plug heave would be $\frac{1}{2} \times 24.9 = 12.45\,\mathrm{m}^3$ divided by the internal area of about $\pi \times 6.5^2/4 = 33.18\,\mathrm{m}$, giving a plug heave of 0.38 m.

Tran *et al.* (2005) found that heave in sand is related to dilation. Tran *et al.* (2007) report centrifuge model test results of suction caisson installation in sand with silt seams. They observed soil heave of up to 20% of the caisson height. Instability of the soil plug was observed, with significant silt scouring. Required underpressures were up to 80% higher than would have been the case without the silt layers.

The installation of a suction caisson into normally consolidated clay will usually cause positive excess pore pressures to develop in the clay. These will dissipate over time as the soil reconsolidates, resulting in a gain in the soil strength with time (Dendani, 2003; Hesar, 2003; Olson *et al.*, 2003). Thixotropy may also be a significant process (Yoshida *et al.*, 2005). Jeanjean (2006) reported data and calculations indicating that 90% consolidation could be reached after about 30 days for caissons in soft clay in the Gulf of Mexico. The effects of set-up can be different inside and outside the caisson.

9.4.4 Ultimate capacity

API RP2SK classifies the analysis and design tools to determine suction anchor capacity as (1) finite element methods, (2) limit equilibrium or limit analysis methods, usually employing the concept of failure mechanisms, or (3) highly simplified, semi-empirical methods such as p–y analysis.

The finite element method is probably the most rigorous general method, and is potentially capable of identifying soil failure mechanisms automatically (Sparrevik, 2002; Aubeny *et al.*, 2003; Maniar *et al.*, 2005; Zdravkovic and Potts, 2005; Cao *et al.*, 2005a,b). Al-Khafaji *et al.* (2003a) describe a finite element analysis used for a caisson for BP's Holstein project in the Gulf of Mexico. The caisson diameter was 5.5 m. The design penetration was 38.4 m into clay varying from soft

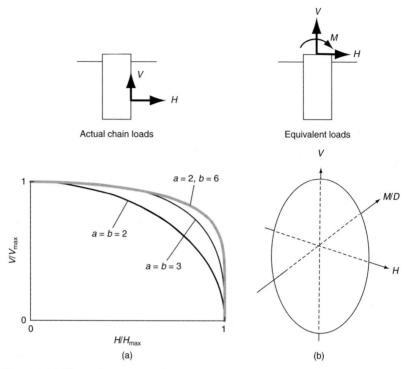

Fig. 9.9 Yield envelope approaches for suction anchors. (a) Envelopes in terms of vertical and horizontal pull-out loads. (b) Envelope in terms of three force resultants

at the seafloor to stiff and very stiff at full penetration. The modified Cam clay model was used to model the soil behaviour. Significant softening was calculated during cyclic loading, due to the response of the model soil at high stress ratios.

A yield envelope or failure interaction diagram approach can be applied for suction caissons in several ways. Figure 9.9a shows an envelope proposed by Senders (2001), given by

$$\left(\frac{V}{V_{\text{max}}}\right)^a + \left(\frac{H}{H_{\text{max}}}\right)^b = 1 \tag{9.3}$$

where V and H are the vertical and horizontal pull-out forces, respectively, and V_{max} and H_{max} are the values that apply when only one of the two forces act. Hesar (2003) found that values of $a = b$ close to 3 fitted data from the Barracuda and Caratinga suction anchors installed in the Campos Basin, offshore Brazil. Zdravkovic et al. (2001) suggested $a = b = 2$ and $H_{\text{max}} = 0.235V_{\text{max}}$, based on finite element analyses

412

relating to the Snorre TLP bucket foundations in soft clay. The parameters involved are affected by the depth of the pad-eye. An alternative approach is to treat the suction anchor unit as a rigid body to which vertical, horizontal, and moment loads are applied, as sketched in Fig. 9.9b. A simple expression would be

$$\left(\frac{V}{V_{\text{ref}}}+\alpha\right)^a+\left(\frac{H}{H_{\text{max}}}\right)^b+\left(\frac{M}{M_{\text{max}}}\right)^c=1 \qquad (9.4)$$

where α, a, b and c are constants. More complex expressions have been discussed by Byrne and Houlsby (1999), Taiebat and Carter (2000, 2005), and others. The force resultants can be related to the anchor load applied to the pad-eye and the position of the pad-eye, so that a given pad-eye position corresponds to a two-dimensional load surface in the three-dimensional loadspace. This more general approach potentially allows a study to be made of the effect of different pad-eye positions.

Plasticity analyses for suction caissons are described by Aubeny and Murff (2004) and others. The caisson itself is usually considered to be a rigid object, so that only the soil fails. The stresses on the caisson are then deduced, and the structural design of the caisson is checked. Finite element analyses can also be of great value, particularly to address complex issues such as the reliability of reverse bearing capacity (Templeton, 2002; Al-Khafaji *et al.*, 2003a; Clukey *et al.*, 2004).

Figures 9.10a and 9.10b show two possible mechanism for pull-out. In the first, the soil plug stays where it is, and the resistance to pull-out is provided solely by the internal and external wall friction. In the second, the wall friction is sufficient to hold the soil plug in place, and the uplift resistance is the weight of the plug plus the effect of the shear stress on the external surface of the caisson. Figures 9.10c and 9.10d show concepts for determining the resistance of a suction anchor to an inclined load. These sketches also indicate the types of laboratory test that most directly model the soil behaviours in different regions around the suction caisson. The laterally loaded pile mode in Fig. 9.10d is further discussed in Section 9.6.3.

Field and model test data for the capacity of suction caissons and skirted foundations under vertical, combined, and cyclic loading have been reported by Helfrich *et al.* (1976), Hogervorst (1980), Steensen-Bach (1992), Clukey *et al.* (1995), El-Gharbawy *et al.* (1998), Randolph *et al.* (1998b), Byrne and Houlsby (1999, 2002a; 2002b), Allersma *et al.* (2000), Byrne (2000), Sharma (2004), Houlsby *et al.* (2005b, 2006), Thorel *et al.* (2005), El-Sherbiny *et al.* (2005), Raines *et al.* (2005),

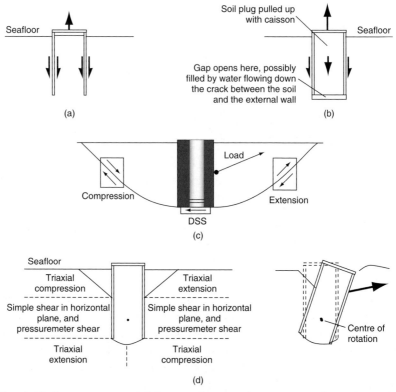

Fig. 9.10 *Some concepts of failure mechanisms for suction anchors. (a) Uplift resistance due to external and internal wall friction alone (adapted from Thorel et al., 2005). (b) Uplift resistance due to the external wall friction and the weight of the soil plug held on the wall (adapted from Thorel et al., 2005). (c) Translational failure mechanism in inclined loading, and related laboratory soil tests (© 2002 Offshore Technology Conference: Jeanjean et al., 1998). (d) Zones (left) and failure mechanism (right) for inclined loading (Aubeny et al., 2003)*

Bang *et al.* (2006), Jeanjean *et al.* (2006), Kelly *et al.* (2006a,b), Jones *et al.* (2007), and Chen and Randolph (2007a,b).

Rittirong *et al.* (2005) found in model tests that the pull-out capacity of caissons in calcareous sand could be increased by up to 120% by the use of electrokinetic and electrochemical techniques.

9.5   Tension foundations

9.5.1   *Objectives and solutions*
The main purpose of a tension foundation is to provide, with an adequate margin of safety, the resistance against uplift required to

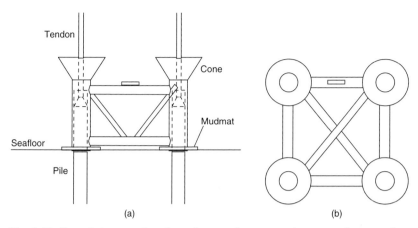

Fig. 9.11 Foundation template for a four-tendon tension leg, using direct tendon-to-pile connection. (a) Elevation. (b) Plan view

balance the tendon force. The foundation is usually installed first, before the tendons are connected, and the foundation must be stable during this operation. Tendons are sometimes unloaded, disconnected, lifted, inspected, and, if necessary, repaired or replaced. The removal may result in a moment being applied to the foundation, which must be resisted with an adequate margin.

The uplift force from the tendon consists of a cyclically varying component associated with wave-loading effects on the floating platform, superimposed on a steady average tension. The tension foundation will also usually be required to support some lateral loads, due partly to drag on the tendon associated with water currents at depths between the water surface and the seafloor. Again, these loads can include cyclic components.

Three arrangements are often considered in design. In an integrated template, the tendons and wellheads are connected to a single foundation unit. This may be a shallow gravity foundation, resisting uplift by its weight, or a piled template, resisting uplift by tension in the piles. Alternatively, in an independent templates system, separate templates are used for the wellhead system and the tendons. In a third solution, a template for the tendons is not used. Each individual tendon is connected directly to its own foundation unit, which is typically a pile.

Figure 9.11 shows a template for a tension leg consisting of four tendons. The template is installed on the seabed first, with temporary support provided by mudmats. The first pile is then lowered into one

415

conical receptacle and driven into the seabed. The next pile is then installed, and so on. The piles are grouted to the template, The tendons are then installed, with each connected to a single pile, or connected to a different part of the template. The mechanical connection may be unlatchable later, so that a tendon can be removed for inspection and/or repair.

Other foundation solutions can be feasible, and are in some instances more economic, including suction anchors (see Section 9.4), and vertically loaded plate anchors (VLAs).

9.5.2   Gravity foundations

A gravity foundation is designed as a shallow foundation. It may also be equipped with skirts, particularly if the upper few metres of the seabed consist of soft clay. The skirts help to transfer vertical load to a stronger underlying soil, act as shear keys so as to partially resist lateral loads, and provide the ability to use suction during installation.

API RP2T gives equations for the uplift and sliding capacity. The uplift capacity equals the net buoyant weight of the gravity foundation, plus contributions due to the skin friction of buried skirts. The sliding capacity equals the base resistance plus contributions due to active and passive components for parts of the foundation below the seafloor.

9.5.3   Piled templates

A piled template is normally installed by first lowering the template to the seafloor, then driving a pile through it, connecting the piles by grout or by mechanical means, and then connecting the tendons. The template is typically a steel frame structure, including conical guides to assist in installing the piles. Before piling, the template may be supported by mudmats and by lower horizontal bracing members bearing on the soil. Geotechnical design of these elements follows the same principles as for jacket platforms.

9.5.4   Tension piles

Tension piles must sustain steady and cyclic uplift, with some steady and cyclic components of lateral loading. In principle, an interaction diagram must exist for the two loading directions. However, its details have not yet been explored. The two load directions are considered separately.

416

Geotechnical design for tension piles is described in API RP2T, and is essentially a straightforward application of the design principles from API RP2A. The ultimate axial capacity Q_t in tension is calculated as

$$Q_t = f_t A_s \tag{9.5}$$

where f_t is the average ultimate unit skin friction over the external surface area of the pile, and A_s is the external surface area. Local and global scour both reduce A_s. Gapping can occur when a pile is laterally loaded, and also reduces the area A_s.

Lateral loading occurs because the tendons may be affected by currents in the water between the TLP and the seafloor. Doyle *et al.* (2004) compared centrifuge model test results with calculations for piles in clay based on API RP2A. They found good agreement with Matlock's (1970) proposals. The upper few metres of soil around the pile become heavily remoulded as a result of cyclic loading, and a gap did not form in the soft clay that was tested. Visual evidence suggested that the remoulded zone extended about three pile diameters below the seafloor.

API RP2T recommended the use of an enhanced factor of safety for tension piles, achieved by multiplying the factors of safety in API RP2A by a factor B that is typically between 1 and 1.5, depending on the confidence in the design parameters and on other factors.

9.5.5 Vertically loaded plate anchors

Plate anchors can be installed horizontally in the seabed, and then loaded by vertical pull-out (Murff *et al.*, 2005; Aubeny and Murff, 2005; Gaudin *et al.*, 2006). Figure 9.12a illustrates the use of a suction caisson to emplace a VLA. The anchor is attached at the bottom of the caisson, and the caisson is then installed in the seabed. The anchor is then released, and the caisson is removed by applying internal water pressure to pull it out of the seabed. The VLA is then pulled through the soil, with the pull angle carefully calculated so that the anchor rotates. Once the correct orientation has been achieved, the anchor pull is switched to the vertical.

Shaheen *et al.* (1987) reviewed several theoretical models for the uplift capacity of plate anchors in sand. They found a wide variation in the predicted uplift capacity. Matsuo's (1967) theory fitted the field data best. The theory assumes the failure mechanism shown in Fig. 9.12b, involving uplift of a volume of material bounded by a compound curve that intersects the ground surface at $45 + \phi'/2$ to

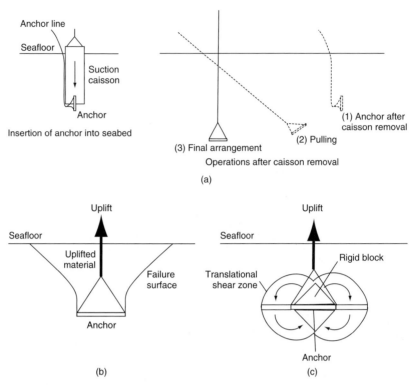

Fig. 9.12 *Vertically loaded anchors. (a) SEMPLA technique: installation of a vertical plate anchor using a suction caisson. (b) Uplift failure mode for a single plate anchor installed close to the seafloor (adapted from Balla, 1961; Matsuo, 1967; Das, 2007). (c) Uplift failure mode for a single plate anchor installed deep beneath the seafloor*

the horizontal. Merifeld *et al.* (2008) presented lower-bound solutions, based on finite element calculations. Kumar and Kouzier (2008) developed a calculation procedure for anchor groups. White *et al.* (2008) developed solutions for strip plate anchors. For deeply buried plate anchors, a flow-around mechanism more like Fig. 9.12c may develop. Consistent with this, DNV-RP-E302 (DNV, 2002) and API RP2SK provide a calculation method based on a bearing capacity approach.

9.6   Anchors

9.6.1   *Purposes and solutions*
An anchoring system is normally required to provide resistance forces that are primarily horizontal, with cyclic as well as static components.

418

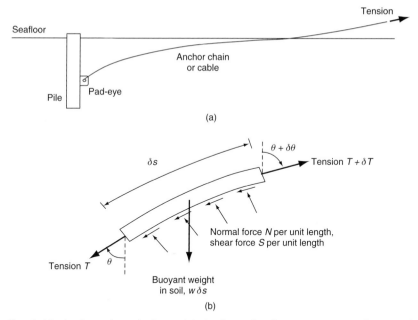

Fig. 9.13 Anchor pile and chain. (a) Anchor pile. (b) Forces on an element of the anchor line (Ruinen, 2005)

The system consists of a mooring chain or cable, and an anchor. Calculation methods for anchoring systems are included in API RP2SK.

Figure 9.13a shows a simple system consisting of an anchor pile and anchor chain. In a catenary mooring system, the chain is laid along the seabed, and the anchoring force that it provides to the floating structure includes affects of the weight of the line, the friction on the seabed, and the frictional resistance from the soil on the buried part of the anchor line, as well as the pull-out resistance of the anchor itself. In a taut mooring system, the line is taut, and rises from the seabed without passing along the seafloor.

The soil resistance along the length of a buried chain or cable can be a significant proportion of the overall anchoring resistance provided by the system (Vivatrat *et al.*, 1982; Stewart, 1992; Neubecker and Randolph, 1995). For the anchor units themselves, the principal practical choices for a TLP and FPSO are anchor piles, suction caissons, and drag-embedment anchors, including suction-emplaced plate anchors (SEMPLAs). Gravity anchors, essentially consisting of heavy weights placed on the seafloor, are also feasible, though not often used.

9.6.2 Resistance along the buried anchor line

The differential equation for the anchor chain or cable in the soil was derived by Reese (1973) and others. In Fig. 9.13b, a segment of anchor cable or chain is of length δs. By considering equilibrium of the forces on the segment, and taking the limit as δs tends to zero, the following differential equations are obtained:

$$\frac{dT}{ds} = S + w \cos \theta \tag{9.6}$$

$$T\frac{d\theta}{ds} = N - w \sin \theta \tag{9.7}$$

where T is the line tension, w is the buoyant weight of the line in the soil per unit length, S is the shear resistance from the soil per unit length of line, and N is the normal resistance from the soil per unit length.

For a wireline, N and S might be estimated by using axial and lateral capacity calculations for a pile of the same diameter. For a chain with a bar diameter d_b in clay, Dutta and Degenkamp (1989) and Degenkamp and Dutta (1989) suggest a normal force per unit length of $2.5d_b N_c s_u$, with $b = 2.4d_b$, and with N_c varying from 5.1 at the seafloor to 7.6 at a depth of $2.4b$. Neubecker and Randolph (1995) indicate that the shear resistance will typically be between 0.4 and 0.6 times the normal resistance.

For any given soil profile, the equations can be solved numerically to give both the tension in the line and the shape of the line. Neubecker and Randolph (1995) give some useful approximate solutions. The shape of the line is typically described as an inverted catenary.

9.6.3 Anchor piles

Reese (1973) describes the concept of an anchor pile (Fig. 9.13a). A pad-eye is attached to a pile and a line is attached to the pad-eye. The pile is then driven into the seabed. The pile may be left with some stick-up, so as to be retrievable later, or may be driven using a follower, which is then removed, leaving the pile installed below the seafloor. After installation, the chain is attached to the line to the floating platform and tightened.

Figure 9.14 shows three soil failure mechanisms for the lateral loading of a short anchor pile or suction pile anchor, ignoring interactions with vertical load components. In Fig. 9.14a, the pad-eye is relatively high on

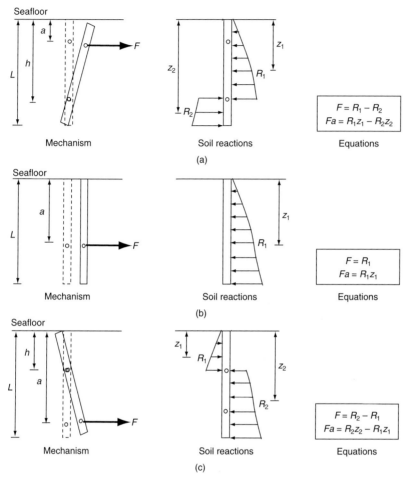

Fig. 9.14 *Short-pile failure modes for a laterally loaded anchor pile.* (a) *High anchor attachment point.* (b) *Optimum anchor attachment point.* (c) *Low anchor attachment point.* (d) *Results for various soil resistance profiles*

the pile, and the pile rotates forwards in the direction of the pull. In Fig. 9.14b, the pad-eye is at a level such that the pile simply translates through the soil, without rotation. This turns out to give the highest horizontal resisting force. In Fig. 9.14c, the pad-eye is low on the pile, and the pile rotates backwards as its base is pulled in the direction of the anchor line. The equations given in each diagram are for the horizontal equilibrium of the pile, and for moment equilibrium about the top of the pile. The quantities R_i are the net soil resistances. The quantities

Resistance P per unit length	R_1	R_2	R_1z_1	R_2z_2
P = constant	Ph	$P(L-h)$	$Ph^2/2$	$P(L^2-h^2)/2$
$P = kz$	$kh^2/2$	$k(L^2-h^2)/2$	$kh^3/3$	$k(L^3-h^3)/3$
$P = kz^n$	$kh^{n+1}/(n+1)$	$k(L^{n+1}-h^{n+1})/(n+1)$	$kh^{n+2}/(n+2)$	$k(L^{n+2}-h^{n+2})/(n+2)$

Optimum can be obtained by putting $h = L$

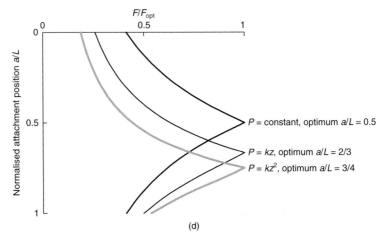

(d)

Fig. 9.14 *Continued*

z_i are the lines of actions of those resistances, so that if h is the depth of the rotation point and P represents the lateral soil resistance per unit length at depth z:

$$R_1 = \int_0^h P \, dz \quad R_2 = \int_h^L P \, dz \tag{9.8}$$

$$R_1z_1 = \int_0^h Pz \, dz \quad R_2z_2 = \int_h^L Pz \, dz \tag{9.9}$$

More complex failure mechanisms can develop for longer piles, involving one or more plastic hinges. The method of analysis is essentially an adaptation of the lateral loading analyses described in Chapter 5. Cao *et al.* (2005a) found that the use of the beam–column method that this approach entails is valid, but recommend using *p*–*y* curves from Stevens and Audibert (1979) instead of those in API RP2A.

As noted in API RP2A, the ultimate resistance P per unit length is different near the soil surface, where a surface failure mechanism dominates, compared with deeper levels, where the deeper failure mechanism applies. Figure 9.14d shows calculation details for simple variations of P with depth, ignoring effects of scour. The limiting lateral load F is plotted in normalised form by dividing by the load F_{opt} obtained when the anchor depth a is at the optimum for a given resistance profile. The optimum attachment point is at half the pile depth if the soil resistance is constant, at two-thirds of the depth if the resistance increases linearly from zero, and at three-quarters of the depth if the resistance is quadratic with depth. In practice:

- the pile is not necessarily installed to the exact design depth
- actual soil strengths may be different from assumed
- changes in the strength may occur after installation, including strength increase due to dissipation of excess pore pressures, or strength decrease due to subsequent cyclic loading.

Consequently, it can be prudent to use an ultimate design load that is smaller than the optimum value.

9.6.4   Drag-embedment anchors

Figure 9.15a shows some features of a drag-embedment fluke anchor. The flukes are designed to cut through the soil during embedment, and act as major providers of subsequent resistance. The stock provides stability while the system is being dragged along the seabed. The crown provides a reaction point that helps to hold the shank in position. The shank offsets the applied anchor load in a way that produces advantageous plasticity mechanisms when the anchor is dragged through the soil. The shank may be able to rotate about a pin, and minimum and maximum values of the fluke angle are set by blocks in the mechanism. For a given anchor, different angles are usually used for sand and clay seabeds.

The anchor capacity is strongly dependent on embedment. This can be calculated by taking account of the soil resistance forces on the anchor and on the anchor chain or cable during embedment (Stewart, 1992). Figure 9.15b shows a simplified assessment of the forces on a drag-embedment anchor as it is dragged through soil. The main components of the soil resistance come from the shank and the flukes. Bransby and O'Neill (1999) developed the following equation for a yield envelope for a plate anchor:

$$\left(\frac{F_n}{F_{nmax}}\right)^q = \left[\left(\frac{M}{M_{max}}\right)^m + \left(\frac{F_s}{F_{smax}}\right)^n\right]^{1/q} = 1 \qquad (9.10)$$

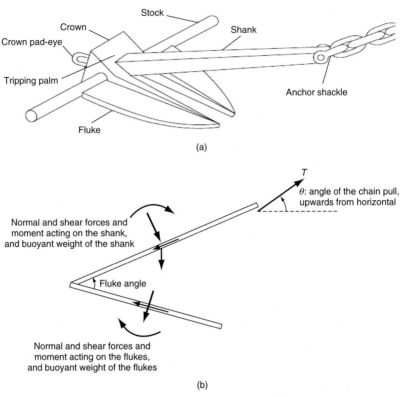

(a)

(b)

Fig. 9.15 Drag-embedment anchor. (a) Components of a single-stock fluke anchor (after API RP2SK). (b) Simplified analysis of forces acting on the anchor (adapted from Neubecker and Randolph, 1996; Bransby and O'Neill, 1999; O'Neill et al., 2003; Ruinen, 2005; Elkhatib and Randolph, 2005)

where F_n, F_s, and M are normal, shear, and moment forces on a plate anchor, respectively; F_{nmax}, F_{smax}, and M_{max} are descriptions of the limiting loads; and m, n, p, and q are constants. Elkhatib and Randolph (2005) provide values of the constants for various anchor geometries in clay, based on finite element calculations.

Vryhof (2000) describes a failure mechanism for shallow embedment with an active failure zone above and behind the anchor, and a passive failure zone in front extending to the soil surface. For deeper embedments, soil flows around the anchor as the anchor moves through the soil. By accounting for the resistance forces and the direction of motion of the anchor (described in a plasticity model by a flow rule), the complete installation trajectory of the anchor can theoretically be predicted (Aubeny et al., 2008b).

After an anchor has been embedded in a normally consolidated clay, an increase in the holding capacity will occur over time, due to dissipation of excess pore pressures that were induced in clay during the process of anchor installation. This set-up effect is termed 'anchor soaking'. It creates an apparent stick–slip effect: if the anchor is loaded to its new capacity, it will move into contact with soil that has not been hardened in this way, where the capacity is less.

The design of anchors to achieve specific load-holding capacities remains somewhat empirical. Anchor tests in cohesionless soil were reported by Walker and Taylor (1983), and in soft silty clay in the Norwegian Trench by Vold and Eie (1983). API RP2SK states that much of its advice for fluke and plate anchors in clay is based on centrifuge model tests by Dunnavant and Kwan (1993). Dahlberg (1998) describes further research on design procedures for deepwater anchors.

9.6.5 Other types of anchor

Kerr (1976) describes a self-burying anchor, which incorporates a water jet that fluidises sand, and a spoil discharge pipe which can be arranged to replace the extracted material in the hole that develops above the horizontal plate anchor. Data for the pull-out capacity of an anchor of this type in sand were reported by Wilson and Sahota (1980) and Sahota and Wilson (1982).

Propellant-embedment anchors have been used to achieve good anchor-holding capacity in corals and soft rocks (Taylor and True, 1976). They are installed by using a gun to fire the anchor into the seabed, which collapses on top of the embedded object.

Small anchors are useful for other tasks, one being the temporary anchoring of an ROV to the seafloor. Newson *et al.* (2005) and Liang *et al.* (2008) investigated the possibility of a lightweight inflatable anchor which an ROV would be able to insert into the seafloor. The anchor would then be inflated, acting like a belled pile anchor. The ROV would deflate the anchor and pull it out to depart.

9.7 Decommissioning

The decommissioning of TLPs has been considered by CDOP (1985). The removal of a deepwater production system involves the cleaning and removal of all of the equipment that is on the seafloor. Tendons are removed by unlatching them from their connections to the tension foundation systems. Suction-installed units can be removed by applying

425

positive relative water pressure inside the unit, causing the unit to push upwards out of the seabed. Tension piles and anchor piles can be partially removed by drilling out the soil plug, then inserting a tool to cut the pile from inside at a depth below the seafloor. The seafloor environment is then able to return to its original condition.

10

Renewable energy

Chapter 10 describes the challenges and principal concepts for support structures for renewable energy offshore, covering how to plan and participate in relevant site investigations, and use applicable standards and references to carry out calculations for monopiles, gravity support structures, suction caissons, jackets, multi-pods, and floaters.

10.1 Introduction

Renewable energy is energy from a source that is continuously replenished by natural processes. The action of the sun's heat on the earth, the earth's rotation, and the moon's rotation around the earth are largely responsible for the major fluid flows on the earth that can be harnessed to provide energy: wind, waves, ocean currents, tides, and weather. These flows also sustain life.

Interest in renewable energy comes from the recognition that the world's reserves of hydrocarbon fuels are limited, and that the associated carbon dioxide emissions contribute to a global climate change that is expected to be adverse (Cassedy, 2000; Avato and Coony, 2008). Energy self-sufficiency is also becoming an important geo-political issue. Renewable marine energy resources that are viable now or in the near future include:

- wind power
- tidal power
- power from ocean currents
- wave power.

Wind energy was the first commercial renewable energy to be developed in a major way offshore. Prototypes of tidal, current, and wave power systems are being tested. Sources for the far future may include ocean thermal energy conversion (OTEC), salinity gradient/osmotic energy, and marine biomass (Fraenkel, 2002a; Bedard, 2007; Kerr, 2007; Leithead, 2007).

10.2   Offshore windfarms

10.2.1 Locations worldwide

Figure 10.1 shows the locations and capacities listed by the European Wind Energy Association (EWEA) as of January 2009. The list shows that operational windfarms in January 2009 provided a total of 1474 MW of power. Windfarms under construction will contribute a further 2604 MW capacity, and planned windfarms will contribute 33 366 MW, including the planned 1000 MW London Array. A grand total capacity of at least 37 444 MW is expected to be in operation before 2020. This is sufficient to power about 25 million homes, and to offset an annual release of about 100 million tonnes of carbon dioxide.

Water depths at the windfarm sites in EWEA's list are mainly less than 30 m, and many are less than 10 m. Amongst these is Blyth Wind Farm, UK, commissioned in 2000. The farm consists of two turbines totalling about 3.8 MW, built on piles in 6 m water depth about 1 km off the Northumberland coast. North Hoyle came online in 2004, with a total capacity of 60 MW (Carter, 2007). The site is 7–8 km off the North Wales coast. Water depths vary across the site between 8 to 11 m, and the tidal range is 8 m. Future 'Round 3' offshore sites in the UK include water depths to about 65 m (Delay and Jennings, 2008). Norway and Italy have structures planned or in testing for water depths of 100 m or more.

The first US offshore windfarm is being developed by Cape Wind off New England. Studies are progressing for farms in a range of water depths, offshore Georgia and in the Gulf of Mexico (Bulpitt *et al.*, 2006; Olmsted, 2006; Schellstede, 2007). It is judged to be feasible to install about 9000 MW capacity in the Northern Gulf of Mexico by the year 2020. Jeng (2007) discusses opportunities offshore Australia.

10.2.2 Elements of an offshore windfarm

An offshore windfarm consists of a number of wind turbines that are supported by towers. The typical spacing between towers is of the order of several hundred metres to 1 km, so that the disturbance to the wind due to one turbine does not significantly reduce the efficiency

Offshore windfarms in operation

European Offshore Wind Power (MW)

Country	Operating	Under construction	Planned	Total
Belgium	30		1416	1446
Denmark	409	449	418	1276
Finland	24		1306	1330
France			1070	1070
Germany	12	733	10 183	10 928
Ireland	25		1578	1603
Italy			827	827
Netherlands	247		2587	2834
Norway	3		1550	1553
Spain			1976	1976
Sweden	133	30	3149	3312
UK	591	1392	6773	8756
Poland			533	533
Totals	**1474**	**2604**	**33 366**	**37 444**

Fig. 10.1 European windfarms as of January 2009 (data from EWEA, 2009)

of another. All the turbines and towers in a given windfarm are typically the same, so that economies of scale can be achieved. The turbines deliver power to sub-sea cables that may pass to an offshore substation that houses electrical switch-gear and step-up transformers. One or two high-voltage sub-sea cables deliver the higher-voltage power to a sub-station onshore. A fibre-optic cable may be bundled with the power

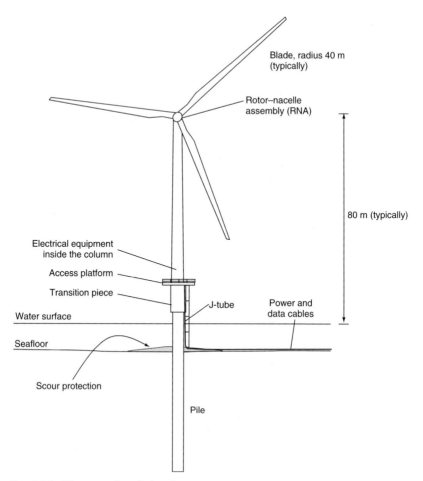

Fig. 10.2 Elements of a piled turbine structure

cables, giving the ability to monitor and control the offshore systems from onshore (Ciamberlano *et al.*, 2006).

Figure 10.2 shows a typical general arrangement for a turbine tower supported by a monopile. The tower may be about 80 m high. The turbine is housed in a nacelle at the top. Presently available turbine capacities range from 2 to 5 MW, with larger units in development. It is driven by rotating windmill blades that can be about 50 m in radius. A 3.5 MW machine including rotor blades typically weighs about 200 tonnes. A 5 MW is about twice as massive. The unit can turn into the wind to take best advantage of the wind direction. Electricity generated by the turbine is passed down the tower to electrical equipment housed at the base of the tower, and then along a cable passing down a J-tube and along the seafloor to the substation or shore.

10.2.3 Foundation options

Figure 10.3 shows a number of foundation options, varying from shallow to very deep water. Monopiles and gravity foundations have been the main choices in windfarms built to date. They are economic in relatively shallow water depths, and have had acceptable dynamic characteristics for the range of soil conditions so far encountered (mainly strong soils and rock).

A monopile solution was the preferred option at North Hoyle. A monopile foundation consists of a single tubular steel pile. The typical diameter is in the range 4–6 m. Prior to installation, the seafloor may be prepared by setting down a thin carpet of gravel to act as temporary scour protection during pile driving. The pile is then lifted into place and driven into the seabed by a hammer. The transition piece is then fitted over the pile and grouted (Klose *et al.*, 2008). This provides the opportunity to correct any small out-of-verticality of the pile. The tower and turbine are then lifted on and attached to the transition piece. The cable is pulled into the J-tube and connected, and the remainder of the scour protection is installed.

A gravity base structure (Figs 10.3b to 10.3d) consists of a wide, heavy unit that resists shear and overturning loads by its weight. The typical base diameter is in the range 15–30 m. Prior to installation, the seafloor may be prepared by shallow dredging and flattening. The gravity base may be constructed onshore and transported by barge to the offshore location, then lifted into place on the seafloor. Alternatively, the base may be designed as a hollow, buoyant unit that is towed onto location, and then set down by controlled flooding. Infill material and scour protection is then placed around the base.

Gravity structures were installed at Middelgrunden (Fig. 10.3b). Monopiles would have been costly because of the presence of a limestone layer in the seabed. The gravity platform also allowed the transformer, switchgear and control systems to be installed on the platform in a dry dock, before floating out to the site. This gave a considerable saving in the offshore installation time later. The upper part of the structures was conical so that an ice sheet moving past would break in bending, thereby limiting the lateral ice loads applied to the foundations. A cone can be fitted to a monopile, but this is more difficult to construct.

431

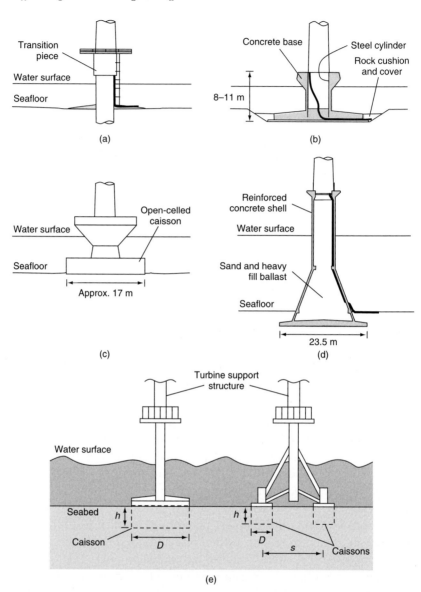

Fig. 10.3 Some foundation options (not to scale). (a) Monopile. (b) Gravity platform of the type used at Middelgrunden (CEEO, 2003). (c) Form used at Nysted, 10 km offshore Denmark stiff clay soil profile (based on COWI, 2009a). (d) Form used at Thornton Park 1, 29 km offshore Belgium: foundation on sand (COWI, 2009b). (e) Suction caissons, as monopod (left) or tripod (right) (from Houlsby et al., 2005b). (f) Multi-pod/multi-pile. (g) Jacket/truss. (h) Guyed tower solution (adapted from Carey, 2002). (i) Tension leg platform: one of several deepwater solutions described by Musial et al. (2006)

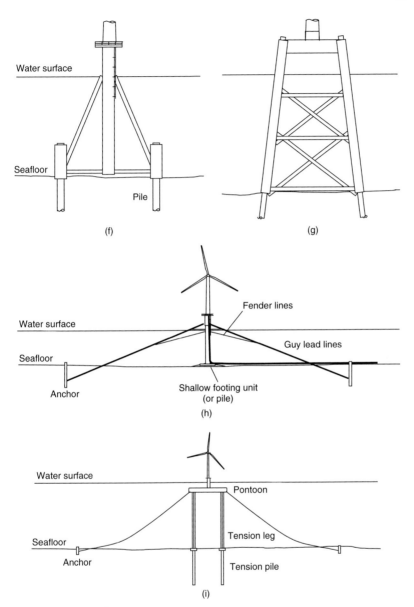

Fig. 10.3 Continued

An upturned cone was used at Nysted for the same reason (Fig. 10.3c). In this case, the base was an open cellular structure, giving a lightweight construction which could be transported offshore by barge. After installation, the cells were filled with ballast and covered over with armour stone. In the gravity cone structures at Thornton Park 1

433

(Fig. 10.3d), a reinforced concrete shell was used, filled with sand and heavy fill ballast. Skirts can be fitted to gravity structures to provide a shear key, and to allow differential water pressures to be used to assist during installation.

Suction caissons (Fig. 10.3e) have been extensively studied at Oxford and Aalborg Universities (Houlsby *et al.*, 2005a,b; Senders, 2005). Two designs have developed: a monopod and a tripod. Installation calculations were presented by Houlsby and Byrne (2005, 2006). Full-scale trials onshore and on beach have demonstrated their feasibility for most soil conditions, excepting very strong seabeds of dense sand, hard clay, or rock. Model tests have shown the importance of ensuring that tensile loading is not generated in the foundation soil, and in this respect they resemble gravity foundations.

In multi-pod and jacket structures (Figs 10.3f and 10.3g), an intermediate structure is used to transfer the high bending moments into several piles. Argyriadis and Klose (2007) describe a prototype jacket installed in 45 m of water in the Moray Firth, Scotland.

For deeper water, Carey (2002) describes a guyed monopile structure. In Fig. 10.3h, the tower may be supported by a relatively lightweight shallow foundation, since it does not need to support a large moment or shear load. The guy line geometry is arranged so that the lines of actions of the line loads is best suited to equilibrate the foundation loads.

For very deep water, Musial *et al.* (2006) discuss several options, including a tension leg platform. A spar-type system may also be feasible. Floating solutions may be economic and technically feasible in deep water depths.

10.2.4 Site Investigation technologies

Geotechnical drilling in very shallow water can require special equipment, because the motion of a large ship relative to a shallow seafloor can severely bend a drillpipe over a small height. The tidal range at some sites is large, and must be catered for over the period of a day or so that is required for a geotechnical investigation at turbine site.

Figure 10.4 shows some of several feasible options. A jackup or liftboat provides a stable fixed platform from which to drill, but is subject to potential punch-through during the site investigation (Hunt *et al.*, 2004). A wide, flat-bottomed barge can be convenient, particularly in sheltered locations. For very shallow waters, a barge can be ballasted down onto the seabed to provide a very stable drilling platform.

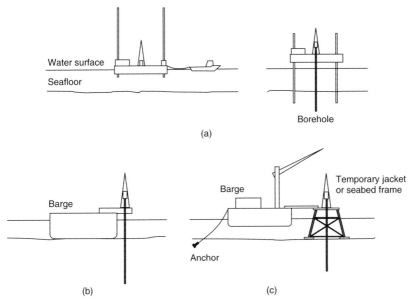

Fig. 10.4 Examples of techniques for shallow-water site investigations. (a) Jackup towed to the site, set down, preloaded, elevated, and the borehole drilled. (b) Barge set down on a shallow seabed. (c) Moored barge and temporary jacket or seabed frame supporting a drilling derrick

Alternatively, a small temporary jacket might be transported by barge to the site, and set down on the seabed, possibly with short pin-piles. A geotechnical drilling rig can then be mounted on the frame, and supplied and powered from the barge. After the investigation, the frame can be lifted off the seabed.

Some investigation companies provide amphibious trucks that can be driven from a beach into water a few metres deep and used as a drilling platform.

10.2.5 Construction technologies

Several special construction vessels have been built to service the windfarm market. Figure 10.5a shows MPI's installation vessel, which is a liftboat or self-propelled jackup. In Fig. 10.5a, it has installed a monopile whose top is visible at the right end of the vessel. A transition piece is about to be lifted on. Figure 10.5b shows the jackup barge *Excalibur* working at North Hoyle. The barge has a special pile gate and gripper system that is used to install a monopile.

Fig. 10.5 Examples of equipment for offshore installation. (a) MPI's installation vessel Resolution *operating at Kentish Flats (© Elsam: from ffrench et al., 2005). (b) The jackup barge* Excalibur *at North Hoyle, showing a monopole held within a pile gate and gripper system (from Carter, 2007). (c) Jacket being lifted into position (reproduced with permission, from Argyriadis and Klose, 2007. © ISOPE). (d) Example of an underwater plough for burying power cables (from Carter, 2007)*

The gravity support platforms at Middlegrunden were built in a dry dock. The foundation weight was 1800 tonnes. The lower part of the steel tower and the electrical equipment there were fitted onto the gravity foundations before they were towed out to the offshore site. On site, the platforms were ballasted down onto the prepared seabed. The remainder of the tower and the rotor–nacelle assembly were

(c)

(d)

Fig. 10.5 Continued

assembled using a floating crane. At Nysted, the gravity foundations were constructed on a barge, which then took them to the offshore location. A floating crane lifted the units off the barge and onto the seabed, and the ballast and armour were then installed.

Turbine support structures are relatively light compared with other offshore platforms. Figure 10.5c shows a jacket being lifted by an offshore crane. The jacket is on its side, with its tip at the right and its foundations on the left. Two of the pile guides can be clearly seen.

The sub-sea cables are also relatively light structures. Figure 10.5d shows a sub-sea ploughing machine that can bury power cables. To pull a cable through a J-tube, a line is first passed down the tube and connected to the cable that has been pre-laid on the seabed with a dogleg.

10.2.6 Foundation costs

Estimates of foundation costs vary, and depend on the design life and other factors. For the 30 turbines at North Hoyle, Carter (2007) quotes a general design life of 20–25 years, with foundations designed for 50 years, presumably so that they can be reused. The total capital expenditure was £82 million for the 60 MW windfarm, including £15.5 million for manufacture, supply, and installation of the monopiles, £5.5 million for cable laying and burial offshore, and £3.5 million for onshore cable laying. Thus, the geotechnical costs were about 30% of the total, two-thirds of which was for the offshore foundations.

10.3   Geotechnical design

10.3.1 General

Geotechnical design for all of the foundation options follows the same principles as for large offshore structures discussed in earlier chapters of this book. However, some caution is needed, partly because the water depths and typical foundation sizes for windfarm support structures can be outside the range of experience of other structures. Also, there are some special aspects of the foundation loading.

10.3.2 Design standards

The API RP2A (API, 2000) standard has been developed over many years, and has been validated by considerable experience and research over that time. However, its focus is on structures that are dimensioned and in environments relating to the offshore petroleum industry. The ISO 19900 series of standards is also intended for the petroleum and natural gas industries.

Saigal *et al.* (2007) discuss API, ISO, and other design standards, and the guidelines being developed by the International Electro-technical Commission: IEC 61400-3, *Design Requirements for Offshore Wind Turbines*. This is sometimes used in conjunction with:

- *Design of Offshore Wind Farm Structures*, DNV-OS-J101, from DNV (2004)

- *Standard for Geotechnical Site and Route Surveys*, from Germanischer Lloyd (2003)
- *Guideline for the Certification of Offshore Wind Turbines*, from Germanischer Lloyd (2005).

Many provisions are identical to API RP2A, not surprisingly since many basic geotechnical issues are similar. The DNV standard has different $t-z$ curves, and contains a useful appendix on scour around a vertical pile. Germanischer Lloyd (2005) includes equations for loads on piles due to breaking waves.

Schellstede (2007) lists 17 codes of design criteria that relate to wind-farm development in the Northern Gulf of Mexico. A code of practice for that region may be different partly because weather conditions there include an average of six major hurricanes making landfall annually.

10.3.3 Design process

Figure 10.6 summarises the IEC 61400-3 design process. A key feature is that the design is separated into two major tasks: design of the support structure and design of the nacelle–rotor assembly. The skills needed for the two tasks are significantly different, but the designs must interface well.

The design basis is written by the developer company or its consultant as early as feasible during the project. Its geotechnical parts can typically include:

- site location
- expected bathymetry data for the site
- design life for the foundations, typically 50 years
- preliminary geohazards data for the site, including an indication of ice hazard and seismic hazard – detailed data may be provided, as these studies may have been completed already
- turbine load data for several possible turbines being considered, including extreme loads, operational loads, cyclic fatigue loading imposed by the turbines and blades, and loads under one or more scenarios of damage to turbine or blades
- expectations for access, usually by boat, and requirements for associated impact load cases
- the design standards to be used.

Geotechnical site investigation data may be pending at the time the design basis is issued. However, some expectations of the range of

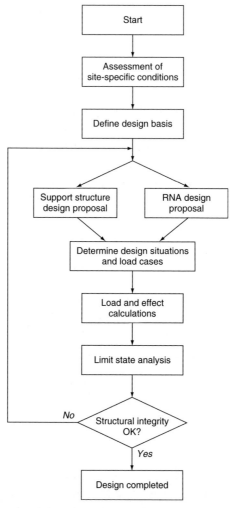

Fig. 10.6 Application of the IEC 61400-3 design process (adapted from Tarp-Johansen et al., 2006)

data may be given, and some of the methods by which the data will be interpreted may be described.

10.3.4 *Foundation loading*

For a monopile and tower that supports a 3.5 MW turbine, the total weight of the tower and turbine is typically around 6 MN or so (Houlsby, 2005; Westgate and deJong, 2005). Typical values for a 5 MW turbine

440

are about twice this (Rosjberg and Gravesen, 2009). Wind loads are typically around 1–2 MN, at a height of around 80 m above sea level. The wave and current load will typically be around 3 MN for a monopile, perhaps at 10–20 m above the seafloor. Other foundation options include a gravity base, for which the wave loading can be significantly larger.

These figures imply that horizontal and moment loading can be the dominant drivers in foundation design, rather than the vertical load. In particular, the ratio of horizontal to vertical loading is higher than can be supported by friction alone. Consequently the foundation must either provide additional mass or be keyed into the soil. Eccentricity in the absence of foundation weight, defined as the overturning moment divided by the vertical load, can be 20 m or so. This means that tensile stresses, and the need to avoid them for the soil, can be a significant design issue. Thus, bottom-founded turbine support structures are essentially outside the range of conditions that are familiar from experience of other offshore structures.

An additional complication is that the wind load can be in one plan direction, while the wave and current load acts in another plan direction. The wind load provides the largest overturning moment, but the wave and current loads provide the largest horizontal force. This multi-directionality of loads, with a separation between horizontal and moment loading, is different from other offshore structures, where the horizontal and moment loads may be more in alignment.

Another complication can arise due to machine vibration effects. The rotor typically rotates at about 20 rpm, although some machines have variable speed rotors. This implies that there will be some structural vibrations at the rotor rotation rate, called the 1P frequency (Houlsby *et al.*, 2005a). As a blade passes the tower, additional wind shear develops, resulting in a complex load being applied to the tower with significant components in a plan direction at right angles to the wind direction. For a three-bladed turbine, this occurs at a frequency called '3P', representing three times the rotator rotation frequency. These loads generate complicated cyclic loading effects in the foundation soils.

Rosjberg and Gravesen (2009) provide a design basis that requires the first natural frequency for a wind turbine structure and bottom-fixed foundation to be in the range 0.275–0.31 Hz for a 3.5 MW structure, and 2.260.29 Hz for a 5 MW structure. These very tight tolerances on resonant frequency imply the need for very accurate modelling of foundation and structural stiffnesses.

10.3.5 The issue of overturning moment

The high lateral loads and overturning moments on the foundation mean that, for a monopile solution, the ultimate lateral capacity and performance can be the dominant design issue. Lesny and Wiemann (2005) and Abdel-Rahman and Achmus (2005) reported finite element calculation results that indicated that the API $p-y$ curves for lateral loading give overestimates of the lateral stiffness for windfarm monopiles. This can have an important effect on the structural dynamics. The conclusions are preliminary, and may be affected by limitations of the soil constitutive model used in the calculations. These authors also cautioned that cyclic loading effects are yet to be explored.

Figure 10.7a illustrates a simplified calculation for the vertical stresses beneath a circular gravity-based support structure of diameter B. If the moment on the foundation is M, and the vertical load from the turbine

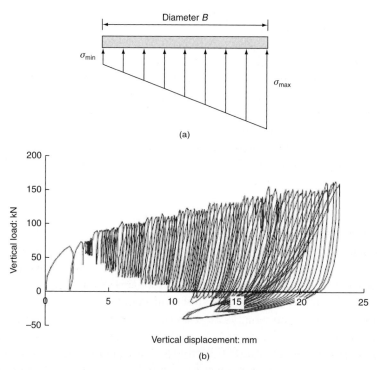

Fig. 10.7 *Issues relating to tension. (a) Simplified analysis of the vertical stress distribution beneath a rigid circular footing under the vertical load* V + W′ *and the moment* M. *(b) Field trial data showing the response of a 1.5 m-diameter suction caisson to cyclic vertical loading, with a large uplift once tension is applied, but net penetration (Houlsby et al., 2006)*

442

is V, and the buoyant weight of the gravity foundation is an additional amount W', then a linear distribution of vertical stress across the base gives minimum stresses of

$$\sigma_{min} = \frac{V + W'}{\pi B^2 / 4} - \frac{M}{\pi B^3 / 32} \tag{10.1}$$

To avoid the linear distribution going into tension, the buoyant weight W' must therefore be greater than $8M/B - V$. Typically M/V may be about 20 m for a 100 m-high tower in shallow water, based on Houlsby *et al.* (2005a). Hence, for a gravity base diameter of $B = 20$ m, the weight of the gravity foundation will need to be about seven times the weight of the turbine and tower in order to avoid tension beneath the foundation.

Figure 10.7b shows data by Houlsby *et al.* (2006) on the application of cyclic vertical uplift to a suction caisson foundation. Provided the vertical load on the soil remains positive, relatively small cyclic vertical displacements occur. However, once the magnitude of the cyclic loading is such that the total vertical stress on the foundation becomes tensile during part of a cycle, relatively large uplift displacements occur in each cycle. Nevertheless, the net movement over a cycle continues to be downwards. Houlsby *et al.* (2006) state that 'the data . . . suggest that caissons should not be loaded in tension for serviceability reasons, as the stiffness of the caisson reduces to a level where foundation movements would render a wind turbine inoperable'; stiffness limitations are usually imposed by the requirement to avoid resonance for frequencies between $1P$ and $3P$, and additional limits on turbine motions may be specified by the turbine manufacturer.

10.3.6 *Other special design issues*
Dynamic structural response is often a dominant design criterion for offshore wind turbines (Tarp-Johansen, 2006); this response is somewhat dependent on the foundation stiffness and damping. The foundation stiffness rather than the ultimate capacity can be the dominant design constraint. Hence, it can be more important to predict foundation stiffness responses accurately, rather than assuming that stiffness issues are addressed implicitly by ensuring satisfactory response in ultimate limit state events. A special aspect is that the turbine and rotor act as a gyroscope, effectively providing a degree of moment fixity at the top of the tower. This can have beneficial effects on the fatigue life of the tower (Wingerde *et al.*, 2006), and perhaps can reduce cyclic loading effects on the soil too.

About one-third of the vertical load on the foundation can be due to the rotor–nacelle assembly, centred 100 m or so above the seafloor. About one-third is the weight of the tower, and about one-third can be due to objects inside the tower. This means that the centre of gravity of the tower and its contents is relatively high, giving a possibility of P–Δ effects affecting the foundation response.

A monopile of diameter 6 m and penetration 25 m has an aspect ratio of only about 4, which is far less than aspect ratios for jacket piles. For this reason, the relative proportions of end effects to side effects are different. The proportions can affect the axial and lateral capacity and performance, as well as the pile driveability. Driving is said to be a straightforward process. However, a special follower may be needed in order to use an available offshore hammer on the relatively large-diameter pile. The mass and stiffness characteristics of the follower can significantly affect the pile driveability.

Because of the differences in water depths, cyclic loading frequencies, and lateral dimensions, wind turbine foundations can have significantly different drainage characteristics, cyclic and dynamic responses, and set-up and consolidation times compared with other offshore structures. The hydraulic instability of the seabed can be an important issue. Water depths for present wind farms are sufficiently shallow, and often in shoaling waters, so that the effects of breaking waves may be different (Rogers and Still, 1999). Water pressures on the seabed will have different characteristics. Issues associated with vortex shedding around a pile may be different. Scour may be more severe at some locations (Hansen and Christensen, 2007; Hansen *et al.*, 2007).

Tadich *et al.* (2007) observe that ultimate wind-induced loads occur at relatively low wind speeds for a turbine, because of the way the control system of the turbine works. Turbines are brought to a rapid stop under some overload conditions. Emergency breaking creates a structural and foundation load scenario that is unique to turbine structures.

10.4 Site investigation

10.4.1 Stages and timescales

All experiences of offshore windfarms to date confirm that comprehensive site survey and assessment is highly desirable, both of the planned turbine site and of potential or planned routes of cables to shore. At North Hoyle, the first site investigations commenced in 1999, 3 years before the start of construction. Eight soil borings were carried out, covering the area to be occupied by the 30 turbines. Carter (2007) indicates that, in hindsight, it would have been helpful to have had one sampling borehole together with in-situ tests at each of the 30 turbine sites.

Feld (2005) recommends that a site assessment includes a geological survey, a geophysical survey, and a geotechnical survey, preferably in that order. The geological survey provides guidance on the nature of some of the geohazards that may be expected. This assists in planning the geophysical survey, which will also include a bathymetric survey as well as sub-bottom profiling over the entire site and cable routes. Germanischer Lloyd (2005) recommends that sub-bottom profiling be done to at least 20 m below the seafloor. These profiles help to identify locally hazardous or unsuitable locations for turbine foundations, and so assist in the planning of economical geotechnical investigations.

Germanischer Lloyd (2005) recommends that geotechnical boreholes be carried out at 10% of the planned turbine sites, and more if the geophysical survey indicates potentially problematic soil conditions. Germanischer Lloyd (2005) also recommends that additional bathymetric and side-scan sonar surveys be done twice a year for the first 2 years of windfarm operations, in spring and late summer, and yearly thereafter. This provides information on sediment dynamics. Unexpected deep scouring and erosion, which can be detrimental to foundation performance, can be identified, and appropriate action taken, if necessary.

10.4.2 Notes on hazard assessment

Offshore windfarms can be affected by all of the geohazards that can affect other offshore structures. Because many are in shallow water relatively close to shore, hydrodynamic and geological hazards can be particularly common, including:

- high water velocities causing scour (Hansen and Christensen, 2007; Hansen *et al.*, 2007)
- lateral variability of soil conditions
- dipping strata
- buried channels
- buried boulders
- loose patches
- sand waves
- rock layers, outcrops, and beds
- geological faults.

Lateral variability is common because the area of an offshore windfarm is large. Dipping strata are significant because of the large separation between turbines. For example, a $1°$ dip translates to a depth offset of $1000 \times \tan 1° \approx 17\,\mathrm{m}$ over a 1 km distance. Consequently, the foundation conditions in the upper 20 m of one turbine site can be totally different from the soils at the next site on the farm.

Other geohazards are likely to be important too. Coastal areas typically contain ancient riverbeds that may have been infilled by transported materials. Boulders occur in areas that were covered by ice in a previous ice age (Bjerrum, 1973). Loose patches of sand can occur in the seafloor as a result of hydrodynamic effects, the actions of marine life, or the previous effects of boat anchors or the use of fishing gear in the area. Where sand waves occur, soil densities can be different at different parts of the waves. Sand waves may move on the seabed, giving foundation conditions that can effectively change between a survey period and a construction period. Limestone and other rock outcrops and layers are common in some European locations, and pose problems for the levelling and installation of piled foundation options.

Some windfarms have been sited or proposed for marine areas subjected to icing, earthquakes, or both. Ice risk is best assessed by a specialist, who will also provide guidance on the selection of a structural shape to best resist ice forces. Seismic risk is also best assessed by a specialist. If necessary, a detailed seismic hazard assessment may be done to quantify the risk and to determine acceleration spectra or time histories for design (Kramer, 1996).

The coastal seafloor is used by many users. Cable routes to shore will often cross telephone, power, and utility cables or pipelines. Thus, several cable crossings may be needed along the route to the shore. Burial is normally advisable to avoid snagging by boat anchors and fishing gear.

10.4.3 Soil borings and in-situ testing

Germanischer Lloyd (2005) provides detailed guidelines on the depths to be investigated below the seabed, and appropriate sampling and in-situ testing intervals. The guidance is very similar to work-scopes for other platforms.

For piled foundations, exploration is required to between one and three pile diameters below the expected pile penetration, depending on whether the critical load case is axial or lateral loading. Sampling is required at 1 m intervals for the first 15 m below the seafloor, followed by sampling at 3 m intervals to 60 m below the seafloor. Subsequent recommended intervals are 8 m, but continuous alternating cone penetration tests and sampling may be necessary to properly charac-terise the soil layering; the extra work is a relatively small additional expenditure. Similar sampling intervals are specified for gravity founda-tions, except that the investigation depth is limited to the depth of the critical failure surface. As this will not be known in advance, and can be

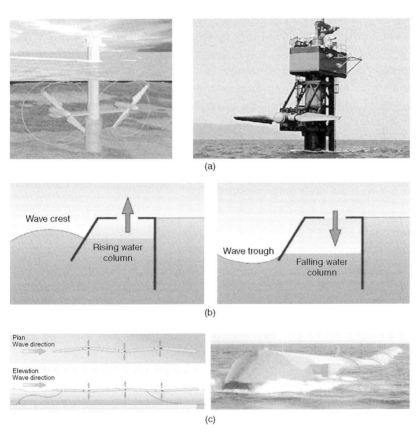

Fig. 10.8 Some other marine energy technologies. (a) Tidal current turbines in operation (Kerr, 2005) and after lifting out of the water in field trials (© 2007 Offshore Technology Conference: Bedard, 2007). (b) Principle of an oscillating column wave power device (Kerr, 2005): power is generated as air is forced through a turbine by the oscillations of the water column inside the closed chamber. (c) Principle of the hinged Polaris generator (Kerr, 2005): hinged rams between the four 4.6 m-diameter cylinders generate power by pumping fluid through turbines as the hinges rotates due to the wave action

447

affected by thin weak layers, a minimum investigation depth is typically at least one to two expected foundation diameters.

Like for other offshore structures, classification tests are normally required on all samples. Strength and consolidation testing will be required for all clay layers. Special cyclic loading tests may be required, particularly for gravity platforms or if a seismic analysis is required.

10.5   Other offshore renewable energy options

Figure 10.8 shows images from Kerr (2005) and Bedard (2007) of several other renewable energy systems that are currently being tested or at the stage of field trials. Geotechnical solutions for these and other marine renewable energy technologies are feasible using the same principles as for other offshore structures.

It seems likely that the tidal current concepts will require foundations that can resist high lateral loads, as well as good scour protection, in view of the possible effect of the turbine blades on water velocities. The oscillating column is likely to induce high vertical cyclic loading of the foundations. The wave energy device is likely to require anchors that can resist high cyclic lateral loads.

References

Abdelnour, R., Sayed, M. and Metpe, M., 1982. Ice Ride-Up on a Man-Made Island. Paper OTC 4313, *Offshore Technology Conference*.

Abdel-Rahman, K. and Achmus, M., 2005. Finite element modelling of horizontally loaded monopile foundations for offshore wind energy converters in Germany. *Proc. Int. Conf. Frontiers in Offshore Geotechnics*, eds S. Gourvenec and M. Cassidy, Taylor and Francis, 391–396.

Abramson, L.W., Lee, T.S., Sharma, S. and Boyce, G.M., 1996. *Slope stability and stabilization methods*, Wiley.

Abu-Hejleh, A.N. and Znidarčić, D., 1995. Dessication Theory for Soft Cohesive Soils. *ASCE Journal of Geotechnical Engineering*, 121(6), 493–502.

Agerton, D.J., 1983. Construction of an Arctic Offshore Gravel Island in 39 ft of Water During Winter and Summer. Paper OTC 4548, *Offshore Technology Conference*.

Airey, D.W., 1984. Clays in simple shear apparatus. Ph.D thesis, Cambridge University.

Airey, D.W., 1987. Some observations on the interpretation of shear-box test results. Technical Report CUED/S-Soils/TR196, Cambridge University Engineering Department.

Airey, D.W. and Wood, D.M., 1987. An evaluation of direct simple shear tests on clay, Géotechnique, 37(1), 25–36.

Akai, K. and Tanaka, Y., 2000. Uncertainties in settlement prediction: KIA International Airport. Advances in Geotechnical Engineering: The Skempton Conference, eds R. Jardine, D.M. Potts, and K.G. Higgins, Thomas Telford, 679–690.

Alba, J.L. and Audibert, J.M.E., 1999. Pile design in calcareous and carbonaceous granular materials: An historical overview. *Proc. Int. Conf. Engineering for Calcareous Sediments*, ed. K.A. Al-Shafei, Balkema, 29–43.

Aldridge, T.R. and Haaland, G., 1991. Assessment of conductor setting depth. Paper OTC 6713, *Offshore Technology Conference*.

Aldridge, T.R., Carrington, T.M. and Kee, N.R., 2005. Propagation of pile tip damage during installation. *Proc. Int. Conf. Frontiers in Offshore Geotechnics*, eds S. Gourvenec and M. Cassidy, Taylor and Francis, 823–827.

Al-Khafaji, Z.A., Audibert, J.M.E., Hossain, M.K., Templeton, J.C. II., Clukey, E.C. and de Jong, P.R., 2003a. Suction Caisson Foundation Design for Vortex-Induced Vibration Loading. Paper OTC 15239, *Offshore Technology Conference*.

449

Al-Khafaji, Z.A., Young, A.G., Degroff, W. and Humphrey, D.G., 2003b. Geotechnical Properties of the Sigsbee Escarpment from Deep Soil Borings. Paper OTC 15158, *Offshore Technology Conference*.

Allard, M.A., Andersen, K.H. and Hermstad, J., 1994. Centrifuge model tests of a gravity platform on very dense sand: Part 1, Testing techniques and results. *Proc. BOSS 94.*

Allen, R.L., Yen, B.C. and McNeill, R.L., 1978. Steroscopic X-ray Assessment of Offshore Soil Samples. Paper OTC 3212, *Offshore Technology Conference*.

Allersma, H.G.B., Brinkgreve, R.B.J., Simon, T. and Kirstein, A.A., 2000. Centrifuge and Numerical Modelling of Horizontally Loaded Suction Piles. *Int. Journal of Offshore and Polar Engineering*, 10(3), 222–228.

Allersma, H.G.B., Jacobse, J.A. and Krabbendam, R.L., 2003. Centrifuge tests on uplift capacity of suction caissons with active suction. *Int. Conf. Offshore and Polar Engineering*, 734–739.

Alm, T. and Hamre, L., 1998. Soil model for driveability calculations. Paper OTC 8835, *Offshore Technology Conference*.

Al-Sharif, M., 2007. Independence Trail – Pipeline Design Considerations. Paper OTC 19056, *Offshore Technology Conference*.

Al-Tabbaa, A., 1984. *Anisotropy of clay*, M. Phil Thesis, Cambridge University.

Alves, A.M.L., Lopes, F.R. and Danzinger, B.R., 2008. Dimensional analysis of the wave equation applied to pile driving. *Proc. Stress Wave 2008*, 8th International Conference on the Application of Stress Wave Theory to Piles, Lisbon, pp. 115–121.

Amundsen, T., Lunne, T., Christoffersen, H.P., Bayne, J.M. and Barnwell, C.L., 1985. Advanced Deep-water soil investigation at the Troll East Field. Chapter 11 of Advances in Underwater technology and Offshore Engineering, Vol. 3, Offshore Site Investigation. Graham and Trotman, 165–186.

Andenæs, E., Skomedal, E. and Lindseth, S., 1996. Installation of the Troll Phase I Gravity Base Platform. Paper OTC 8122, *Offshore Technology Conference*.

Andersen, K.H., 1991. Foundation design of offshore gravity structures. Chapter 4 of Cyclic Loading of Soils, eds M.P. O'Reilly and S.F. Brown, Blackie, 122–173.

Andersen, K.H. and Jostad, H.P., 1999. Foundation Design of Skirted Foundations and Anchors in Clay. Paper OTC 10824, *Offshore Technology Conference*.

Andersen, K.H. and Lauritzsen, R., 1988. Bearing Capacity for Foundations with Cyclic Loads. *ASCE Journal of Geotechnical Engineering*, 114(5), 540–555.

Andersen, K.H. and Lunne, T., 1994. A method to determine conductor setting depth in clay. *Proc. Int. Conf. BOSS 94*, Behaviour of offshore structures. 173–187.

Andersen, K.H., Rawling, G.G., Lunne, T.A. and Bye, T.H., 1994. Estimation of hydraulic fracture pressure in clay. *Canadian Geotechnical Journal*, 31(6), 817–828.

Andersen, K.H., Jostad, H.P. and Dyvik, R., 2008. Penetration Resistance of Offshore Skirted Foundations and Anchors in Dense Sand. *ASCE Journal of Geotechnical and Geoenvironmental Engineering*, 134(1), 106–116.

Andersen, K.H., Kleven, A. and Heien, D., 1988. Cyclic soil data for design of gravity structures. *ASCE Journal of Geotechnical Engineering*, 114(5), 517–539.

Andersen, K.H., Dyvik, R., Schøeder, K., Hansteen, O.E. and Bysveen, S., 1993. Field Tests of Anchors in Clay. Predictions and Interpretation. *ASCE Journal of Geotechnical Engineering*, 113(10) 1532–1549.

Andersen, K.H., Allard, M.A. and Hermstad, J., 1994. Centrifuge model tests of a gravity platform on very dense sand: Part 2, Interpretation. *Proc. BOSS 94*.

Andersen, K.H., Murff, J.D., Randolph, M.F., Clukey, E., Erbrich, C.T., Jostad H.P., Hansen, B., Aubeny, C.P., Sharma, P. and Supachawarote, C., 2005. Suction anchors for deepwater applications. *Proc. Int. Symp. on Frontiers in Offshore Geotechnics* (ISFOG), Perth, 3–30.

Andresen, A., Berre, T., Klevem A. and Lunne, T., 1979. Procedures used to obtain soil parameters for foundation engineering in the North Sea. *Marine Geotechnology*, 3(3), 201–266.

Anderson, L.M. and Ledidersdorf, C.B., 1988. Arctic Island Abandonment: Planning and Implementation for Mukluk Island. Paper OTC 5686, *Offshore Technology Conference*.

Angeli, M., Orange, D., Egan, J., Hooper, J. and Demetrious, D., 2005. Successive Geohazard Assessments in a Tectonically Active Shallow Gas Environment. Paper 17444, *Offshore Technology Conference*.

Angus, N.M. and Moore, R.L., 1982. Scour repair methods in the Southern North Sea. Paper OTC 4410, *Offshore Technology Conference*.

Antani, J.K., Dick, W.T., Balch, D. and van der Leij, T., 2008. Design, Fabrication and Installation of the Neptune Export PLETs. Paper OTC 19688, *Offshore Technology Conference*.

API, 1997. *RP2T, Recommended Practice for Planning, Designing and Constructing Tension Leg Platforms*, American Petroleum Institute.

API, 2000. *RP2A, Recommended Practice for Planning, Designing and Installing Fixed Offshore Platforms – Working Stress Design*, 21st edition, and subsequent updates, American Petroleum Institute.

API, 2005. *RP2SK, Design and Analysis of Stationkeeping Systems for Floating Structures*, American Petroleum Institute.

API 2006. *Gulf of Mexico Jackup Operations for Hurricane Season – Interim Recommendations*, API Recommended Practice 95J, American Petroleum Institute.

Argyriadis, K. and Klose, M., 2007. Analysis of offshore wind turbines with jacket structures. *Proc. Int. Offshore and Polar Engineering Conf*, 328–334.

Arthur, T.T., Cook, E.L. and Chow, J.K., 1994. Installation of the Mobile Bay Offshore Pipeline System. Paper OTC 7572, *Offshore Technology Conference*.

Ashford, R.A., 1984. Engineering and Construction of Mukluk Island. Paper OTC 4670, *Offshore Technology Conference*.

ASTM, 2009. American Society for Testing and Materials. Volume 04.08, Soil and Rock (I): D420 – D5779, and Volume 04.09, Soil and Rock (II): D5780 – latest; Geosynthetics.

ASTM, 2009. D6032.

Atakan, K. and Ojeda, A., 2005. Stress transfer in the Storegga area, offshore mid-Norway. *Marine and Petroleum Geology* 22(1–2): 161–170.

Atkins, W.S., 2004. *Risk implications in site characterisation and analysis for offshore engineering and design*, Research Report 286 by W.S. Atkins Limited to the UK Health and Safety Executive.

451

Atkinson, J.H., 2000. Non-linear soil stiffness in routine design. *Geotechnique*, 50(5), 487–508.

Atkinson, J.H. and Bransby, P.L., 1978. *The Mechanics of Soils: An introduction to critical soil mechanics*, McGraw-Hill.

Aubeny, C. and Biscontin, G., 2008. Interaction Model for Steel Compliant Riser on Soft Seabed. Paper OTC 19493, *Offshore Technology Conference*.

Aubeny, C., Han, W-W. and Murff, J.D., 2003. Suction Caisson Capacity in Anisotropic, Purely Cohesive Soil. *ASCE Int. Journal of Geomechanics*, 3(2), 225–235.

Aubeny, C.P. and Murff, J.D., 2003. Simplified Limit Solutions for Undrained Capacity of Suction Anchors. *Int. Symp. Deepwater Mooring Systems*, ASCE, 76–90.

Aubeny, C.P. and Murff, J.D., 2004. Simplified limit solutions for the capacity of suction anchors under undrained conditions. *Ocean Engineering*, 32(7), 864–877.

Aubeny, C.P. and Murff, J.D., 2005. Suction Caissons and Vertically Loaded Anchors: Design Analysis Methods. Prepared for the Minerals Management Service, MMS Project No. 362.

Aubeny, C.P., Murff, D.J. and Roesset, J.M., 2001. Geotechnical issues in deep and ultra deep waters. In *Computer methods and Advances in Geomechanics*, ed. C.S. Desai, Balkema, 13–26.

Aubeny, C.P., Shi, H. and Murff, J.D., 2005. Collapse load for cyclinder embedded in trench in cohesive soil. *ASCE Int. J. Geomechanics*, 5(4), 320–325.

Aubeny, C.P., Murff, J.D. and Kim, B.M., 2008a. Prediction of Anchor Trajectory during Drag-Embedment in Soft Clay. *Int. J. Offshore and Polar Engineering*, 18(4), 314–319.

Aubeny, C., Gaudin, C. and Randolph, M.F., 2008b. Cyclic Tests of Model Pipe in Kaolin. Paper OTC 19494, *Offshore Technology Conference*.

Audibert, J.M.E., Neubecker, S. and Stewart, W.P., 2008. Detailed Geotechnical Investigation Around In-Place Mat Foundation Including T-Bar and CPT Comparisons. Paper OTC 19580, *Offshore Technology Conference*.

Aurora, R.P., 1980. Case studies of pile setup in the Gulf of Mexico. Paper OTC 3824. *Offshore Technology Conference*.

Aurora, R.P., 1984. Experience with driving 84 in. piles with Underwater and Abovewater Hammers at the South Brae Platform, North Sea. Paper OTC 4803, *Offshore Technology Conference*.

Aust, 1997. Accident to the Mobile Offshore Drilling Unit Maersk Victory on November 16 1996. MESA Report Book RB 97/24, Mines and Energy Resources, South Australia.

Austin, D., Carriker, B., McGuire, T., Pratt, J., Priest, T. and Pulsipher, A.G., 2004. *History of the offshore oil and gas industry in southern Louisiana: Interim report; Volume I: Papers on the evolving offshore industry*, U.S. Dept. of the Interior, Minerals Management Service, Gulf of Mexico OCS Region, New Orleans, LA. OCS Study MMS 2004–049.

Avato, P. and Coony, J., 2008. Accelerating Clan Energ Technology Research, Development, and Deployment. World Bank Working Paper 138, International Bank for Reconstruction and Development, Washington.

Ayres, A. and Theilen, F., 2001. Natural gamma-ray activity compared to geotechnical and environmental characteristics of near surface marine sediments. *Journal of Applied Geophysics*, 48(1), 1–10.

452

Baerheim, M., Fossen, T.I. and Erlksen, K., 1990. Design and installation of the Veslefrikk jacket. Paper OTC 6307, *Offshore Technology Conference*.

Baglioni, V.P., Chow, G.S. and Endley, S.N., 1982. Jackup Rig Foundation Stability in Stratified Soil Profiles. Paper OTC 4409, *Offshore Technology Conference*.

Bai, Y. and Bai, Q., 2005. *Subsea Pipelines and Risers*, Elsevier.

Bainbridge, C.A., 1975. Certification of Fixed Steel Platforms in the North Sea. Paper OTC 2410, *Offshore Technology Conference*.

Baker, J.H.A., Bruton, D.A.S. and Matheson, I.C., 2006. Monitoring and Effective Integrity Management of Laterally Buckled Flowlines in Deep Water. Paper OTC 17932, *Offshore Technology Conference*.

Baldi, G., Bellotti, R., Ghionna, V., Jamiolkowski, M. and Pasqualini, E., 1986. Interpretation of CPTs and CPTU's: 2nd Part: Drained penetration of sands. *Proc. 4th Int. Geotechnical Seminar, Singapore*, 143–156.

Baligh, M.M. and Levadoux, J.N., 1986. Consolidation after undrained piezocone penetration. II. Interpretation. *ASCE Journal of the Soil Mechanics and Foundation Engineering Division*, 112(7), 727–745.

Baligh, M.M., Assouz, A.S. and Chin, C.T., 1987. Disturbance due to ideal tube sampling. *ASCE Journal of the Geotechnical Engineering Division*, 113(GT7), 739–757.

Balla, A., 1961. The resistance of breakout of mushroom foundations for pylons. *Proc. 5th Int. Conf. Soil Mechanics and Foundation Engineering*, 1, 569–576.

Banerjee, P.K. and Driscoll, R.M.C., 1978. *Program for the analysis of pile groups of any geometry sbject to horizontal and vertical loads and moments, PGROUP (2.1)*, Report HECB/B/7 Department of Transport, HECB London.

Bang, S., Leahy, J.C., Cho, Y. and Kwon, O., 2006. Horizonatl Bearing Capacition of Suction Piles in Sand. Transportation Research Record, NRC Washington.

Barbour, R.J. and Erbrich C.T., 1994. Analysis of in-situ reformation of flattened large diameter foundation piles using ABAQUS. *Proc. UK ABAQUS Users Conf.*, Oxford.

Bardet, J.P., 2000. *EERA, A computer program for Equivalent Earthquake Site Response Analyses of Layered Soil Deposits*, Department of Civil Engineering, University of Southern California.

Bardet, J., 2002. Advances in Analysis of Soil Liquefaction during Earthquakes. In *International handbook of earthquake and engineering seismology*, Academic Press, 1175–1201.

Barron, R.A., 1948. Consolidation of Fine-Grained Soils by Drain Wells. *Trans., ASCE*, Vol. 113, pp. 718–754.

Basarir, H., Karpuz, C. and Tutluoglu, L., 2007. A fuzzy logic based rippability classification system. *Journal of the South African Institute of Mining and Metallurgy*, 107, 817–831.

Baudet, B.A. and Ho, E.W.L., 2004. On the behaviour of deep-ocean sediments. *Geotechnique*, 54(9), 571–580.

Baxter, C.D.P., 1999. *An experimental study of the aging of sands*, Ph.D Thesis, Virginia Tech.

Bayne, J.M. and Tjelta, T.-I., 1987. Advanced Cone Penetrometer Development for In-Situ Testing at Gulllfaks C. Paper OTC 5420, *Offshore Technology Conference*.

Bea, R.G., 1991. Earthquake geotechnology in offshore structures. *Proc. 2nd Int. Conf. Recent Advances in Geotechnical Earthquake Engineering and Soil Dynamics*, University of Missouri-Rolla.

Bea, R.G., Vahdani, S., Guttman, S.I., Meith, R.M. and Paulson, S.F., 1986. Analysis of the Performance of Piles in Silica Sands and Carbonate Formations. Paper OTC 5145, *Offshore Technology Conference*.

Bedard, R., 2007. Overview of Wave and Current Energy: Resource, Technology, and Business Issues. Paper OTC 19094, *Offshore Technology Conference*.

Bell, R.W., 1991. The analysis of offshore foundations subjected to combined loading. M.Sc. Thesis, University of Oxford.

Bender, C.H., Lyons, C.G. and Lowery, L.L., 1969. Applications of Wave Equation Analysis to Offshore Pile Foundations. Paper OTC 1055, *Offshore Technology Conference*.

Berge, J.O., 2005. North Sea Pipelines – Pushing the Technology Front. *Proc. Int. Conf.*, Offshore and Polar Engineering, 12–17.

Berger, W.J. III, Lanier, D.L. and Jeanjean, P., 2006. Geological Setting of the Mad Dog Mooring System. Paper OTC 17914, *Offshore Technology Conference*.

Berner, D.E., Haggerty, B. and Gerwick, B.C., 1989. 260-meter Deep Tremie Concrete Placement for Belled Foundation Rehabilitation of the North Rankin A. Paper OTC 6145, *Offshore Technology Conference*.

Berthin, J.C., Hudson, W.L. and Myrabo, D.O., 1985. Installation of the Maureen Gravity Platform Over a Template. Paper OTC 4876, *Offshore Technology Conference*.

Berzins, W.E. and Hewitt, K.J., 1984. The Use of Hydraulically Placed Sand in Island Construction. Paper OTC 4671, *Offshore Technology Conference*.

Bhattacharya, S., Carrington, T.M. and Aldridge, T.R., 2005. Buckling considerations in pile design. *Proc. Int. Conf. Frontiers in Offshore Geotechnics*, eds S. Gourvenec and M. Cassidy, Taylor and Francis, 815–821.

Bieniawski, Z.T., 1979. The Geomechanics Classification in Rick Engineering Applications, 41–48.

Bienen, B., Byrne, B.W., Houlsby, G.T. and Cassidy, M.J., 2006. Investigating six-degree-of-freedom loading of shallow foundations on sand. *Geotechnique*, 56(6), 367–379.

Bienen, B., Byrne, B.W., Houlsby, G.T. and Cassidy, M.J., 2007. Discussion: Investigating six-degree-of-freedom loading of shallow foundations on sand. *Geotechnique*, 57(5), 483–484.

Bishop, A.W., 1966. The Strength of Soils as Engineering Materials. *Geotechnique*, 16, 91–130.

Bishop, A.W. and Henkel, D.J., 1957. *The triaxial test*, Edward Arnold.

Bishop, A.W., Webb, D.L. and Lewin, P.I., 1965. Undisturbed samples of London Clay from the Ashford Common shaft: strength-effective stress relationships. *Geotechnique*, 15(1), 1–31.

Bjerkas, M., 2004. Global Design Ice Loads Dependence on Failure Mode. *Int. Offshore and Polar Engineering Conf.*, 1, 871–877.

Bjerrum, L., 1967. Engineering Geology of Norwegian Normally-Consolidated Marine Clays as Related to the Settlement of Buildings. *Geotechnique*, 17, 81–118.

Bjerrum, L., 1973. Geotechnical problems involved in foundations of structures in the North Sea. *Geotechnique*, 23(3), 319–358.

454

Bjerrum, L., Nash, J.K.T.L., Kennard, R.M. and Gibson, R.E., 1972. Hydraulic Fracturing in Field Permeability Testing. *Geotechnique*, 22(2), 319–322.

Blenkarn, K.A., 1970. Measurement of ice forces on Cook Inlet structures. Paper OTC 1261, *Offshore Technology Conference*.

Boade, R.R., Chin, L.Y. and Siemers, W.T., 1988. Forecasting of Ekofisk Resrvoir Compaction and Subsidence by Numerical Simulation. Paper OTC 5622, *Offshore Technology Conference*.

Bogard, D. and Matlock, H., 1983. Procedurs for Analysis of Laterally Loaded Pile Groups in Soft Clay. *Proc. Geotechnical Practice on Offshore Engineering*, ASCE, 499–535.

Boggs, S., 2006. *Principles of Sedimentology and Stratigraphy*, Prentice-Hall.

Bolt, B., 2005. *Earthquakes*, W.H. Freeman.

Bolton, M.D., 1986. The strength and dilatancy of sands. *Geotechnique*, 36(1), 65–78.

Bonin, J.P., Deleuil, G. and Zaleski-Zamenhof, L.C., 1976. Foundation Analysis of Marine Gravity Structures Submitted to Cyclic Loading, Paper OTC 2475, *Offshore Technology Conference*.

BonJean, D. and Zhang, J., 2008. Pipeline Flotation in Liquefiable Soil. Paper OTC 19668, *Offshore Technology Conference*.

Boon, C., Gouvenot, D., Gau, M. and Geffriaud, H.-F., 1977. Stability of gravity-type platforms by filling under the raft. Paper OTC 2693, *Offshore Technology Conference*.

Boone, D.J., 1980. The Construction of an Artificial Drilling Island in Intermediate Water Depths in the Beaufort Sea. Paper OTC 3873, *Offshore Technology Conference*.

Bordieri, E., Barbosa, V.C. and Dias, R., 2008. An Overview of the Roncador Field Development, a Case in Petrobras Deepwater Production, Paper OTC 19254, *Offshore Technology Conference*.

Borel, D., Puech, A., Dendani, H. and de Ruijter, M., 2002. High quality sampling for deepwater engineering: the Stacor[®] experience. Ultra Deep Engineering and Technology (UDET), Brest, France.

Borel, D., Puech, A., Dendani, H. and Colliat, J.L., 2005. Deepwater geotechnical site investigation practice in the Gulf of Guinea. *Proc. Int. Conf. Frontiers in Offshore Geotechnics*, eds S. Gourvenec and M.J. Cassidy, Taylor and Francis, 921–926.

Boulanger, R.W. and Idriss, M., 2007. Evaluation of Cyclic Softening in Silts and Clays. *ASCE Journal of Geotechnical and Geoenvironmental Engineering*, 133(6), 641–652.

Boussinesq, J., 1878. Equilbre d'elasticite d'un solide isotrope sans pesanteur, supportant differents poids, Comptes Rendus Acad. Sci. Paris, Vol. 86, 1260–1263.

Bowles, J.E., 1996. *Foundation Analysis and Design*, McGraw-Hill.

Bradshaw, H., Barton, R.R. and McKenzie, R.H., 1984. The Hutton TLP Foundation Design. Paper OTC 4807, *Offshore Technology Conference*.

Bradshaw, H., Stokes, E.G. and Leece, M.J., 1985. Hutton TLP Installation. Paper OTC 4913, *Offshore Technology Conference*.

Bradshaw, A.S., Silva, A.J. and Bryant, W.R., 2000. Stress–strain and strength behavior of marine clays from continental slope, Gulf of Mexico. ASCE Engineering Mechanics Divisions (EMD 2000) Conference, Austin, TX.

Bransby, M.F. and O'Neill, M.P., 1999. Drag anchor fluke-soil interaction in clays. *Int. Symp. Numerical Models in Geomechanics*, Balkema, 489–494.

Bransby, M.F. and Randolph, M.F., 1997. Finite element modelling of skirted strip footings subject to combined loading. *Proc. Int. Offshore and Polar Engineering Conference.*

Bransby, M.F. and Randolph, M.F., 1998. The Effect of Skirted Foundation Shape on Response to Combined V-M-H Loadings. *Proc. Int. Offshore and Polar Engineering Conference.*

Bransby, M.F. and Yun, G.J., 2009. The undrained capacity of skirted strip foundations under combined loading. *Geotechnique*, 59(2), 115–125.

Bransby, M.F., Yun, G.J., Morrow, D.R. and Brunning, P., 2005. The performance of pipeline ploughs in layered soils. *Proc. Int. Conf. Frontiers in Offshore Geotechnics*, eds S. Gourvenec and M.J. Cassidy, Taylor and Francis, 597–605.

Brekke, J.N., Murff, J.D., Campbell, R.B. and Lamb, W.C., 1989. Calibration of Jackup Leg Foundation Model Using Full-Scale Structural Measurements. Paper OTC 6127, *Offshore Technology Conference.*

Brekke, J.N., Campbell, R.B., Lamb, W.C. and Murff, J.D., 1990. Calibration of a Jackup Structural Analysis Procedure Using Field Measurements From a North Sea Jackup. Paper OTC 6465, *Offshore Technology Conference.*

Brennan, A.J., Thusytharan, N.I. and Madabhushi, S.P.G., 2005. Evaluation of Shear Modulus and Damping in Dynamic Centrifuge Tests. *ASCE Journal of Geotechnical and Geoenvironmental Engineering*, 131(12), 1488–1497.

Brennan, R., Diana, H., Stonor, R.W.P., Hoyle, M.J.R., Cheng, C.-P., Martin, D. and Roper, R., 2006. Installing Jackups in Punch-Through-Sensitive Clays. Paper OTC 18268, *Offshore Technology Conference.*

Breslau, L.R., James, J.E. and Trammell, M.D., 1970. The Underwater Shape of a Grounded Ice Island off Prudhoe Bay, Alaska. Paper OTC 1305, *Offshore Technology Conference.*

Brewer. R., 1964. *Fabric and Mineral Analysis of Soils*, Wiley.

Broere, W. and van Tol, A.F., 2006. Modelling the bearing capacity of displacement piles in sand. *Proc. ICE Geotechnical Engineering*, 159(GE3), 195–206.

Broms, B.B., 1964a. Lateral resistance of piles in cohesive soils. *ASCE Journal of the Soil Mechanics and Foundation Engineering Division*, 90(SM2), 27–63.

Broms, B.B., 1964b. Lateral resistance of piles in cohesionless soils. *ASCE Journal of the Soil Mechanics and Foundation Engineering Division*, 90(SM3), 123–156.

Broms, B.B., 1965. Design of laterally loaded piles. *ASCE Journal of the Soil Mechanics and Foundation Engineering Division*, 91(SM3), 77–99.

Broughton, P., Davies, R.L., Aldridge, T. and Carrington, T., 2002. Foundation design for the refloat of the Maureen steel gravity platform, Paper 12735. *Proc. ICE, Geotechnical Engineering*, 2, 111–118.

Brown, D.A., Reese, L.C. and O'Neill, M.W., 1987. Cyclic Lateral Loading of a Large Scale Pile Group. *ASCE Journal of the Geotechnical Engineering Division*, 113(11), 1326–1343.

Brown, J.D. and Meyerhof, G.G., 1969. Experimental study of bearing capacity in layered clays. *Proceedings of the 7th International Conference on Soil Mechanics and Foundation Engineering* (ICSMFE), Mexico City, 2, 45–51.

Brown, R.E., 1977. Vibroflotation Compaction of Cohesionless Soils. *ASCE Journal of the Geotechnical Engineering Division*, 103(GT12), 1437–1451.

Brown, R.J., 2006. Past, Present, and Future Towing of Pipelines and Risers. Paper OTC 18047, *Offshore Technology Conference*.

Brown, R.J. and Palmer, A.C., 1985. Submarine Pipeline Trenching by Multipass Ploughs. Paper OTC 3925, *Offshore Technology Conference*.

Brunner, M.S., Qi, X., Zheng, J. and Chao, J.C., 2006. Combined Effect of Flowline Walking and Riser Dynamic Loads on HP/HT Flowline Design. Paper OTC 17086, *Offshore Technology Conference*.

Bruton, D.A.S., Bolton, M.D. and Nicolson, C.T., 1998. Poseidon Project – Pipeline Design for Weak Clay. *Offshore Technology Pipeline Conference*.

Bruton, D.A.S., White, D.J., Cheuk, C.Y., Bolton, M.D. and Carr, M.C., 2006. Pipe–soil interaction behaviour during lateral buckling, including large amplitude cyclic displacement tests by the Safebuck JIP. Paper OTC 17944, *Offshore Technology Conference*.

Bruton, D.A.S., White, D.J., Carr, M. and Chuek, J.C.Y., 2008. Pipe–Soil Interaction During Lateral Buckling and Pipeline Walking – the SAFEBUCK JIP. Paper OTC 19589, *Offshore Technology Conference*.

Bruton, D.A.S., White, D.J., Langford, T. and Hill, A.J., 2009. Techniques for assessment of pipe/soil interaction forces for future deepwater developments. Paper OTC 20096, *Offshore Technology Conference*.

Bryn, P., Berg, K., Forsberg, C.F., Solheim, A. and Kvalstad, T.J., 2005. Explaining the Storegga Slide. *Marine and Petroleum Geology*, 22(1–2): 11–19.

Bryn, P., Andersen, E.S. and Lien, R., 2007. The Ormen Lange Geohazard Experience: Best Practice for Geohazard Evaluations of Passive Continental Margins. Paper OTC 18712, *Offshore Technology Conference*.

BSI 1990. *BS 1377, Methods of Test for Soils for Civil Engineering Purposes*, British Standards Institution.

BSI 1999. *BS 5930. Code of practice for site investigations*, British Standards Institution.

Bulpitt, W.S., Stewart, S.W., Hunt, M.H. and Shelton, S.V., 2006. Feasibility of Offshore Wind Power in the South Atlantic Bight. Paper OTC 18351, *Offshore Technology Conference*.

Burgess, N.C., Hughes, J.M.O., Innes, R. and Gladowe, J., 1983. Site Investigation and In Situ Testing Techniques in Arctic Seabed Sediments. Paper OTC 4583, *Offshore Technology Conference*.

Burland, J.B., 1973. Shaft friction of piles in clay – a simple fundamental approach. *Ground Engineering*, 6(3), 30–42.

Butterfield, R., 1979. A natural compression law for soils an advance on e-log p'. *Geotechnique*, 29, 469–480.

Butterfield, R. and Douglas, R.A., 1981. *Flexibility coefficients for the design of piles and pile groups*, Technical Note No. 108, CIRIA UK.

Butterfield, R. and Gottardi, G., 1994. A complete three-dimensional failure envelope for shallow footings on sand. *Geotechnique*, 44(1), 181–184.

Butterfield, R. and Ticof, J., 1979. Design parameters for granular soils (discussion contribution). *Proc. 7th European Conf. Soil Mechanics and Foundation Engineering*, Brighton, Vol. 4, pp. 259–261.

Byrne, B.W., 2000. *Investigations of Suction Caissons in Dense Sand*, Ph.D Thesis, Oxford University.

Byrne, B.W. and Cassidy, M.J., 2002. Investigating the Response of Offshore Foundations in Soft Clay Soils. *Proc. Int. Conf. Offshore Mechanics and Arctic Engineering*, Oslo.

Byrne, B.W. and Houlsby, G.T., 1999. Drained Behaviour of Suction Caisson Foundations on Very Dense Sand. Paper OTC 10994, *Offshore Technology Conference*.

Byrne, B.W. and Houlsby, G.T., 2001. Observations of footing behaviour on loose carbonate sands. *Geotechnique*, 51(5), 463–466.

Byrne, B.W. and Houlsby, G.T., 2002a. Experimental Investigations of Response of Suction Caissons to Transient Vertical Loading. *ASCE Journal of Geotechnical and Geoenvironmental Engineering*, 128(11), 926–939.

Byrne, B.W. and Houlsby, G.T., 2002b. Experimental Investigations of the Response of Suction Caissons to Transient Combined Loading. *ASCE Journal of Geotechnical and Geoenvironmental Engineering*, 130(3), 240–253.

Byrne, B.W. and Houlsby, G.T., 2003. Foundations for Offshore Wind Turbines. *Philosophical Transactions of the Royal Society*, London, Series A, Vol. 371, 2909–2930.

Byrne, B.W., Schupp, J., Martin, C.M., Oliphant, J., Maconochie, A. and Cathie, D.N., 2008. Experimental Modelling of the Unburial Behaviour of Pipelines. Paper OTC 18573, *Offshore Technology Conference*.

Calladine, C.R., 2002. *Plasticity for engineers*. Ellis-Horwood.

Camerlenghi, A., Cita, M.B., Della Vedova, B., Fusi, N., Mirabile, L. and Pellis, G., 1995. Geophysical Evidene of Mud Diapirism on the Mediterranean Ridge Accretionary Complex. *Marine Geophysical Researches*, 17, 115–141.

Camp, J.J. and Langley, W.E., 1991. Main Pass 299 Sulphur Mine: Offshore Design in a Soil Subsidence Bowl. Paper OTC 6666, *Offshore Technology Conference*.

Campanella, R.G. and Davies, M.P., 1994. The seismic piezocone: a practical site investigation tool. In *Geophysical Characterization of Sites*, ISSMFE; Technical Committee No. 10 for XIII ICSMFE, New Delhi, India. Balkema.

Campanella, R.G. and Kokan, M.J., 1993. A new approach to measuring dilatancy in saturated sands. *Geotechnical Testing Journal*, ASTM, 16(4), 485–495.

Campbell, K.J., Quiros, G.W. and Young, A.G., 1988. The Importance of Integrated Studies to Deepwater Site Investigation. Paper OTC 5757, *Offshore Technology Conference*.

Campbell, K.J., Burrell., R., Kucera, M.S. and Audibert, J., 2005. Defining Fault Exclusion Zones at Proposed Suction Anchor Sites using an AUV Micro 3D Seismic Survey, Paper OTC 17669, *Offshore Technology Conference*.

Campbell, K.J., Humphrey, G.D. and Litte, R.L., 2008. Modern Deepwater Site Investigation: Getting it Right the First Time. Paper OTC 19535, *Offshore Technology Conference*.

Cao, J., Li, Y., Tjok, K-M. and Audibert, J.M.E., 2005a. Validation of the use of beam-column method for suction caisson design. *Proc. Int. Conf. Frontiers in Offshore Geotechnics*, eds S. Gourvenec and M.J. Cassidy, Taylor and Francis, 325–331.

Cao, J., Audibert, J.M.E., Tjok, K-M. and Hossain, M.K., 2005b. Validation of the use of finite element method for suction caisson design. *Proc. Int. Conf. Frontiers in Offshore Geotechnics*, eds S. Gourvenec and M.J. Cassidy, Taylor and Francis, 333–339.

458

Caquot, A. and Kerisel, J., 1953. Sur le terme de surface dan le calcul des fondations en milieu pulverent. *Proc. 3rd Int. Conf. Soil Mechanics and Foundation Engineering*, Zurich, 1, 336–337.

Carey, J.M., 2002. Guyed Support Structures For Offshore Wind Turbines. *2nd Symposium Offshore Wind Energy – Construction and Environmental Aspects*, Hannover.

Carr, M., Sinclair, F. and Bruton, D., 2006. Pipeline Walking – Understanding the Field Layout Challenges, and Analytical Solutions developed by the SAFE-BUCK JIP. Paper 17945, *Offshore Technology Conference*.

Carrillo, N., 1942. Simple Two- and Three-Dimensional Cases in the Theory of Consolidation of Soils. *Journal of Mathematics and Physics*, 21(1), 1–5.

Carrington, T., Hodges, W., Aldridge, T., Osborne, J. and Mirrey, J., 2003. Jackup advanced foundation analysis by automatic remeshing (large strain) FEA Methods. *Proc. 9th Int. Conf. The Jackup Platform*, City University, London.

Carter, J.M.F., 2007. North Hoyle offshore wind farm: design and build. *Proc. ICE Energy*, 160(EN1), 21–29.

Carter, J.P., Davies, P.J. and Krasnostein, P., 1999. The future of offshore site investigation – robotic drilling on the sea-bed. *Australian Geomechanics*, 34(3), 77–84.

Carter, J.P., Airey, D.W. and Fahey, M., 2000. A review of laboratory testing of calcareous soils. *Proc. Int. Conf. Engineering for Calcareous Sediments*, ed. K.A. Al-Shafei, Balkema, 401–431.

Casagrande, A., 1948. Classification and Identification of Soils. *ASCE Transactions*, p. 901.

Cassedy, E.S., 2000. *Prospects for Sustainable Energy: A Critical Assessment*, Cambridge University Press.

Cassidy, M.J., 1999. *Nonlinear Analysis of Jackup Structures Subject to Random Waves*, Ph.D Thesis, Oxford University.

Cassidy, M.J., 2007. Experimental observations of the combined loading behaviour of circular footings on loose silica sand. *Geotechnique*, 57(4), 397–401.

Cassidy, M.J. and Byrne, B.W., 2001. Drum Centrifuge Model Tests Comparing the Performance of Spudcans and Caissons in Kaolin Clay. Report No. OUEL 2248/01, University of Oxford.

Cassidy, M.J. and Houlsby, G.T., 2002a. On the Modelling of Foundations for Jackup Units on Sand. Paper OTC 10995, *Offshore Technology Conference*.

Cassidy, M.J. and Houlsby, G.T., 2002b. Vertical bearing capacity factors for conical footings on sand. *Geotechnique*, 52(9), 687–692.

Cassidy, M.J., Taylor, R.E. and Houlsby, G.T., 2001. Analysis of jack-up units using a Constrained New Wave methodology. *Applied Ocean Research*, 23, 221–234.

Cassidy. M.J., Houlsby, G.T., Hoyle, M. and Marcom, M.R., 2002a. Determining appropriate stiffness levels for spudcan foundations using jack-up case records. *Proc. OMAE, Int. Conf. Offshore Mechanics and Arctic Engineering*.

Cassidy, M.J., Taylor, P.H., Taylor, R.E. and Houlsby, G.T., 2002b. Evaluation of long-term extreme response statistics of jack-up platforms. *Ocean Engineering*, 29, 1603–1631.

Cassidy, M.J., Byrne, B.W. and Houlsby, G.T., 2002c. Modelling the behaviour of circular footings under combined loading on loose carbonate sand, *Geotechnique*, 52, No. 10, 705–712.

Cassidy, M.J., Byrne, B.W. and Randolph, M.F., 2004a. A comparison of the combined load behaviour of spudcan and caisson foundations on soft normally consolidated clay. *Geotechnique*, 54(2), 91–106.

Cassidy, M.J., Martin, C.M. and Houlsby, G.T., 2004b. Development and application of force resultant models describing jack-up foundation behaviour. *Marine Structures*, 17, 165–193.

Cassidy, M.J., Airey, D.W. and Carter, J.P., 2005. Numerical Modeling of Circular Footings Subjected to Monotonic Inclined Loading on Uncemented and Cemented Calcareous Sands. ASCE *Journal of Geotechnical and Geoenvironmental Engineering*, 131(1), 52–63.

Cassidy, M.J., Randolph, M.F. and Byrne, B.W., 2006. A plasticity model describing caisson behaviour in clay. *Applied Ocean Research*, 28(5), 345–358.

Castelli, F. and Motta, E., 2003. A non-linear approach for settlement prediction of single pile and pile groups under vertical load. *Proc. ICE Geotechnical Engineering*, 156, 183–192.

Castelli, F. and Motta, E., 2005. Discussion: A non-linear approach for settlement prediction of single pile and pile groups under vertical load. *Proc. ICE Geotechnical Engineering*, 158(GE3), 175–177.

Castro, G., 1969. Liquefaction of sands. Ph.D thesis, *Harvard Soil Mechanics Series*, No. 81.

Castro, G. and Poulos, S.J., 1977. Factors affecting liquefaction and cyclic mobility, *Journal of the Geotechnical Engineering Division*, ASCE, 103(6), 501–516.

Cathie, D.N., 2001. Advances in burial assessment and performance prediction, International Cable Protection Committee, Plenary Session, Tokyo.

Cathie, D.N. and Wintgens, J.F., 2001. Pipeline trenching using plows: performance and geotechnical hazards, Paper OTC 13145, *Offshore Technology Conference*.

Cathie, D.N., Jaeck, C., Ballard, J.C. and Wintgens, J.-F., 2005. Pipeline geotechnics – state-of-the-art. *Proc. Int. Conf. Frontiers in Offshore Geotechnics*, eds S. Gourvenec and M. Cassidy, Taylor and Francis, 95–114.

Cauquil, E. and Adamy, J., 2008. Seabed Imagery and Chemosynthetic Communities: Examples for Deep Offshore West Africa. Paper OTC 19352, *Offshore Technology Conference*.

Cedergren, H.R., 1997. *Seepage, Drainage and Flownets*, Wiley.

CEEO, 2003. *Middelgrunden Offshore Wind Farm*, Copenhagen Environment and Energy Office.

Cerruti, V. 1884. Sulla deformazione di uno strato isotropo indefinito limitato da due piani paralleli. Atti Acad. Nazl Lincei Rend, Serie 4, Vol. 1, pp. 521–522.

Chakrabarti, S.K., 2003. *Hydrodynamics of Offshore Structures* (2 vols). WIT Press.

Chakrabarti, S.K., Halkyard, J. and Capanoglu, C., 2005. Historical development of offshore structures. Chapter 1 of *Handbook of Offshore Structures*, ed. S.K. Chakrabati, Elsevier, 1, 1–38.

Chamberlain, E.J., 1983. Frost heave of Saline Soils. *4th Int. Conf. Permafrost*, Fairbanks Alaska, available from http://www.mms.gov/tarprojects/051.htm.

Chandler, R.J., 1988. The in situ measurement of undrained shear strength using the field vane. *ASTM STP1014 Int. Symp. on Laboratory and Field Vane Strength Testing*, Tampa, Florida, 13–44.

Chen, L.-S., 1948. An investigation of stress–strain and strength characteristics of cohesionless soils by triaxial testing. *Proc. ICSMFE*, Vol. 5, 35.

Chen, W. and Randolph, M.F., 2007a. Uplift Capacity of Suction Caissons under Sustained and Cyclic Loading in Soft Clay. *ASCE Journal of Geotechnical and Geoenvironmental Engineering*, 133(11), 1352–1363.

Chen, W. and Randolph, M.F., 2007b. External radial stress changes and axial capacity for suction caissons in soft clay. *Geotechnique*, 57(6), 499–511.

Chen, W-F. and Liu, X.L., 1990. *Limit Analysis in Soil Mechanics*, Elsevier.

Chen, W.-F. and Scawthorn, C., 2003. *Earthquake Engineering Handbook*, CRC Press.

Cheng, Y.M. and Lau, C.K., 2008. *Slope Stability Analysis and Stabilization*, Routledge.

Cheuk, C.Y., 2005. Soil–Pipe interaction at the seabed. Ph.D thesis, Cambridge University.

Cholley, J.A., Thomas, J.P., Lebois, G. and Maniere, P., 2008. Heavy Production Platform for Offshore LNG Development. Paper OTC 19393, *Offshore Technology Conference*.

Chu, J. and Lo, S.-C.R., 1994. Asymptotic behaviour of a granular soil in strain path testing. *Geotechnique*, 44(1), 65–82.

Ciamberlano, F., Nitschke, J., Kragelund, N., Thiede, J., Fusselbaugh, M., Johst, M. and van de Veide, F., 2006. Engineering Insurance of Offshore Wind Turbines. *Proc. 29th IMIA Conf.*, Boston, International Association of Engineering Insurers.

Clarke, B.G., 1995. Pressuremeter in Geotechnical Design. Blackie Academic and Professional.

Clarke, J., 1993. *Large-scale pile tests in clay*, Thomas Telford.

Clark, A.R. and Walker, B.F., 1977. A proposed scheme for the classification and nomenclature for use in the engineering description of Middle Eastern sedimentary rocks. *Geotechnique*, 17(1), 93–99.

Clausen, C.J.F. and Aas, P.M., 2001. Capacity of Driven Piles in Clays and Sands on the Basis of Pile Load Tests. *Int. Conf. Offshore and Polar Engineering*, 581–586.

Clausen, C.J.F., Dimaggio, E., Duncan, J.M. and Andersen, K.H., 1975. Observed Behaviour of the Ekofisk Oil Storage Tank Foundation, Paper OTC 2373, *Offshore Technology Conference*.

Clayton, C.R.I. and Siddique, A., 2001. Discussion: Tube sampling dusturbance – forgotten truths and new perspectives. *Proc. ICE Geotechnical Engineering*, 149(3), 195–200.

Clayton, C.R.I., Matthews, M.C. and Simons, R.E., 1982. Site Investigation. Department of Civil Engineering, University of Surrey.

Clukey, E.C., 2005. Suction caisson soil displacement during installation. *Proc. Int. Conf. Frontiers in Offshore Geotechnics*, eds S. Gourvenec and M.J. Cassidy, Taylor and Francis, 229–234.

Clukey, E., Cacchione, D.A. and Nelson, C.H., 1980a. Liquefaction Potential of the Yukon Prodelta, Bering Sea. Paper OTC 3773, *Offshore Technology Conference*.

Clukey, E.C., Jackson, C.R., Vermersch, J.A. and Lamb, W.C., 1980b. Natural Densification by Wave Action of Sand Surrounding a Buried Offshore Pipeline. Paper OTC 6151, *Offshore Technology Conference*.

461

Clukey, E.C., Morrison, M.J., Garnier, J. and Corte, J.-F., 1995. The Response of Suction Caissons in Normally Consolidated Clays to Cyclic TLP Loading Conditions. Paper OTC 7796, *Offshore Technology Conference*.

Clukey, E.C., Templeton, J.S. III, Randolph, M.F. and Phillips R., 2004. Suction Caisson Response Under Sustained Loop Current Loads. Paper OTC 16843, *Offshore Technology Conference*.

Clukey, E.C., Israel, K., Jones, C. and Ziegler, C.K., 2007. Pipeline Risk Assessment in Deep-Sea Furrow Regions. Paper OTC 18939, *Offshore Technology Conference*.

Clukey, E.C., Jacob, P. and Sharma, P., 2008. Investigation of Riser Seafloor Interaction Using Explicit Finite Element Methods. Paper OTC 19432, *Offshore Technology Conference*.

Coker, J.W.A., 1991. Design of gas and oil riser installations for offshore platforms. Paper OTC, *Offshore Technology Conference*.

Coleman, J.M., Prior, D.B. and Garrison, L.E., 1978. Submarine Landslides in the Mississippi River Delta. Paper OTC 3170, *Offshore Technology Conference*.

Collett, T.S., 2008. Geology of Marine Gas Hydrates and their Global Distribution. Paper OTC 19241, *Offshore Technology Conference*.

Colliat, J.L., Vergobbi, P. and Puech, A., 1993. Friction, Degradation and Set-Up in Hard Clays Offshore Congo and Angola. Paper OTC 7192, *Offshore Technology Conference*.

Conlin, B.H., Jefferies, M.G. and Maddock, W.P., 1985. As Assessment of the Behaviour of Foundation Clay at Tarsuit N-44 Caisson Retained Island. Paper OTC 4884, *Offshore Technology Conference*.

Coop, M.R., 1990. The mechanics of uncemented carbonate sands. *Geotechnique*, 40(4), 607–626.

Coop, M.R., 2000. The Influence of in-situ state on the behaviour of carbonate sands. *Proc. Int. Conf. Engineering for Calcareous Sediments*, ed. K.A. Al-Shafei, Balkema, 379–400.

Cornforth, D.H., 2005. *Landslides in Practice. Investigation, Analysis, and Remedial/Preventative Options in Soils*, Wiley.

COWI, 2009a. *Nysted Offshore Windfarm at Rødand, Denmark*, COWI.

COWI, 2009b. *Thornton Park 1 Offshore Windfarm – Phase 1, Belgium*, COWI.

Cox, W.R., Reese, L.C. and Grubbs, B.R., 1974. Field testing of laterally loaded piles in sand. Paper OTC 2079, *Offshore Technology Conference*.

Cox, W.R., McClure, S.C. and Sorensen, K.H., 1990. Settlement of Mat-Supported Mobile Units in very Soft Clays. Paper OTC 6468, *Offshore Technology Conference*.

Craig, W.H., 1998. Spudcan foundations: installation with deep penetration and subsequent removal. *Geotechnical Engineering*, 131(3), 146–151.

Craig, R.F., 2004. *Craig's Soil Mechanics*, Spon Press.

Craig, W.H. and Chua, K., 1990. Extraction forces for offshore foundations under undrained loading. *ASCE Journal of Geotechnical Engineering*, 116(5), 868–884.

CSLC, 2009. Final Environmental Impact Report for the AT and T Asia America Gateway Fibre Optic Cable Project, State Clearinghouse Report No. 2007111029, CSLC EIR No. 745, Califirnia State lands Commission: Appendix I, Geological Conditions. Available as download from www.slc.csa.gov.

Cundall, P.A., 2001. A discontinuous future for numerical modelling in geomechanics? Paper 12211. *Proc. ICE Geotechnical Engineering*, 149, 41–47.

Cundall, P.A., Drescher, A. and Strack, O.D.L., 1982. Numerical experiments on granular assemblies. IUTAM Conference on Deformation and Failure of Granular Materials, Delft, 355–370.

Dahlberg, R., 1998. Design Procedures for Deepwater Anchors in Clay. Paper OTC 8837, *Offshore Technology Conference*.

Dahlberg, R., Ronold, K.O., Strom, P.J., Mathisen, J., Andersen, K.H. and Jostad, H.-P., 2006. Calibrated Geotechnical Design Code for Suction Anchors in Clay. Paper OTC 18036, *Offshore Technology Conference*.

Danziger, B.R., Costa, A.M., Lopes, F.R. and Pacheco, M.P., 1999. Back analysis of offshore pile driving with an improved soil model. *Geotechnique*, 49, No. 6, 777–799.

Dao, K.M., Tang, B. and Penton, R., 1985. Geohazard Surveying in the Yellow Sea. Paper OTC 4967, *Offshore Technology Conference*.

D'Appolonia, D.J., Poulos, H.G. and Ladd, C.V., 1971. Initial settlement of structures on clay. *Journal of the Soil Mechanics and Foundations Division*, ASCE, 93(SM10), 1357–1377.

Darr, K.A., Reese, L.C. and Wang, S.T., 1990. Coupling effects of uplift loading and lateral loading on capacity of piles. Paper OTC 6320, *Offshore Technology Conference*.

Das, B.M., 2004. *Principles of Foundation Engineering*, Thomson Brooks/Cole.

Das, B.M., 2005. *Fundamentals of Geotechnical Engineering*, Thomson Brooks/Cole.

Das, B.M., 2007. *Earth Anchors*, J. Ross Publishing.

Datta, M., Gulhati, S.K. and Rao, G., 1980. An appraisal of the existing practice in determining the axial load capacity of deep penetration piles in calcareous sands. Paper OTC 3867, *Offshore Technology Conference*.

Davies M.C.R. and Newson T.A., 1992. A critical state constitutive model for anisotropic soil. *Proceedings of the Wroth Memorial Symposium*, Oxford University, July, 219–229, Thomas Telford, London.

Davis, E.H. and Booker, J.R., 1973. The effect of increasing strength with depth on the bearing capacity of clay. *Geotechnique*, 234, 551–553.

Davis, R.O. and Selvadurai, A.P.S., 1996. *Elasticity and Geomechanics*, Cambridge University Press.

Davis, R.O. and Selvadurai, A.P.S., 2002. *Plasticity and Geomechanics*, Cambridge University Press.

Day, R.W., 2007. *Geotechnical Earthquake Engineering Handbook*, McGraw-Hill.

Dean, E.T.R., 2007a. Thermodynamic derivation of yield envelope shapes. *Proc. ICCES 07, Int. Conference on Advances in Computational and Experimental Engineering Sciences*, Miami, 529–540.

Dean, E.T.R., 2007b. Thermodynamic derivation of an asymptotic flow rule. *Proc. ICCES 07, Int. Conference on Advances in Computational and Experimental Engineering Sciences*, Miami, 599–611.

Dean, E.T.R., 2008. Consistent preload calculations for jackup spudcan penetration in clays. *Canadian Geotechnical Journal*, 45(5), 705–714.

Dean, E.T.R. and Metters, R., 2009. Cyclic stiffness degradation in non-linear jackup dynamics. Paper OTC 19998, *Offshore Technology Conference*.

Dean, E.T.R. and Serra, H., 2004. Concepts for mitigation of spudcan-footprint interaction in normally consolidated clay. *Int. Conf. Offshore and Polar Engineering*, 721–728.

Dean, E.T.R., James, R.G., Schofield, A.N., Tan, F.S.C. and Tsukamoto, Y., 1993. The bearing capacity of conical footings on sand in relation to the behaviour of spudcan footings of jack-ups. *Proc. Wroth Memorial Symp. Predictive Soil Mechanics*, Oxford, 230–253.

Dean, E.T.R., Hsu, Y.S., James, R.G., Schofield, A.N., Murff, J.D. and Wong, P.C., 1995. Centrifuge Modelling of 3-Leg Jackups with Non-Skirted and Skirted Spuds on Partially Drained Sand. Paper OTC 7839, *Offshore Technology Conference*.

Dean, E.T.R., James, R.G., Schofield, A.N. and Tsukamoto, Y., 1997a. Theoretical modeling of spudcan behaviour under combined load. *Soils and Foundations*, 37(2), 1–15.

Dean, E.T.R., James, R.G., Schofield, A.N. and Tsukamoto, Y., 1997b. Numerical modeling of three-leg jackup behaviour subject to horizontal load. *Soils and Foundations*, 37(2), 17–26.

Dean, E.T.R., James, R.G., Schofield, A.N. and Tsukamoto, Y., 1998. Drum centrifuge study of three-leg jackup models on clay. *Geotechnique*, 48(6), 761–785.

Dean, E.T.R., Gay, D., Ibrahim, J. and Shrivastava, G.S., 2008. Oceanographic and civil engineering aspects of an offshore island in Otaheite Bay. Chapter 13 of *Aluminum Smelting: Health, Environmental and Engineering Perspectives*, edited by M. Khare, C.K. Sankat, G.S. Shrivastava, and C. Venkobachar, Ian Randle Publishers, 191–215.

Dearman, W.R., 1995. Description and classification of weathered rocks for engineering purposes: the background to the BS5930:1981 proposals. *Quarterly Journal of Engineering Geology*, 28, 267–276.

Deeks, A.J., 1992. *Numerical Analysis of Pile Driving Dynamics*, Ph.D. Thesis, University of Western Australia.

Degenkamp, G. and Dutta, A., 1989. Soil resistances to embedded anchor chains in soft clay. *ASCE Journal of the Geotechnical Engineering Division*, 115(10), 1420–1438.

de Groot, M.B., Bolton, M.D., Foray, P., Meijers, P., Palmer, A.C., Sandven, R., Sawicki, A. and Teh, C.H., 2006. Physics of liquefaction around marine structures. *ASCE Journal of Waterway, Port, Coastal, and Ocean Engineering*, 132(4), 227–243.

Demars, K.R., 1983. Transient stresses induced in sandbed by wave loading. *ASCE Journal of Geotechnical Engineering*, 109(4), 591–602.

Demars, K.R. and Vanover, E.A., 1985. Measurement of wave-induced pressures and stresses in a sand bed. *Marine Geotechnique*, 6(1), 29–59.

De Mello, V.F.B., 1969. Foundations of Buildings on Clay: State of the Art Report. *Proc. 7th ICSMFE*, 1, 49–136.

Denbigh, P.N., 1989. Swath bathymetry: principles of operation and an analysis of errors. *IEEE Journal of Oceanic Engineering*, 14(4), 289–298.

Dendani, H., 2003. Suction Anchors: Some critical aspects for their design and installation in clayey soils. Paper OTC 15376, *Offshore Technology Conference*.

De Nicola, A. and Randolph, M.F., 1997. The plugging behaviour of driven and jacked piles in sand. *Geotechnique*, 47(4), 841–856.

Diaz-Rodriguez, J.A., Leroeuil, S. and Aleman, J.D., 1992. Yielding of Mexico City Clay and other Natural Clays. *ASCE Journal of Geotechnical Engineering*, 118(7), 981–995.

Dier, A. and Carroll B., 2004. *Guidelines for jackup rigs with particular reference to foundation integrity*, Research Report 289 by MSL Engineering Limited for UK Health and Safety Executive, HSE Books.

Digre, K.A., Brasted, L.K. and Marshall, P.W., 1989a. The Design of the Bullwinkle Platform. Paper OTC 6050, *Offshore Technology Conference*.

Digre, K.A., Pelletier, J.H., Larrabee, R.E., Marshall, P.W. and Piter, E.S., 1989b. Design Consideration for the Bullwinkle mudmats. Paper OTC 6097, *Offshore Technology Conference*.

Ding, J., Liu, H. and Hu, L., 2007. Response of Marine Clay to Cyclic Loading. *Proc. Int. Conf. Offshore and Polar Engineering*, 1188–1192.

DNV, 1992. Classification Notes 30.4, Foundations. Det Norske Veritas.

DNV, 2002, Design and Installation of Plate Anchors in Clay. DNV-RP-E302, Det Norske Veritas.

DNV, 2004. Design of Offshore Wind Farm Structures. DNV-OS-J101, Det Norske Veritas.

Doyle, E.H., 1998. The Integration of Deepwater Geohazard Evaluations and Geotechnical Studies. Paper OTC 8590, *Offshore Technology Conference*.

Doyle, E.H., 1999. Pile Installation Performance for Four TLP's in the Gulf of Mexico. Paper OTC 10826, *Offshore Technology Conference*.

Doyle, E.H., Dean, E.T.R., Sharma, J.S., Bolton, M.D., Valsangkar, A.J. and Newlin, J.A., 2004. Centrifuge Model Tests on Anchor Piles for Tension Leg Platforms. Paper OTC 16845, *Offshore Technology Conference*.

Droz, L., Marsset, T., Ondreas, H., Lopez, M., Savoye, B. and Spy-Anderson, F.-L., 2003. Architecture of an active mud-rich turbidite system: The Zaire Fan (Congo-Angola margin southeast Atlantic: Results from ZaiAngo 1 and 2 cruises. *AAPG Bulletin*, 87(7), 1145–1168.

Drucker, D.C. and Prager, W., 1952. Soil Mechanics and Plastic Analysis for Limit State Design. *Quarterly Journal of Applied Mathematics*, 10(2), 157–165.

Drucker, D.C., Gibson, R.E., Henkel, D.J., 1957. Soil mechanics and work-hardening theories of plasticity. *ASCE Journal of the Soil Mechanics and Foundations Division*, 122, 338–346.

Dunlap, W.A., Bryant, W.R., Bennett, R. and Richards, A.F., 1978. Pore pressure measurements in underconsolidated sediments. Paper OTC 3168, *Offshore Technology Conference*.

Dunnavant, T.W. and Kwan, C.-T.T., 1993. Centrifuge Modelling and Parametric Analyses of Drag Anchor behaviour. Paper OTC 7202, *Offshore Technology Conference*.

Dutt, R.N. and Ingram, W.B., 1988. Bearing capacity of jack up footings in carbonate granular sediments. *Proc. Int. Conf. on Calcareous Sediments*, Perth, 1, 291–296.

Dutt, R.N., Doyle, E.H., Collins, J.T. and Ganguly, P., 1995. A simple model to predict soil resistance to driving for long piles in deepwater normally consolidated clays. Paper OTC 7668, *Offshore Technology Conference*.

Dutta, A. and Degenkamp, G., 1989. Behaviour of embedded mooring chains in clay during chain tensioning. Paper OTC 6031, *Offshore Technology Conference*.

Edwards, D., Potts, D. and Zdravkovic, L., 2006. The bearing capacity of a footing under punchthrough failure. *Ground Engineering*, October, pp. 42–44.

Ehlers, C.J., Chen, J., Roberts, H.H. and Lee, Y.C., 2005. The origin of near-seafloor 'crust zones' in deepwater. *Frontiers in Offshore Geotechnics* (ISFOG 2005), eds S. Gourvenec and M.J. Cassidy, Taylor and Francis, 927–933.

Ehlers, C.J., Lobley, G.M., Spikula, D.R. and Brand, J.R., 2008. Site Characterization through the Integration of Geophysical and Geotechnical Data. Paper OTC 19349, *Offshore Technology Conference*.

Eide, O. and Andersen, K.H., 1984. *Foundation Engineering for Gravity Structures in the northern North Sea*, Publication No. 154, Norwegian Geotechnical Institute.

Eiksund, G., Brennodden, H., Paulsen, G. and Witso, S.A., 2008. Ormen Lange Pipelines – Geotechnical Challenges. *Int. Offshore and Polar Engineering Conference*, 457–462.

Eklund, T., Hogmoen, K. and Paulsen, G., 2007. Ormen Lane Pipelines Installation and Seabed Preparation. Paper OTC 18967, *Offshore Technology Conference*.

Elgamel, A., Yang, Z., Parra, E. and Ragheb, A., 2003. Modeling of cyclic mobility in saturated cohesionless soils. *Int. J. Plasticity*, 19, 883–905.

El-Gharbawy, S.L., Iskander, M.G. and Olson, R.E., 1998. Application of Suction Caisson Foundations in the Gulf of Mexico. Paper OTC 8832, *Offshore Technology Conference*.

Elkhatib, S. and Randolph, M.F., 2005. The effect of interface friction on the performance of drag-in plate anchors. *Frontiers in Offshore Geotechnics* (ISFOG 2005), eds S. Gourvenec and M.J. Cassidy, Taylor and Francis, 171–177.

Ellinas, C.P., Supple, W.J. and Vstenholt, H., 1990. Prevention of Upheaval Buckling of Hot Submarine Pipelines by Means of Intermittent Rock Dumping. Paper OTC 6332, *Offshore Technology Conference*.

El Naggar, M.H. and Novak, M., 1995. Effect of Foundation Nonlinearity on Modal Properties of Offshore Towers. *ASCE Journal of Geotechnical Engineering*, 121(9), 660–668.

El Naggar, M.H. and Novak, M., 1996. Influence of Foundation Nonlinearity on Offshore Tower Response. *ASCE Journal of Geotechnical Engineering*, 122(9), 717–724.

El-Sherbiny, R.M., Olson, R.E., Gilbert, R.B. and Vanka, S.K., 2005. Capacity of suction caissons under inclined loading in normally consolidated clay. *Proc. Int. Conf. Frontiers in Offshore Geotechnics*, eds S. Gourvenec and M.J. Cassidy, Taylor and Francis, 281–287.

Eltaher, A., Rajapaksa, Y. and Chang, K.-T., 2003. Industry Trends for Design of Anchoring Systems for Deepwater Offshore Structures. Paper OTC 15265, *Offshore Technology Conference*.

Erbrich, C.T., 2004. A New Method for the Design of Laterally Loaded Anchor Piles in Soft Rock. Paper OTC 16441, *Offshore Technology Conference*.

Erbrich, C.T., 2005. Australian frontiers – spudcans on the edge. Keynote paper, *Frontiers in Offshore Geotechnics* (ISFOG 2005), eds S. Gourvenec and M.J. Cassidy, Taylor and Francis, 49–74.

Erbrich, C.T. and Hefer, P., 2002. Installation of the Laminaria suction piles – a case history. Paper OTC 14240. *Offshore Technology Conference.*

EWEA, 2009. Offshore Statistics. European Wind Energy Association.

Eyles, N. and Meulendyk, T., 2008. Ground-penetrating radar study of Pleistocene ice scours on a glaciolacustrine sequence boundary. *Boreas*, 37(2), 226–233.

Faÿ, J.-B., Montarges, T., Le Tirant, P. and Brucy, F., 1985. Use of the PAM Self-boring Pressuremeter and the STACOR Large-size Fixed-piston Corer for Deep Seabed Surveying. Chapter 12 of *Advances in Underwater Technology and Offshore Engineering, Vol. 3, Offshore Site Investigation*, Graham and Trotman, 187–199.

Feld, T., 2005. Geotechnical Analysis Requirements. *Proc. Int. Conf. Copenhagen Offshore Wind 2005.*

Felix, M. and Peakall, J., 2006. Transformation of debris flows into turbidity currents: mechanisms inferred from laboratory experiments. *Sedimentology*, 53, 107–123.

ffrench, R., Bonnett, D. and Sandon, J., 2005. Wind power: a major opportunity for the UK. Paper 14298, *Proc. ICE Civil Engineering*, 158, 20–27.

Fine, I.V., Rabinovich, A.B., Bornhold, B.D., Thomson, R.E. and Kulikov, E.A., 2005. The Grand Banks landslide-generated tsunami of November 18, 1929: preliminary analysis and numerical modeling. *Marine Geology*, 215(1–2): 45–57.

Finn, W.D.L., Siddharthan, W.D. and Martin, G.R., 1983. Response of seafloor to ocean waves. ASCE Journal of Geotechnical Engineering, 109(4), 556–572.

Finn, W.D.L., Siddharthan, W.D., Lee, F. and Schofield, A.N., 1984. Seismic Response of Offshore Drilling islands in a Centrifuge Including Soil-Structure Interaction. Paper OTC 4693, *Offshore Technology Conference.*

Finn, W.D.L., Steedman, R.S., Yogendrakumar, M. and Ledbetter, R.R., 1985. Seismic response of Gravity Structures in a Centrifuge. Paper OTC 4885, *Offshore Technology Conference.*

Fleming, W.G.K., Weltman, A.J., Randolph, M.F. and Elson, W.K., 1992. *Piling Engineering*, Blackie Academic and Professional.

Florin, V.A. and Ivanov, P.L., 1961. Liquefaction of saturated sand soil. *Proc. 5th ICSFME*, Paris.

Focht, J.A. and Koch, K.J., 1973. Rational Analysis of the Lateral Performance of Offshore Pile Groups. Paper OTC 1896, *Offshore Technology Conference.*

Focht, J.A., Johnson, G.W. and Rivette, C.A., 1986. Results of Recent Cone Penetration Testing in the Gulf of Mexico. Paper OTC 5104, *Offshore Technology Conference.*

Fortin, G., Good, R.L., Norminton, E.J. and Hunter, J.A., 1987. The use of a 12-channel eel for shallow refraction surveying of ice-bearing sediments in the Canadian Beaufort Sea. Paper OTC 5516, *Offshore Technology Conference.*

Foss, I., Dahlberg, R. and Kvalstad, T., 1978. Foundation Design for Gravity Structures with respect to Failure in Cyclic Loading. Paper OTC 3114, *Offshore Technology Conference.*

Fraenkel, P., 2002a. Ocean Energy. Chapter 9 of *The Future for Renewable Energy 2. Prospects and Directions*, EUREC Agency, James and James (Science Publishers), London, 207–221.

Fraenkel, P.L., 2002b. Power from marine currents. *IMECH E Journal of Power and Energy*, 216(1), 1–14.

France, J.W. and Sangrey, D.A., 1977. Effects of drainage in Repeated Loading of Clays. *ASCE Journal of the Geotechnical Engineering Division*, 103(GT7), 769–785.

Fredlund, D.G., 2006. Unsaturated Soil Mechanics in Engineering Practuce, *ASCE Journal of Geotechnical and Geoenvironmental Engineering*, 123(3), 286–321.

Fredlund, D.G. and Rahardjo, H., 1993. *Soil Mechanics for Unsaturated Soils*, Wiley.

Frydman, S. and Burd, H.J., 1997. Bearing capacity of plane strain footings on layered soils. *Canadian Geotechnical Journal*, 34, 241–253.

Fugro, 2005. *Geophysical and Geotechnical techniques for the Investigation of Near-Seabed Soils and Rocks*, Fugro NV, downloadable from www.fugro.com.

Fujii, T., Kobayashi, T. and Tagaya, K., 1989. Punch-Through Encountered in India and Indonesia. Paper OTC 6124, *Offshore Technology Conference*.

Fung, Y.C., 1965. *Foundations of solid mechanics*, Prentice-Hall.

Gadd, P.E., Hearon, G., Liedersdorf, C.B., McDougal, W.G., Ellsworth, J. and Thomas, D., 2001. Slope Armor Design North Star Production Island. *Proc. 16th Int. Conf. Port and Ocean Engineering under Arctic Conditions*, POAC 01, Canada.

Gadd, P.E., Gibson, D.H., Nagel, R.H. and Sonu, C.J., 1982. Natural Barrier Island Migration and Change – No Name Island, Beaufort Sea, Alaska. Paper OTC 4222, *Offshore Technology Conference*.

Gafeira, J., 2009. Ph.D thesis, University of Edinburgh.

Gajo, A. and Muir Wood, D., 1999. A kinematic hardening constitutive model for sands: the multiaxial formulation, *International Journal for Numerical and Analytical Methods in Geomechanics*, 23, 925–965.

Galavazi, M., Moore, R., Lee, M., Brunsden, D. and Austin, B., 2006. Quantifying the Impact of Deepwater Geohazards. Paper OTC 18083, *Offshore Technology Conference*.

Games, K.P., 1985. High-resolution Geophysical Surveys for Engineering Purposes. Chapter 7 of *Advances in Underwater Technology and Offshore Engineering, Vol. 3, Offshore Site Investigation*, Graham and Trotman, 85–98.

Garrison, C.J. and Stacey, R., 1977. Wave loads on North Sea Gravity Platforms: A Comparison of Theory and Experiment. Paper OTC 2794, *Offshore Technology Conference*.

Gaudin, C., O'Loughlin, C.D., Randolph, M.F. and Lowmass, A.C., 2006. Influence of the installation process on the performance of suction embedded plate anchors. *Geotechnique*, 56(6), 381–391.

George, P.J. and Shaw, P.G.H., 1976. Certification of Concrete Gravity Platforms in the North Sea. Paper OTC 2436, *Offshore Technology Conference*.

Georgiadis, M. and Butterfield, R., 1988. Displacements of footings on sands under eccentric and combined loads. *Canadian Geotechnical Journal*, 25, 199–212.

Georgiadis, M. and Michalopoulos, P., 1985. Bearing Capacity of Gravity Bases on Layered Soils. *ASCE Journal of Geotechnical Engineering*, 111(6), 712–729.

Germanischer Lloyd, 2003. Standard for Geotechnical Site and Route Surveys.

Germanischer Lloyd, 2005. Guideline for the Certification of Offshore Wind Turbines.

468

Gerwick, B.C., 2004. Pile Installation in Difficult Soils. *ASCE Journal of Geotechnical and Geoenvironmental Engineering*, 130(5), 454–460.

Gerwick, B.C., 2007. *Construction of Marine and Offshore Structures*, CRC Press.

Ghionna, V.N. and Porcino, D., 2006. Liquefaction Resistance of Undisturbed and Reconstututed Samples of Natural Coarse Sand from Undrained Cyclic Triaxial Tests. *ASCE Journal of Geotechnical and Geoenvironmental Engineering*, 132(2), 194–202.

Gibson, R.E. and Dowse, B.E.W., 1981. The influence of geotechnical engineering on the evolution of offshore structures in the North Sea. *Canadian Geotechnical Journal*, 18, 171–178.

Gidwani, J.M. and Renault, J.P., 1990. Boat impact ultimate capacity analyses of jacket structures. Paper OTC 6484, *Offshore Technology Conference*.

Gijzel, T.G., Thomason, R.A.A. and Athmer, J.B.E.M., 1985. Installation of the Mobile Arctic Caisson Molikpaq. Paper OTC 4942, *Offshore Technology Conference*.

Gilbert, R.B., Nodine, M.C., Wright, S.G., Cheon, J.Y., Wrzyszczynski, M., Coyne, M. and Ward, R.E., 2007. Impact of Hurricane-Induced Mudslides on Pipelines. Paper OTC 18983, *Offshore Technology Conference*.

Gosse, C.G. and Barksdale, G.L., 1969. The Marine Riser – A Procedure for Analysis. Paper OTC 1080, *Offshore Technology Conference*.

Gottardi, G., Houlsby, G.T. and Butterfield, R., 1999. The plastic response of circular footings under general planar loading. *Geotechnique*, 49(4), 453–470.

Gourvenec, S., 2007a. Failure envelopes for offshore shallow foundations under general loading. *Geotechnique*, 57(9), 715–728.

Gourvenec, S., 2007b. Shape effects on the capacity of rectangular footings under general loading. *Geotechnique*, 57(8), 637–646.

Gourvenec, S., 2008. Effect of embedment on the undrained capacity of shallow foundations under general loading. *Geotechnique*, 58(3), 177–185.

Gourvenec, S. and Cassidy, M. (eds) 2005. *Frontiers in Offshore Geotechnics*, Taylor and Francis.

Graham, J., Crooks, J.H.A. and Lau, S.L.K., 1988. Yield envelopes: identification and geotechnical properties. *Geotechnique*, 38(1), 125–134.

Griffiths, D.V. and Marquez, R.M., 2007. Three-dimensional slope stability analysis by elasto-plastic finite elements. *Geotechnique*, 57(6), 537–546.

Guijt, J., 1990. Upheavel buckling of Offshore Pipelines: Overvie and Introduction. Paper OTC 6487, *Offshore Technology Conference*.

Guo, B., Song, S., Chacko, J. and Ghalambor, A., 2005. *Offshore Pipelines*, Elsevier.

Guo, W.D. and Ghee, E.H., 2005. A preliminary investigation into the effect of axial load on piles subjected to lateral soil movement. *Proc. Int. Conf. Frontiers in Offshore Geotechnics*, eds S. Gourvenec and M. Cassidy, Taylor and Francis, 865–871.

Hagen, D., Andenaes, E. and Korstad, G.M., 1998. Innovative Suction Anchor Design and Installation. Paper OTC 8833, *Offshore Technology Conference*.

Hall, J.D. and Perry, C.J., 2008. Oooguruk Field Development Concept and Execution. Paper OTC 19526, *Offshore Technology Conference*.

Halpin, S.M. and Morrison, M.L., 2009. Marine UXO Identification and Avoidance for a Shallow-Water Pipeline Route. Paper OTC 19957, *Offshore Technology Conference*.

Hambly, E.C., 1985. Punchthrough instability of jackup on seabed. *ASCE Journal of Geotechnical Engineering*, 116(4), 704–709.

Hambly E.C., Imm, G.R. and Stahl, B., 1990. Jackup performance and foundation fixity under developing storm conditions, Paper OTC 6466, *Offshore Technology Conference*.

Hambly, E.C. and Nicholson, B.A., 1991. Jackup dynamic stability under extreme storm conditions. Paper OTC 6590, *Offshore Technology Conference*.

Hanna, A.M. and Meyerhof, G.G., 1980. Design charts for ultimate bearing capacity of foundations on sand overlying soft clay. *Canadian Geotechnical Journal*, 17, 300–303.

Hansen, E.A. and Christensen, E.D., 2007. Scour Holes or Scour Protection around Offshore Wind Turbine Foundations: Effect on Loads. *Proc. European Wind Energy Conference, Scientific Proceedings*, 139–142.

Hansen, E.A., Simsonen, H.J., Nielsen, A.W., Pedersen, J. and Hogedal, M., 2007. Scour Protection around Offshore Wind Turbine Foundations: Full Scale Measurements. *Proc. European Wind Energy Conference, Scientific Proceedings*, 132–138.

Hansen, J.B., 1970. *A Revised and Extended Formula for Bearing Capacity*, Bulletin No. 28, Danish Geotechnical Institute.

Hardin, B.O., 1978. The nature of stress–strain behaviour of soils. *Proc, Earthquake Engineering and Soil Dynamics*, ASCE Pasadena, Vol. 1, 3–89.

Hardin, B.O. and Black, W.L., 1968. Vibration Modulus of Normally Consolidated Clay. *ASCE Journal of Soil Mechanics and Foundation Engineering*, 94(SM2), 353–369.

Hardin, B.O. and Drnevich, V.P., 1972a. Shear modulus and damping parameters in soils: measurement and parameter effects. *ASCE Journal of the Soil Mechanics and Foundation Engineering Division*, 98(SM6), 603–624.

Hardin, B.O. and Drnevich, V.P., 1972b. Shear modulus and damping parameters in soils: design equations and curves. *ASCE Journal of the Soil Mechanics and Foundation Engineering Division*, 98(SM7), 667–692.

Harris, J.S., 1995. *Ground Freezing in Practice*, Thomas Telford, London.

Harris, G. and Stone, G.C.H.B., 1990. Vertically constructed and installed jacket for the Gyda field. Paper OTC 6396, *Offshore Technology Conference*.

Harrison, G.E., Brunner, M.S. and Bruton, D.A.S., 2003. King Flowlines – Thermal Expansion design and Implementation. Paper OTC 14310, *Offshore Technology Conference*.

Harte, G., Kavanagh, K., Taberner, D. and Van-der-Linden, N., 2006. Post-Extreme-Event Assessment of SCR Integrity: Strength and Fatigue Effects on the Matterhorn Gas Export SCR from Hurricane Ivan. Paper OTC 18313, *Offshore Technology Conference*.

Hashiguchi, K., 1985. Macrometric Approaches – Static – Intrinsically Time Independent. In *Constitutive Laws of Soils, Report of the ISSMFE Subcommittee on Constitutive Laws of Soils and Proc. Discussion Session 1A IX ICSMFE*, San Francisco, pp. 25–65.

Hashiguchi, K., 1995. On the linear relations of V-lnp and lnV-lnp for isotropic consolidation of soils. *Int. J. Numerical and Analytical Methods in Geomechanics*, 19, 367–376.

Hatherley, A., Fraser Bransby, M., Lauder, K. and Brown, M., 2008. Model testing to reveal the mechanics of ploughing in mega-ripples. *Int. Offshore and Polar Engineering Conf*, 2, 60–66.

Haugen, R., Dalberg, P. and Hogmoen, K., 1983. Development of an Ultrasonic Inspection Pig for In-Service Wall Thickness Measurements of Gas Pipelines. Paper OTC 4568, *Offshore Technology Conference.*

Hayward, M., Hoyle, M.J.R. and Smith, N.P., 2003. Determining Acceptable Rack Phase Difference for Jack-up Legs. *9th Int. Conf. The Jackup Platform*, City University.

Hazen, A., 1892. *Physical properties of sands and gravels with reference to their use in filtration*, Rept. Mass. State Board of Health, p. 539.

Head, K.H., 2006. *Manual of Soil Laboratory Testing* (3 vols). Whittles Publishing.

Hearn, C.G., 2004. *Circuits in the Sea: The Men, the Ships, and the Atlantic Cable*, Praeger Publishers.

Heerema, E.P., 1978. Predicting Pile Driveability: Heather as an Illustration of the Friction Fatigue theory. *Proc. European Offshore Petroleum Conference*, London, 1, 413–422.

Heerema, E.P., 1980. An Evaluation of Hydraulic vs. Steam Pile Driving Hammers. Paper OTC 3829, *Offshore Technology Conference.*

Heerema, E.P., 1981. Dynamic point resistance in sand and clay, for pile driveability analysis. Ground Engineering, September, pp. 30–37 and 46.

Heezen, B.C., Menzies, R.J., Schneider, E.D., Ewing, W.M. and Granelli, N.C.L., 1964. Congo submarine canyon: *AAPG Bulletin*, 48(7), 1126–1149.

Heidari, M. and James, R.G., 1982. Centrifugal modelling of earthquake induced liquefaction in a column of sand. *Proc. Int. Conf. Soil Dynamics and Earthquake Engineering*, Southampton, 271–281.

Helfrich, S.C., Brazill, R.L. and Richards, A.F., 1976. Pullout Characteristics of a Suction Anchor in Sand. Paper OTC 2469, *Offshore Technology Conference.*

Helfrich, S.C., Young, A.G. and Ehlers, C.J., 1980. Temporary seafloor support of jacket structures. Paper 3750, *Offshore Technology Conference.*

Helland, K., Kvalstad, T.J., Karlsen, V., Fjeld, S. and Hermstad, J.M., 1991. The Brage Platform: A New Generation of Gravity-Base Structures. Paper OTC 6699, *Offshore Technology Conference.*

Henkel, D.J., 1956. Discussion on 'Earth Movement affecting L.T.E. Railway in Deep Cutting East of Uxbridge'. *Proc. Inst. Civ. Eng.*, Part II, 5, 320–323.

Henkel, D.J., 1970. The role of waves in causing submarine landslides. *Geotechnique*, 20(1), 75–80.

Herbich, J.B., 2000a. *Handbook of Coastal Engineering*, McGraw-Hill.

Hesar, M., 2003. Geotechnical Design of the Barracude and Caratinga Suction Anchors. Paper OTC 15137, *Offshore Technology Conference.*

Hettinger, F. and Machin, J., 2005. Cable and Pipeline Burial at 3,000 metres. *Proc. Oceans 2005*, Washington.

Hicks, M.A. and Smith, I.M., 1988. Class A prediction of Arctic caisson performance, *Geotechnique*, 38, 589–612.

Hight, D.W., 1993. A review of sampling effects in clays and sands. In *Advances in Underwater Technology, Ocean Science and Offshore Engineering, Vol. 28, Offshore Site Investigation and Foundation Behaviour, Proc. Conf., Society for Underwater Technology*, Kluwer, 115–146.

Hight, D.W., Georgiannou, V.N. and Ford, C.J., 1994. Characterisation of clayey sands. *Proc. BOSS 94 Behaviour of Offshore Structures, Vol. 1 Geotechnics*, eds

C. Chryssostomidos, M.S. Triantafyllou, A.J. Whittle, and Hoo Fatt, M.S., Pergamon, 321–340.

Hill, R., 1950. *The Mathematical Theory of Plasticity*, Oxford Clarendon Press.

Hill, A.J. and Jacob, H., 2008. In-Situ measurement of Pipe–Soil Interaction in Deep Water. Paper OTC 19528, *Offshore Technology Conference*.

Hiroyuki, T., Raj, S.D. and Masanori, T., 2003. Applicability of shansep method to six different natural clays, using triaxial and direct shear tests. *Soils and Foundations*, 43(3), 43–55.

Hirsch, T.J., Koehler, A.M. and Sutton, V.J.R., 1975. Selection of Pile Driving Equipment and Field Evaluation of Pile Bearing Capacity during Driving for the North Sea Forties Field. Paper OTC 2247, *Offshore Technology Conference*.

Hirst, T.J., Steele, J.E. and Remy, N.D., 1976. Performance of Mat-Supported Jackup Drilling Rigs. Paper OTC 2503, *Offshore Technology Conference*.

Hitchings, G.A., Bradshaw, T.D. and Labiosa, T.D., 1976. The Planning and Execution of Offshore Site Investigations for a North Sea Gravity Platform. Paper OTC 2430, *Offshore Technology Conference*.

Hobbs, R.E., 1984. In service buckling of heated pipelines. ASCE *Journal of Transportation Engineering*, 110(2), 175–189.

Hoffmans, G.J.C.M. and Verheij, H.J., 1997. *Scour Manual*, Balkema.

Hogan, P., Lane, A., Hooper, J., Broughton, A. and Romans, B., 2008. Geohazard Challenges of the Woodside Ocean Way Secure Energy LNG Development, Offshore Southern California. Paper OTC 19563, *Offshore Technology Conference*.

Hogervorst, J.R., 1980. Field trials with large diameter suction piles. Paper OTC 3817, *Offshore Technology Conference*.

Holloway, D.M., Clough, G.W. and Vesic, A.S., 1978. The Effects of Residual Driving Stresses on Pile Performance under Axial Loads. Paper OTC 3306, *Offshore Technology Conference*.

Horsnell, M.R., Aldridge, T.R. and Erbrich, C., 1990. Lateral Group Behavior of Piles in Offshore Soil Conditions. Paper OTC 6246, *Offshore Technology Conference*.

Hossain, M.S., Hu, Y. and Randolph, M.F., 2003. Spudcan Foundation Penetration into Uniform Clay. *Proc. 13th Int. Offshore and Polar Engineering Conference*, 647–652.

Hossain, M.S., Hu, Y., Randolph, M.F. and White, D.J., 2005a. Limiting cavity depth for spudcan foundations penetrating clay. *Géotechnique*, 55(9), 679–690.

Hossain, M.S., Hu, Y., Randolph, M.F. and White, D.J., 2005b. Punch-through of spudcan foundations in two-layer clay. *Proc. Int. Conf. Frontiers in Offshore Geotechnics*, eds S. Gourvenec and M. Cassidy, Taylor and Francis, 535–541.

Hossain, M.S., Randolph, M.F., Hu, Y. and White, D.J., 2006. Cavity Stability and Bearing Capacity of Spudcan Foundations on Clay. Paper OTC 17770, *Offshore Technology Conference*.

Hossain, M.S. and Randolph, M.F., 2009. New Mechanism-Based Design Approach for Spudcan Foundations on Stiff-over-soft Clay. Paper OTC 19907, *Offshore Technology Conference*.

Houlsby, G.T., 1990. *Pressuremeters*, A British Geotechnical Society Symposium. Thomas Telford.

472

Houlsby, G.T., 2005. Discussion: Editorial. *Geotechnique*, 55(5), 416–417.

Houlsby, G.T. and Byrne, B.W., 2005. Design procedures for installation of suction caissons in clay and other materials. Paper 13817, *Proc. ICE Geotechnical Engineering*, 158(GE2), 75–82.

Houlsby, G.T. and Byrne, B.W., 2006. Design procedures for installation of suction caissons in sand. Paper 13818, *Proc. ICE Geotechnical Engineering*, 159(GE3), 135–144.

Houlsby, G.T. and Cassidy, M.J., 2002. A plasticity model for the behaviour of footings on sand under combined loading. *Geotechnique*, 52(2), 117–129.

Houlsby, G.T. and Martin, C.M., 2003. Undrained bearing capacity factors for conical footings on clay. *Geotechnique*, 53(5), 513–520.

Houlsby, G.T. and Wroth, C.P., 1982. Direct Solution of Plasticity Problems in Soils by the Method of Characteristics. *Proceedings of the 4th International Conference on Numerical Methods in Geomechanics*, Vol. 3, Edmonton, June, pp. 1059–1071.

Houlsby, G.T. and Wroth, C.P., 1983. Calculations of stresses on shallow penetrometers and footings. Chapter 9 of *Seabed Mechanics*, 107–112.

Houlsby, G.T., Evans, K.M. and Sweeney, M., 1988. End bearing capacity of model piles in layered carbonate soils. *Proc. Int. Conf. on Calcareous Sediments*, Perth, Australia, Balkema, 1, 209–214.

Houlsby, G.T., Bo Ibsen, L. and Byrne, B.W., 2005a. Suction Caissons for Wind Turbines. *Proc. Int. Conf. Frontiers in Offshore Geotechnics*, eds S. Gourvenec and M. Cassidy, Taylor and Francis, 75–93.

Houlsby, G.T., Kelly, R.B., Huxtable, J. and Byrne, B.W., 2005b. Field trials of suction caissons in clay for offshore wind turbine foundations. *Géotechnique*, 56(1), 3–10.

Houlsby, G.T., Vassidy, M.J. and Einav, I., 2005c. A generalised Winkler model for the behaviour of shallow foundations. *Geotechnique*, 55(6), 449–460.

Houlsby, G.T., Kelly, R.B., Huxtable, J. and Byrne, B.W., 2006. Field trials of suction caissons in sand for offshore wind turbine foundations. *Géotechnique*, 55(4), 287–296.

Howarth, M., Dier, A., Jones, W. and Hunt, R.J., 2003. Jack-up Response to Wave-in-deck Loads during Extreme Storms. *Proc. 9th Int. Conf. The Jackup Platform: Design, Construction and Operation*, City University, London.

Hubbert, M.K. and Willis, D., 1957. Mechanics of Hydraulic Fracturing. *Trans. AIME*, 210, 153–166.

Hsu, Y.S., 1998. *Excess pore pressures under cyclically loaded model jack-up foundations*, Ph.D, Cambridge University.

Huhnerbach, V. and Masson, D.G., 2004. 'Landslides in the North Atlantic and its adjacent seas: an analysis of their morphology, setting and behaviour', *Marine Geology*, 213(1–4): 343–362.

Hunt, R.J., 1999. Jack-up and jacket relative motions, prediction and measurements. *7th Int. Conf., The Jack-up Platform: Design, Construction and Operation*, City University, London.

Hunt, R.J., Ahilan, R., Quarrington, J. and Simpson, M., 2004. Management of Marine Risk in Offsore Wind Farm Installation and Maintenance. *Proc. Int. Conf. The British Wind Energy Association*, Manchester, UK.

Hunt, R.J., Dier, A.F. and Jones, W., 2001. Further interpretation of North sea jack-up motion measurements. *8th Int. Conf., The Jack-up Platform: Design, Construction and Operation*, City University, London.

Hunt, R.E., 2005. *Geotechnical Engineering Investigation Handbook*, Taylor and Francis.

Huslid, C., 2001. Full-Scale Monitoring of Troll A Concrete Platform: A Huge Gravity Based Structure on Soft Clay. *Proc. Int. Conf. Offshore and Polar Engineering*, 647–655.

Huynh, T.L., Clark, W.J. and Luther, D.C., 1997. Structural Design of the Iceberg Resistant Hibernia Reinforced Concrete GBS. Paper OTC 8398, *Offshore Technology Conference*.

Hyde, A.F.L. and Conn, G.M., 1987. Cyclic triaxial tests on remoulded clays. *ASCE Journal of Geotechnical Engineering*, 113(6), 665–667.

Hyde, A.F.L. and Ward, S.J., 1986. The effect of cyclic loading on the undrained shear strength of a silty clay. *Marine Geotechnology*, 6(3), 299–314.

Hyde, A.F.L., Higuchi, T. and Yasuhara, K., 2006. Liquefaction, Cyclic Mobility, and Failure of Silt. *ASCE Journal of Geotechnical and Geoenvironmental Engineering*, 132(6), 716–735.

Idelovichi, J-L. and Zundel, J.-P., 2004. Girassol: Two Years after First Oil – Active Development Activity with Record Production. Paper OTC 16575, *Offshore Technology Conference*.

Ippen, A.T., 1966. *Estuary and Coastline Hydrodynamics*, McGraw-Hill.

Isaacson, M. and Cheung, K.-F., 1992. Nonlinear Diffraction of Irregular Waves Around a Large Structure. Paper OTC 6816, *Offshore Technology Conference*.

Ishihara, K., Tatsuoka, F. and Yasuda, S., 1975. Undrained deformation and liquefaction of sand under cyclic stresses. *Soils and Foundations*, 15, 29–44.

Ishihara, K. and Yamazaki, A., 1984. Wave-induced liquefaction in seabed deposits of sand. In *Seabed Mechanics*, Denness (ed.), Graham & Trotman, London, 139–148.

Islam, M.K., Carter, J.P. and Airey, D.W., 2004. Comparison of the Yield Locus and Stress-Dilatancy Function of Some Critical State Constitutive Models with Experimental Data for Carbonate Sand. *Journal of the Institution of Engineers*, India, 84, 267–274.

ISO, 2005. *International Standard ISO 19901-7. Petroleum and natural gas industries: Specific requirements for offshore structures Part 7: Stationkeeping systems for floating offshore structures and mobile offshore units*, International Standards Organization.

ISO, 2006. *International Standard ISO 19903. Petroleum and natural gas industries: Fixed concrete offshore structures*, International Standards Organization.

ISO, 2007. *International Standard ISO 19902. Petroleum and natural gas industries: Fixed steel offshore structures*, International Standards Organization.

ISO, 2009. *International Standard ISO 19906. Petroleum and natural gas industries: Arctic offshore structures*, International Standards Organization.

ISSMFE, 1989. International Reference Test Procedure for Cone Penetration Test (CPT). Report of the ISSMFE Technical Committee on Penetration Testing of Soils – TC 16. Also published as Appendix A of Lunne et al. (1997).

ISSMGE TC1 2005. *Geotechnical and Geophysical Investigations for Offshore and Nearshore Developments*, Technical Committee 1 of the International

Society for Soil Mechanics and Geotechnical Engineering. Downloadable from www.offshoregeohazards.org.

Jackson, G. and Bell, T.A., 1990. The Design of the Ravenspurn North Concrete Gravity Substructure: An Innovative Application of Conventional Technology. Paper OTC 6394, *Offshore Technology Conference*.

Jackson, N. and Dhir, R.K., 1996. *Civil Engineering Materials*, Palgrave.

Jacob, P. and Stewart, W., 2008. Seismic Time History Response of the Maleo Producer. Paper OTC 19480, *Offshore Technology Conference*.

Jaky, J., 1944. The coefficient of earth pressure at rest, *Magyar Mérnök és Epitész Egglet Közlönye*.

Jamiolkowski, M., Ladd, C.C., Germaine, G.T. and Lancellotta, R., 1985. New developments in field and laboratory testing of soils. *Proc. 11th Int. Conf. Soil Mechanics and Foundation Engineering*, Vol. 1, 57–153.

Jamiolkowski, M., Ghionna, V.N., Lancellotta, R. and Pasqualini, E., 1988. New Correlations of Penetration Tests for Design Practice, in De Ruiter, J. (ed.), Penetration Testing 1988: Proceedings First Intl. Symp. on Penetration Testing, ISOPT-1, Orlando, Balkema, 1, 263–296.

Jamiolkowski, M., Leroeusil, S. and LoPresti, D.C.F., 1991. Theme lecture: Design parameters from theory to practice. *Proc. Geocoast '91*, Yokohama, Japan, 1–41.

Janbu, N., 1967. *Settlement computation based on the tangent modulus concept*, Three Guest Lectures at Moscow State University, Bulletin No. 2, Soil Mechanics, Norwegian Institute of Technology, Trondheim.

Janbu, N., 1985. Soil models in offshore engineering. *Geotechnique*, 35, 243–281.

Jardine, R.J. and Chow, F.C., 1996. *New Design Methods for Offshore Piles*, Publication 96/103, Marine Technology Directorate Limited, London.

Jardine, R.J., Kovacevic, N., Hoyle, M.J.R., Sidhu, H.K. and Letty, A., 2001. A Study of Eccentric Jack-Up Penetration Into Infilled Footprint Craters. *Proc. 8th Int. Conf. The Jackup Platform*, City University, London, eds C. D'Mello and L. Boswell.

Jardine, R.J., Standing, J.R. and Chow, F.C., 2006. Some observations of the effects of time on the capacity of piles driven in sand. *Geotechnique*, 56(4), 227–244.

Jeanjean, P., 2006. Setup Characteristics of Suction Anchors for Soft Gulf of Mexico Clays: Experience from Field Installation and Retrieval. Paper OTC 18005, *Offshore Technology Conference*.

Jeanjean, P., 2009. Reassessment of p–y curves for soft clays from centrifuge testing and finite element modelling. Paper OTC 20158, *Offshore Technology Conference*.

Jeanjean, P., Andresen, K.H. and Kalsnes, B., 1998. Soil Parameters for Design of Suction Caissons for Gulf of Mexico Deepwater Clays. Paper OTC 8830, *Offshore Technology Conference*.

Jeanjean, P., Liedtke, E., Clukey, E.C., Hampson, K. and Evans, T., 2005. An operator's perspective on offshore risk assessment and geotechnical design in geohazard-prone areas. *Proc. Int. Conf. Frontiers in Offshore Geotechnics*, eds S. Gourvenec and M. Cassidy, Taylor and Francis, 115–143.

Jeanjean, P., Znidaric, D., Phillips, R., Ko, H.-Y., Pfister, S., Cinicioglu, O. and Schroeder, K., 2006. Centrifuge Testing on Suction Achors: Double-Wall, Over-Consolidated Clay, and Layered Soil Profile. Paper OTC 18007, *Offshore Technology Conference*.

Jefferies, M.G. and Been, K., 2006. *Soil Liquefaction*, Taylor and Francis.

Jeng, D.S., 2007. Potential of Offshore Wind Energy in Australia. Paper OTC 18578, *Offshore Technology Conference*.

Jewell, R.J. and Khorshid, M.S., 2000. A historical perspective, 1988 to 1999. *Proc. Int. Conf. Engineering for Calcareous Sediments*, ed. K.A. Al-Shafei, Balkema, Vol. 2, 305–312.

Jeyatharan, K., 1991. *Partial liquefaction of sand fill in a mobile arctic caisson under ice loading*, Ph.D thesis, Cambridge University.

Johnson, J.P., Rhett, D.W. and Siemers, W.T., 1988. Rock Mechanics in the Ekofisk Reservoir in the Evaluation of Subsidence. Paper OTC 5621, *Offshore Technology Conference*.

Johnston, M. and Timco, G.W., 2003. *Proc. 17th Int. Conf. Port and Ocean Engineering under Arctic Conditions*, 1, 213–222.

Jones, K.D., Bang, S. and Cho, Y., 2007. Pullout capacity of embedded suction anchors in sand. *Ocean Engineering*, 34, 2107–2114.

Jostad, H.P. and Andersen, K.H., 2006. Potential benefits of Using Skirted Foundations for Jackup Platforms. Paper OTC 18016, *Offshore Technology Conference*.

Judd, A.G. and Hovland, M., 2007. *Seabed fluid flow: the impact of geology, biology and the marine environment*, Cambridge University Press.

Jukes, P., Wang, J. and Durin, B., 2008. Solving Pipeline Challenges in the GOM by Innovation, Advanced Analysis Tools, and Engineering Competency. Paper OTC 19504, *Offshore Technology Conference*.

Kamphuis, J.W., 2002. *Introduction to Coastal Engineering and Management*, World Scientific.

Karunakaran, D., Spidsøe, N. and Dalane, J.I., 1992. Nonlinear dynamic response of two deep water jack-up platforms, 2nd Offshore and Polar Engineering Conference, San Francisco, 1, 278–287.

Karunakaran, D. and Spidsøe, N., 1997. Verification of methods for simulation of nonlinear dynamic response of jack-up platforms, Marine Structures, 10.

Karunakaran, D., Baerheim, M. and Spidsøe, N., 1998. Measure and Simulated Dynamic Response of a Jacket and a Large Jackup Platform in the North Sea. Paper OTC 8827, *Offshore Technology Conference*.

Karunakaran, D., Baerheim, M. and Spidsøe, N., 1999. Full-scale measurements from a large deepwater jack-up platform, Marine Structures, 12.

Kaynia, A.M. and Kausel, E., 1982. Dynamic behaviour of Pile Groups. *Proc. 2nd Int. Conf. Numerical methods in Offshore Piling*, 509–532.

Kearey, P., Brooks, M. and Hill, I., 2002. *An Introduction to Geophysical Exploration*, Blackwell.

Keller, G.H., 1967. Shear strength and some other physical properties of sediments from some ocean basins. *Proc. ASCE Conference on Civil Engineering in the Oceans*, San Francisco, 391–417.

Kellezi, L. and Stromann, H., 2003. FEM Analysis of of jack-up spudcan penetration for multi-layered critical soil conditions. *Spudcan penetration*, GEO, Lyngby, Denmark.

Kellezi, L., Hofstede, H.W.I. and Hansen, P.B., 2005a. Jackup footing penetration and fixity analyses. *Proc. Int. Conf. Frontiers in Offshore Geotechnics*, eds S. Gourvenec and M. Cassidy, Taylor and Francis, 559–565.

Kellezi, L., Kudsk, G. and Hansen, P.B., 2005b. FE Modelling of spudcan–pipeline interaction. *Proc. Int. Conf. Frontiers in Offshore Geotechnics*, eds S. Gourvenec and M. Cassidy, Taylor and Francis, 551–557.

Kelly, R., Airey, D.W. and Tabucanon, J.T., 2003. Design and Performance of a 1 m Diameter Ring Shear Apparatus. ASTM *Geotechnical Testing Journal*, 26(4).

Kelly, R.B., Houlsby, G.T. and Byrne, B.W., 2006a. A comparison of field and laboratory tests of caisson foundations in sand and clay. *Geotechnique*, 56(9), 617–626.

Kelly, R.B., Houlsby, G.T. and Byrne, B.W., 2006b. Transient vertical loading of model suction caissons in a pressure chamber. *Geotechnique*, 56(10), 665–675.

Kelly, W.E., Nacci, V.A. and Demars, K.R., 1974. Engineering Properties of Cemented Deep-Ocean Sediments. Paper OTC 2091, *Offshore Technology Conference*.

Kennedy, M.J., Skinner, G. and Moore, I.D., 2004a. Elastic calculations of limiting mud pressures to control hydrofracturing during HDD. *Proc., 2004, No-Dig Conf.*

Kennedy, M.J., Skinner, G. and Moore, I.D., 2004b. Limiting mud pressures to control hydrofracturing during HDD in an elasto-plastic soil. *Proc. Canadian Geotechnical Conf.*

Kenny, S., Barett, J., Phillips, R. and Popescu, R., 2007. Integrating geohazard demand and structural capacity modelling within a probabilistic design framework for offshore arctic pipelines. *Proc. Int. Conf. Offshore and Polar Engineering* (ISOPE 2007), 3057–3064.

Kerr, D., 2005. Marine Energy: getting power from tides and waves. Paper 14294, *Proc. ICE Civil Engineering*, 158, 32–39.

Kerr, D., 2007. Marine Energy. *Phil. Trans. Royal Society* A, 265, 971–992.

Kerr, N., 1976. A Self-Burying Anchor of Considerable Holding Power. Paper OTC 2466, *Offshore Technology Conference*.

Kim, Y.T. and Leroueil, S., 2001. Modeling the viscoplastic behaviour of clays during consolidation: application to Berthierville clay in both laboratory and field conditions. *Canadian Geotechnical Journal*, 38: 484–497.

Kim, D-S. and Choo, Y.-W., 2005. Dynamic deformation Characteristics of Dry and Saturated Sands under Cyclic Loadings. *Proc. Int. Conf. Offshore and Polar Engineering*, 703–710.

King, R.W., Van Hooydonk, W.R., Kolk, H.K. and Windle, D., 1980. Geotechnical investigations of calcareous soils of the North West Shelf Australia. Paper OTC 3773, *Offshore Technology Conference*.

Kitiyodom, P., Sonoda, R. and Matsumoto, T., 2005. Simplified analysis of single pile subjected to dynamic active and passive loadings. *Proc. Int. Conf. Frontiers in Offshore Geotechnics*, eds S. Gourvenec and M. Cassidy, Taylor and Francis, 837–843.

Kitney, N. and Penman, A., 2008. ACG Offshore Platforms Temporary Pin-Pile Foundations. Paper 19217, *Offshore Technology Conference*.

Klar, A. and Frydman, S., 2002. Three-Dimensional Analysis of Lateral Pile Response using Two-Dimensional Explicitly Numerical Scheme, *ASCE Journal of Geotechnical and Geoenvironmental Engineering*, 128(GT9), 775–784.

477

Klose, M., Faber, T., Schaumann, P. and Lochte-Holtgreven, S., 2008. Grouted Connections for Offshore Wind Turbines. *Proc. Int. Offshore and Polar Engineering Conf*, 425–430.

Kolk, H.J., 2000. Deep foundations in calcareous sediments. *Proc. Int. Conf. Engineering for Calcareous Sediments*, ed. K.A. Al-Shafei, Balkema, 2, 313–344.

Kolk, H.J. and Wegerif, J., 2005. Offshore site investigations: New frontiers. *Proc. Int. Conf. Frontiers in Offshore Geotechnics*, eds S. Gourvenec and M. Cassidy, Taylor and Francis, 145–161.

Kolk, H.J., Baaijens, A.E. and Vergobbi, P., 2005. Results from axial load tests on pipe piles in very dense sands; the EURIPIDES JIP. *Proc. Int. Conf. Frontiers in Offshore Geotechnics*, eds S. Gourvenec and M. Cassidy, Taylor and Francis, 661–667.

Koumoto, T. and Houlsby, G.T., 2001. Theory and practice of the fall cone test. *Geotechnique*, 51(8), 701–712.

Kraft, L.M. and Murff, J.D., 1975. A Probabilistic Investigation of Foundation Design for Offshore Structures. Paper OTC 2370, *Offshore Technology Conference*.

Kraft, L.M., Ray, R.P. and Kagawa, T., 1981a. Theoretical t–z Curves. *ASCE Journal of the Geotechnical Engineering Division*, 107(GT11), 1543–1561.

Kraft, L.M., Focht, J.A. and Amerasinghe, S.F., 1981b. Friction Capacity of Piles Driven Into Clay. *ASCE Journal of the Geotechnical Engineering Division*.

Kramer, S.L., 1988. Development of p–y curves for analysis of laterally loaded piles in Western Washington. Task 31 in Research Project Y-3399, Report prepared for the Washington State Transportation Commission.

Kramer, S.L., 1996. *Geotechnical Earthquake Engineering*, Prentice-Hall.

Kreysig, E., 1999. *Advanced Engineering Mathematics*, Wiley.

Kulhawy, F.H. and Mayne, P.W., 1990. *Manual on estimating soil properties for foundation design*, Electric Power Research Institute, Palo Alto, California, USA.

Kumar, J. and Kouzier, K.M., 2008. Vertical uplift capacity of a group of shallow horizontal anchors in sand. *Geotechnique*, 58(10), 821–823.

Kusakabe, O., Yamaguchi, H. and Morikage, A., 1991. Experimental and analysis on the scale effect of $N\gamma$ for circular and rectangular footings. *Proc. Centrifuge '91*, Boulder, CO, 179–186.

Lacasse, S., 1999. Ninth OTRC Honors Lecture: Geotechnical Contributions to Offshore Development. Paper 10822, *Offshore Technology Conference*.

Lacasse, S. and D'Orazio, T.B., 1988. Soil Reaction Stresses on Offshore Gravity Platforms. *ASCE Journal of Geotechnical Engineering*, 114(11), 1277–1299.

Lacasse, S., Robbetstad, L., Boisard, P. and Ohm, K., 1991. The Foundation of the Frigg CDP-1 platform: a Case Study. Paper OTC 6512, *Offshore Technology Conference*.

Lacasse, S., Iversen, K., Sandboekken, G. and Morstad, P., 1984. *Radiography Offshore to Assess Sample Quality*, Publication No. 153, NGI Oslo.

Ladd, C.C. and Assouz, A.S., 1983. Stress History and Strength of Stiff Offshore Clays. *Geotechnical Practice in Offshore Engineering, Proc. Conf.*, Austin, Texas, ASCE, 65–80.

Ladd, C.C. and Foott, R., 1974. New Design Procedure for Stability of Soft Clays. *ASCE Journal of the Geotechnical Engineering Division*, 100(GT7), 763–786.

Ladd, C.C., Foott, R., Ishihara, K., Schlosser, F. and Poulos, H.G., 1977. Stress, deformation and strength characteristics: State of the Art Report. *Proc. 9th ICSMFE*, Tokyo, 2, 421–494.

Ladd, R.S., 1974. Specimen preparation and liquefaction of sands. *ASCE Journal of the Geotechnical Engineering Division*, 100(GT10), 1180–1184.

Ladd, R.S., 1977. Specimen preparation and cyclic stability of sands. *ASCE Journal of the Geotechnical Engineering Division*, 103(GT6), 535–547.

Lade, P.V. and Duncan, J.M., 1973. Cubical Triaxial Tests on Cohesionless Soil. *J. Soil Mech. Found. Division*, ASCE, 99(SM10), 793–812.

Lade, P.V. and Duncan, J.M., 1975. Elastoplastic Stress–Strain Theory for Cohesionless Soil. *ASCE Journal of the Geotechnical Engineering Division*, 101(GT10), 1037–1053.

Lambe, T.W. and Whitman, R.V., 1979. *Soil Mechanics – SI version*, Wiley.

Lane, A., 2005. Overcoming Deepwater Geohazards in West Africa. Paper OTC 17496, *Offshore Technology Conference*.

Larrson, R. and Sallfors, G., 1981. Hypothetical yield envelope at stress rotation. *Proc. 10th Int. Conf. Soil Mech and Foundation Engineering*, Stockholm, 1, 693–696.

Lauritzen, R. and Schjetne, K., 1976. Stability calculations for offshore gravity structures. Paper OTC 2431B, *Offshore Technology Conference*.

Le, M.-H., Nauroy, J.-F., De Gennaro, V., Delage, O., Flavigny, E., Than, N., Colliat, J.-L., Puech, A. and Meunier, J., 2008. Characterization of Soft Deepwater West Africa Clays: SHANSEP Testing is Not Recommended for Sensitive Structured Clays. Paper OTC 19193, *Offshore Technology Conference*.

Le Tirant, P., 1992. *Design guide for offshore structures, Vol. 3, Offshore Pile Design*, Editions Technip.

Le Tirant, P., Nauroy, J-F. and Marshall, N., 1994. *Design guide for offshore structures, Vol. 5, Foundations in carbonate soils.* Editions Technip.

Lee, K.K., Randolph, M.F. and Cassidy, M.J., 2009. New simplified conceptual model for spudcans on sand overlying clay soils. Paper OTC 20012, *Offshore Technology Conference*.

Lee, K.L. and Focht, J.A., 1975. Cyclic Testing of Soil for Ocean Wave Loading Problems. Paper OTC 2183, *Offshore Technology Conference*.

Lee, K.L. and Seed, H.B., 1967. Drained strength characteristics of sands. *ASCE Journal of the Soil Mechanics and Foundations Division*, 93(SM6), 117–141.

Lee, K.M., Shen, C.K., Leung, H.K. and Mitchell, J.K., 1999. Effects of Placement Method on Geotechnical Behavior of Hydraulic Fill Sands. *ASCE Journal of Geotechnical and Geoenvironmental Engineering*, 125(10), 832–846.

Lee, Y.C., Audibert, J.M.E. and Tjok, K.-M., 2005. Lessons learned from several suction caisson installation projects in clay. *Proc. Int. Conf. Frontiers in Offshore Geotechnics*, eds S. Gourvenec and M. Cassidy, Taylor and Francis, 235–241.

Lefebvre, G. and Poulin, C., 1979. A new method of sampling in sensitive clay. *Canadian Geotechnical Journal*, 16(1), 226–233.

Leghorn, J., Brookes, D.A. and Shearman, M.G., 1996. The Foinaven and Schiehallion Developments. Paper OTC 8033, *Offshore Technology Conference*.

Lehane, B.M., Gaudin, C., Richards, D.J. and Rattley, M.J., 2008. Rate effects on the vertical uplift capacity of footings founded in clay. *Geotechnique*, 58(1), 13–21.

Leidersdorf, C.B., Gadd, P.E., Hearon, G.E., Hall, J.D. and Perry, C.J., 2008. Coastal Engineering design of the Oooguruk Project. Paper OTC 19369, *Offshore Technology Conference*.

Leithead, B., 2007. Wind Energy. *Phil. Trans. Royal Society* A, 265, 957–970.

Lekkerkerk, H.-J., Van der Velden, R., Roders, J., Haycock, T., de Vries, R. and Beemster, C., 2006. *Handbook of Offshore Surveying, Vol. 1 Preparation and positioning, and Vol. 2 Acquisition and Processing*, Clarkson Research Services Ltd, London.

Leon, E., Gassman, S.L. and Talwani, P., 2006. Accounting for soil aging when assessing liquefaction potential. *ASCE Journal of Geotechnical and Geoenvironmental Engineering*, 132(3), 363–373.

Lesny, K. and Wiemann, J., 2005. Design aspects of monpiles in German offshore wind farms. *Proc. Int. Conf. Frontiers in Offshore Geotechnics*, eds S. Gourvenec and M. Cassidy, Taylor and Francis, 383–389.

Leung, C.F. and Shen, R.F., 2008. Performance of gravity caisson on sand compaction piles. *Canadian Geotechnical Journal*, 45, 393–407.

Leung, C.F., Xie, Y. and Chow, Y.K., 2006. Centrifuge model study of spudcan–pile interaction. *Int. Offshore and Polar Engineering Conf*, 530–535.

Li, X.S. and Dafalias, Y., 2004. A constitutive framework for anisotropic sand including non-proportional loading. *Geotechnique*, 54(1), 41–55.

Liang, Y., Newson, T., Hinchberger, S. and Larkin, P., 2008. Numerical study of the mechanics of inflatable anchors in clay. *Int. Offshore and Polar Engineering Conference*, 546–551.

Liedtke, E., Jeanjean, P. and Humphrey, G., 2006. Geotechnical Site Investigation for the Mad Dog SPAR Anchors. Paper OTC 17862, *Offshore Technology Conference*.

Lieng, J.T., 1989. A Model for Group Behavior of Laterally Loaded Piles. Paper OTC 6004, *Offshore Technology Conference*.

Lieng, J.T. and Bjørgen, H.P., 1995. New flow-through mudmat design for the Heidrun subsea structure. Paper OTC 7671, *Offshore Technology Conference*.

Likins, G., Piscsalko, G., Roppel, S. and Rausche, F., 2008. PDA Testing: State of the Art. *Proceedings of the Eighth International Conference on the Application of Stress Wave Theory to Piles*, Lisbon, Portugal, 395–402.

Litkouhi, S. and Poskitt, T.J., 1980. Damping constants for pile driveability calculations. *Geotechnique*, 30(1), 77–86.

Liu, P.L., 1973. Damping of water waves over poous bed. *ASCE Journal of the Hydraulics Division*, 99(HY12), 2263–2271.

Locart, J. and Mienert, J. (eds), 2002. *Int. Symp. Submarine Mass Movements and Their Consequences*, Springer.

Loken, A.E. and Olsen, O.A., 1976. Diffraction Theory and Statistical Methods to Predict Wave Induced Motions and Loads for Large Structures. Paper OTC 2502, *Offshore Technology Conference*.

Long, M., 2003. Sampling disturbance effects in soft laminated clays. *Proc. ICE Geotechnical Engineering*, 156(4), 213–244.

Long, M., 2006. Sampling disturbance effects on medium plasticity clay/silt. *Proc. ICE Geotechnical Engineering*, 159(GE2), 99–111.

Loret, B., 1990a. An Introduction to the Classical Theory of Elastoplasticity. Chapter 8 of *Geomaterials, Constitutive Laws and Modelling*, ed. F. Darve, Elsevier, 149–186.

Loret, B., 1990b. Geomechanical Applications of the Theory of Multimechanisms. Chapter 9 of *Geomaterials, Constitutive Laws and Modelling*, ed. F. Darve, Elsevier, 187–211.

Lowe, J. and Zaccheo, P.F., 1991. Subsurface explorations and sampling. Chapter 1 of *Foundation Engineering Handbook*, 2nd edition, ed. H-Y. Fang, Chapman and Hall, 1–71.

Lowry, W., Mason, N., Chipman, V., Kisiel, K. and Stockton, J., 1999. In-Situ Permeability Measurements with Direct Push Techniques: Phase II Topical Report. Report No. SEASF-TR-98–207. Submitted to DOE Federal Energy Technology Center, FETC Contract No. DE-AC21–96MC33124, USA.

Lucas, J.C., Masterson, D.M., Hall, J.D. and Perry, C.J., 2008. Arctic Offshore Projects and Technologies: Alaskan Beaufort Sea Exploration and Production Islands – Civil design and construction. Paper OTC 19343, *Offshore Technology Conference*.

Lunne, T., 2001. In Situ Testing in Offshore Geotechnical Investigations. *Proc. Int. Conf. In Situ Measurement of Soil Properties and Case Histories*, Bali, 61–78.

Lunne, T. and Christoffersen, H.P., 1983. Interpretation of Cone Penetrometer Data for Offshore Sands. Paper OTC 4464, *Offshore Technology Conference*.

Lunne, T., Myrvoll, F. and Kjekstad, O., 1981. Observed settlements of five North Sea gravity platforms. Paper OTC 4146, *Offshore Technology Conference*.

Lunne, T., Jonsrud, R., Eidsmoen, T. and Lacasse, S., 1987. The Offshore Dilatometer. Norwegian Geotechnical Institute, Report No. 52157-2.

Lunne, T., Robertson, P.K. and Powell, J.J.M., 1997. *Cone Penetration Testing in Geotechnical Engineering*, Blackie Academic and Professional, London.

Lunne, T., Berre, T. and Strandvk, S., 1998. Sample disturbance effects in deep water soil investigations. *Proc. Offshore Site Investigation and Foundation Behaviour*, SUT, 199–220.

Lunne, T., Randolph. M.F., Chung, S.F., Andersen, K.H. and Sjursøn, M., 2005. Comparison of cone and T-bar factors in two onshore and one offshore clay sediments. *Proc. Int. Conf. Frontiers in Offshore Geotechnics*, eds S. Gourvenec and M.J. Cassidy, Taylor and Francis, 981–989.

Lunne, T., Berre, T., Andersen, K.H., Strandvik, S. and Sjursen, M., 2006. Effects of sample disturbance and consolidation procedures on measured shear strength of soft marine Norwegian clays. *Canadian Geotechnical Journal*, 43, 726–750.

Lunne, T., Tjelta, T.I., Walta, A. and Barwise, A., 2008. Design and Testing Out of Deepwater Seabed Sampler. Paper OTC 19290, *Offshore Technology Conference*.

Luong, M.P. and Sidaner, J.F., 1981. Undrained behaviour of cohesionless soils under cyclic and transient loading. *Proc. Int. Conf. Recent Advances in Geotechnical Engineering and Soil Dynamics*, St. Louis, Vol. 1, 215–220.

Macara, J.C., 2002. Malampaya Deep Water Gas Pipeline and Flowlines: Technical and Engineering Challenges Faced in the Execution of the Malampaya Pipeline Scope. Paper OTC 14040, *Offshore Technology Conference*.

Mancini, C.V., Dowse, B.E.W. and Chevalier, J.-M., 1983. Caisson Retained Island for Canadian Beaufort Sea – Geotechnical Design and Construction Considerations. Paper OTC 4581, *Offshore Technology Conference*.

Maniar, D.R., Vasquez, L.F.G. and Tassoulas, J.L., 2005. Suction Caissons: Finite Element Modelling. *Proc. 5th GRACM International Congress on Computational Mechanics*, Limassol.

Marchetti, S., 1997. The flat dilatometer; design applications. Keynote lecture. *Third Geotechnical Engineering Conference*, Cairo University.

Marcuson, W.F. and Townsend, F.C., 1978. The effects of specimen reconstitution on cyclic triaxial test results. *Proc. 6th Symp. Earthquake Engineering*, Univ. Roorkee, Vol. 1, 113–118.

Marsden, P. and Whiteman, T., 1999. ConExpo-Con/Agg 99. Top 10 Construction Achievements of the 20th Century. KHI Publishers.

Martin, C.M., 1994. *Physical and Numerical Modelling of Offshore Foundations under Combined Loads*, Sc thesis, Oxford University.

Martin, C.M., 2001. Vertical bearing capacity of skirted circular foundations on Tresca soil. *Proceedings of the 15th International Conference on Soil Mechanics and Foundation Engineering* (ICSMFE), Istanbul, 1, 743–746.

Martin, C.M. and Houlsby, G.T., 1999. Jackup Units on Clay: Structural Analysis with Realistic Modelling of Spudcan Behaviour. Paper OTC 10996, *Offshore Technology Conference*.

Martin, C.M. and Houlsby, G.T., 2000. Combined loading of spudcan foundations on clay: laboratory tests. *Geotechnique*, 50(4), 325–338.

Martin, C.M. and Houlsby, G.T., 2001. Combined loading of spudcan foundations on clay: numerical modelling. *Geotechnique*, 51(8), 687–699.

Martin, C.M. and Randolph, M.F., 2006. Upper bound analysis of lateral pile capacity in cohesive soil. *Geotechnique*, 56(2), 141–145.

Masing, G., 1926. Eiganspannungen und verfestigung beim messing. *Proc. 2nd Int. Congress of Applied Mechanics*, Zurich, 332–335.

Masson, D.G., Harbitz, C.B., Wynn, R.B., Pedersen, G. and Lovholt, F., 2006. Submarine landslides: processes, triggers, and hazard prediction. *Phil. Trans. R. Soc.*, A 364, 2009–2039.

Mather, A., 2000. *Offshore Engineering, An Introduction*, Clarkson Research Services Ltd, London.

Matlock, H., 1970. Correlations for Design of Laterally Loaded Piles in Soft Clay. Paper OTC 1204, *Offshore Technology Conference*.

Matlock, H. and Foo, S.C., 1979. Axial analysis of piles using a hysteretic and degrading soil model. *Proc. Conf. Numerical Methods in Offshore Piling*, ICE, London, 165–185.

Matlock, H., Ingram, W.B., Kelley, A.E. and Bogard, D., 1980. Field Tests of the Lateral Load behaviour of Pile Groups in Clay. Paper OTC 3871, *Offshore Technology Conference*.

Matsuo, M., 1967. Bearing Capacity of Anchor Foundations. *Soils and Foundations*, 8(1), 18–48.

Mayne, P.W. and Kulhawy, F.H., 1982. Ko-OCR relationships in soil. *ASCE Journal of Geotechnical Engineering*, 108 (GT6), 851–872.

Mayne, P.W., Christopher, B.R. and DeJong, J., 2001. *Manual on Subsurface Investigations*, National Highway Instutute, Publication No. FHWA NHI-01-031, Federal Highway Administration, Washington DC.

McCarron, W.O. and Broussard, M.D., 1992. Measured jack-up response and spud can–seafloor interaction for an extreme storm event. *Proc. Int. Conf. Behaviour of Offshore Structures*, BOSS 92, London, 1, 349–361.

McClellan III, J.E. and Dorn, H., 2006. *Science and Technology in World History: An Introduction.* John Hopkins University Press, Baltimore.

McClelland, B., 1974. Design of deep penetration piles for ocean structures. ASCE *Journal of the Geotechnical Engineering Division*, 100(GT7), 705–747.

McClelland, B., Young, A.G. and Remmes, B.D., 1982. Avoiding jackup rig foundation failures. *Geotechnical Engineering*, 13(2), 151–188.

McClure, L. and Dixon, M., 2008. Offshore Routing of Large Diameter Pipelines through High Relief Outcrops. Paper OTC 19521, *Offshore Technology Conference.*

McKenzie, K.J., Sturbys, A.F. and Caulfield, D.D., 1984. The use of Processed High-Resolution Seismic Data in Geotechnical Engineering. Paper OTC 4719, *Offshore Technology Conference.*

McNeilan, T.W. and Bugno, W.T., 1985. Jackup Rig Performance in Predominantly Silty Soils, Offshore California. Paper OTC 5082, *Offshore Technology Conference.*

McNeilly, C.C., Redwine, R.V. and Higgs, W.G., 2006. Benguela-Belize Project Overview. Paper OTC 18200, *Offshore Technology Conference.*

Menard, H.W., 1964. *Marine Geology of the Pacific*, International Series in the Earth Sciences. McGraw-Hill, New York.

Mendoza, M.J. and Orozco, M., 1999. Fast and Accurate Techniques for Determination of Water Content in Soils. ASTM *Geotechnical Testing Journal*, 22(4), 301–307.

Menzies, D. and Roper, R., 2008. Comparison of Jackup Rig Spudcan Penetration Methods in Clay. Paper OTC 19545, *Offshore Technology Conference.*

Merifeld, R., White, D.J. and Randolph, M.F., 2008. The ultimate undrained resistance of partially embedded pipelines. *Geotechnique*, 58(6), 461–470.

Mes, M.J., Luttenberger, C., Landau, H. and Gustavsen, K., 1995. Automatic GPS Satellite Based Subsidence Measurements for Ekofisk. Paper OTC 7650, *Offshore Technology Conference.*

Mesri, G. and Castro, A., 1987. C_α/C_c concept and Ko during secondary compression. ASCE *Journal of Geotechnical Engineering*, 113(3), 230–247.

Mesri, G. and Godlewski, P.M., 1977. Time and stress-comoressibility interrelationship. ASCE *Journal of the Geotechnical Engineering Division*, 128(5), 416–425.

Mesri, G. and Vardhanabhuti, B., 2005. Secondary Compression. ASCE *Journal of Geotechnical and Geoenvironmental Engineering*, 131(3), 398–401.

Meyerhof, G.G., 1963. Some recent research on the bearing capacity of foundations. *Canadian Geotechnical Journal*, 1, 16–26.

Meyerhof, G.G., 1972. Stability of Slurry Trench Cuts in Saturated Clay. *Proc. ASCE Speciality Conf. on Performance of Earth and Earth-Supported Structures*, 1451–1466.

Meyerhof, GG., 1984. An Investigation of the Bearing Capacity of Shallow Footings on Dry Sand. *Proc. 2nd Int. Conf. Soil Mechanics and Foundation Engineering*, Rotterdam.

Meyerhof, G.G. and Chaplin, T.K., 1953. The compression and bearing capacity of cohesive layers. *British Journal of Applied Physics*, No. 4.

Meyerhof, G.G. and Hanna, A.M., 1978. Ultimate bearing capacity of foundations on layered soils under inclined load. *Canadian Geotechnical Journal*, 15, 565–572.

Michalowski, R.L., 1997. An estimate of the influence of soil weight on bearing capacity using limit analysis. *Soils and Foundations*, 37(4), 57–64.

Mienert, J., Vanneste, M., Bunz, S., Andreassen, K., Haflidason, H. and Sejrup, H.P., 2005. Ocean warming and gas hydrate stability on the mid-Norwegian margin at the Storegga Slide. *Marine and Petroleum Geology*, 22(1–2): 233.

Mimura, M. and Yang, W., 2003. Evaluation of time-dependent behavior of Osaka Pleistocene clay by elasto-viscoplastoic finite element analysis. Paper 46B in *Annals of the Disaster Prevention Institute*, Kyoto University, Japan.

Mindlin, R.D., 1936. Force at a point in the interior of a semi-infinite solid. *Physics*, 7, 195–202.

Mirza, S., Skinner, J., Mathea, A. and Ekstrom, L., 2006. Hurricane Ivan – Pipeline Damage, Integrity Assessment, and On-Bottom Stability Observations. Paper OTC 18183, *Offshore Technology Conference*.

Mirza, U.A., Sweeney, M. and Dean, A.R., 1988. Potential effects of jackup spudcan penetration on jacket piles. Paper OTC 5762, *Offshore Technology Conference*.

Mitchell, J.K., 1960. Fundamental Aspects of Thixotropy in Soils. *ASCE Journal of the Soil Mechanics and Foundation Engineering Division*, 86(SM3), 19–52.

Mitchell, J.K. and Soga, K., 2005. *Fundamentals of Soil Behavior*, Wiley.

Mitchell, J.K. and Idriss, I.M., 2001. *Selected Geotechnical Papers of James K. Mitchell*, ASCE Publications.

Mo, O., 1976. Concrete drilling and production platforms: review of construction, installation and commissioning. *Proc. Offshore North Sea Technical Conference and Exhibition*, Stavanger.

Mokkelbost, K.H. and Strandvik, S., 1999. Development of NGI's Deepwater Gas Probe, DGP. *Proc. Conference on Offshore and Nearshore Geotechnical Engineering*, Geoshore, Panvel, India, 107–112.

Moksnes, J., Hoff, G.C., Gudmestad, O.T. and Fjeld, S., 1994. Concrete Platforms: History, Technological Breakthroughs, and Future. Paper OTC 7630, *Offshore Technology Conference*.

Moorhouse, D.C. and Sheehan, J.V., 1968. Predicting Safe Capacity of Pile Groups. *ASCE Civil Engineering*, 38(10), 44–48.

Morandi, A.C., 2003. Impact of changes to TandR 5–5A on jack-up system reliability levels. Research Report 037, UK Health and Safety Executive.

Morandi, A.C., Karunakaran, D., Dixon, A.T. and Bærheim, M., 1998. Comparison of full-scale measurements and time domain irregular sea analysis for a large deepwater jack-up. Paper OTC 8828, *Offshore Technology Conference*.

Morrow, D.R. and Larkin, P.D., 2007. The Challenges of Pipeline Burial. *Proc. Int. Conf. Offshore and Polar Engineering*, 900–907.

Mroz, Z., Boukpeti, N. and Drescher, A., 2003. Constitutive Model for Static Liquefaction. *Int. J. Geomech.*, 3(2), 133–144.

MSL, 1998. *West Epsilon Jackup Rig Data Analysis*, Offshore Technology Report 98/082. Prepared by MSL Engineering Limited for the Health and Safety Executive.

MSL, 2001. *A study of pile fatigue during driving and in-service and of pile tip integrity*, Offshore Technology Report 2001/018. Prepared by MSL Engineering Limited for the Health and Safety Executive, HSE Books.

MSL, 2002a. *Assessment of the effect of wave-in-deck loads on a typical jack-up*, Offshore Technology Report 2001/034, UK Health and Safety Executive, HSE Books.

MSL, 2002b. *Interpretation of full-scale monitoring data from a jack-up*, Offshore Technology Report 2001/035, UK Health and Safety Executive, HSE Books.

Muir Wood, D., 1991a. *Soil Behaviour and Critical State Soil Mechanics*, Cambridge University Press.

Muir Wood, D., 1991b. Approaches to modelling the cyclic stress–strain response of soils. Chapter 2 of Cyclic Loading of Soils, eds M.P. O'Reilly and S.F. Brown, Blackie, 19–69.

Mulder, T. and Cochonat, P., 1996. Classification of offshore mass movements. *Journal of Sedimentary Research*, 66(1), 43–57.

Mulilis, J.P., Seed, H.B., Chan, C.K., Mitchell, J.K. and Arulanandan, K., 1977. Effects of sample preparation on sand liquefaction, *Journal of Geotechnical Engineering Division*, ASCE, 103(2), 91–108.

Mulilis, J.P., Townsend, F.C. and Horz, R.C., 1978. Triaxial testing techniques and sand liquefaction, ASTM *Special Technical Publication No. 654*, 265–279.

Mullee, J., 1995. Oman-India Pipeline Route Survey. Paper OTC 7676, *Offshore Technology Conference*.

Murff, J.D., 1987. Pile Capacity in Calcareous Sediments: State of the Art Review. ASCE *Journal of Geotechnical Engineering*, 113(GT5), 490–507.

Murff, J.D., 1994. Limit analysis of multi-footing foundation systems. *Proc. 8th Int. Conf. Computer Methods and Advances in Geomechanics*, Morgantown, 1, 223–244.

Murff, J.D., 1996. The Geotechnical Centrifuge in Offshore Engineering. Paper OTC 8265, *Offshore Technology Conference*.

Murff, J.D. and Miller, T.W., 1977. Stability of Offshore Gravity Structure Foundations by the Upper Bound method. Paper OTC 2896, *Offshore Technology Conference*.

Murff, J.D. and Young, A.G., 2008. Overturning Analysis of Maleo Jackup Mat Foundation on Soft Clay. Paper OTC 19553, *Offshore Technology Conference*.

Murff, J.D., Hamilton, J.M., Dean, E.T.R., James, R.G., Kusakabe, O. and Schofield, A.N., 1991. Centrifuge testing of Foundation Behavior using Full Jackup Rig Foundation Models. Paper OTC 6516, *Offshore Technology Conference*.

Murff, J.D., Prins, M.D., Dean, E.T.R., James, R.G. and Schofield, A.N., 1992. Jackup rig foundation modelling. Paper OTC 6807, *Offshore Technology Conference*.

Murff, J.D., Randolph, M.F., Ejkhatib, S., Kolk, H.J., Ruinen, R.M., Strim, P.J. and Thorne, C.P., 2005. Vertically loaded plate anchors for deepwater applications. *Proc. Int. Conf. Frontiers in Offshore Geotechnics*, eds S. Gourvenec and M.J. Cassidy, Taylor and Francis, 31–48.

Musial, W., Butterfield, S. and Ram, B., 2006. Energy from Offshore Wind. Paper OTC 18355, *Offshore Technology Conference*.

Mylonakis, G. and Gazetas, G., 1998. Settlement and additional internal forces of grouped piles in layered soil. *Geotechnique*, 48(1), 55–72.

Nataraja, R., Hoyle, M.J.R., Nelson, K. and Smith, N.P., 2003. Calibration of Seabed Fixity and System Damping from GSF Magellan Full-Scale Measurements. *9th Int. Conf. The Jackup Platform*, City University, London.

Nauroy, J.F., Dubois, J.C., Meunier, J., Marsset, B., Puech, A., Lapierre, F., Kervadec, J.P. and Kuhn, H., 1994. Tests in Offshore Monaco of New Techniques for a Better Integration of Geotechnical and Seismic Data. Paper OTC 7375, *Offshore Technology Conference*.

Nebrija, E.L., Welkie, C.J. and Meyer, R.P., 1978. Geophysical–Geological Exploration and Evaluation of Offshore Sand and Gravel Deposits. Paper OTC 3185, *Offshore Technology Conference*.

Nelson, K., Smith, P., Hoyle, M., Stoner, R. and Versavel, T., 2000. Jack-up response measurements and the underprediction of spud-can fixity by SNAME 5–5A. Paper OTC 12074, *Offshore Technology Conference*.

Nelson, K., Stonor, R.W.P. and Versave, T., 2001. Measurements of seabed fixity and dynamic behaviour of the Santa Fe Magellan jack-up, Marine Structures 14(4–5), 451–483.

Neubecker, S.R. and Randolph, M.F., 1995. Performance of Embedded Anchor Chains and Consequences for Anchor Design. Paper OTC 7712, *Offshore Technology Conference*.

Neubecker, S.R. and Randolph, M.F., 1996. The Static Equilibrium of Drag Anchors in Sand. Paper OTC 7712, *Canadian geotechnical Journal*, 33, 574–583.

Neurauter, T.W. and Bryant, W.R., 1989. Gas hydrates and their association with mud diapir/mud volcanoes on the Louisiana continental slope. Paper OTC 5944, *Offshore Technology Conference*.

Newman, J.R., 1977. *Marine Hydrodynamics*, WIT Press.

Newson, T.A., Smith, F.W. and Brunning, P., 2005. The use of inflatable anchors in offshore sandy soils. *Proc. Int. Conf. Frontiers in Offshore Geotechnics*, eds S. Gourvenec and M.J. Cassidy, Taylor and Francis, 221–226.

Ng, T.G. and Lee, F.H., 2002. Cyclic settlement behaviour of spudcan foundations. *Geotechnique*, 52(7), 469–480.

Niedoroda, A.W., Dalton, C. and Bea, R.G., 1981. The Descriptive Physics of Scour in the Ocean Environment. Paper OTC 445, *Offshore Technology Conference*.

Niedoroda, A.W., Reed, C.W., Hatchett, L., Young, A., Lanier, D., Kasch, V., Jeanjean, P., Orange, D. and Bryant, W., 2003. Analysis of Past and Future Debris Flows and Turbidity Currents Generated by Slope Failures along the Sigsbee Escarpment in the Deep Gulf of Mexico. Paper OTC 15162, *Offshore Technology Conference*.

Nissar, A., 2008. Seismic Design Criteria for the Maleo Producer, Madura Straits. Paper OTC 19583, *Offshore Technology Conference*.

Noad, J., 1993. Successful Cable Burial – Its Dependence on the Correct Use of Plough Assessments and Geophysical Surveys. *Advances in Underwater Technology, Ocean Science and Offshore Engineering, Vol. 28, Offshore Site Investigation and Foundation Behaviour*, SUT, Kluwer, 39–56.

Noble Denton Europe and Oxford University, 2006. The Calibration of SNAME Spudcan Footing Equations with Field Data. Report No L19073/NDE/mjrh, Rev. 5, Noble Denton Europe.

Noorany, I., 1984. Phase relations in Marine Soils. ASCE *Journal of Geotechnical Engineering*, 110(4), 539–543.

Norbury, D.R. *et al.*, 1986. A critical review of BS 5930, soil and rock descriptions, Geology Society, *Engineering Geology*, Special Publication, No. 2.

486

Nova, R. and Montrasio, L., 1991. Settlements of shallow foundations on sand, *Géotechnique*, 41(2), 243–256.

Novello, E.A., 2000. From static to cyclic p–y data in calcareous sediments. *Proc. Int. Conf. Engineering for Calcareous Sediments*, ed. K.A. Al-Shafei, Balkema, 17–27.

Nowacki, F., Solhjell, E., Nadim, F., Liedtke, E., Andersen, K.H. and Andresen, L., 2003. Deterministic Slope Stability Analyses of the Sigsbee Escarpment. Paper OTC 15160, *Offshore Technology Conference*.

Ochtman, J.A. and den Boer, J.S., 1980. Post plowing for rigid lines – controlled trench depth and high progress rate. Paper OTC 3738, *Offshore Technology Conference*.

Oda, M., 1972. The mechanicsm of fabric changes during compressional deformation of sand. *Soils and Foundations*, 12(2), 1–18.

Oda, M., 1978. Significance of fabric in granular mechanics. US-Japan Seminar, Sendai 1977. Gakujustsu Bunken, Fukyu-kai, Tokyo, 7–26.

OGP, 2003. *Disposal of Disused Offshore Concrete Gravity Platforms in the OSPAR Maritime Area*, Report No. 338, International Association of Oil and Gas Producers.

Olmsted, C., 2006. Status of Cape Wind Offshore Wind Project. Paper OTC 18353, *Offshore Technology Conference*.

Olson, R.E., 1977. Consolidation under Time Dependent Loading. *ASCE Journal of the Geotechnical Engineering Division*, 103(GT1), 55–60.

Olson, R.E., 1989 and Li, J., 2002. *Application of Terzaghi's Theory of Consolidation to Problems involving radial flow*, Unit 4, Advanced Soil Mechanics, Department of Construction Engineering, Chaoyang University of Technology.

Olson, R.E., Rauch, A.F., Luke, A.M., Mania, D.J., Tassoulas, J.L. and Mecham, E.C., 2003. Soil Reconsolidation Following the Installation of Suction Anchors. Paper OTC 15263, *Offshore Technology Conference*.

O'Neill, M.W., 1983. Group action in offshore piles. *Proceedings of the Conference on Geotechnical Practice in Offshore Engineering*, Austin, TX, 25–64.

O'Neill, M.W. and Ha, H.B., 1982. Comparative modelling of vertical pile groups. *Proc. 2nd Int. Conf. Numerical methods in Offshore Piling*, 399–418.

O'Neill, M.W., Bransby, M.F. and Randolph, M.F., 2003. Drag anchor fluke-soil interaction in clays. *Canadian Geotechnical Journal*, 40, 78–94.

Ooley, M. and Stewart, W.P., 2008. The Maleo MOPU Project – Project Overview and Keynote Address. Paper OTC 19581, *Offshore Technology Conference*.

O'Riordan, N.J. and Clare, D.G., 1990. Geotechnical Considerations for the Installation of Gravity Based Structures. Paper OTC 6381, *Offshore Technology Conference*.

Osborne, J.J., Trickey, J.C., Houlsby, G.T. and James, R.G., 1991. Findings from a Joint Industry Study on Foundation Fixity of Jackup Units. Paper OTC 6615, *Offshore Technology Conference*.

Osborne, J.J., Colwill, R., Rowan, D. and Phillips, D., 1993. Review of the Design Development of a High Performance Anchor System. *Advances in Underwater Technology, Ocean Science and Offshore Engineering, Vol. 28, Offshore Site Investigation and Foundation Behaviour*, SUT, Kluwer, 393–416.

Oser, M.S. and Huston, G.J., 1992. New Generation Liftboat: Refined Engineering Analysis Expands Operating Envelope. Paper OTC 6976, *Offshore Technology Conference.*

OSIF, 1999. *Guidance notes on geotechnical investigations for marine pipelines*, Report by the Subsea Working Group of the Offshore Soil Investigation Forum.

Ou, C.-Y., 2006. *Deep Excavation: Theory and Practice*, Taylor and Francis.

Overy, R.F. and Dean, A.R., 1986. Hydraulic fracture testing of cohesive soil. Paper OTC 5226, *Offshore Technology Conference.*

Paikowsky, S.G. and Chernauskas, L.R., 2008. Dynamic analysis of open-ended pipe piles. Keynote Paper. *Proc. Stress Wave 2008*, 8th International Conference on the Application of Stress Wave Theory to Piles, Lisbon, pp. 59–76.

Palmer, A.C., 1994. Deepwater Pipelines: Improving State of the Art. Paper OTC 7541, *Offshore Technology Conference.*

Palmer, A.C. and King, R.A., 2006. *Subsea pipeline engineering*, Pennwell.

Palmer, A.C. and Williams, P.J., 2003. Frost heave and pipeline upheaval buckling. *Canadian Geotechnical Journal*, 40(5), 1033–1038.

Palmer, A.C., Ellinas, C.P., Richards, D.M. and Guijt, J., 1990a. Design of Submarine Pipelines Against Upheaval Buckling. Paper OTC 6335, *Offshore Technology Conference.*

Palmer, A.C., Konuk, I., Comfort, G. and Been, K., 1990b. Ice gouging and the safety of marine pipelines. OTC Paper 6371, *Offshore Technology Conference.*

Palmer, A.C., Konuk, I., Niedoroda, A.W., Been, K. and Croasdale, K.R., 2005. Arctic seabed ice gouging and large sb-gouge deformations. *Proc. Int. Conf. Frontiers in Offshore Geotechnics*, eds S. Gourvenec and M.J. Cassidy, Taylor and Francis, 645–650.

Palmer, R.W., Oksuzler, Y., Campo, J.J., Kessler, K.J. and Sanzgiri, S.M., 1990c. South Marsh island 205-A: Lifted jacket in a Water Depth of 437 ft. Paper OTC 6476, *Offshore Technology Conference.*

Pan, J., 1999. *The behaviour of shallow foundations on calcareous soil subjected to inclined load*, Ph.D Thesis, The University of Sydney.

Pande, G.N. and Sharma, K.G., 1983. Multilaminate model of clays – a numerial analysis of the influence of rotation of the principal stress axes. *Int. J. Num. and Anal. Meths in Geomechanics*, 7, 397–418.

Pappin, J.W., 1991. Design of foundations and soil structures for seismic loading. Chapter 7 of *Cyclic Loading of Soils*, eds M.P. O'Reilly and S.F. Brown, Blackie, 306–366.

Park, S-S. and Byrne, P.M., 2004. Practical constitutive model for soil liquefaction. Proceedings of the Ninth International Symposium on 'Numerical Models in Geomechanics' – Numog IX, eds G.N. Pande, S. Pietruszczak, Taylor and Francis.

Parker, E.J., Moore, R. and Evans, T., 2008. Evaluation of Landslide Impact on Deepwater Submarine Pipelines. Paper OTC 19459, *Offshore Technology Conference.*

Parry, R.H.G., 1958. Correspondence on 'On the Yielding of Soils', *Géotechnique*, 8, 184–186.

Parry, R.H.G., 2004. *Mohr Circles, Stress Paths and Geotechnics*, E. and F.N. Spon.

PDI, 1998. *GRLWEAP (Computer Program for) Wave Equation Analysis of Pile Driving*, Version 1998. Pile Dynamics Inc.

PDI, 2003. *GRLWEAP (Computer Program for) Wave Equation Analysis of Pile Driving*, Version 2003–1. Pile Dynamics Inc.

Pedotti, G., Dubois, J-C. and Meunier, J., 1990. SHRIMP: A New Equipment for Precise Subsurface Soil Investigation by High-Resolution Seismic Refraction. Paper OTC 6230, *Offshore Technology Conference*.

Pelletier, J.H. and Sgouros, G.E., 1987. Shear Transfer Behavior of a 30-in Pile in Silty Clay. Paper OTC 5407, *Offshore Technology Conference*.

Pelletier, J.H., Doyle, E.H. and Dutt, R.N., 1997. Deepwater Geotechnical Investigations in the Gulf of Mexico. *Int. Journal Society for Underwater Technology*, 2292, 63–74.

Penzien, J. and Tseng, W.S., 1976. Seismic Analysis of Gravity Platforms Including Soil-Structure Interaction Effects, Paper OTC 2674, *Offshore Technology Conference*.

Peuchen, L.J. and Raap, C., 2007. Logging, sampling and testing for offshore geohazards, Paper OTC 18664, *Offshore Technology Conference*.

Phillips, M., Springman, S.M. and Arenson, L.U. (eds), 2003. *Permafrost. Proc. 8th Int. Conf.*, Taylor and Francis.

Pliskin, L., 1979. Removal of concrete gravity platforms. Paper OTC 3475, *Offshore Technology Conference*.

Polyanin, A.D., 2002. *Handbook of Linear Partial Differential Equations for Engineers and Scientists*, Chapman and Hall.

Porcino, D. and Marciano, V., 2008. Effect of Initial Fabric on Cyclic and Monotonic Undrained Shear Strength of Gioia Tauro Sand. Seismic Engineering Conference, American Instuitute of Physics, Conference Proceedings, Volume 1020, pp. 448–455.

Porter, B.W. and Ingram, W.B., 1989. Post Driving Prediction of Pile Capacity. Paper OTC 6003, *Offshore Technology Conference*.

Poulos, H.G., 1979. Settlement of single piles in non-homogeneous soil. *ASCE Journal of the Geotechnical Engineering Division*, 105(GT5), 627–641.

Poulos, H.G., 1980. *Users Guide to program DEFPIG, Deformation Analysis of Pile Groups*, School of Civil Engineering, University of Sydney.

Poulos, H.G., 1988. *Marine Geotechnics*, Unwin.

Poulos, H.G., 2006. Use of stiffness inserts in pile groups and piled rafts. *Proc. ICE Geotechnical Engineering*, 159(GE3), 153–160.

Poulos, H.G. and Chua, K.F., 1985. Bearing capacity of foundations on calcareous sand. *Proc. 11th Int. Conf. on Soil Mechanics and Foundation Engineering*, Vol. 3, pp. 1619–1622.

Poulos, H.G. and Randolph, M.F., 1983. Pile Group Analysis: A Study of Two Methods. *ASCE Journal of the Geotechnical Engineering Division*, 109(3), 335–372.

Power, P., Galavazi, M. and Wood, G., 2005. Geohazards need not be – redefining project risk. Paper OTC 17634, *Offshore Technology Conference*.

Prandtl, L., 1921. Uber die Eindringungfestigkeit (Härte) plasticher Baustoffe und dei Festigkeit von Schneiden. *Zeitschrift für Angewandte Mathematik und Mechanik*, Basle 1(1), 15–20.

Prandtl, L., 1923. *Zeitschrift für Angewandte Mathematik und Mechanik*, Basle, 3, 401ff.

Prevost, J.H. and Hughes, T.J.R., 1978. Analysis of Gravity Offshore Structure Foundations subject to Cyclic Wave Loading. Paper OTC 3261, *Offshore Technology Conference*.

Price, D.G., 2008. *Engineering Geology: Principles and Practice*, Springer.

Prior, D.B. and Doyle, E.H., 1984. Geological Hazard Surveying for Exploratory Drilling in Water depths of 2000 metres. Paper OTC 4747, *Offshore Technology Conference*.

Puech, A. and Tuenter, H.-J., 2002. Continuous Burial Assessment of Pipelines and Cables: a State-of-practice. Offshore Site Investigation and Geotechnics: Diversity and Sustainability. *Proc. Int. Conf., Society for Underwater Technology*, London, 153–162.

Puech, A., Bustamente. M. and Auperin, L., 1990. Foundation problems in coral soils: A case history – the Oil Terminal of Matanzas, Cuba. Paper OTC 6238, *Offshore Technology Conference*.

Puech, A., Dendani, H., Nauroy, J-F. and Meunier, J., 2004a. Characterisation of Gulf of Guniea deepwater soils for geotechnical engineering: successes and challenges. Seatech Week, Brest, Coolloque *Caracterisation in situ des sols marins*.

Puech, A., Rivoallan, X. and Cherel, L., 2004b. The Use of Surface Waves in the Characterisation of Seabed Sediments: Development of a MASW System for Offshore Applications. Seatech Week, Brest, France, *Colloque Caractérisation In Situ des Fonds Marins*, 21 et 22 October 2004.

Purwana, O.A., Leung, C.F., Chow, Y.K. and Foo, K.S., 2005a. Influence of base suction on extraction of jack-up spudcans. *Geotechnique*, 55(10), 741–753.

Purwana, O.A., Leung, C.F., Chow, Y.K. and Foo, K.S., 2005b. Extraction of jack-up foundations. *Proc. Int. Conf. Frontiers in Offshore Geotechnics*, eds S. Gourvenec and M. Cassidy, Taylor and Francis, 517–522.

Putnam, J.A., 1949. Loss of wave energy due to percolation in a permeable sea bottom. *Trans American Geophysical Union*, 38, 662–666.

Pyke, R., 1979. Non-linear soil models for irregular cyclic loading. *ASCE Journal of the Geotechnical Division*, 105(GT6), 715–726.

Quiros, G.W. and Little, R.L., 2003. Deepwater soil properties and their impact on the geotechnical program. Paper OTC 15262, *Offshore Technology Conference*.

Rahman, M.S., Seed, H.B. and Booker, J.R., 1977. Pore Pressure Development under Offshore Gravity Structures. *ASCE Journal of the Geotechnical Engineering Division*, 103(GT12), 1419–1436.

Raine, B., Powell, J., Jackson, G. and Thomas, G., 2007. Offshore LNG Storage in Concrete Gravity Caissons: Project Development and Procurement. Paper OTC 18981, *Offshore Technology Conference*.

Raines, R.D., Ugaz, O. and Garnier, J., 2005. Centrifuge modelling of suction piles in clay. *Proc. Int. Conf. Frontiers in Offshore Geotechnics*, eds S. Gourvenec and M.J. Cassidy, Taylor and Francis, 303–308.

Randell, C., Morgan, V. and Ralph, F., 2008. Protection and Risk Mitigation Strategies for Subsea Infrastructure in Ice Environments. Paper OTC 19272, *Offshore Technology Conference*.

Randolph, M.F., 1983. Design Considerations for Offshore Piles. *ASCE Speciality Conference on Geotechnical Practice in Offshore Engineering*, Austin, 422–439.

Randolph, M.F., 1985. RATZ – load transfer analysis of axially loaded piles: User's Manual. Technical Report, Cambridge University Engineering Department.

Randolph, M.F., 2003a. *PIGLET: Analysis and design of pile groups. Users' Manual*, Version 4–2, University of Western Australia, Perth.

Randolph, M.F., 2003b. Science and empiricism in pile foundation design. *Geotechnique*, 53(10), 847–875.

Randolph, M.F., 2004. Characterisation of soft sediments for offshore applications. Keynote Lecture. *Proc. 2nd International Conference on Site Characterisation*, Porto, 1, 209–231.

Randolph, M.F. and Andersen, K.H., 2006. Numerical Analysis of T-Bar Penetration in Soft Clay. *ASCE Int. Journal of Geomechanics*, 6(6), 411–420.

Randolph, M.F. and Erbrich, C., 1999. Design of shallow foundations for calcareous sediments. *Proc. 2nd Int. Conf. on Engineering for Calcareous Sediments*, Bahrain, pp. 361–378.

Randolph, M.F. and Murphy, B.S., 1985. Shaft Capacity of Driven Piles in Clay. Paper 4883, *Offshore Technology Conference*.

Randolph, M.F. and Simons, H.A., 1986. An improved soil model for one-dimensional pile driving analysis. *Proc. 3rd Int. Conf. Numerical Methods in Offshore Piling*, Nantes, 3–17.

Randolph, M.F. and White, D.J., 2008a. Pipeline Embedment in Deep Water: Processes and Quantitative Assessment. Paper OTC 19128, *Offshore Technology Conference*.

Randolph, M.F. and White, D.J., 2008b. Upper-bound yield envelopes for pipelines at shallow embedment in clay. *Geotechnique*, 58(4), 297–301.

Randolph, M.F. and Wroth, C.P., 1978. Analysis of Deformation of Vertically-Loaded Piles, *ASCE Journal of the Geotechnical Engineering Division*, 104(GT12), 1465–1488.

Randolph, M.F. and Wroth, C.P., 1979. An analytical solution for the consolidation around a driven pile. *Int. J. Numer. Anal. Methods Geomech*, 3(3), 217–229.

Randolph, M.F., Finnie, I.M. and Joer, H., 1993. Performance of shallow and deep foundations on calcareous soil. *Proc. Symp. on Foundations of Difficult Soils*, Kagoshima, Japan.

Randolph, M.F., Hefer, P.A., Geise, J.M. and Watson, P.G., 1998a. Improved seabed strength profiling using T-Bar penetrometer. *Proc. Int. Conf. Offshore site Investigations and Foundation Behaviour*, SUT, London, 221–236.

Randolph, M.F., O'Neill, M.P. and Stewart, D.P., 1998b. Performance of Suction Anchors in Fine-Grained Calcareous Soils. Paper OTC 8831, *Offshore Technology Conference*.

Randolph, M.F., Cassidy, M., Gourvenec, S. and Erbrich, C., 2005. Challenges of offshore geotechnical engineering. State of the art paper. *16th International Conference on Soil Mechanics and Foundation Engineering*, Millpress Science Publishers, Vol. 1, 123–176.

Rausche, F. and Hussein, M., 2000. Pile driving in calcareous sediments. *Proc. Int. Conf. Engineering for Calcareous Sediments*, ed. K.A. Al-Shafei, Balkema, 2, 345–359.

Reese, L.C., 1973. A Design Method for an Anchor Pile in a Mooring System. Paper OTC 1745, *Offshore Technology Conference*.

Reese, L.C. and Matlock, H.S., 1956. Non-dimensional solutions for laterally loaded piles with soil modulus proportional to depth. *Proc. 8th Texas Conf. Soil Mechanics and Foundation Engineering*, 1–41.

Reese, L.C. and Van Impe, W.F., 2001. *Single Piles and Pile Groups under Lateral Loading*, Balkema.

491

Reese, L.C., Cox, W.R. and Koop, F.D., 1974. Analysis of laterally loaded piles in sand. Paper OTC 2080, *Offshore Technology Conference*.

Reese, L.C., Cox, W.R. and Koop, F.D., 1975. Field testing and analysis of laterally loaded piles in stiff clay. Paper OTC 2312, *Offshore Technology Conference*.

Reese, L.C., Isenhower, W.M. and Wang, S.-T., 2006. *Analysis and Design of Shallow and Deep Foundations*, Wiley.

Reeve, D., Chadwick, A. and Fleming, C., 2004. *Coastal Engineering: Processes, Theory, and Design Practice*, E. and F.N. Spon.

Reimnitz, E., Kamperna, E. and Ross, C.R., 1982. Observations on the Mode and rate of Decay of an Artificial Ice island in the Alaskan Beaufort Sea. Paper OTC 4310, *Offshore Technology Conference*.

Reissner, H., 1924. Zum Erddruckproblem. *Proc. 1st Int. Conf. Applied Mathematics*, Delft, 295–311.

Rendulic, L., 1935. Der hydrodynamische spannungsausgleich in zentral entwasserten tanzylindern. *Wasser-wirtschaft*, 2, 250–253.

Reppe, T. and Helsø, E., 1994. Towage and Installation of Concrete Gravity-Based Structures. Paper OTC 7503, *Offshore Technology Conference*.

Rhodes M., 1989. *Introduction to Particle Technology*, Wiley.

Rittirong, A., Shang, J.Q., Ismail, M.A. and Randolph, M.F., 2005. Electrokinetic and electrochemical stabilization of caissons in calcareous sand. *Proc. Int. Conf. Frontiers in Offshore Geotechnics*, eds S. Gourvenec and M.J. Cassidy, Taylor and Francis, 267–272.

Roberts, J., 1990. Innovation in Concrete Gravity Substructures: The Ravenspurn North Platform and beyond. Paper OTC 6347, *Offshore Technology Conference*.

Robertson, P.K., Campanella, R.G., Gillespie, D.G. and Grieg, J., 1986. Use of piezocone data. *ASCE Specialty Conf. In-Situ 86: Use of In-Situ Tests in Geotechnical Engineering*, 1263–1280.

Rogers, N. and Still, D., 1999. Structural dynamics of Offshore Wind Turbines Subject to Extreme Wave Loading. *Proc. European Wind Energy Conference*, 369–372.

Ronalds, B.F., 2001. Jacket design to resist ship impact. *Proc. ICE Structures and Buildings 146*, 3, 285–294.

Roscoe, K.H. and Burland, J.B., 1968. On the generalised stress–strain behaviour of 'wet' clay. In *Engineering Plasticity*, eds J. Heyman and F.A. Leckie, Cambridge University Press, 535–608.

Roscoe, K.H. and Schofield, A.N., 1956. The stability of short pier foundations in sand. *British Welding Journal*, August, pp. 343–354.

Rosjberg, S. and Gravesen, H., 2009. *OWA Offshore Wind Farm Foundations, UK Round 3, Design Basis. Version 1*, Grontmij, Carl Bro.

Rowe, P.W., 1962. The stress–dilatancy relation for static equilibrium of an assembly of particles in contact. *Proc. R. Soc. London, Ser. A*, 269, 500–527.

Rowe, P.W., 1969. The relation between the shear strength of sands in triaxial compression, plane strain and direct shear. *Geotechnique*, 19(1), 75–86.

Rowe, P.W., 1983. Use of large centrifugal models for offshore and nearshore works. *Proc. Int. Symp. Geotechnical Aspects of Coastal and Offshore Structures*, Bangkok, eds Yudbhir and A.S. Balasubrananiam, Balkema, 21–33.

Rowe P.W. and Craig W.H., 1976. Studies of offshore caissons founded on Oosterschelde sand. *Design and Construction of Offshore Structures*, Institution of Civil Engineers, 49–55.

Rudolph, D., Arnout C., Bos, K.J., Rietema, K., 2005. Scour around spudcans – analysis of field measurements, *15th Int. Offshore and Polar Engineering (ISOPE) Conference.*

Ruinen, R.M., 2005. Influence of anchor geometry and soil properties on numerical modeling of drag anchor behavior on soft clay. *Proc. Int. Conf. Frontiers in Offshore Geotechnics*, eds S. Gourvenec and M.J. Cassidy, Taylor and Francis, 165–169.

Sahota, B.S. and Wilson, Q., 1982. The Break-out Behavior of Suction Anchors Embedded in Submered Sands. Paper OTC 4175, *Offshore Technology Conference.*

Saigal, R.K., Dolan, D., Der Kiureghian, A., Camp, T. and Smith, C.E., 2007. Comparison of Design Guidelines for Offshore Wind Energy Systems. Paper OTC 18984, *Offshore Technology Conference.*

Salgado, R., Lyamin, A.V., Sloan, S.W. and Yu, H.S., 2004. Two- and three-dimensional bearing capacity of foundations in clay. *Geotechnique*, 54(5), 297–306.

Sangrey, D.A., Clukey, E.C. and Molnia, B.F., 1979. Geotechnical engineering analysis of underconsolidated sediments from Alaska coastal waters. Paper OTC 3436, *Offshore Technology Conference.*

Santagata, M.C. and Germaine, J.T., 2002. Sampling Disturbance in Normally Consolidated Clays. *ASCE Journal of Geotechnical and Geoenvironmental Engineering*, 128(12), 997–1006.

Schaminée, P.E.L., Zorn, N.F. and Schotman, G.J.M., 1990. Soil Response for Pipeline Upheaval Buckling Analyses: Full-Scale Laboratory Tests and Modelling. Paper OTC 6486, *Offshore Technology Conference.*

Schellstede, H.J., 2007. Wind Power: Wind Farms of the Northern Gulf of Mexico. Paper OTC 19092, *Offshore Technology Conference.*

Schnaid, F., 2009. *In Situ Testing in Geotechnics: The Main Tests*, Taylor and Francis.

Schneider, J.A., Randolph, M.F., Mayne, P.W. and Ramsey, N.R., 2008. Analysis of Factors Influencing Soil Classification using Normalized Piezocone Tip Resistance and Pore Pressure Parameters. *ASCE Journal of Geotechnical and Geoenvironmental Engineering*, 134(11), 1569–1586.

Schofield, A.N., 1980. Cambridge Geotechnical Centrifuge Operations. *Geotechnique*, 30(3), 227–268.

Schofield, A.N., 2005. *Disturbed soil properties and geotechnical design*, Thomas Telford.

Schofield, A.N. and Wroth, C.P., 1968. *Critical State Soil Mechanics*, McGraw-Hill.

Schotman, G.J.M., 1987. Pipe–Soil Interaction: A Model for Laterally Loaded Pipelines in Clay. Paper OTC 5588, *Offshore Technology Conference.*

Schotman, G.J.M., 1989. The effects of displacements on the stability of jack-up spud-can foundations. Paper OTC 6026, *Offshore Technology Conference.*

Schotman, G.J.M. and Hospers, B., 1992. An improved method for conductor setting depths in sand. *Proc. Int. Conf. BOSS 92, Behaviour of offshore structures*, 543–554.

Schrag, D.P., 2008. Carbon storage in deep sea sediments: an important part of the CCS portfolio. Paper OTC 19515, *Offshore Technology Conference.*

Schroeder, K., Andersen, K.H. and Jeanjean, P., 2006a. Predicted and Observed Installation Behavior of the Mad Dog Anchors. Paper OTC 19261, *Offshore Technology Conference.*

Schroeder, K., Andersen, K.H. and Tjok, K.-M., 2006b. Laboratory Testing and Detailed Geotechnical Design of the Mad Dog Anchors. Paper OTC 17950, *Offshore Technology Conference*.

Schweiger, H.F., Wiltafsky, C., Scharinger, F. and Galavi, V., 2009. A multilaminate framework for modelling induced and inherent anisotropy of soils, *Geotechnique*, 59(2), 87–102.

Scott, R.F., 1985. Plasticity and constitutive relations in soil mechanics. *ASCE Journal of Geotechnical Engineering*, 111(5), 563–605.

Scott, W.J., Laing, J.S. and Botha, W.J., 1983. Water Borne Resistivity/Induced Polarization Survey in Prudhoe Bay. Paper OTC 4468, *Offshore Technology Conference*.

Seed, H.B. and Idriss, I.M., 1970. *Soil moduli and damping factors for dynamic response analyses*, Report EERC 70–10, Earthquake Engineering Research Center, University of California, Berkeley.

Seed, H.B. and Idriss, I.M., 1971. Simplified procedure for evaluating soil liquefaction potential. *ASCE Journal of the Soil Mechanics and Foundations Division*, 107(SM9), 1249–1274.

Seed, H.B. and Peacock, W.H., 1971. Test procedures for measuring soil liquefaction characteristics. *ASCE Journal of the Soil Mechanics and Foundations Division*, 97(SM8), 1099–1119.

Seed, H.B. and Rahman, M.S., 1977. Wave-induced pore pressures in relation to ocean floor stability of cohesionless soils. *Marine Geotechnology*, 3(2), 123–150.

Seed, H.B. and Reese, L.C., 1957. The action of soft clay along friction piles. *ASCE Transactions*, Vol. 122, 731–754.

Seed, H.B., Chaney, R.C. and Pamukcu, S., 1991. Earthquake effects on soil-foundation systems. Chapter 16 of *Foundation Engineering Handbook*, 2nd ed, eds H.-Y. Fang, Chapman and Hall, 594–672.

Seed, R.B., Dickinson, S.E., Riemer, M.F., Bray, J.D., Sitar, N., Mitchell, J.K., Idriss, I.M., Kayen, A., Kropp, R.E., Harder, L.F. and Power, M.S., 1990. Preliminary report on the principal geotechnical aspects of the October 17, 1989 Loma Prieta Earthquake, Earthq. Engrg. Res. Cen. Rept. UCB/EERC-90/05, University of California, Berkeley, Calif.

Sekiguchi, H. and Ohta, K., 1977. Induced anisotropy and time dependence in clay. In Constitutive Equations for Soils. *Proc. 9th ICSMFE (Specialty Session 9)*, JSSMFE, 229–238.

Selnes, P.B., 1982. *Geotechnical problems in offshore earthquake engineering*, Report No. 140, Norwegian Geotechnical Institute.

Semple, R.M. and Gemeinhardt, J.P., 1981. Stress History Approach to Analysis of Soil Resistance to Pile Driving. Paper OTC 3969, *Offshore Technology Conference*.

Semple, R.M. and Rigden, W.J., 1983. Site Investigation for Magnus. Paper OTC 4466, *Offshore Technlogy Conference*.

Senders, M., 2001. Contribution to Workshop: 'Design Methodologies and Criteria for Suction Caissons for Deepwater Mooring Applications', ed. Gilbert, R.B. and Murff, J.D., OTRC, Houston.

Senders, M., 2005. Tripods with suction caissons as foundations for offshore wind turbines on sand. *Proc. Int. Conf. Frontiers in Offshore Geotechnics*, eds S. Gourvenec and M.J. Cassidy, Taylor and Francis, 397–403.

Senpere, D. and Auvergne, G.A., 1982. Suction Anchor Piles – A Proven Alternative to Driving or Drilling. Paper OTC 4206, *Offshore Technology Conference.*

Serpas, R.J., Chandra, T.K., Popp, D.E. and Sircar, S., 1990. Installation of the Kiluea Jacket and Piles and Full Scale Validation of Analytical Predictions. Paper OTC 6265, *Offshore Technology Conference.*

Shaheen, W.A., Change, C.S., and Demars, K.R., 1987. Field Evaluation of Plate Anchor Theories in Sand. Paper OTC 5419, *Offshore Technology Conference.*

Sharma, P.P., 2004. *Ultimate Capacity of Suction Caisson in Normally and Lightly Overconsolidated Clays,* MSc Thesis, Texas AandM University.

Sharples, M., 2002. *Post Mortem Failure of MODUs during Hurricane Lili.* Report by Offshore Risk and Technology Consulting Inc to the US Minerals Management Service, MMS Order 0103PO72450.

Sharples, M., 2004. *Post Mortem Failure of MODUs during Hurricane Ivan.* Report by Offshore Risk and Technology Consulting Inc to the US Minerals Management Service, MMS Order 0105PO39221.

Sharples, M. and Stiff, J., 2009. Post Mortem Analysis of MODUs in Hurricanes Katrina and Ivan. Paper OTC 20143, *Offshore Technology Conference.*

Shaw, P.G.H., Coayes, A.D., Hobbs, R. and Schumm, W., 1977. Analytical and Field Data Studies of the Dynamic Behavior of Gravity Structures and Foundations. Paper OTC 3008, *Offshore Technology Conference.*

Sheta, M. and Novak, M., 1982. Vertical vibration of pile groups. *ASCE Journal of the Geotechnical Engineering Division,* 108(GT4), 570–590.

Shi, Q., 1988. Centrifuge modelling of surface footings subject to combined loading. Ph.D Thesis, Cambridge University.

Shipley, T.H., Houston, M.H. and Buffler, R.T., 1979. Widespread Occurrence of Possible Gas-Hydrate Horizons from Continental Slopes as Identified on Seimic Reflection Profiles. Paper OTC 3570, *Offshore Technology Conference.*

Shiri, H. and Pashnehtala, M.H., 2006. A geotechnical database development and applying data mining techniques to extract the common trendes of offshore geotechnical properties of South Pars gas Field/Persian Gulf IR-Iran. *Soft Soil Engineering,* eds D. Chan and K.T. Law, Taylor and Francis.

Siciliano, R.J., Hamilton, J.M., Murff, J.D. and Phillips, R., 1990. Effect of jackup spudcans on piles. Paper OTC 6467, *Offshore Technology Conference.*

Silver, M.L., Chan, C.K., Ladd, R.S., Lee, K.L., Tiedemann, D.A., Townsend, F.C., Valera, J.E. and Wilson, J.H., 1976. Cyclic triaxial strength of a standard test sand. *ASCE Journal of the Geotechnical Engineering Division,* 102(GT5), 511–524.

Sims, M.A., Smith, B.J.A. and Reed, T., 2004. Bayu-Undan Substructure Foundations: Conception, Design and Installation Aspects. Paper OTC 16158, *Offshore Technology Conference.*

Siriwardane, H.J. and Smith, D.H., 2006. Gas hydrate induced seafloor stability problems in the Blake Ridge. *Proc. Int. Conf. Offshore and Polar Engineers* (ISOPE 2006), 294–298.

Smith, E.A.L., 1962. Pile Driving Analysis by the Wave Equation. Paper 3306, *ASCE Transactions,* 127, Part 1, 1145–1193.

Smith, S.F., Hoyle, M.J.R., Ahilan, R.V., Hunt, R.J. and Marcom, M.R., 2006. 3D Nonlinear Wave Spreading on Jackup Loading and Response and its Impat on Current Assessment Practoce. Paper OTC 18266, *Offshore Technology Conference*.

SNAME, 1991. *Guidelines for Site-Specific Assessment of Mobile Jackup Units*, Rev. 1, Technical and Research Bulletin 5-5A. Society of Naval Architects and Marine Engineers.

SNAME, 2002. *Guidelines for Site-Specific Assessment of Mobile Jackup Units*, Rev. 2, Technical and Research Bulletin 5-5A. Society of Naval Architects and Marine Engineers.

Sokolovskii, W.W., 1946. *Theory of Plasticity*, USSR Academy of Sciences, Moscow.

Solberg, L. and Gjertveit, E., 2007. Constructing the world's longest subsea pipeline – Langeled gas export. Paper OTC 18962, *Offshore Technology Conference*.

Solheim, A., Bryn, P., Berg, K., Sejrup, H.P. and Mienert, J., (ed.), 2005. *Ormen Lange – An Integrated Study for Safe Field Development in the Storegga Submarine Area*, Elsevier.

Solheim, A., Forsberg, C.F., Yang, S., Kvalstad, T.J., Longva, O. and Rise, L., 2007. The Role of Geological History and Depositional History in Offshore Slope Instability. Paper OTC 18720, *Offshore Technology Conference*.

Sorensen, R.M., 1997. *Basic Coastal Engineering*, Springer.

Soros, P. and Koman, B., 1974. Artificial Island Trans-Shipment Terminal. Paper OTC 2099, *Offshore Technology Conference*.

Soulsby, R., 1998. *Dynamics of Marine Sands*, Thomas Telford.

Sparrevik, P., 2002. Suction Pile Technology and Installation in Deep Waters. Paper OTC 14241, *Offshore Technology Conference*.

Spencer, A.J.M., 2004. *Continuum Mechanics*, Dover Publications.

Spidsøe, N. and Hilmarsen, B., 1983. Measured Dynamic Behaviour of North Sea Gravity Platforms under Extreme Environmental Conditions. Paper OTC 4613, *Offshore Technology Conference*.

Spidsøe, N. and Karunakaran, D., 1996. Nonlinear dynamic behaviour of jack-up platforms, *Marine Structures*, 9.

Spidsøe, N. and Skjastad, O., 1986. Measured Soil–Structure Interaction Properties of a Gravity Platform. Paper OTC 5222, *Offshore Technology Conference*.

Spidsøe, N. and Skjastad, O., 1987. Measured Storm-Induced Variations of the Soil-Structure Interaction Properties of a Gravity Platform. Paper OTC 5410, *Offshore Technology Conference*.

Spriggs, T.F., 1971. Conceptual Design of a Man-Made island for a Seawater Desalting and Power Plant. Paper OTC 1369, *Offshore Technology Conference*.

Springett, C.N., Stonor, R.W.P. and Wu, X., 1994. North sea jackup measurement program reduces response uncertainty. *Petroleum Engineering International*, 66(4), 46–48, 51, 53, April.

Springett, C.N., Stonor, R.W.P. and Wu, X., 1996. Results of jack-up measurement program in the North Sea and their comparison with the structural analysis, *Marine Structures*, 9(1), 53–70.

Spingman, S., 2002. *Constitutive and centrifuge modeling: two extremes*, Taylor and Francis.

Srbulov, M., 2008. *Geotechnical Earthquake Engineering: Simplified Analyses with Case Studies and Examples*, Springer.

Staff, 2003. Coast to coast for caissons. *European Foundations*, May, 17–18.

Stark, T.D. and Contreras, I.A., 1996. Constant volume ring shear apparatus. *Geotechnical Testing Journal*, ASTM, 19(1).

Stark, T.D. and Eid, H.T., 1998. Performance of Three-Dimensional Slope Stability Methods in Practice. *ASCE Journal of Geotechnical and Geoenvironmental Engineering*, 124(11), 1049–1060.

Steensen-Bach, J.O., 1992. Recent Model tests with Suction Piles in Clay and Sand. Paper OTC 6844, *Offshore Technology Conference*.

Stevens, J.B. and Audibert, J.M.E., 1979. Re-examination of p–y curve formulations. Paper 3402, *Offshore Technology Conference*.

Stevens, R.F. and Al-Shafei, K.A., 1996. The Applicability of the Ras Tanajib Pile Capacity Method to Long Offshore Piles. Paper OTC 7974, *Offshore Technology Conference*.

Stevens, R.S., 1988. The effects of a soil plug on pile driveability in clay. *Proc. 3rd Int. Conf. Application of Stress Wave Theory to Piles*, 861–868.

Stevens, R.S., Wiltsie, E.A. and Turton, T.H., 1982. Evaluating Pile Driveability for Hard Clay, Very Dense Sand, and Rock. Paper OTC 4205, *Offshore Technology Conference*.

Stewart, D.P., Boyle, R.S. and Randolph, M.F., 1998. Experience with a new drum centrifuge. *Proc. Int. Conf. Centrifuge '98*, Tokyo, 1, 35–40.

Stewart, H.R. and Hodge, W.E., 1988. Molikpaq Core Densification with Explosives at Amauligak F-24. Paper OTC 5684, *Offshore Technology Conference*.

Stewart, H.R., Jefferies, M.G. and Goldby, H.M., 1983. Berm Construction for the Gulf Canada Mobile Arctic Caisson. Paper OTC 4552, *Offshore Technology Conference*.

Stewart, W.P., 1992. Drag Embedment Anchor Performance Prediction in Soft Soils. Paper OTC 6970, *Offshore Technology Conference*.

Stewart, W.P., 2007. Mat-Supported Jack-up Foundation on Soft Clay – Overturning Storm Stability. *Proc. 11th Int. Conf. The Jackup Platform*, City University, London.

Stockard, D.M., 1981. Structural design considerations for temporary seafloor support of jacket structures. Paper OTC 3972, *Offshore Technology Conference*.

Stockard, D.M., 1986. Case Histories: Pile Driving Offshore India. Paper OTC 5227, *Offshore Technology Conference*.

Stonor, R.W.P., Hoyle, M.J.R., Nelson, K., Smith, N.P. and Hunt, R.J., 2003. Recovery of an elevated jackup with leg bracing member damage. *Proc. 9th Int. Conf. The Jackup Platform*, City University, London.

Strout, J.M. and Tjelta, T.I., 2007. Excess Pore Pressure Measurement and Monitoring for Oiffshore Instability Problems. Paper OTC 18706, *Offshore Technology Conference*.

Sultan, N., Voisset, M., Marsset, B., Marsset, T., Cauquil, E. and Colliat, J.-L., 2007. Potential role of compressional structures in generating submarine slope failures in the Niger Delta. *Marine Geology*, 237(3–4), 169–190.

Sundborg, A., 1956. The River Klaralven, A Study of Fluvial Processes. *Geografiska*, A(38).

Sulak, R.M. and Danielsen, J., 1988. Reservoir Aspects of Ekofisk Subsidence. Paper OTC 5618, *Offshore Technology Conference*.

Sully, J.P., Sgambatti, J., Templeton, J.S., Perez, F. and Laya, E., 1995. Geotechnical Characterization of Rio Caribe Soils. Paper OTC 7662, *Offshore Technology Conference*.

Sumer, B.M., Bundgarrd, K. and Fredsøe, J., 2005. Global and Local Scour at Pile Groups. *Proc. International Offshore and Polar Engineering Conference*, 577–583.

Svanø, G. and Tjelta, T.-I., 1993. Skirted Spudcans – Extending Operational Depth and Improving Performance. 4th City University Jack up Platform Conference, London.

Svein, F. and Andreasson, B., 1982. Soil–Structure Interaction of Multi-footing Gravity Structures. Paper OTC 4413, *Offshore Technology Conference*.

Sweeney, M., Webb, R.M. and Wilkinson, R.H., 1988. Scour around jackup rig footings. Paper OTC 5764, *Offshore Technology Conference*.

Tadich, J.K., Ronold, K.O. and Feld, T., 2007. Revision of DNV Standard for Offshore Wind Turbine Structures. *Proc. European Wind Energy Conference, Scientific Proceedings*, paper associated with Poster Session, 128.

Taiebat, H.A. and Carter, J.P., 2000. Numerical studies of the bearing capacity of shallow foundations on cohesive soil subjected to combined loading. *Géotechnique*, 50(4), 409–418.

Taiebat, H.A. and Carter, J.P., 2005. A failure surface for caisson foundations in undrained soils. *Proc. Int. Conf. Frontiers in Offshore Geotechnics*, eds S. Gourvenec and M.J. Cassidy, Taylor and Francis, 289–295.

Takahara, H., Handa, K., Ishii, K. and Kuboki, E., 1984. Research and Development Project of Manganese Nodule Mining System in Japan. Paper OTC 4782, *Offshore Technology Conference*.

Tan, F.S.C., 1990. *Centrifuge and theoretical modelling of conical footings on sand*, Ph.D thesis, Cambridge University.

Tan, X.M., Guo, J.Y. and Lu, C., 2006. Effect of Spudcan Penetration on Neighboring Existing Pile. *Proc. International Offshore and Polar Engineering Conference*, 516–523.

Tanaka, H., 1984. *Bearing capacity of footings for jack-up platforms*, M. Phil thesis, Cambridge University.

Tarp-Johansen, N.J., Manwell, J.F. and McGowan, J., 2006. Application of Design Standards to the Design of Offshore Wind Turbines in the US. Paper OTC 18359, *Offshore Technology Conference*.

Taylor, R.N. (ed.), 1995. *Geotechnical Centrifuge Technology*, Blackie Academic and Professional.

Taylor, R.J. and True, D.G., 1976. Use of Propellant-Actuated Anchors in Underwater Construction. Paper OTC 2465, *Offshore Technology Conference*.

Teh, C.I. and Houlsby, G.T., 1988. Analysis of the cone penetration test by the strain path method. *Numerical Methods in Geomechanics*, Balkema, 397–402.

Teh, C.I. and Houlsby, G.T., 1991. An analytical study of the cone penetration test in clay. *Geotechnique*, 41(1), 17–34.

Teh, K.L., Cassidy, M.J., Leung, C.F., Chow, Y.K., Randolph M.F. and Quah, C.K., 2008. Revealing the bearing capacity mechanisms of a penetrating spudcan through sand overlying clay. *Geotechnique*, 58(10), 793–804.

Teh, K.L., Leung, C.F., Chow, Y.K. and Handidjaja, P., 2009. Prediction of punch-through for spudcan penetration in sand overlying clay. Paper OTC 20060, *Offshore Technology Conference*.

498

Temperton I., Stonor, R.W.P. and Springett, C.N., 1999. Measured spud can fixity: analysis of instrumentation data from three North Sea jack-ups and correlation to site assessment procedures. *Marine Structures*, 12.

Templeton, J.S. III., 2002. The Role of Finite Element Analysis in Suction Foundation Design. Paper OTC 14235, *Offshore Technology Conference*.

Templeton, J.S. III., 2006. Jackup Foundation Performance in Clay. Paper OTC 18367, *Offshore Technology Conference*.

Templeton, J.S. III., 2007. Spud Can Fixity in Clay, Findings from Additional Work in a Study for IADC. *Proc. 11th Int. Conf.*, The Jackup Platform, City University, London.

Templeton, J.S. III., 2008. Time Domain FE Seismic Analysis of Mat-Supported Jackup Structure on Soft Clay. Paper OTC 19645, *Offshore Technology Conference*.

Templeton, J.S. III., 2009. Finite element analysis of conductor/seafloor interaction. Paper OTC 20197, *Offshore Technology Conference*.

Templeton, J.S. III, Murff, J.D., Goodwin, R.H. and Klejbuk, L.W., 1985. Evaluating Soils and Hazards in the Mississippi Canyon. Paper OTC 4964, *Offshore Technology Conference*.

Templeton, J.S. III, Lewis, D.R. and Brekke, J.N., 2009. Assessment of Jackup survival in severe storms. Paper OTC 20255, *Offshore Technology Conference*.

Terzaghi, K., 1936. The shearing resistance of saturated soils and the angles between the planes of shear. *1st Int. Conf. Soil Mechanics and Foundation Engineering*, Cambridge, 1, 161–165.

Terzaghi, K., 1943. *Theoretical Soil Mechanics*, Wiley.

Terzgahi, K., Peck, R.B. and Mesri, G., 1996. *Soil Mechanics in Engineering Practice*, Wiley.

Tetlow, J.H., Ellis, N. and Mitra, J.K., 1983. The Hutton Tension Leg Platform. *Design in offshore structures*, Thomas Telford, 137–150.

Thompson, G.R. and Long, L.G., 1989. Hibernia geotechnical investigation and site characterization. *Canadian Geotechnical Journal*, 26, 653–678.

Thompson, R.S.G., 1996. *Development of non-linear numerical models appropriate for the analysis of jack-up units*, D. Phil. Thesis, University of Oxford.

Thorel, L., Garnier, J., Rault, G. and Bisson, A., 2005. Vertical uplift capacity of suction caisson in clay. *Proc. Int. Conf. Frontiers in Offshore Geotechnics*, eds S. Gourvenec and M.J. Cassidy, Taylor and Francis, 273–279.

Thusyanthan, I., 2009. Personal communication.

Ticof, J., 1977. *Surface footings on sand under general planar loads*, Ph.D Thesis, University of Southampton.

TJA, 1999. Guidelines for Trenching Design of Submarine Pipelines. Report No. OTH 561, prepared by Trevor Jee Associates for the UK Health and Safety Executive, HSE Books.

Tjelta, T.I., 1993. Foundation Behaviour of Gullfaks C. *Advances in Underwater Technology, Ocean Science and Offshore Engineering, Vol. 28, Offshore Site Investigation and Foundation Behaviour*, SUT, Kluwer, 451–467.

Tjelta, T.I., 1994. Geotechnical Aspects of Bucket Foundations Replacing Piles for the Europipe 16/11-E Jacket. Paper OTC 7379, *Offshore Technology Conference*.

Tjelta, T.I., 1995. Geotechnical Experience from the Installation of the Europipe Jacket with Bucket Foundations. Paper OTC 7795, *Offshore Technology Conference*.

Tjelta, T.I. and Haaland, G., 1993. Novel Foundation Concept for a Jacket Finding its Place. In *Advances in Underwater Technology, Ocean Science and Offshore Engineering*, Vol. 28, Offshore Site Investigation and Foundation Behaviour, Kluwer, 716–728.

Tjelta, T.I., Tieges, A.W.W., Smits, F. P., Geise, J.M. and Lunne, T., 1985. In situ density measurements by nuclear backscatter for an offshore soil investigation. Paper OTC 6473, *Offshore Technology Conference*.

Tjelta, T.I., Aas, P.M., Hermstad, J. and Andenaes, E., 1990. The Skirt Piled Gullfaks C Platform Installation. Paper OTC 6473, *Offshore Technology Conference*.

Toolan, R.E. and Fox, D.A., 1977. Geotechnical Planning for Piled Foundations for Offshore Platforms. *Proc. ICE London*, Part 1, 221–243.

Topolnicki, M., Gudehus, G. and Mazurkiewicz, B.K., 1990. Observed stress–strain behavior of remoulded saturated clay under plane strain conditions. *Geotechnique*, 40(2), 155–187.

Toume, F.T. and Sadiq, M.I., 2000. Foundations on the Red Sea coastal coral in Jeddah area. *Proc. Int. Conf. Engineering for Calcareous Sediments*, ed. K.A. Al-Shafei, Balkema, 1, 167–177.

Townsend, D.L., Stewart, H.R. and Myers, R.M., 1983. Experience with Alert and Evacuation, Tarsuit Island, Summer 1982. Paper OTC 4521, *Offshore Technology Conference*.

Townsend, F.C., 1978. A review of factors affecting cyclic triaxial tests. ASCE Special Technical Publication 654, 356–383.

Tran, M.N. and Randolph, M.F., 2008. Variation of suction pressure during caisson installation in sand. *Geotechnique*, 58(1), 1–11.

Tran, M.N., Randolph, M.F. and Airey, D.W., 2005. Study of sand heave formation in suction caissons using Particle Image Velocimetry (PIV). *Proc. Int. Conf. Frontiers in Offshore Geotechnics*, eds S. Gourvenec and M.J. Cassidy, Taylor and Francis, 259–265.

Tran, M.N., Randolph, M.F. and Airey, D.W., 2007. Installation of Suction Caissons in Sand with Silt layers. ASCE *Journal of Geotechnical and Geoenvironmental Engineering*, 133(10), 1183–1191.

Tricker, R.A.R., 1964. *Bores, Breakers, Waves and Wakes*, Mills and Boon.

Tsukamoto, Y., 1994. *Drum centrifuge tests of three-leg jackup models on sand*, Ph.D thesis, Cambridge University.

Turner, E.L., Chevallier, J. and Rapaport, V., 1987. Placement of Mat-Supported Jackup Rig on Very Weak Soil. Paper OTC 5358, *Offshore Technology Conference*.

Ugaz, O.G., Nowacki, F. and Hanrik, L., 1997. Foundation Analysis of the Hibernia GBS. Paper OTC 8403, *Offshore Technology Conference*.

UKHO, 2004. Admiralty Tide tables (several volumes giving world-wide coverage). United Kingdom Hydrographic Office.

UKOOA, 1997. Guidelines for Conduct of Mobile Drilling Rig Site Surveys. United Kingdom Offshore Operators Association, Surveying and Positioning Committee.

Vaid, Y.P. and Chern, J.C., 1985. Cyclic and monotonic response of saturated sands. *Advances in the Art of Testing Soils under Cyclic Conditions*, ed. V. Khosla, ASCE, 120–147.

Vaid, Y.P., Sivathayalan, S. and Stedman, D., 1999. Influence of specimen-reconstituting method on the undrained response of sand. *Geotechnical Testing Journal*, 22(3), 187–195.

Van der Zwaag, G., 2006. Personal communication.

Van Langen, H. and Hospers, B., 1993. Theoretical Model for Determining Rotational Behavior of Spudcans. Paper OTC 7302, *Offshore Technology Conference*.

Van Langen, H., Wong, P.C. and Dean, E.T.R., 1999. Formulation and Validation of a Theoretical Model for Jack-Up Foundation Load-Displacement Assessment. *Marine Structures*, 12(4) 215–230.

Van Santen, J.A. and de Werk, K., 1976. On the typical qualities of SPAR type structures for initial or permanent field development. Paper OTC 2716, *Offshore Technology Conference*.

Vazquez, J.H., Michel, R.P., Alford, J.H., Quah, M. and Foo, K.S., 2005. *Jackup Units. A Technical Primer for the Offshore Industry Professional*, www.bbengr.com and www.keppelfels.com.sg.

Veletsos, A.S. and Boaz, I.B., 1979. Effects of Soil–Structure Interaction on Seismic Response of a Steel Gravity Platform. Paper OTC 3404, *Offshore Technology Conference*.

Vesic, A.S., 1963. Bearing Capacity of Deep Foundations in Sand. National Academy of Sciences, National Research Council, *Highway Research Record*, 39, 112–153.

Vesic, A.S., 1969. Experiments with Instrumented Pile Groups in Sand. *ASTM Special Technical Publication No. 444, Performance of Deep Foundations*, 172–222.

Vesic, A.S., 1971. Breakout Resistance of Objects Embedded in Ocean Bottom. *ASCE Journal of the Soil Mechanics and Foundation Engineering Division*, 97(SM9), 1183–1205.

Vesic, A.S., 1973. Analysis of Ultimate Loads on Shallow Foundations. *ASCE Journal of the Soil Mechanics and Foundation Engineering Division*, 99(SM1), 45–73.

Vesic, A.S., 1977. Design of Pile Foundations. National Cooperative Highway Research Program, Synthesis of Practice No. 42, Transportation Research Board, Washington DC.

Vijayvergiya, V.N., 1977. Load–Movement Characteristic of Piles., *Ports 1977 Conference*, Long Beach, California, 269–284.

Vijayvergiya, V.N. and Focht, J.A., 1972. A new way to predict the capacity of piles in clay. Paper OTC 1718, *Offshore Technology Conference*.

Vivatrat, V., Valent, P.J. and Ponterio, A.A., 1982. The Influence of Chain Friction on Anchor Pile Design. Paper OTC 4178, *Offshore Technology Conference*.

Vold, R.C. and Eie, J., 1983. Anchor Holding Tests in the Norwegian Trench. Paper OTC 4529, *Offshore Technology Conference*.

Voldsund, T.-A., 2007. *Modelling and Control of Offshore Ploughing Operations*, M.Sc. Thesis, Norwegian University of Science and Technology.

Vryhof, 2000. *Anchor Manual*, Vryhof, the Netherlands.

Wallingford, 1992. *Vibration of Pipeline Spans: 3, Development of Guidelines for Assessment of Submarine Pipeline Spans*, Report No. OTI 92 555 by HR Wallingford Limited for the UK Health and Safety Executive, HSE Books.

Walker, G.R. and Taylor, R.J., 1983. Model Anchor Tests in Cohesionless Soil. Paper OTC 4528, *Offshore Technology Conference*.

Waltham, A.C., 2000. Towards a classification of karst ground conditions. *Proc. 2nd Int. Conf. Engineering for Calcareous Sediments*, Balkema, Vol. 2, pp. 443–453.

Wang, M.C., Demars, K.R. and Nacci, V.A., 1977. Breakout Capacity of Model Suction Anchors in Soil. *Canadian Geotechnical Journal*, 14(2), 246–257.

Wang, M.C., Demars, K.R. and Nacci, V.A., 1978. Applications of Suction Anchors in Offshore Technology. Paper OTC 3203, *Offshore Technology Conference*.

Wang, S. and Lu, X., 2008. Post-cyclic strength degradation of undisturbed and remolded marine silty clay. *Proc. Int. Conf. Offshore and Polar Engineering*, 621–624.

Warrington, D.C., 1997. *Closed form solutions for the wave equation*, M.Sc Thesis. University of Tennessee at Chattanooga.

Watt, B.J., Boaz, I.B. and Dowrick, D.J., 1976. Response of Concrete Gravity Platforms to Earthquake Excitations. Paper OTC 2673, *Offshore Technology Conference*.

Weaver, J.M., 1975. Geological factors significant in the assessment of rippability. *Civil Engineering in South Africa*, Vol. 17, 131–136.

Weaver, J.S. and Berzins, W., 1983. The Tarsuit Island Monitoring Program. Paper OTC 4519, *Offshore Technology Conference*.

Weaver, T.O. and Brinkmann, C.R., 1995. Calibration of a dynamic analysis procedure using measurements from a North sea jack-up in a severe storm. Paper OTC7840, *Offshore Technology Conference*.

Webster, S., Givet, R. and Griffith, A., 2008. Offshore Pile Acceptance Using Dynamic Pile Monitoring. *Proceedings of the Eighth International Conference on the Application of Stress Wave Theory to Piles*, Lisbon, Portugal, 655–661.

Weiss, R.T., Wright, B. and Rogers, B., 2001. In-Ice Performance Of The Molikpaq Off Sakhalin Island. *Proceedings of the 16th International Conference on Port and Ocean Engineering under Arctic Conditions POAC '01*, Ottawa, Ontario, Canada.

Wesselink, B.D., Murff, J.D., Randolph, M.F., Nunez, I.L., Hyden, A.M., 1988. Analysis of centrifuge model test data from laterally loaded piles in calcareous sand. *Engineering for Calcareous Sediments, Proc. Int. Conf.*, eds. Jewell, R.J. and Andrews, D.C., Vol. 1, pp. 261–270, Perth.

Westgate, Z.J. and deJong, J.T., 2005. Geotechnical Considerations for Offshore Wind Turbines. Report, Centre for Offshore Foundations Systems, Australia.

Wetmore, S.B., 1984. The Concrete Island Drilling System: Super Series. Paper OTC 4801, *Offshore Technology Conference*.

Wichers, J., Andenacs, E. and Bonniemaire, B., 2007. Development of an ISO Standard on Marine Operations. Paper OTC 19039, *Offshore Technology Conference*.

White, D.J., 2005. A general framework for shaft resistance on displacement piles in sand. *Proc. Int. Conf. Frontiers in Offshore Geotechnics*, eds S. Gourvenec and M. Cassidy, Taylor and Francis, 697–703.

White, D.J. and Bolton, M.D., 2004. Displacement and strain paths during plane-strain model pile installation in sand. *Geotechnique*, 54, No. 6, 375–397.

White, D.J. and Randolph, M.F., 2007. Seabed characterization and models for pipeline–soil interaction. *Proc. Int. Conf. Offshore and Polar Engineering*, 758–769.

White, D.J., Barefoot, A.J. and Bolton, M.D., 2001. Centrifuge modelling of upheaval buckling in sand. *Int. Journal of Physical Modelling in Geotechnics*, 2, 19–28.

White, D.J., Cheuk, C.Y. and Bolton, M.D., 2008a. The uplift resistance of pipes and plate anchors buried in sand. *Geotechnique*, 58(10), 771–779.

White, D.J., Teh, K.L., Leung, C.F. and Chow, Y.K., 2008b. A comparison of the bearing capacity of flat and conical circular foundations on sand. *Geotechnique*, 58(10), 781–792.

White, E.I. and Drake, K.R., 1994. The Design, Fabrication, and Installation of the Alba Northern Jacket. Paper OTC 7467, *Offshore Technology Conference*.

Whitehouse, R.J.S., 1998. *Scour at Marine Structures, A Manual for Practical Applications*, Thomas Telford.

Will, S.A., Mascorro, E., Roberson, W., Hussain, K. and Paulson, S., 2006. Benguela-Belize Compilant Piled Tower: Tower Design. Paper OTC 18068, *Offshore Technology Conference*.

Williams, A.F., Dunnavant, T.W., Anderson, S., Equid, D.W. and Hyden, A.M., 1988. The Performance and Analysis of Lateral Load tests on 356 mm dia piles in reconstituted calcareous sand. *Proc. Int. Conf. Engineering for Calcareous Sediments*, Perth, 271–282.

Williams, G.N., Dunlap, W.A. and Hansen, B., 1981. Storm-induced bottom sediment data – Seaswab II Results. Paper OTC 3974, *Offshore Technology Conference*.

Williams, J.P. and Aurora, R.P., 1982. Case Study of an Integrated Geophysical and Geotechnical Site Investigation Program for a North Sea Platform. Paper OTC 4168, *Offshore Technology Conference*.

Williamson, S.C., Zois, N. and Hewitt, A.T., 2008. Integrated Site Investigation of Seafloor Features and Associated Fauna, Shenzi Field, Deepwater Gulf of Mexico. Paper OTC 19356, *Offshore Technology Conference*.

Willis, N.R.T., Parker, E.J. and Johnson, W.J., 2008. Geohazard Assessment and Avoidance on the GAZA Marine Subsea Development. Paper OTC 19310, *Offshore Technology Conference*.

Wilson, Q. and Sahota, B.S., 1980. Pull-out Parameters for Buried Suction Anchors. Paper OTC 3816, *Offshore Technology Conference*.

Wiltsie, E.A., Hulett, J.M., Murff, J.D., Brown, J.E., Hyden, A.M. and Abbs, A.F., 1988. Foundation design for external strut strengthening system for Bass Strait first generation platforms. *Proc. Int. Conf Engineering for Calcareous Sediments*, eds R.J. Jewell and D.C. Andrews, Vol. 1, 321–330.

Wingerde, A.M. van, Delft, D.R.V. van, Packer, J.A. and Janssen, I.G.J., 2006. Survey of support structures for offshore wind turbines. *Proc. Int. Symp. Tubular Structures IX*, Quebec, Taylor and Francis, 51–57.

Winterwerp, J.C., 2005. *Fine Sediment Dynamics in the Marine Environment*, Elsevier.

Wisch, D.J. and Mangiavacchi, A., 2008. API Offshore Structures Standards: Changing Times. Paper OTC 19606, *Offshore Technology Conference*.

Witney, K.C. and Muller, B., 1986. Installation and Results of the Molikpag Instrumentation System. Paper OTC 5116, *Offshore Technology Conference*.

Wolters, G., Müller, G., Bruce, T. and Obhrai, C., 2005. Large scale experiments on wave downfall pressures. Paper 13682. *Proc. ICE Maritime Engineering*, 158(MA4), 137–145.

Wong, P.C., Chao, J.C., Murff, J.D., Dean, E.T.R., James, R.G., Schofield, A.N. and Tsukamoto, Y., 1993. Jack up Rig Foundation Modeling II. Paper OTC 7303, *Offshore Technology Conference*.

Wong, P.C., Taylor, B.B. and Audibert, J.M.E., 2008. Differences in Shear Strength between Jumbo Piston Core and Conventional Rotary Core Samples. Paper OTC 19683, *Offshore Technology Conference*.

Wright, N., Tamboezer, A.J., Windle, D., van Hooydonk, W.R. and Ims, B.W., 1982. Pile Instrumentation and Monitoring During Pile Driving Offshore Northwest Borneo. Paper OTC 4204, *Offshore Technology Conference*.

Wroth, C.P., 1979. Correlations of some engineering properties of soils. *Proc. 2nd BOSS Conf.*, London, 121–132.

Wroth, C.P. and Houlsby, G.T., 1985. Soil Mechanics – Property Characterization and Analysis Procedures. Keynote lecture. *Proc. 11th Int. Conf. on Soil Mechanics and Foundation Engineering* (ICSMFE), San Francisco, 1–55.

Wroth, C.P. and Wood, C.M., 1978. The correlation of index properties with some basic engineering properties of soils. *Canadian Geotechnical Journal*, 15, 137–145.

Wu, A.K.H., Kuhlemeyer, R.L. and To, C.W.S., 1989. Validity of Smith Model in Pile Driving Analysis. *ASCE Journal of Geotechnical Engineering*, 115(9), 1285–1302.

Wu, T.H., Martinez, R.E. and Kjekstad, O., 1983. Stability of Ekofisk Tank: Reliability Analysis. *ASCE Journal of Geotechnical Engineering*, 110(7), 938–956.

Xia, H.W. and Moore, I.D., 2006. Estimation of maximum mud pressure in purely cohesive material during directional drilling. *Int. J. Geomechanics and Geoengineering*, 1(1), 3–11.

Xu, X.T., Liu, H.L. and Lehane, B.M., 2006. Pipe pile installation effects in soft clay. *Proc. ICE Geotechnical Engineering*, 159(GE4), 285–296.

Yafrate, N.J. and DeJong, J.T., 2005. Considerations in evaluating the remoulded undrained shear strength from full flow penetrometer testing. *Proc. Int. Conf. Frontiers in Offshore Geotechnics*, eds S. Gourvenec and M.J. Cassidy, Taylor and Francis, 991–997.

Yalçıner, A.C., Pelinovsky, E.N., Okal, E. and Synolakis, C.E. (eds), 2003. *Submarine landslides and tsunamis*, Springer.

Yamamoto, N., Randolph, M.F. and Einav, I., 2005. Numerical study of shallow foundations on calcareos sand. *Proc. Int. Conf. Frontiers in Offshore Geotechnics*, eds S. Gourvenec and M.J. Cassidy, Taylor and Francis, 443–449.

Yamamoto, N., Randolph, M.F. and Einav, I., 2008a. Simple formulae for the response of shallow foundations on compressible sands. *Int. J. for Geomechanics*, ASCE.

Yamamoto, N., Randolph, M.F. and Einav, I., 2008b. A numerical study of the effect of foundation size for a wide range of sands, *ASCE Journal of Geotechnical and Geoenvironmental Engineering*.

Yamamuro, J.A. and Kaliakin, V.A., 2005. *Soil Constitutive Models, Evaluation Selection and Calibration*, ASCE Geotechnical Special Publication No. 128.

Yang, Z. and Elgamal, A., 2001. Sand Boils and Liquefaction-Induced Lateral Deformation. *15th Int. Conf. Soil Mechanics and Geotechnical Engineering*, Istanbul, Turkey, 345–350.

Yang, Z.X., Li, X.S. and Yang, J., 2008. Quantifying and modelling fabric anisotropy of granular soils. *Geotechnique*, 58(4), 237–248.

Yergin, D., 1993. *The Prize: The Epic Quest for Oil, Money and Power*, Free Press.

Yeung, S.K. and Carter, J.P., 1989. An Assessment of the Bearing Capacity of Calcareous and Silica Sands. *Int. J. Numerical and Analytical Methods in Geomechanics*, 13, 19–26.

Yew, C.H., 1997. *Mechanics of Hydraulic Fracturing*, Gulf Professional Publishing.

Yoshida, Y., Masui, N. and Ito, M., 2005. Evaluation of recovery of wall friction after penetration of skirts with laboratory and field tests. *Proc. Int. Conf. Frontiers in Offshore Geotechnics*, eds S. Gourvenec and M.J. Cassidy, Taylor and Francis, 251–257.

Youd, T.L., Idriss, I.M., Andrus, R.D., Arango, I., Castro, G., Christian, J.T., Dobry, R., Finn, W.D.L., Harder, L.F., Hynes, M.E., Ishihara, K., Koester, J.P., Liao, S.S.C., Marcuson, W.F. III, Martin, G.R., Mitchell, J.K., Moriwaki, Y., Power, M.S., Robertson, P.K., Seed, R.B. and Stokoe, K.H., II, 2001. Liquefaction resistance of soils: Summary report from the 1996 NCEER and 1998 NCEER/NSF Workshop on Evaluation of Liquefaction Resistance of Soils. *ASCE Journal of Geotechnical and Geoenvironmental Engineering*, Vol. 127, No. 10, 817–833.

Younes, A.J., Gibson, J.L. and Shipp, R.C., 2005. Geohazard Assessment of the Deepwater Princess Field in the Northeastern Gulf of Mexico: Example of Evaluating Complex Faulting in a Subsea Development. Paper OTC 17577, *Offshore Technology Conference*.

Young, A.G. and Focht Jr, J.A., 1981. Subsurface hazards affect mobile jackup rig operations. *Sounding*, McClelland Engineers, Houston, 3(2), 4–9.

Young, A.G., Kraft, L.M. and Focht, J.A., 1975. Geotechnical Considerations in Foundation Design of Offshore Gravity Structures. Paper OTC 2371, *Offshore Technology Conference*.

Young, A.G., House, F., Turner, R.D. and Helfrich, S.C., 1981. Foundation Performance of Mat-Supported Jackup Rigs in Soft Clays. Paper OTC 4143, *Offshore Technology Conference*.

Young, A.G., Remmes, B.D. and Meyer, B.J., 1984. Foundation performance of offshore jackup drilling rigs. *ASCE Journal of Geotechnical Engineering*, 110(7), 841–859.

Young, A.G., Phu, D.R., Spikula, D.R., Rivette, J.A., Lanier, D.L. and Murff, J.D., 2009. An Approach for using Integrated Geoscience Data to avoid Deepwater Anchoring Problems. Paper OTC 20073, *Offshore Technology Conference*.

Yusifov, M. and Rabinowitz, P.D., 2004. Classification of mud volcanoes in the South Caspian Basin, offshore Azerbaijan. *Marine and Petroleum Geology*, 21(8), 965–975.

Zaaijer, M.B. and Henderson, A.R., 2004. Review of Current Activities in Offshore Wind Energ. *Proc. Int. Conf. Offshore and Polar Engineering*, 101–108.

Zakeri, A. and Nadim, F., 2008. Submarine Debris Flow Impact on Pipelines: Drag Forces, Mitigation and Control. Paper OTC 19173, *Offshore Technology Conference*.

Zdravkovic, L. and Potts, D.M., 2005. Parametric finite element analyses of suction anchors. *Proc. Int. Conf. Frontiers in Offshore Geotechnics*, eds S. Gourvenec and M.J. Cassidy, Taylor and Francis, 297–302.

Zdravkovic, L., Potts, D.M. and Jardine, R.J., 2001. A parametric study of the pull-out capacity of bucket foundations in soft clay. *Geotechnique*, 51(1), 55–67.

Zelinski, G.W., Gunleiskrud, T., Sættem, J., Zuidberg, H.M. and Geise, J.M., 1986. Deep heatflow measurements in quaternary sediments on the Norwegian continental shelf. Paper OTC 5183, *Offshore Technology Conference*.

Zentech, 2000. Validity of wave response analysis for jackup rigs. Offshore Technology Report 2000/094, UK Health and Safety Executive.

Zhang, J., Randolph, M.F. and Stewart, D.P., 1999. An elasto-plastic model for pipe–soil interaction of unburied pipelines. *Proc. Int. Offshore and Polar Engineering Conference*, 185–192.

Zhang, X.Y., Lee, F.H. and Leung, C.F., 2009a. Response of caisson breakwater subjected to repeated impulsive loading. *Geotechnique*, 59(1), 3–16.

Zhang, X.Y., Lee, F.H. and Leung, C.F., 2009b. Tilt displacement of caisson breakwater due to wave loading. *Geotechnique*, 59(1), 17–27.

Zhou, X.X., Chow, Y.K. and Leung, C.F., 2009. Numerical modelling of extraction of spudcans. *Geotechnique*, 59(1), 29–39.

Zhu, J.K. and Yin, J.-H., 2001. Drained creep behaviour of soft Hong Kong marine deposits. *Geotechnique*, 51(5), 471–474.

Zuidberg, H.M. and Vergobbi, P., 1996. EURIPIDES, Load tests on Large Driven Piles in Dense Silica Sands. Paper 7977, *Offshore Technology Conference*.

Index

Page numbers in *italics* denote figures.

507